W. D.
1980

Physiography of the United States

A Series of Books in Geology
Editors: JAMES GILLULY, A. O. WOODFORD

Physiography
of the United States

CHARLES B. HUNT

The Johns Hopkins University

W. H. FREEMAN AND COMPANY
San Francisco and London

Preface

My purpose in this book is to present a broad view of the natural features and resources of the United States. The book is an outgrowth of a course offered at The Johns Hopkins University for students not majoring in one of the earth sciences. In this course I attempt to describe the physical geography, geology, climate, soils, vegetation, resources, and related phenomena in the natural regions of the United States and consider some of the ways in which they have shaped our history.

The United States is uniquely rich in resources, and its residents live upon what must be acknowledged as the most valuable piece of real estate on this planet. But the abundance and variety of resources that we enjoy today cannot be taken for granted; their proper use and management urgently need our best thought and our most careful study.

I hope this book will serve to provide students, and a larger audience as well, not only with some understanding of the physical characteristics of our land but also with a greater appreciation of our good fortune. For out of such understanding and appreciation can come, as increasingly it must, the use of our lands and resources in ways that will best serve ourselves, our children, and the rest of mankind.

Charles B. Hunt

Baltimore, Maryland
August 1966

6441

Contents

General Physiography

The Natural
1 *Regions*

The face of our land is the net result of a complex of processes and changes that occurred in the past and continue to occur today, but the basic differences between various parts of the land surface are structural. The natural regions into which the earth's surface is divided are controlled mostly by the kinds of structural members that make up the different parts of the earth's crust and by their relationship to one another. These structural differences may be further accentuated by changes in climate, which governs the processes that shape the landscape—weathering, erosion, and sedimentation. But the structural differences prevail even where the regimens of climate, erosion, and sedimentation are similar.

The United States is divided, primarily on the basis of structure, into 34 natural regions called physiographic provinces, which are grouped in 11 major divisions. Each province has characteristics peculiar to itself—a distinctive structural framework giving rise to distinctive landforms expressing their structure and, for the most part, distinctive climate, vegetation, soils, water, and other resources. Moreover, each physiographic province has its own economy, and each has numerous distinctive cultural traits despite similarities in the outward appearances of their banks, billboards, and beauty shops.

Table 1.1 lists the major divisions and the provinces in the United States and briefly describes some of their outstanding characteristics (see Fig. 1.1; for Alaska, Fig. 18.2; for Hawaii, Fig. 19.3; for Puerto Rico, Fig. 20.2). Some provinces are divided into *sections;* these will be discussed as the provinces are described in Part II.

The boundaries between the provinces, for the most part, are sharp, reflecting the fact that the chief differences are structural. Some examples are: the break marked by a line of falls between the Coastal Plain and the more elevated Piedmont Province; the foot of the Blue Ridge, which forms the inner boundary of the Piedmont Province; the so-called knob belt that forms the western edge of the Appalachian Plateaus; the foot of the Front Range in the Southern Rocky Mountains, which marks the western edge of the Great Plains; the southern rim of the Colorado Plateau, which overlooks the much lower Basin and Range Province in central and western Arizona; the northern edge of the Snake River Plains at the foot of the Northern Rocky Mountains in Idaho; and the base of the mountains on both the east and the west sides of the Cascade-Sierra Nevada Province.

At a few places, however, the provinces are not sharply bounded but grade into one another over wide areas, even though they are structurally distinct. Perhaps the best ex-

TABLE 1.1   Major Divisions and Physiographic Provinces of the United States.

Major Divisions	Provinces	Characteristics
Laurentian Upland	Superior Upland	An upland with altitudes up to 2,000 feet, but without much local relief; drainage irregular; many lakes; extends far north in Canada around both sides of Hudson Bay.
Atlantic Plain	Continental Shelf	Submarine plain sloping seaward to depth of about 600 feet; the submerged part of the Coastal Plain.
	Coastal Plain	Broad plain rising inland; shores mostly sandy beaches backed by estuaries and marshes; mud flats at mouth of Mississippi River; some limestone bluffs on west coast of Florida; inland ridges parallel the coast; altitudes less than 500 feet; along Atlantic coast the surface slopes northeast and northern valleys are tidal inlets.
Appalachian Highlands	Piedmont Province	Rolling upland; altitudes 500 to 2,000 feet in the south; surface slopes northeast (like the Coastal Plain) and altitudes at the north are below 500 feet.
	Blue Ridge Province	**Easternmost ridge of the Appalachian Highlands; altitudes above 5,000 feet.**
	Valley and Ridge Province	Parallel valleys and mountainous ridges; altitudes mostly between 1,000 and 3,000 feet; lower to the north like the Coastal Plain and Piedmont provinces.
	Appalachian Plateaus	Plateau; surface mostly 2,000 to 3,000 feet; slopes west; deeply incised by winding stream valleys; considerable local relief; hillsides steep.
	New England Province	Mostly hilly upland with altitudes below 1,500 feet; locally mountainous with altitudes above 5,000 feet; coast irregular and rocky.
	Adirondack Province	Mountains rising to more than 5,000 feet.
	St. Lawrence Valley	Rolling lowland with altitudes below 500 feet.
Interior Plains	Central Lowland	Vast plain, 500 to 2,000 feet; the agricultural heart of the country.
	Great Plains Province	Western extension of the Central Lowland rising westward from 2,000 to 5,000 feet; semiarid.
	Interior Low Plateaus	Plateaus; less than 1,000 feet; rolling uplands with moderate relief.
Interior Highlands	Ozark Plateaus	Rolling upland; mostly above 1,000 feet.
	Ouachita Province	Like the Valley and Ridge Province; altitudes 500 to 2,000 feet.

Rocky Mountain System	Southern Rocky Mountains	A series of mountain ranges and intermontane basins, mostly trending north; high part of the continental divide; altitudes 5,000 to 14,000 feet.
	Wyoming Basin	Elevated semiarid basins; isolated low mountains; altitudes mostly between 5,000 and 7,000 feet.
	Middle Rocky Mountains	An assortment of different kinds of mountains with differing trends and semiarid intermontane basins; features here resemble those of the neighboring provinces; altitudes mostly 5,000 to about 12,000 feet.
	Northern Rocky Mountains	Linear blocky mountains and basins in the east; highly irregular granitic mountains without linear trends in the southwest; altitudes mostly between 4,000 and 7,000 feet.
Intermontane Plateaus	Colorado Plateau	Highest plateaus in the country; surface mostly above 5,000 feet and up to 11,000 feet; canyons; semiarid.
	Basin and Range Province	Mostly elongate, blocky mountains separated by desert basins and trending north; pattern more irregular in the south; altitudes from below sea level (Death Valley, Salton Sea) to more than 12,000 feet, but relief between mountains and adjoining basins generally no more than about 5,000 feet; most basins in the north are without exterior drainage.
	Columbia Plateau	Mostly a plateau of lava flows; altitudes mostly below 5,000 feet; semiarid but crossed by two major rivers, the Columbia and Snake.
Pacific Mountain System	Cascade-Sierra Nevada	Northerly trending mountains; Cascades a series of volcanos; Sierra Nevada a blocky mass of granite with steep eastern slope and long gentle western slope; altitudes up to 14,000 feet; western slopes humid, eastern slopes semiarid.
	Pacific Border Province	Coastal Ranges with altitudes mostly below 2,000 feet and separated from the high Cascade-Sierra Nevada Province by troughs less than 500 feet in altitude.
	Lower California Province	Northern end of the granitic ridge forming the Lower California Peninsula.
Alaska	Southeastern Coast Mountains	Rugged coastal mountains up to 9,000 feet in altitude; glaciers, fjords.
	Glaciered Coast	Coastal Mountains up to 20,000 feet in altitude; 5,000 square miles of glaciers; perpetual snow above 2,500 feet.
	South-central Alaska	Mountain ranges and troughs in arcs curving around the Gulf of Alaska; altitudes up to 20,000 feet.
	Alaska Peninsula and Aleutian Islands	**Chiefly a chain of volcanoes; altitudes mostly less than 6,000 feet except at the north; bordered on the south by the Aleutian trough, an oceanic trench 20,000 feet deep.**
	Interior Alaska	Mostly the Yukon River valley between Alaska Range on the south and Brooks Range on the north; deltaic flat at the west; mostly dissected upland in the east with uplands 1,000 to 2,000 feet higher than the rivers.

(Continued on next page.)

Alaska (cont.)	Seward Peninsula and Bering Coast Uplands	Rugged plateau, mostly 1,000 to 2,500 feet in altitude; most ground is permanently frozen.
	Arctic Slope	Long slope north from the Brooks Range to broad coastal plain bordering the Arctic Ocean; permanently frozen ground.
Hawaii	Hawaii	Oceanic volcanic islands in part bordered by coral reef; altitudes up to 13,000 feet.
Puerto Rico	Puerto Rico	Oceanic island bordered on north by a trench more than 30,000 feet deep; an east-west trending ridge extends the length of the island; long slope to north; shorter, more-precipitous slope to south; shores partly bordered by coral reef.

amples are the boundaries of the Middle Rocky Mountains and the Basin and Range Province, for these provinces grade into the mountains, plateaus, and basins of neighboring provinces. The boundaries at such places are necessarily arbitrary.

Almost a half of the United States consists of plains. The central part of the United States is a vast plain that extends northward across Canada to the Arctic Ocean and southward to the part of the Coastal Plain that borders the Gulf of Mexico. Along the northern part of the Atlantic coast the Coastal Plain narrows and becomes fragmented where it slopes northeastward under the Atlantic Ocean. The northeastward slope is the result of tilting of the surface by earth movements. This tilting is responsible for the drowned valleys at Chesapeake, Delaware, and New York Bays. East of New York only the tops of the highest hills remain above sea level, as islands; beyond Cape Cod the plain is wholly submerged. Other less extensive areas of plains occur in the structural basins that separate some of the western mountains, like the broad valley of the Sacramento and San Joaquin Rivers in California, many of the basins in the Basin and Range Province, and the Wyoming Basin.

About a quarter of the country is made up of plateaus. In order of increasing height the six major plateaus are: the Piedmont Province, Interior Low Plateaus, Ozark, Appalachian, Columbia, and Colorado plateaus. No two of these are alike; not only have earth movements raised them to different heights, but their rock formations are different. The four eastern plateaus are much older than the two western ones; the eastern plateaus are humid, the western ones semiarid, and there are consequent differences in the weathering and erosional processes that have shaped the landforms.

Mountains make up about a quarter of the country. The central plains are flanked on the east and on the west by mountains—the mountains of the Appalachian Highlands on the east and the Rocky Mountain System on the west. The western mountains and plateaus differ from the eastern ones in many ways and for many reasons. The kinds of rocks and their structures are different; the western mountains and plateaus are younger and higher; they are less worn down partly because they are younger. The landforms differ partly for these reasons and partly because the processes of erosion, at least in the western interior, are those of a semiarid rather than humid climate.

Structural differences are reflected too in the great differences between the shorelines along the two sides of the country. The Atlantic Coast south of New England is a plain with extensive, sandy beaches; the Pacific Coast is mountainous with comparatively few beaches. The coast of southeastern Alaska is mountainous with glaciers and fjords.

The offshore areas differ too. Off the Atlantic Coast the continental shelf is more than a hundred miles wide, but along the Pacific Coast it is quite narrow. The south shore of the Alaska Peninsula, the Aleutian Islands, and the north shore of Puerto Rico are bordered by oceanic trenches several miles deep.

Drawing Maps—The Way To Learn Physiography

Studying physiography involves studying maps, and for many this will mean acquiring new habits and techniques. Gazing at maps is not enough; one must draw them. In the study of physiography, drawing maps serves the same purpose as does dissection in the study of anatomy. The spatial relationships must be drawn to be understood clearly. As in the other arts, practice brings improvement; most students find that their later efforts are done better and more easily than their first.

Figure 1.1, the map showing the physiographic provinces, is basic to our study. One must know clearly and exactly where the boundaries are located relative to state boundaries and to each other; such understanding can be acquired by drawing the provinces on an outline map showing the state lines. In the course of study at The Johns Hopkins University this is drawn first in class, again as a homework assignment, a third time in a quiz, and finally as a standard question in the final examination, and so promised at the beginning of the term. Students who do well draw the map more times than that!

There is reason for so much emphasis on this map, for it is *the basic physiographic map.* If this map is thoroughly known, most of the others will be easy to master, for to a considerable degree they are derived from it. The pattern of boundaries of the physiographic provinces reappears prominently in the other physiographic maps. The one to be looked at next is a good example.

Topography and topographic maps

Topographic maps show the configuration of the land surface by means of *contour lines,* which represent imaginary lines on the ground surface at a constant elevation above sea level. One who follows a contour on the ground goes neither uphill nor downhill, but on a level. Figure 1.2, which shows ranges of altitude in the United States, is a form of contour map. The shoreline is a contour at sea level; it is the zero contour. If sea level were to rise 500 feet, the shoreline would be along the 500-foot contour. This is not entirely hypothetical either, because sea level was at about that position in the not very distant geologic past (see Chapter 10). Every contour represents such a level line.

Contours provide a means for showing the slope of the land surface. For example, where the Missouri River joins the Mississippi the altitude is just under 500 feet (Fig. 1.2), but 500 miles west the altitude is 2,000 feet. This 1,500-foot difference in altitude represents an average slope of 3 feet per mile. Two hundred miles farther west, on the Great Plains in Colorado, the altitude is 5,000 feet; in this 200 miles the slope averages 15 feet per mile. From the foot of the Rocky Mountains, say at Denver, to the summit, the rise is about 9,000 feet in 30 miles, which is an average slope of 300 feet per mile.

With contours as widely spaced as those in Figure 1.2, one cannot know whether the actual configuration of the surface is smooth or irregular, but such differences show on more detailed maps having contours that are more closely spaced.

Figure 1.3 illustrates how slopes determined from contour maps are projected and plotted to scale to obtain a topographic *profile*

Figure 1.1 *Physiographic provinces of the United States.*

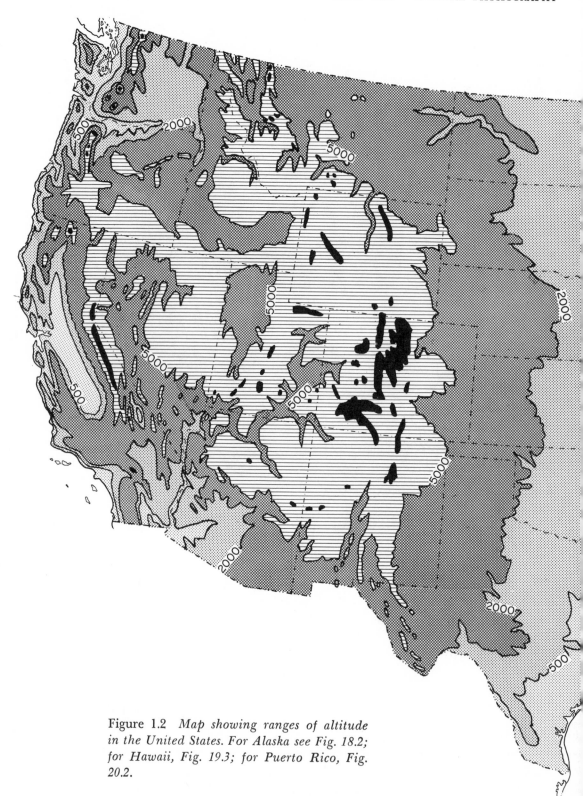

Figure 1.2 *Map showing ranges of altitude in the United States. For Alaska see Fig. 18.2; for Hawaii, Fig. 19.3; for Puerto Rico, Fig. 20.2.*

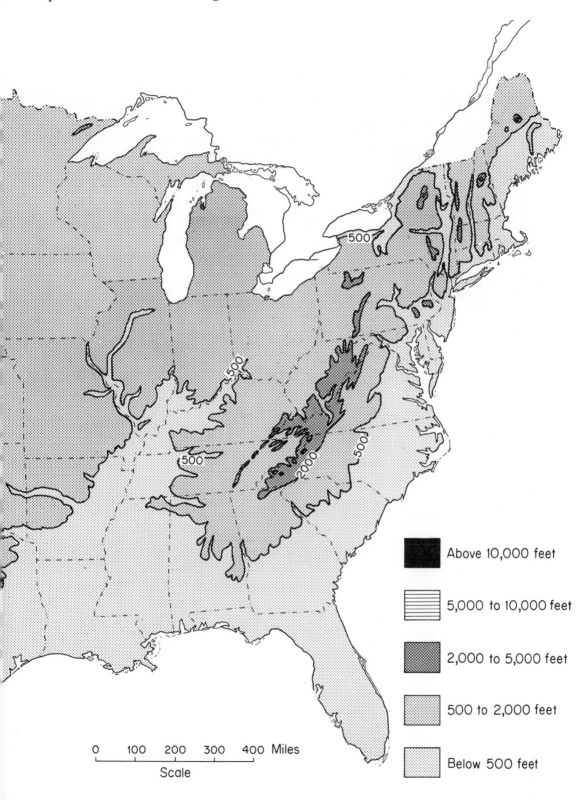

Above 10,000 feet

5,000 to 10,000 feet

2,000 to 5,000 feet

500 to 2,000 feet

Below 500 feet

0   100   200   300   400 Miles

Scale

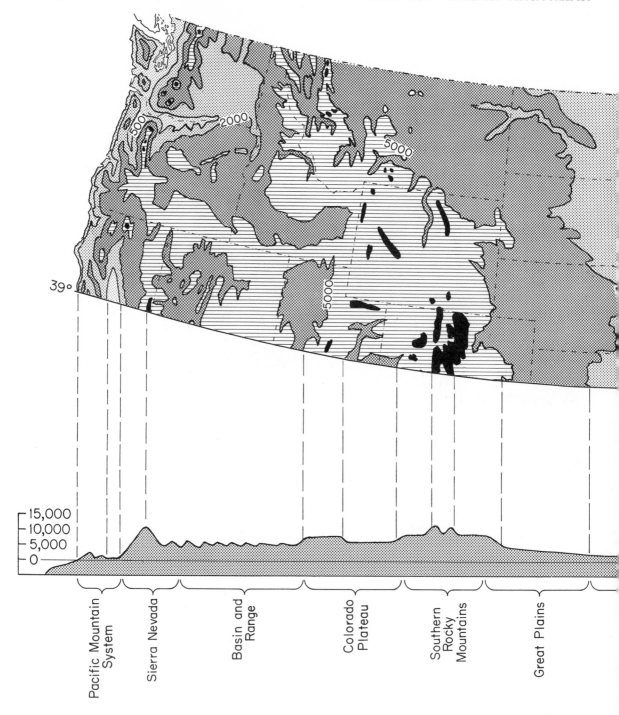

Figure 1.3 *Profile across the United States along the 39th parallel.*

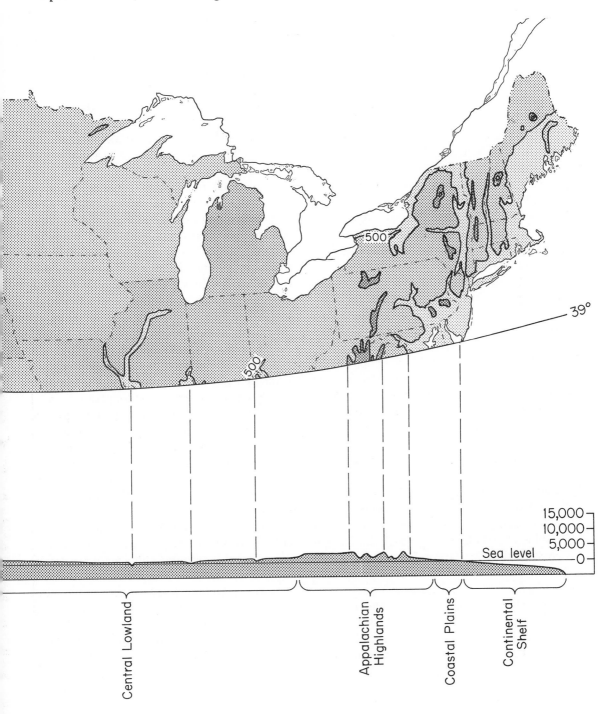

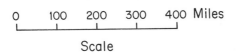

across an area. The projected contours provide the control points along the profile. Known topographic irregularities that do not have sufficient relief to show between the contours, like some indicated in the Basin and Range Province, can be added by sketching. But the relief on such irregularities must be less than the difference in height of the contours on either side.

Altitudes in the United States differ from province to province. Figure 1.2 shows that the Colorado Plateau is higher than the Columbia Plateau and that these are higher than the Ozark and Applachian plateaus. To a considerable degree the province boundaries coincide with contours.

The 500-foot contour almost coincides with the inner edge of the Coastal Plain from Virginia to the Rio Grande. The contour has a serrate pattern where the province boundary is smooth because where contours cross valleys they curve upstream, but this need not obscure the general accordance of the contour and the province boundary. This 500-foot contour along the inner boundary of the Coastal Plain is a clear indication that altitudes on the plain are below 500 feet.

The 500-foot contour also outlines the St. Lawrence Valley and the extension of the Valley and Ridge Province along the Hudson River Valley. On the Pacific Coast it outlines the physiographic sections at Puget Trough in Washington, Willamette Trough in Oregon, Central Valley in California, and the Salton Sink at the north end of the depression occupied by the Gulf of California.

The boundary of the Appalachian Highlands nearly coincides with the 1,000-foot contour, which is not shown in Figure 1.2.

The boundary between the Central Lowland and the Great Plains coincides roughly with the 2,000-foot contour in that area. Along the Pacific coast this contour and the 5,000-foot contour outline the Cascade-Sierra Nevada Province.

The 5,000-foot contour roughly outlines the Northern Rocky Mountains and southern edge of the Colorado Plateau. The 7,500-foot contour (not shown) approximately outlines the Southern Rocky Mountains, Wyoming Basin, Middle Rocky Mountains, and western edge of the Colorado Plateau.

These relationships illustrate that if the physiographic provinces are known, it is not difficult to draw a topographic map of the country. This, too, is required in the study of physiography.

In addition to contours, relief is shown on some maps by means of shading, which gives a pictorial, three-dimensional effect. Some topographic maps are published as relief models. In looking at such models, or at the profile in Figure 1.3, one must remember that the vertical scale is greatly exaggerated, about 40 times in Figure 1.3. The earth's relief is insignificant in comparison with its diameter. The earth, if reduced to the size of a billiard ball, would be equally smooth.

Figure 1.2 has been used to illustrate some principles about topographic maps, but it is hardly representative of the topographic maps available for the United States. Topographic maps are prepared and distributed by the United States Geological Survey. They are issued as quadrangles bounded by meridians of longitude and parallels of latitude. Some of the old quadrangle maps cover one degree; more recent ones cover 15 minutes of latitude and longitude. The most recent and most detailed quadrangle maps cover $7\frac{1}{2}$ minutes of latitude and longitude. These maps are drawn at different scales.

Scale can be indicated by a bar or a fraction. Scales commonly used on maps in the United States are illustrated in Table 1.2. The bar scales need no explanation, but the fractional scales are not widely understood. The fraction 1/62,500 means that one unit on the map equals 62,500 of the same units on the ground —for example, 1 inch on the map equals 62,500 inches on the ground. If the fraction were 1/63,360 the scale would be 1 inch equals 1 mile (1 mile equals 63,360 inches; that is, 12 inches/foot × 5,280 feet). A scale of 1/31,680

TABLE 1.2 Some map scales commonly used in the United States.

Bar scales	Fractional scales	
0 — 200 — 400 miles	1/15,000,000	Roughly the scale of Figures 1.1 and 1.2.
0 — 25 — 50 — 75 — 100 miles	1/2,500,000	This scale commonly used for wall maps of the United States.
0 — 10 — 20 miles	1/500,000	This scale commonly used for state maps.
0 — 5 — 10 miles	1/250,000	Scale of one of the series of topographic maps; topographic maps at this scale are available for all parts of the United States including Alaska.
0 — 2.5 — 5 miles	1/125,000	Scale of 30-minute quadrangle maps.
0 — 1 — 2 miles	1/63,360	One inch equals one mile. 15-minute quadrangle maps at 1/62,500 are available for two thirds of the United States.
0 — $\frac{1}{2}$ — 1 mile	1/31,680	One inch equals one half mile.
0 — 1 mile	1/24,000	Scale of 7$\frac{1}{2}$-minute quadrangle maps; in 1963, maps at this scale are available for a quarter of the United States.

means that 1 inch on the map equals 31,680 inches on the ground; that is, 1 inch equals $\frac{1}{2}$ mile. Map scales are commonly referred to as large or small, but this refers to the size of the fraction and not to the area covered.

Parts of numerous topographic quadrangle maps are reproduced in this book to illustrate details of the physiographic provinces. It should be noted that where the land is nearly flat a small contour interval is used, as on contour maps that show parts of the bottom lands along the Mississippi River. On such maps the contour interval is 5 feet. In hummocky areas a contour interval of 10 feet may be used, as in Figure 12.3, which shows some glacial features in the Central Lowland. Topographic maps of the eastern mountains and plateaus commonly have a contour interval of 20 feet, as in Figures 12.15 and 12.16; those showing the more rugged western mountains may have contour intervals of 40 feet (Fig. 17.9), 50 feet (Fig. 13.4), or even more.

In this book the geologic and topographic maps are reproduced in black and white, but the originals are printed in color, and a standard series of colors is used for distinguishing different classes of map features. Man-made features (cultural features) such as roads, buildings, place names, and boundaries are shown in black. Lakes, rivers, canals, glaciers and other water features are shown in blue. Contours are brown. Woodland cover is shown in green, and patterns of green are used to distinguish orchards from natural growth. Important roads and urban areas are shown in red.

The reader may wonder why so many of the topographic maps used in this book to illustrate landforms are taken from old editions on which the cultural features are out of date. The reason is that the old editions were published at scales more suitable for use in a book. Most modern maps are published at larger scales, show much more detail, but are too large for use in a book.

Index circulars showing all available topographic maps can be obtained by request addressed to the United States Geological Survey, Washington 25, D.C. The U. S. Geological Survey also distributes an explanation chart showing topographic map symbols.

General Physiographic References

ATWOOD, W. W., 1940, *The physiographic provinces of North America:* Ginn, Boston, 536 p. with map by Raisz showing landforms in the United States.

BOWMAN, ISAIAH, 1909, *Forest physiography:* Wiley, New York.

FARB, P., 1963, *The face of North America, the natural history of a continent:* Harper & Row, New York, 316 p.

FENNEMAN, N. M., 1931, *Physiography of western United States:* McGraw-Hill, New York, 534 p.

———, 1938, *Physiography of eastern United States:* McGraw-Hill, New York, 689 p.

KROEBER, A. L., 1947, *Cultural and natural areas of native North America:* Univ. Calif. Press, Berkeley, 242 p.

LOOMIS, F. B., 1938, *Physiography of the United States:* Doubleday, New York, 350 p.

PATERSON, J. H., 1963, *North America, a regional geography:* Oxford Univ. Press, 454 p.

POWERS, W. E., 1966, *Physical geography:* Appleton-Century-Crofts, New York, 566 p.

THORNBURY, W. D., 1965, *Regional geomorphology of the United States:* Wiley, New York, 609 p.

U. S. Geological Survey, map showing physical divisions of the United States, (scale 1/7,-000,000).

———, Index to topographic mapping. Available for each state, on request.

———, 100 topographic maps illustrating physiographic features.

Structural Framework

2 of the Provinces

Bedrock Geology

The structural framework of the provinces is determined by their bedrock geology, and the provinces differ from one another mainly because their geologic structures differ. A map of the bedrock geology of the United States is shown in Figure 2.1. The general geologic structure and resulting landforms are illustrated in Figure 2.2. The geology of Alaska, Hawaii, and Puerto Rico is described in the chapters on those areas.

A geologic map can be very attractive if printed in color, as are those published by the U. S. Geological Survey. Although most people find geologic maps to be pretty much a hodgepodge of color patterns and not very meaningful, one does not have to be a geologist to read a great deal from them. We need first to distinguish the three principal types of rocks—sedimentary, igneous, and metamorphic—and to do this will look briefly at some of the physiographic provinces in which the types are particularly well developed.

Sedimentary Rocks

If we were to visit the outcrops (natural exposures of rock) on the Coastal Plain, we would find that the rock formations designated K (Cretaceous) in Figure 2.1 overlie the formations on the landward side, but extend under the formations designated T (Tertiary) that crop out on the seaward side. The Tertiary formations overlie the Cretaceous but extend seaward under those designated Q (Quaternary).

These formations were deposited mostly as nearshore marine sediments, although some nonmarine sediments were deposited in such fresh-water environments as estuaries or deltas. They were derived by erosion of older rocks inland from the Coastal Plain. The youngest strata, or layers, are at the top. From the superposition of strata it is ascertained that the Cretaceous formations are younger than those on the landward side; the Tertiary are still younger, and the Quaternary are the youngest. The geologic time table, derived in just this manner, by observing relationships between rock formations all over the world, is given in Table 2.1. Learning this time table is a *must* in physiography. The task is no more difficult than learning the seasons and months of the year. A year is divided into 4 seasons; geologic time is divided into 4 *eras*. A year is further divided into 12 months; geologic time, after the Precambrian, is divided into 12 *periods*.

Figure 2.1 *Bedrock geology of the United States. (After U.S.G.S.)*

Quaternary sedimentary deposits. Shown only where the deposits are thick enough and extensive enough to completely conceal the bedrock formations; deposits shown are mostly fluvial but include some marine sedimentary deposits along the coasts; dune sand in Nebraska; glacial drift in Minnesota; playa deposits, lake beds, alluvium, and gravel fans in the western interior.

Tertiary formations. Sedimentary and mostly of marine origin along the coasts; some volcanic along the Washington-Oregon coast; in western interior mostly lake and stream deposits but include considerable volcanic material.

Mostly volcanic rocks. Some minor intrusions. Mostly of Cenozoic age but including some that are Mesozoic.

Granitic batholiths. Late Mesozoic and early Cenozoic.

Late Mesozoic. Mostly sedimentary Cretaceous formations; marine and continental deposits intertongued.

Early Mesozoic formations (Triassic and Jurassic). Red beds in eastern United States; mostly red beds and canyon-forming sandstones in Rocky Mountain region; mostly marine and metamorphic rocks in westernmost United States.

Upper Paleozoic formations (Mississippian, Pennsylvanian, and Permian). Marine and continental sedimentary deposits; not metamorphosed except in the Pacific Mountains where formations include volcanics and are metamorphics.

Lower Paleozoic formations (Cambrian, Ordovician, Silurian, and Devonian). Sedimentary deposits, mostly of marine origin.

Paleozoic formations. Not divided in western United States; sedimentary rocks.

Metamorphic rocks. Mostly Precambrian in interior United States; considerable infolded Paleozoic metamorphic rocks along both coasts.

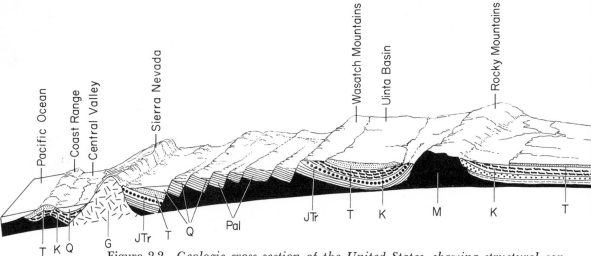

Figure 2.2 *Geologic cross section of the United States, showing structural control of the major topographic features.* **Q,** *Quaternary;* **T,** *Tertiary;* **K,** *Cretaceous;*

The periods are divided into *epochs,* but only those of the Cenozoic need concern us. These are:

Period	Epoch	Estimated ages of the time boundaries in millions of years
Quaternary	Recent Pleistocene	
	Pliocene	2
	Miocene	11
Tertiary	Oligocene	25
	Eocene	40
	Paleocene	60
		70

The original sediments of the Coastal Plain Province—mud and sand, together with their contained sea shells—became firm rocks by compaction and cementation. Shells became fossils. Gravels consolidated into *conglomerates;* sands consolidated into *sandstones;* fine-grained muds consolidated into *shales;* the sediments composed of intermediate-size grains became *siltstones, shaly sandstones,* or *sandy shales.* Marls, or calcareous oozes (composed of calcium carbonate), consolidated into *limestones* (limestone containing much magnesium is called *dolomite*). In addition there are deposits of salts, such as gypsum (calcium sulfate) and rock salt (sodium chloride). Peat

and related swamp deposits compacted and altered to *lignite* and then to *coal.* All these are now sedimentary rocks; they were once squishy sediments.

These different kinds of sediments grade laterally into each other. For example, sands deposited near shore grade into muds deposited offshore, and the muds in turn grade into marls deposited in very quiet water. These different kinds of deposits are referred to as *facies,* and each contains remains of the fauna peculiar to the particular environment.

At times deposition was interrupted. An unusual storm, for example, may erode layers already deposited in quiet water, and subsequently deposited beds then rest *unconformably* upon the older. Such discontinuities in the sedimentary sequence may represent brief intervals of time, or if there has been earth movement and deep erosion, the discontinuity may represent considerable time, perhaps an entire period. For example, in North Carolina and Virginia, the landward edges of the Cretaceous formations were eroded before the Tertiary beds were deposited, and the Cretaceous formations there do not crop out at the surface, but are buried under the Tertiary formations (Fig. 2.1).

During Cretaceous time the edge of the ocean was about at the inner boundary of the Cretaceous deposits. The shore gradually shifted seaward and at the beginning of Tertiary time stood about along the boundary

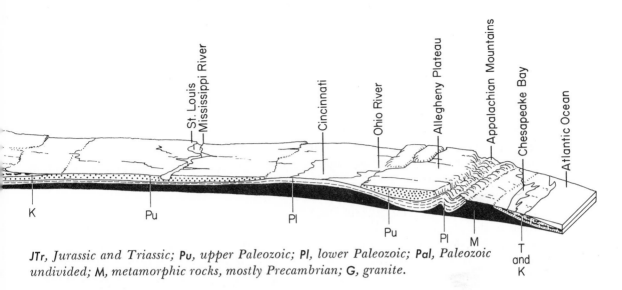

JTr, Jurassic and Triassic; **Pu,** *upper Paleozoic;* **Pl,** *lower Paleozoic;* **Pal,** *Paleozoic undivided;* **M,** *metamorphic rocks, mostly Precambrian;* **G,** *granite.*

between the Cretaceous and Tertiary formations. The shore continued its shift seaward and by Quaternary time stood at the inner edge of the deposits mapped as Quaternary, except in the Mississippi embayment, where there are river deposits called *alluvium.* This retreat of the ocean is shown in Figure 10.24; in a different way the geologic map shows the growth of this part of the United States during approximately the last 100 million years.

Whereas the Coastal Plain deposits are largely marine, other sedimentary deposits are

TABLE 2.1   Major divisions of geologic history.

Era	Period	Estimated ages of time boundaries in millions of years
Cenozoic (Age of mammals)	Quaternary (Age of man)	
		2
	Tertiary	
		70
Mesozoic (Age of reptiles, notably the dinosaurs; first appearance of birds)	Cretaceous	
		135
	Jurassic	
		180
	Triassic	
		225
Paleozoic (Invertebrate forms abundant and varied; first appearance of fishes, amphibians, and land plants)	Permian	
		270
	Pennsylvanian	
		310
	Mississippian	
		350
	Devonian	
		400
	Silurian	
		440
	Ordovician	
		500
	Cambrian	
		600
Precambrian (Primitive life forms)		
		5,000

entirely *nonmarine*—for example, the Tertiary formations on the Great Plains. The sediments that formed these deposits were derived by erosion of the Rocky Mountains, which became uplifted in late Cretaceous and early Tertiary time. These sediments, washed from the mountains onto the plains, are mostly stream, or *fluviatile*, deposits.

Another kind of nonmarine sedimentary deposit is exemplified by the Tertiary and Quaternary fills in the western basins, like those in the Basin and Range Province. In the central part of the basins are lake, or *lacustrine*, deposits, laid down in ancient ephemeral lakes. As these basins are situated in what are now desert or near-desert environments, the former lakes are bare mud flats, or *playas*, except in wet seasons. Fluviatile deposits are represented by gravel fans spreading basinward from the foot of the adjoining mountains. These gravel deposits grade laterally into the muds of the playas; gradational sandy belts between the fans and playas supply sand that winds collect into dunes.

Many of the basins contain brines, natural solutions of salts concentrated by evaporation. These give rise to still another kind of sedimentary deposit, chemical precipitates called *evaporites*. The deposits are much like those that form in an evaporating dish in a chemical laboratory, and consist of an outer carbonate zone, an intermediate sulfate zone, and a central chloride zone (Fig. 2.3). These natural basins differ from the chemist's evaporating dish only in size; the evaporating dish covers a few square inches, whereas the natural basins cover scores or hundreds of square miles.

Other and older sedimentary deposits are represented by the Mesozoic formations on the Colorado Plateau. Still older ones are the Paleozoic formations in the Valley and Ridge Province and westward to the Great Plains. As can be seen in Figure 2.2 these Paleozoic formations extend under the Cretaceous and Tertiary formations on the Great Plains and reappear where turned up against the uplifted Rocky Mountains.

Igneous Rocks

Igneous rocks were once molten, but subsequently froze and crystallized to become rock, though it must be remembered that this freezing temperature is hot as Hell, 600° to more than 1,000°C. Some igneous rocks occur as *extrusions* at the surface, like lavas; others

Figure 2.3 *Zonation of the salts, and history of the salt pan, in Death Valley, California. The salt pan is analogous to the residue that forms in an evaporating dish. As a brine is evaporated the least-soluble salts precipitate first (A). These are mostly calcium and magnesium carbonates (c). As the brine evaporates further and the salinity continues to increase, sodium and potassium sulfates are deposited (s). Finally, when maximum salinity is reached, sodium and potassium chlorides and magnesium sulfate are deposited in the interior (h). In Death Valley, while the salts were being deposited, the pan was tilted eastward, and the salts are crowded against that side of the valley (B).*

occur as *intrusions,* masses that formed below the surface. Intrusions, in large part at least, represent masses of molten rock that were physically injected into the surrounding rocks. Most granites are intrusions. Where erosion has removed the overlying rocks, intrusions have become exposed at the surface. The Columbia Plateau and the Cascade Province are vast fields of extrusive rocks; central Idaho and the Sierra Nevada consist largely of intrusive granitic rocks (Fig. 2.1). Igneous rocks also are extensive in the Southern Rocky Mountains, Colorado Plateau, Basin and Range Province, and Alaska. The Hawaiian Islands are wholly of volcanic origin.

Igneous rocks are of many kinds depending on the composition of the original molten mass, or *magma,* the pressures and temperatures that caused the igneous activity, and the physical conditions that prevailed where the magma froze. Magmas that cool rapidly may freeze to form a glass, such as *obsidian.* If a magma cools slowly, large minerals crystallize from it and the resulting rock is crystalline, like granite. Still other rocks, known as *porphyries,* consist of large crystals in a matrix of fine-grained ones.

The magmas, and the rocks developed from them, generally contain more than 50 percent silica (SiO_2); some igneous rocks contain as much as 75 percent silica. The chief other constituents are iron, aluminum, magnesium, calcium, sodium, and potassium. In general, the igneous rocks low in silica are dark; for example, *gabbro* and its eruptive equivalents *basalt* and *diabase.* The lavas of the Columbia Plateau are largely basalt. Igneous rocks containing much silica tend to be light in color, like granite and its eruptive equivalent, *rhyolite.*

As a magma cools, the minerals that form crystallize in a definite order that reflects their relative solubilities under the particular temperature and pressure. The general sequence in which the more common rock-forming minerals crystallize is illustrated in Table 2.2. This sequence illustrates several related features.

1. The minerals that form early contain less silica than those that form late.
2. The early-forming, dark minerals generally occur with the early-forming, light ones; the late-forming, dark minerals generally occur with the late-forming, light ones.
3. The dark igneous rocks like basalt and gabbro, are composed of early-forming minerals. The light igneous rocks like rhyolite and granite, are composed of late-forming minerals.
4. The susceptibility of these minerals to weathering and to soil formation is in the same order as the sequence of crystallization (see p. 24).

With Table 2.2 in mind one can infer a lot about the composition of the large granitic masses shown on the geologic map (**B** in Fig. 2.1). They are composed principally of late-forming minerals, whereas the basaltic lavas of the Columbia Plateau are composed chiefly of early-forming minerals.

GRANITE AND BASALT

Granite and basalt are the most common kinds of igneous rocks. Most granites are the result of older rocks being melted and the magma being intruded into another part of the crust (p. 27); some granites, however, have formed as a result of metamorphism (p. 27).

The term "granite" is applied to many kinds of rock used for facing stone on large buildings and for monuments, curbstones, paving blocks, riprap, road materials, ballast, and even poultry grits. A few kinds of granite, especially the very coarse-grained forms (*pegmatite*), are useful as a source of certain kinds of minerals.

Different kinds of granites are distinguished by their mineral composition and texture. True granite consists of quartz and alkali feldspar, especially potash feldspar (orthoclase). Mica (biotite or muscovite) is usually present along with hornblende (see Table 2.2). Granite, the most siliceous of the common igneous rocks, has the following average composition (in percent):

SiO_2	70	MgO	1.0
Al_2O_3	15	K_2O	4.0
Fe_2O_3	1.5	Na_2O	3.25
FeO	1.5	other	1.5
CaO	2.25		

Granitic rocks composed chiefly of sodic-calcic feldspar and with little or no potash feldspar are known as diorite (Table 2.2), which has the following average composition (in percent):

SiO_2	58	MgO	4.
Al_2O_3	16.5	K_2O	2
Fe_2O_3	3	Na_2O	3.5
FeO	4.5	other	1.75
CaO	6.75		

If quartz is present, the silica content is higher and the rock is known as quartz diorite. Instead of mica, diorite generally contains hornblende or augite (Table 2.2) and magnetite (magnetic iron oxide, Fe_3O_4).

Most of the volcanic rocks shown in Figure 2.1 are basalt. The Columbia Plateau and the Hawaiian Islands are almost entirely basalt. Basalt also occurs in the Triassic formations (JTr on Fig. 2.1) in the Piedmont Province.

Basalt, the least siliceous of the common igneous rocks, is composed chiefly of dark minerals (Table 2.2)—silicates of iron and magnesium (olivine and augite), and oxides of iron oxide (magnetite and hematite). The light mineral in basalt is mostly plagioclase feldspar. Basalts are remarkably uniform in

TABLE 2.2   The common rock-forming silicate minerals and their compositions.

Sequence of crystallization	Susceptibility to weathering	Dark minerals	Light minerals	Rock types volcanic (fine-grained or glassy)	intrusive (coarsely crystalline)
early	least resistant	Olivine $(Mg,Fe)_2SiO_4$	Calcic plagioclase $CaAl_2Si_2O_8$	basalt (mostly dark minerals)	gabbro (mostly dark minerals)
		Augite $(Ca,Mg,Fe,Al)_2(Al,Si)_2O_6(OH)_2$	Calcic plagioclase with sodium	andesite	diorite
		Hornblende $(Ca,Na,Fe,Mg,Al)_7(Al,Si)_8O_{22}(OH)_2$	Sodic plagioclase with calcium	latite	monzonite
		Biotite (dark mica) $K(Mg,Fe)_3(Al,Si_3)O_{10}(OH,F)_2$	Sodic plagioclase $NaAlSi_3O_8$		
			Potash feldspar $KAlSi_3O_8$	rhyolite (mostly light minerals)	granite (mostly light minerals)
			Muscovite (white mica) $KAl_2(Al,Si_3)O_{10}(OH,F)_2$		
late	most resistant		Quartz SiO_2		

Table 2.2. The common, rock-forming, silicate minerals and their composition. The minerals are arranged in their general order of crystallization from molten magmas, their susceptibility to weathering, and their occurrence in various rock types.

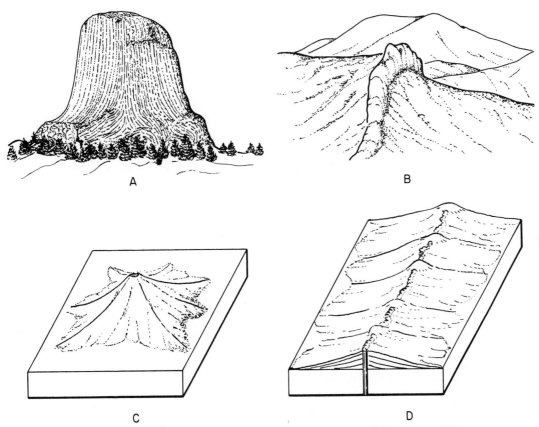

Figure 2.4 (*A*) *Devils Tower, Wyoming, a volcanic neck.* (*B*) *Dike forming a rock wall that extends across the countryside, Spanish Peaks area, Colorado.* (*C*) *Central type volcano.* (*D*) *Fissure type volcano.*

composition, both mineralogically and chemically. The average chemical composition (in percent) is:

SiO_2	49	MgO	6
Al_2O_3	16	K_2O	1.5
Fe_2O_3	5.5	Na_2O	3
FeO	6.5	H_2O	1.5
TiO_2	1.5	other	0.5
CaO	9		

STRUCTURAL FORMS OF IGNEOUS ROCKS

Volcanoes are the most familiar examples of igneous activity. They may be of the central type, which produces volcanic cones (Figs. 17.10, 18.10), or of the fissure type, which produces lava ridges. Erosion of the central type may expose a basaltic plug (*volcanic neck*), like Devils Tower, Wyoming (Fig. 2.4,A) or like some on the Colorado Plateau (Fig. 14.6). Erosion of the fissure type may expose vertical sheets, or *dikes,* of the igneous rock (Fig. 2.4,B). Basaltic necks and dikes are well exposed on the Colorado Plateau, but are virtually absent on the Columbia Plateau because of insufficient erosion.

Basaltic magmas are fluid enough so that the lavas may spread for miles in flows only 10 to 15 feet thick. Quiet eruptions of basaltic lava form broad low cones, but these eruptions are interrupted by explosive eruptions that produce steep-sided cinder cones. The cinders are like the porous cinders, or clinker, from a furnace—glassy rock frothed by air bubbles. Some cinders are as porous as cotton and nearly as light (pumice).

Highly explosive eruptions, which produce detritus rather than lavas, throw out quantities of hot, finely comminuted rock together with liquid magma that becomes spun out in fine threads that quickly freeze to glass. These fall to the ground as threads, like cotton, or as dust-size particles to form beds of *volcanic ash* or *tuff*. The term is misleading because volcanic ash is not the waste product of combustion in the usual sense of the word "ash." Crater Lake (Fig. 17.12) in the Cascade Range is the product of an explosive eruption that produced an extensive ash deposit; the 1912 eruption of Mount Katmai in Alaska (p. 429) is another very recent and well-documented example of this kind of eruption.

In places a crust may form over a lava flow and the underlying liquid drain out to leave a tunnel or cave in the lava. The surface of the lava may be slabby if the crust is broken. It may be smooth and wavey (*pahoehoe type*), or rough and cindery (*aa type*). Some lavas on the Columbia Plateau flowed into lakes and developed rounded structures about the size and shape of pillows, and are called *pillow lavas;* but most flowed on the land and, as they cooled, developed columnar jointing, a highly characteristic and physiographically important feature of basaltic lavas.

The columns are generally 4- to 6-sided, 18 to 36 inches in diameter, and many feet long. They developed at right angles to the cooling surface. In a lava flow they are vertical, with a main set extending downward from the top of the flow and a smaller set extending upward from the base. In a dike they are horizontal and in two sets that meet in the middle (Fig. 2.5,B). In a volcanic neck they are radial in ground plan, and they curve upward in the interior of the neck (Fig. 2.5,C). These patterns of jointing provide an important structural control for the landforms developed from basaltic rocks. The lava flows tend to form cliffs as the columnar blocks spall away.

Dikes generally form walls with vertical sides (Fig. 2.4,B). Volcanic necks have tops narrower than their bases because of the curvature of the joints (Fig. 2.4,A).

Until basaltic lavas are softened by weathering and by an overgrowth of vegetation, they form a somber, forbidding terrain. Washington Irving, in his account of the travels of Captain Bonneville, described fresh lava surfaces in the Snake River Plain as ground "where nothing meets the eye but a desolate and awful waste; where no grass grows nor water runs, and where nothing is to be seen but lava." In warm humid areas like Hawaii

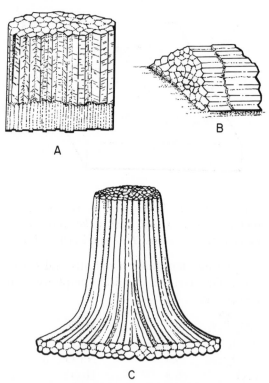

Figure 2.5 *Structure of columnar jointing in basaltic lava flows (A), dikes (B), and volcanic necks (C). The surfaces of flows and the tops of necks generally are cindery (scoriaceous) and lack columnar joints. Along the walls of dikes and necks there is a narrow selvage of platy joints parallel to the walls. These layers have been omitted in order to emphasize the columns.*

lava flows may become overgrown with vegetation in 50 years, but on the Columbia Plateau, and in other semiarid provinces, the lavas remain barren for hundreds of years.

Intrusive rocks also may assume a variety of forms, depending on the structure of the surrounding rocks, the viscosity of the magma, and the rate of its injection. In a sense, the feeders to volcanoes are intrusions, like the cylindrical necks of central-type volcanoes and the dikes of fissure-type volcanoes.

An intrusion being squeezed upward may encounter the base of a strong formation, and if unable to penetrate it, may spread laterally along the base of the layer. Intrusive sheets of more or less uniform thickness are termed *sills;* highly bulbous ones that dome the overlying rocks are termed *laccoliths.* In general, viscous magmas, or those injected rapidly, form laccoliths; fluid magmas, or those injected slowly, form sills.

Another common form of intrusion, roughly cylindrical but much larger than a volcanic neck, is referred to as a *stock.* Stocks may be a mile or several miles in diameter. Many stocks —probably most—were formed by magmas that penetrated the surrounding rocks and domed them upward (Fig. 14.8), just as a nail punched into a book will penetrate many pages and dome those that it does not penetrate.

The tremendous bodies of granite in central Idaho and in the Sierra Nevada cover thousands of square miles and are referred to as *batholiths.* The three-dimensional form of these vast intrusions is poorly known, and how they became emplaced is a matter of much speculation. They appear to be a complex of stocks.

Metamorphic Rocks

Turning back to the Atlantic seaboard we look next at the Piedmont Province (Fig. 2.1), which consists largely of the third major class of rocks—*metamorphic rocks.* These originally were sedimentary or igneous rocks, but they have been subjected to pressures and temperatures so great that not only have the constituent minerals been recrystallized to form new kinds but the new minerals have been arranged in bands or layers—a textural pattern called *foliation.* These rocks are extensively exposed in the Piedmont Province but occur also in New England, the Superior Upland, central Texas, in the cores of several of the mountain uplifts in the Rocky Mountain region and Alaska, and in the bottom of Grand Canyon. Rocks of Precambrian age generally are highly metamorphosed; they constitute the basement complex underlying the sedimentary rocks of Paleozoic, Mesozoic, and Cenozoic age (Fig. 2.2).

Metamorphic equivalents of some of the rocks already described are:

Original rock	Metamorphic equivalent
sandstone	quartzite
shale	slate, schist
limestone	marble
basalt	greenstone
granite	gneiss

If the pressure and heat are great enough, the metamorphic rock becomes a magma, and the resulting rock, by definition, is igneous. A schist, for example, can be metamorphosed to granite.

Folding and Faulting

Another important property of rocks is that, despite being hard and brittle when in masses the size that might be quarried or used for throwing-stones, the same rock in a slab miles thick and covering the area of a state would bend if a corner could be raised, just as a large sheet of glass can be bent without breaking. Rocks are pliable when acted upon in large masses and over long periods of time.

The bending of rocks is called *folding.* If folding progresses fast enough, or far enough, the slab will break, and the resulting fractures are called *faults.* Upfolds are called *anticlines;* downfolds are called *synclines* (Fig. 2.6).

The rock formations in all the physiographic provinces are, to at least some degree, folded and faulted. Folding is best illustrated, however, in the Valley and Ridge Province. In this province the rock formations, which are of Lower Paleozoic age, are strongly folded, and south of New York State these folded rocks form elongate fold mountains paralleling the linearity of the province. Immediately to the east are the folded, faulted, and metamorphosed rocks of the Blue Ridge, Piedmont, and New England provinces. West of the folded belt is a broad structural basin

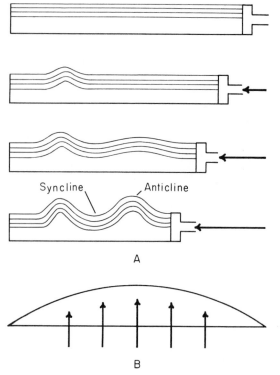

Figure 2.6 *Two kinds of folding. (A) Folding due to horizontal compression, as if by a piston shoving against a set of beds contained in a box. (B) Folding due to vertically directed forces.*

containing Upper Paleozoic formations that are folded parallel to those of the Valley and Ridge Province, but not nearly so high structurally. The intensity of the structural deformation decreases westward; rock formations in the eastern provinces are more deformed than those in the Valley and Ridge, and the formations in the Valley and Ridge are more deformed than those in the Appalachian Plateaus. Moreover, the three quite different structural belts, and the individual structures within them, are overlapped and cut off at the south by the Cretaceous and younger formations in Alabama (Fig. 2.1). The geologic map shows the relative age of these rocks and of the structures—the structural features of the Appalachian Highlands formed before the Cretaceous formations were deposited. From other evidence we know that the principal structural features of the Appalachian Highlands formed at the end of the Paleozoic.

The structural features that control mountains like the Appalachians are in part regional in extent and in part local. Regions that have been elevated, such as the Rocky Mountain region and the adjoining Colorado Plateau and High Plains (Fig. 2.2), are referred to as *geanticlines.* Regions that are downwarped below sea level, and flooded, are referred to as *geosynclines.* The Gulf of Mexico, the Aleutian Trench, and the Puerto Rico Trench are present-day examples. The Mediterranean Sea is another. The more localized earth movements produce the folds and faults within the geanticline and geosyncline.

Regional earth movements in past eras are responsible for the structural framework that is so important in physiography. During Paleozoic time, a geosyncline existed in the area now occupied by the Appalachian Mountains, and another existed in the area now occupied by the Basin and Range Province (Fig. 2.7,A). Other geosynclines formed during the Mesozoic (Fig. 2.7,B and C). In each of these, great thickness (30,000 to 40,000 feet) of sediments were deposited, and each of these

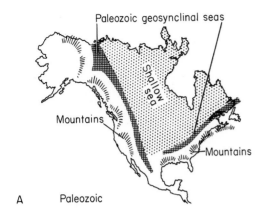

A Paleozoic

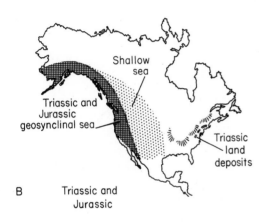

B Triassic and Jurassic

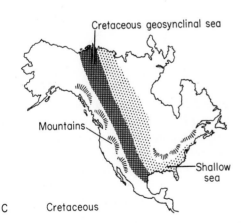

C Cretaceous

Figure 2.7 *Paleogeographic maps of North America, showing principal Paleozoic and Mesozoic mountains and geosynclinal seas.*

tremendous accumulations of sediments became uplifted, folded, and faulted to form mountain chains. Probably a similar future is ahead for the sediments being deposited in the Gulf of Mexico and in the Aleutian and Puerto Rico Trenches. This kind of folding probably is caused by horizontal compressional forces; folds developed over intrusions, such as over the top of a laccolith, are due chiefly to vertical forces.

In some places, such as along the Appalachians, the folding of the rocks progresses far beyond mere wrinkling. The rocks may be strongly folded and the folds asymmetrical (Fig. 2.8). The folding may be accompanied by fracturing—that is, by faulting. Faults are classed as *normal* faults, *tear* faults, and *thrust* faults, depending on the relationship

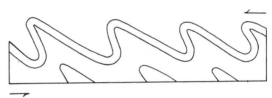

Figure 2.8 *Asymmetrical folding.*

between the beds on opposite sides of the plane of fracture (Figs. 2.9 and 2.10). Closely spaced fractures along which there has been little or no slippage of the two blocks are known as *joints*.

The displacements due to folding and to faulting may be measurable in scores of miles, although in most individual folds and faults the displacements are moderate and are measurable in hundreds or thousands of feet. The displacements are the result of intermittent small movements, as can be seen along the San Andreas fault in California.

Movement on this fault was the cause of the great earthquake in California in April, 1906. The displacement was almost entirely horizontal, the western block moving northward with respect to the eastern block, as is clearly shown by offsets in roads, fences, or-

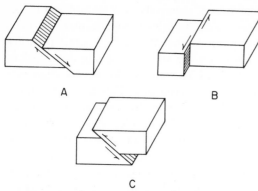

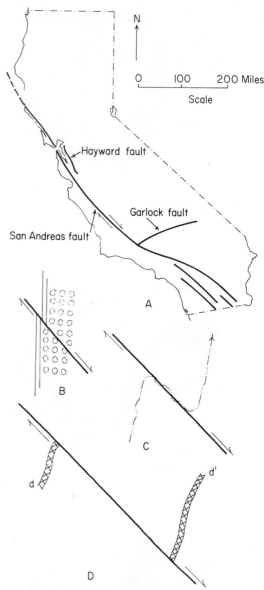

Figure 2.9 (A) Normal fault with mostly vertical movement; the fault plane dips toward the downthrown block (B) Tear fault with mostly horizontal movement. (C) Reverse fault with mostly vertical movement; the fault plane dips toward the upthrown block, as if the upthrown block had been pushed onto the downthrown block.

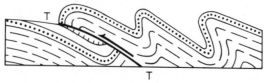

Figure 2.10 Continued deformation at asymmetrical folds, like those shown on Fig. 2.8, may lead to the development of thrust faults (T-T) by which one set of beds is thrust laterally onto another.

chards, and other features. The maximum displacement was about 20 feet. However, the older features along the fault are displaced much more than that; the older the feature, the greater the displacement (Fig. 2.11). The courses of small streams, for example, may have been offset hundreds or even thousands of feet. Offsets in still older features, such as some rock formations, are measurable in miles. Formations as old as Cretaceous may be offset a few hundred miles, and this could readily be accomplished by an average movement of only a foot in a hundred years.

Displacement is going on at the present time, with stress building up along the old fracture, but the fracture remains sealed be-

Figure 2.11 (A) The San Andreas fault, California. The dramatic horizontal displacement along this fault is the result of many small movements over a long period of time. (B) The most recent displacement took place in 1906, when roads and orchards were offset as much as 20 feet. (C) Earlier movements on the fault are recorded by stream courses, some of which have been offset hundreds of feet. (D) Displacements of rock formations, older than the streams, are measurable in miles.

cause of friction between the two earth blocks. Eventually, however, a stage will be reached when the stress exceeds the friction, and the rocks that have been bending will flip along the fracture, producing an earthquake.

In the central United States the Paleozoic formations are thinner than under the Applachians (Fig. 2.2) and, for the most part, form broad shallow synclines (structural basins) and broad, low anticlines (structural upwarps). The bluegrass area of central Kentucky and the Nashville area in Tennessee are structural domes that expose lower Paleozoic rocks flanked by formations of upper Paleozoic age dipping off the domes. Southern Illinois and Michigan are broad structural basins in which the upper Paleozoic formations are still preserved. The Lake Superior region is an upwarp of Precambrian metamorphic rocks. Other small areas of Precambrian rocks, also marking uplifts, are located in the Ozark Plateau of Missouri and in central Texas.

Westward, on the plains, these Paleozoic formations and their structures are unconformably overlapped by Cretaceous formations of marine origin, and farther west on the plains these are overlapped unconformably by Tertiary formations of continental origin that were as already noted derived by erosion of the Rocky Mountains. Accordingly, the Rocky Mountains are younger than the Cretaceous deposits and older than the Tertiary ones. The mountains are formed of uplifts of Precambrian rocks flanked by Paleozoic and Mesozoic (including the Cretaceous) formations, which are turned up steeply at the edges of those uplifts (Fig. 2.2).

The continuity of the Rocky Mountains is broken by a structural basin in Wyoming that is partly filled with Tertiary formations similar to those on the Great Plains. Similar but smaller Tertiary basins located in Utah (Uinta Basin) and in New Mexico (San Juan Basin) contain deposits washed from the western slopes of the Rocky Mountains. These basins are part of the Colorado Plateau.

Between the Colorado Plateau and the Sierra Nevada is a highly faulted area, the Basin and Range Province, which consists of elongate mountain ranges and intervening valleys. There and to the west, in California, earth movements of considerable magnitude are continuing.

Mineral Deposits

Mineral deposits may be classified in many ways: on the basis of commodity, use, worth, strategic importance, method of extracting the ores, need for metallurgical or other treatment, and origin. The United States government classes minerals as strategic or critical, depending on adequacy of supply and importance in case of war (see p. 129).

On the basis of origin minerals are classified into several groups. One such group consists of *sedimentary deposits:* peat; coal; oil and gas; phosphates; fire clay; sand suitable for glassmaking; some iron ores; some manganese deposits; limestone for cement; gypsum, potash, and other salts; sand and gravel; and concentrates of heavy metals. Minerals may also be deposited in sedimentary rocks by vaporous or liquid emanations from magmatic intrusions. These deposits are closely related to those that occur in igneous rocks, and generally they are found in orderly zones analogous to those in salt deposits (Fig. 2.3).

Other mineral deposits occur within intrusions and may be finely disseminated throughout the igneous rock. These, referred to as *disseminated ore deposits,* include many of our largest copper deposits in the western states. Still other deposits consist of minerals that have filled cavities or fissures (joints, faults) to form *veins.* In some, the hot, mineralizing solutions dissolved portions of the surrounding rocks, especially the limestones, and deposited new minerals in their place. These last are known as *replacement deposits.*

Weathering and erosion of any of these

kinds of deposits may give rise to *placer deposits*—stream sands or gravels containing heavy and durable minerals and metals, like gold, washed from mountain deposits. Weathering and erosion of a rock mass containing gold reduces the rocks to clay, silt, sand, and gravel, freeing particles of the heavy minerals, of which gold is one of the heaviest. The gold discovery in California that led to the gold rush of 1849 was made in just such a placer deposit. Washing—subjecting the sands and gravels of a placer deposit to the action of running water—separates the light minerals from the heavy ones, in much the same way that a prospector separates them by washing in a gold pan. The gold, together with a concentrate of dark, heavy minerals, commonly magnetic iron, are left behind, and the light minerals—mostly quartz, feldspar, and clay, which are also light in color—are washed away.

Lode deposits are those still contained within the rock formations, and to remove these ores requires underground mining by pits, tunnels, or shafts.

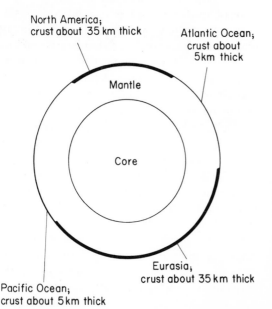

Figure 2.12 *Section through the earth, showing the core, mantle, and crust.*

The value of a mineral deposit and the ore from it depends on the comparative value of the final product and the costs of mining and concentrating the ore at a mill. Mining by any method involves removal of barren rock as well as "pay dirt."

A second factor affecting value derives from the occurrence of more than one metal—for example, lead and silver—in a single deposit. A mine may become unprofitable if either metal becomes priced below a certain minimum, or both metals may be produced if either is priced high enough.

There may be a third factor if one of the associated metals is particularly difficult to separate from the others. For example, zinc is present in some lead-silver ores and is difficult to separate. Consequently a penalty is charged for its presence.

Crustal and Subcrustal Structure

The solid earth consists of three main zones. The outer zone consists of the continental land masses, which are about 20 miles thick, and the ocean floors, which are about 3 miles thick. This zone has an average composition and density between that of granite (about 2.7) and basalt (about 3.3). Although it is composed of many kinds of rocks, this is called the granitic shell, or *crust* (Fig. 2.12).

Below the crust, and extending to a depth of about 2,000 miles, is a denser zone called the *mantle*. Below this and extending to the center is a zone of still denser material, called the *core*. The dimensions and certain physical properties of these layers can be estimated by the manner in which they transmit earthquake waves and by their gravitational and magnetic effects.

The differences in seismic, gravitational, and magnetic properties between the materials at the surface and those at depth probably are due partly to differences in composition and partly to differences in temperature and pressure. Temperatures in the outer 500 kilometers of the mantle have been estimated to exceed 1500°C and may exceed 2000°C. Pressures at a depth of 500 kilometers have been estimated to be about 20 million atmospheres. Rock at such temperatures and pressures behaves very differently from the rocks we know at the surface, where the temperature averages perhaps 30°C and the pressure is 1 atmosphere (14.7 pounds per square inch).

The continents can be thought of as slabs of light rock floating on the denser mantle. Being light, at least comparatively, they rise higher than the ocean basins, and their base is deep in the mantle, like an iceberg in a sea.

Tidal and other stresses that cause movement in the mantle can produce folds and faults in the overlying, more-rigid crust. According to one theory on crustal movements, the convection-cell hypothesis, differences between the densities of the inner and outer parts of the mantle develop as a result of slow heat transfer, which causes convection currents like those resulting from unequal heating of air in a room or of water in a pan, a process illustrated in Figure 2.13,A. Two adjoining units in the mantle, rotating in opposite directions like geared wheels, could cause a wedge of the crust to be dragged downward or raised, depending on the direction of rotation. The part dragged downward could become the site of a geosyncline, like those referred to earlier.

Another theory holds that the crust is drifting across the top of the mantle. This, the theory of continental drift, attributes the bends in the Cordillera of western North America to clockwise rotation of the continent, and the bends in the Cordillera in South America to counterclockwise rotation (Fig. 2.13,B). Probably neither theory is right, but either one would account for the kinds of forces required to create mountains and to move them, and to that extent we may rest easier.

Earthquakes

If all the faults and other fractures in the rocks of the crust were lubricated to eliminate friction, perhaps movement would be continuous, and there would be no earthquakes. Earthquakes and volcanic eruptions com-

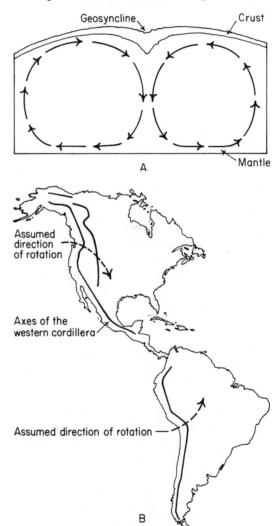

Figure 2.13 *Two hypothetical crustal structures that would explain the forces required to cause crustal warping and folding. (A) The convection-cell hypothesis. (B) The hypothesis of continental drifting assumes that the crust is drifting on top of the mantle.*

monly are thought of as occurring together, but earthquakes may be caused by earth movements that are not at all related to volcanic action. The association, however, has some basis, in that most volcanic eruptions are accompanied by earth tremors.

An earthquake actually originates at a point within the earth's crust. This point is called the *focus,* and the point on the surface directly above it is called the *epicenter.* From the epicenter outward in all directions the intensity of the earthquake diminishes, and around the epicenter can be drawn lines, called *isoseismals,* connecting the points of equal intensity of the shock. Intensities of earthquakes are expressed in terms of various scales. A simple one, called the Modified Mercalli scale, has been much used until recently:

Modified Mercalli Intensity Scale for Earthquakes (1956 version, abridged)

  I. Not felt; detected by seismographs.

  II. Felt by some persons at rest.

 III. Felt indoors. Hanging objects swing. Vibrations like passing of light trucks. May not be recognized as an earthquake.

 IV. Hanging objects swing. Vibration like passing of heavy trucks. Windows, dishes, doors rattle.

  V. Felt outdoors. Sleepers awakened. Liquids spilled. Small objects displaced or upset. Doors, shutters, pictures move.

 VI. Felt by all. Many frightened. Persons walk unsteadily. Windows, dishes, glassware broken. Pictures off walls. Furniture moved or overturned. Plaster and weak masonry cracked. Trees, bushes shake and rustle.

 VII. Difficult to stand. Noticed by drivers of motor cars. Furniture broken. Weak chimneys broken. Fall of plaster. Waves on ponds. Small slides along sand and gravel banks. Large bells ring.

VIII. Steering of motor cars affected. Fall of stucco and some masonry walls. Twisting and falling of chimney, monuments, and elevated tanks. Some frame houses moved on foundations. Branches broken from trees. Cracks in wet ground and on steep slopes.

 IX. General panic. Most masonry seriously damaged. Some frame structures shifted off their foundations. Underground pipes broken. Conspicuous cracks in ground.

  X. Most masonry and frame structures destroyed. Large landslides. Rails bent slightly.

 XI. Rails bent greatly. Underground pipelines completely out of service.

 XII. Damage nearly total.

Earthquake *intensity* refers to the effects on the works of man; earthquake *magnitude* refers to the energy released by the earth movement. Magnitude (Richter scale) is measured by the effects on the seismograph, the amplitude of swing of the arms; each unit increase in magnitude represents a 10-fold increase in effect on the seismograph. Thus an earthquake of magnitude 8 is a hundred times greater than an earthquake of magnitude 6.

Although the 1906 earthquake in California and the resulting fire in San Francisco caused much damage and the loss of hundreds of lives, the losses were small compared to those caused by other major earthquakes and the resulting fires or other disasters. The table below lists some of the major earthquakes that have occurred during this century.

Country	Date	Number of deaths
India	1905	20,000
Italy	1908	75,000
Italy	1915	30,000
China	1920	180,000
China	1932	70,000
Japan	1923	143,000
Turkey	1939	thousands
India	1935	60,000
Morocco	1960	12,000
Chile	1960	5,700
Iran	1957	2,500
Iran	1962	8,000

By comparison, the United States has suffered only minor losses due to earthquakes. Even in this respect we have been favored, partly by our physiography and partly because we have been able to afford better construction.

Figure 2.14 shows the epicenters of the principal earthquakes that have been recorded in the United States (see also Figs. 3.6 and 18.12).

Earth Magnetism

Two manifestations of earth magnetism that are significant physiographically are the earth's general magnetic field and the magnetic properties of certain rock masses that cause deviations in the earth's general field. The magnetic pole is in northern Canada in the northern part of Prince of Wales Island, at about longitude 100°W, latitude 73°. A compass needle points to the north magnetic pole, not to the north geographic pole, and the difference in angle between these two directions is referred to as *declination*. In the United States magnetic north coincides with true north along a line that approximates the 85th meridian. East of this line the compass points west of north; west of this line the compass points east of north. The amount of declination in various parts of the United States is shown in Figure 2.15. A compass taken across the country must be corrected for declination.

Another correction must be made if a compass is taken north. As the pole is approached the needle increasingly dips toward the ground, and at the magnetic poles stands vertically. In the central United States the needle dips about 65 degrees to the north. Compass needles in the United States must

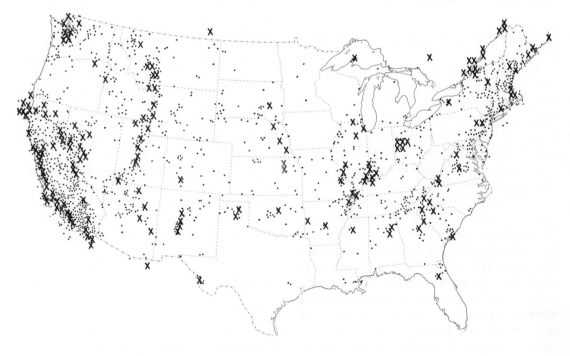

Figure 2.14 *Epicenters of earthquakes in and immediately adjacent to the United States.* X = *destructive and near-destructive earthquakes. (After Coast and Geodetic Survey.)* • = *minor earthquakes. (After American Geophysical Union.)*

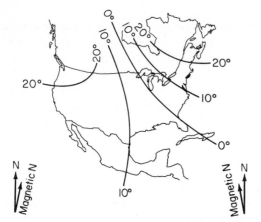

Figure 2.15 *Lines of equal magnetic declination (isogonic lines) are given for each 10 degrees (declinations as of 1960). In the northern United States the north ends of compass needles are drifting westward roughly 2 to 4 minutes annually; in the southern United States they are drifting eastward at a maximum of about 2 minutes annually.*

have a weight on the south end to maintain them level.

An effect of declination may be seen in the street pattern in Baltimore, which is not noted for having an orderly system of streets. Baltimore streets that supposedly lead north are alined about 3 degrees west of north, and the east-west system is similarly misoriented. The survey evidently was not corrected properly for declination.

Rock formations containing magnetic minerals can affect both the direction and dip of a compass needle, and this property can be used to locate such formations, thus serving as an aid to the study of buried rock structures. Deviations caused by magnetic rocks are called *magnetic anomalies*. Weakly magnetic masses or strongly magnetic ones that are deeply buried produce anomalies with low amplitude; depth of burial and the nature of the edges of the magnetic masses— that is, whether gradational with or sharply separated from surrounding nonmagnetic rock—determine the magnetic gradient or the steepness of the sides of the anomalies. Some

examples are given in Figure 2.16, which illustrates some of the kinds of magnetic anomalies in the United States and their relation to exposed and buried rock masses.

The metamorphic and igneous rocks in the Piedmont and New England Provinces give sharp, high-amplitude anomalies; on the Coastal Plain, similar anomalies, except for having low amplitude, leave no doubt about the continuity of the metamorphic and igneous rocks beneath the Coastal Plain formations.

Iron-bearing formations in the Superior Upland produce high-amplitude linear anomalies trending southwestward. Similar anomalies, except for having low amplitude, extend southwestward to Nebraska and leave no doubt that the iron-bearing formations extend at least that far under the cover of Paleozoic and Cretaceous formations (Fig. 2.1).

The magnetic properties of some kinds of rock formations also can be used to determine shifts in the positions of the magnetic poles, or possible crustal changes, in the geologic past. For example, in some intrusions and lava flows, as the magma solidified, the magnetic minerals oriented themselves in the earth's magnetic field as it existed at the time the rock body formed. This so-called *relict magnetism* can be determined and used to measure the difference between an earlier magnetic field and that of the present. If enough such rock masses can be found, it may be possible to reconstruct progressive changes in the earth's magnetic field.

Gravity

All matter exerts a force that attracts other matter, and this force varies as the product of two masses of matter and inversely as the square of the distance between them. The force of gravity is the attraction of the earth for matter around it. If the earth were homogeneous and had a smooth surface, the force

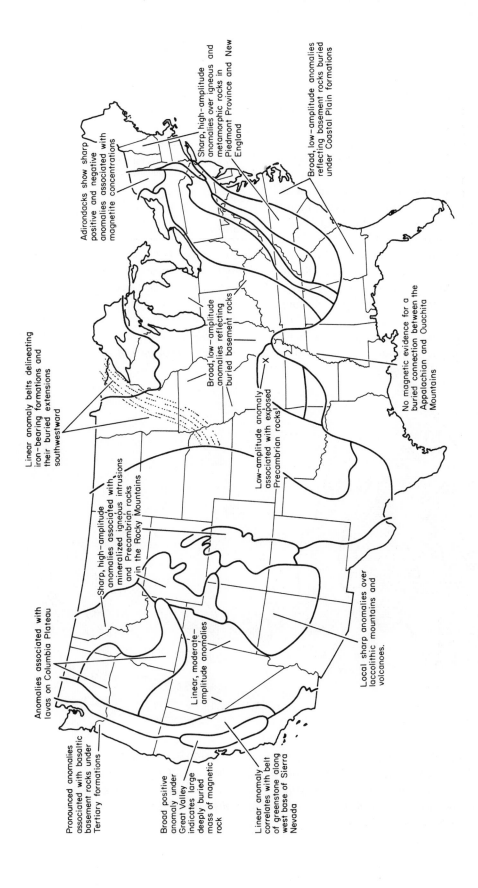

Figure 2.16 *Some magnetic anomalies in the United States. (Generalized from U.S.G.S.)*

of gravity would be uniform all over the surface. But the earth is not homogeneous; some rock masses are dense and exert greater pull than others that are less dense.

Surveys that measure these gravity differences indicate that the rocks under the ocean basins are more dense than those that form the continents. These surveys also reveal irregularities in the continental slabs. Figure 2.17 illustrates the great thickness of crustal rocks inferred under the Sierra Nevada as compared with either the Great Basin to the east or the Pacific Ocean to the west. Figure 2.18 shows irregularities in the force of gravity in the United States. The gravity contours are calculated for sea level. The milligal, the unit by which gravity is measured, is roughly a millionth of the gravitational acceleration

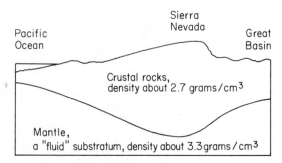

Figure 2.17 *Diagrammatic cross section through the Sierra Nevada from the Great Basin to the Pacific Ocean. Under the Sierra Nevada the layer of light crustal rocks is believed to be about seven times as thick as under the ocean, and about twice as thick as under the western part of the Great Basin.*

Figure 2.18 *Gravity map of the United States. Contour interval 100 millegals. The continent is light rock and gives negative values; off the coasts dense rocks give positive values. The high-altitude western states have extensive areas with values less than −200 milligals, and evidently are underlain by a thick layer of light rock. (From U.S.G.S.)*

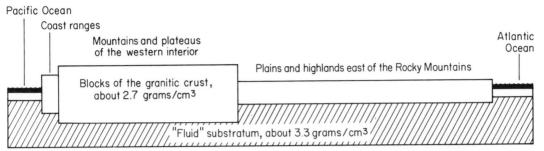

Figure 2.19 *Simplified interpretation of the gravity map of the United States envisages blocks of the granitic crust (density about 2.7) floating in a denser substratum. The crustal blocks are thin under the oceans, but they are thick and sink deeply into the substratum under the high mountains and plateaus in the western United States.*

at the earth's surface. Masses of light rock, like those under the western physiographic provinces, give negative values; masses of dense rock give positive values. Figure 2.19 shows diagrammatically an interpretation of the possible structural significance of the variation in gravity across the country.

Figure 2.20 offers an interpretation of the configuration of the base of the crust beneath the United States. The high mountains and plateaus in the western United States have deep roots. The Appalachians, which are lower, have shallow roots. Seismic studies show that the still lower mountains of the Superior Upland do not have roots of light rock, although this seems to be expressed in Figure 2.18. These differences may be related to differences in the ages and histories of the mountains as well as to the differences in their heights; the western mountains are Cenozoic, the Appalachians are Paleozoic, and the mountains of the Superior Upland are Precambrian. If the continents are drifting across the mantle, perhaps the roots of the older mountains have been sheared off.

Geologic History

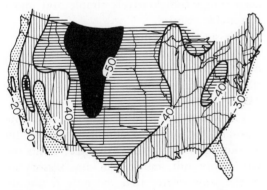

Figure 2.20 *An interpretation of the configuration of the base of the crust under the United States. Contours show the inferred depths of the base in kilometers below sea level. Depths are greatest under the Southern and Middle Rocky Mountains, the northern Great Plains, and the Sierra Nevada. Depths are least under the Pacific coast and under the Atlantic coast. (From U.S.G.S.)*

In attempting to summarize the major events of earth history that have controlled the structural framework of the physiographic provinces, we will assume the earth to be 5 billion years old. This is slightly older than the currently popular estimate, based on radioactive age determinations on meteorites and on ancient rocks in the crust. But until we know *how* the earth was formed, we cannot be sure what event we should take for the beginning. It could be that the earth is many times older

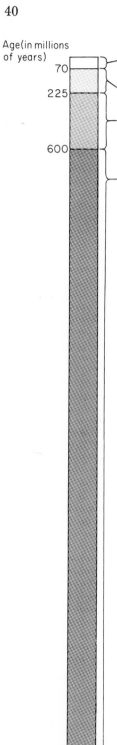

Age(in millions of years)

70 — Cenozoic Era, about which we know most, is the age of mammals and of the Rocky Mountains. The Quaternary Period, the age of Man, is represented by the width of the top line.

225 — Mesozoic Era, the age of dinosaurs and of Pacific Coast Mountains ancestral to the present ones.

— Paleozoic Era, the age of invertebrates, of great coal swamps, and of the Appalachian Mountains.

600

— Precambrian time, about which we know very little.

Figure 2.21 *Relative duration of the geologic eras.*

5,000

than 5 billion years, and perhaps that date merely represents the last time the earth's inhabitants became sufficiently civilized to demolish the planet!

The beginning of geologic time is as uncertain and mysterious as the limits, if there are any, to outer space, but if we limit our attention to the last 5 billion years, we can keep things comparatively simple and under reasonable control.

The ages and durations of the eras and periods are shown in Table 2.1. The relative duration of the eras is more clearly emphasized by proportions on a linear scale (Fig. 2.21).

The system of dividing geologic time into eras and periods was adopted because, for measuring geologic time, the year is an unsatisfactory unit, and for the same reason and to the same degree that the mile is unsatisfactory for measuring stellar space. Our planet is only a speck of dust in stellar space, and a year is only a split second in geologic time.

Geologic processes operate exceedingly slowly, but they cause tremendous changes because they operate for so long a time. A foot of uplift in a thousand years is not a breathtaking rate of earth movement. Indeed, many parts of the United States are moving today at rates greater than that. But uplift continued at that rate for 10 million years—which is not a long time geologically speaking—can build a 10,000 foot mountain range. Slow and easy does it!

The basis for subdividing geologic history lies in the fossil record, the subject of the science called *paleontology*. Species change from one era or period to another, because extinct species never reappear, and new species are never quite like more ancient ones. As we look backward into older and older formations, the faunas increasingly differ from those of the present.

Since some species survive without change longer than others, an individual fossil may be misleading. Rather, the whole *fauna,* not the individual fossil or individual species, must be considered. By analogy, a modern kitchen may contain colonial antiques, but one has little difficulty identifying the age of the kitchen on the basis of the total assemblage of utensils and equipment.

Differences may also exist between contemporaneous faunas, because of differences in environment within a depositional basin. For example, noticeable differences in shellfish faunas may be noted between the Mississippi River, its mouth, and the deeper and saltier offshore water. These differences, which are analogous to the differences between a kitchen, a dining room, and a living room, usually can be correctly identified and understood by noting the changes in texture and composition of the fossil-bearing formation as it is traced away from or toward the original source of the sediments. Such studies are the concern of *paleogeography* and *paleoecology*.

The Precambrian is noteworthy because of the vast time represented by it, almost 90 percent of all geologic time. Precambrian rocks, however, are exposed in only a few places in the United States (Fig. 2.1)—in the Appalachian Highlands, Lake Superior Region, central Texas, and in parts of the Rocky Mountain region, the West Coast, and Alaska.

The record preserved in these rocks is not only fragmentary but is difficult to decipher. Many of the rocks are so altered that one cannot be sure what they were like originally. Precambrian history was inscribed on a vast number of pages of which only a few are preserved for our inspection. Moreover, the writing on many of those pages is illegible, and we cannot be sure of the sequence of the pages we have recovered.

For our purpose, the Precambrian rocks are important chiefly because those in the Lake Superior region contain this nation's principal iron deposits, and elsewhere they provide the basement foundation for the Paleozoic, Mesozoic, and Cenozoic rocks and structures.

Fossil remains in Precambrian rocks are those of primitive forms (algae, radiolaria, sponges, and possible foraminifera), but the absence of higher-order forms does not necessarily mean that all living things were primitive. Soft parts of animals rarely are preserved, and the fossil record must be reconstructed largely from hard parts, such as shells and bones. Late Precambrian animals may have included large and complex forms that were composed wholly of soft, nonmineral tissue. The still unknown ancestor of the fish may have been a complex organism without hard parts.

Paleozoic rocks, which represent the next 8 percent of geologic time, are widespread, from the Appalachians to the Rocky Mountains. During this time there were uplands and probably mountains along the Atlantic seaboard, and a mediterranean sea occupied a trough, or geosyncline, along the site of the Appalachian Mountains (Fig. 2.7). Other uplands or mountains existed at or near the site of the Gulf Coast, and there were seas north of them. Still other uplands existed at the western edge of the continent, and a mediterranean sea occupied a geosyncline that extended northward across the western states. Most of the interior states were alternately slightly below and slightly above sea level, and apparently then, as now, had little relief.

Sediments eroded from the mountains and uplands were deposited in the geosynclines to a thickness of about 30,000 feet. This does not mean that the seas were 6 miles deep. On the contrary, both the fossils and the physical geology indicate that much of the time the seas were shallow. Evidently the coast under those seas gradually sank as sediments accumulated in them. And during the same long period, the bordering mountains must have been maintained, despite erosion, by a prolonged series of small uplifts.

We cannot be sure whether the segment of the earth's crust that comprises North America was isolated from other present-day continental segments during Paleozoic time. In any case, the uplands or mountains of that time were located along or near what later became the margins of our continent, and the geosynclinal seas of that time were located along the site of many of the present mountains. The physical geography was different!

In the central and eastern states the Paleozoic deposits are noted for their mineral fuels—oil, gas, and coal. Other important mineral deposits of this age are the salt beds in New York, West Virginia, Michigan, Ohio, Illinois, and Kansas, and the so-called Clinton iron beds that extend along the Appalachians from New York to Alabama.

When the Paleozoic ended, the sediments that filled the geosyncline became folded and became part of the Appalachian Mountains, which had been forming since early Paleozoic time. In the Mesozoic Era, which represents about 3 percent of geologic time, there were dinosaurs, and toward the close of the Mesozoic the first suckling mammals and toothless birds appeared. Also, in Cretaceous time, flowering plants appear in abundance for the first time, and perhaps bees and wasps date from then.

The principal areas of Mesozoic rocks in the United States are shown in Figure 2.1. These rocks are a rich source of the energetic minerals—coal, oil, gas, and uranium. The locations of the principal geosynclinal seas and bordering mountains indicated by the Mesozoic rocks are shown in Figure 2.7,B and C. In Triassic and Jurassic time (Fig. 2.7,B) a geosynclinal sea extended along much of the Pacific coast of the United States, and a thin sheet of sediments was deposited far to the east in an area that was alternately shallow sea and land. In the eastern United States terrestrial deposits of Triassic age were laid down along the eastern foot of the Appalachians, which had risen where the Paleozoic sea had been. This kind of history was repeated in Cretaceous time (Fig. 2.7,C) when mountains rose at the site of what had been the Triassic and Jurassic sea, and happened again at the beginning of Cenozoic time when the Rocky Mountains were formed along the position occupied by the Cretaceous geosynclinal sea. In geology, evidently, what goes down must come up!

Uplift of the Rocky Mountains at the site of the Cretaceous geosynclinal sea occurred 60 million years ago. The time since then, embracing the Cenozoic, is about 1 percent of geologic time. The western mountains had begun forming in California and Nevada during Jurassic time, but did not occupy the positions of present-day mountains, nor did they look like them. At the end of Cretaceous time, the mountain-making movements extended eastward to central Colorado, and for the first time the physical geography of the country, including the outline of the continent, began assuming the shapes we know today. Although the Rocky Mountains began forming in early Tertiary time, the general uplift to their present high altitudes occurred during the latter part of the Tertiary.

During the Tertiary Period, mammals became dominant. These were small and strange ones at first, like *Eohippus*. This ancestral horse was little bigger than a dog and had five toes. Later in the Tertiary the animals became larger and by Pliocene time consisted mostly of those familiar to us today. During the first part of the Tertiary period, the coastal plain along the Atlantic and Gulf coasts was partly submerged (Fig. 10.31). It emerged to take approximately its present form in late Tertiary time, and that area is blanketed with Cenozoic rocks, as are the Great Plains and western basins, where sediments eroded from the newly formed mountains were deposited. Many of these sedimentary deposits are rich in mineral fuels, particularly oil and gas in California and along the Gulf Coast in Texas and Louisiana. The tremendous oil-shale deposits in the western interior are of Tertiary age.

At the end of Pliocene time, roughly 2 million years ago, *Australopithecus, Pithecanthropus,* and other primitive ape-men appeared in the eastern hemisphere. *Homo sapiens* appeared no earlier than a few hundred thousand years ago. During this last period, the Quaternary, continental glaciers spread southward into Europe and North America. The deposits left by the glaciers, called *glacial drift,* record a succession of climatic changes (p. 68ff.). The last big glaciers retreated to the polar caps some 10,000 years ago. Before that time man had migrated to North America.

During the periods of mountain building in the western United States, there was much volcanic and other igneous activity (p. 25ff.), and as a result, extensive areas there are blanketed by volcanic and related rocks (Fig. 2.1). The great volcanoes of the Cascade Range formed during the Quaternary period, and this volcanism continued until historic time. Such volcanism and related igneous activity in the western states gave rise to the abundant and varied metallic mineral deposits of that region.

3 The Landforms

General Considerations of Scale and Origin

Hills record at least two quite different chapters of geologic history: one, recorded by the rocks in the hill, involves ancient geologic history; the second is comparatively recent history and concerns the processes and events that caused the hill to be sculptured from those rocks.

These two chapters of earth history may be separated by hundreds of millions of years —a fact that removes some of the mystery about sea shells found on the tops of some mountains. The shells are there not because the mountains were ever submerged but because the rocks containing them were deposited as muds or other sediments in a sea. Subsequently, those sediments became compacted and hardened—*lithified*—by pressure or heat due to their burial beneath younger deposits. Eons later they were raised by earth movements to the altitudes at which we now find them. Still later, erosion carved the mountains from those fossil-bearing rocks.

Landforms and the processes by which they have developed—the subject of *geomorphology*—may be considered on four very different scales (Fig. 3.1). The largest, represented by the continents and the oceanic deeps, have horizontal dimensions measurable in thousands of miles and a vertical relief of more than 10 miles. The processes by which these developed involve the geologic history of the mantle.

The next smaller scale of landforms is that represented by the physiographic provinces, especially on the continents, although the ocean bottoms can be divided into physiographic provinces too. The provinces, whether on the land or under the sea, are characterized by a distinctive kind of geologic structure, and are scores or hundreds of miles wide. Figure 3.1,B, illustrates the structural differences that control landforms in the provinces along the middle Atlantic seaboard.

The next smaller scale of landforms reflects differences in process or position within the physiographic provinces. The differences between valley bottoms, valley sides, and hilltops are examples. Figure 3.1,C, illustrates some landforms in the littoral zone that are attributable to differences in processes operating at various distances from shore. The smallest scale of landforms is measurable in centimeters or inches; every location has its peculiar microrelief, such as mudcracks on the tidal flats, tussock mounds on the sand dunes, and ripple marks where the inshore water is shallow (Fig. 3.1,D).

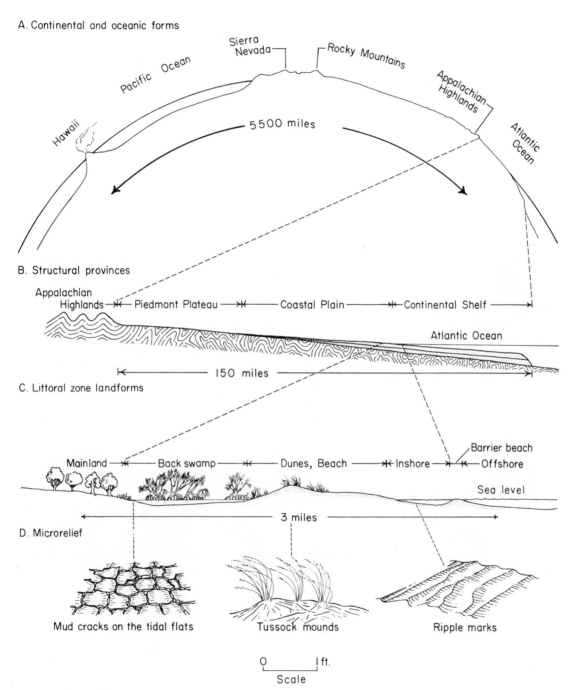

A. Continental and oceanic forms

B. Structural provinces

C. Littoral zone landforms

D. Microrelief

Mud cracks on the tidal flats   Tussock mounds   Ripple marks

Figure 3.1 *Four scales of landforms. The largest (A) are represented by the continents and the oceanic deeps. Next largest (B) are the physiographic provinces, each characterized by distinctive geologic structure. Within the provinces (C) are smaller differences reflecting differences in local structure or different processes. The smallest features (D) are represented in microrelief.*

The three major factors that control the shape of landforms are structure, process, and stage. In the geomorphic sense of the word, *structure* involves two quite different properties, one pertaining to differences in the resistance of rocks to erosion, the other pertaining to the way the rock formations have been deformed—that is, whether they are tilted, folded, faulted, or have remained horizontal though uplifted. By way of example, landforms developed on folded resistant rocks differ from those developed on similarly folded nonresistant rocks. And these landforms differ from those developed where the formations are horizontal or tilted. The two larger scales of landforms are governed primarily by their structures.

Many different *processes* shape landforms. Some are erosional; others are depositional. The agents of erosion and deposition are streams, waves, glacial ice, and wind, and each process develops distinctive landforms. Valleys eroded by streams tend to have V-shaped cross sections; valleys deepened by glaciers have U-shaped cross sections. Streams build alluvial fans, glacial ice builds terminal moraines, and wind builds dunes. Along the coasts wave erosion and shore currents develop cliffs, stacks, and arches. The coastal outline may be straight, like the east coast of Florida; cuspate between spits, like the coast of North Carolina; or built of great capes, like Cape Cod.

The two smaller scales of landforms illustrated in Figure 3.1 are governed primarily by the processes of erosion and sedimentation that shaped them.

Stage pertains to the duration of a particular process and to its intensity—that is, whether the effects are those of a feeble process, one just beginning to operate, or those of a vigorous process that is well advanced. Stage is merely a modifying factor that controls the shape of landforms; the chief factors are structure and process.

Nevertheless, differences in the forms of stream valleys have been attributed to stage of erosion. Deep narrow valleys and those having roughened gradients have been described by geologists as *youthful*. Valleys that have intermediate width, shape, and longitudinal profile have been described as *mature*. Valleys that are open and have low gradients have been described as *old*. This concept, though, is much over-simplified, for the major differences in landforms result chiefly from structure and, to a lesser extent, process. There is no reason to suppose, for example, that the broad open valleys on top of the Appalachian Plateaus are older than the deeper and narrower valleys of the main streams. A more extreme example is illustrated by some mountains formed by igneous rock, which is resistant to erosion. The surrounding sedimentary rocks erode more readily and their surface is lowered faster, which leaves the mountain of igneous rock higher and usually more rugged. Such mountains appear more youthful as they become older.

There are two other reasons why stage is not very important in shaping the landforms of the provinces. First, most landforms have been evolving throughout the latter part of the Cenozoic Era, a period of many millions of years during which the climates have changed greatly. As a result, the capacity of streams to erode and to transport debris also has changed greatly; episodes of downcutting have alternated with episodes during which streams were unable to cut downward and instead deposited alluvium in their valleys. Second, during the long time that the landforms have been evolving, structural movements have modified stream gradients in many regions and thereby affected their capacity to erode and to transport sediment. In still other regions stream courses have been modified as a result of damming by lava flows.

Figure 3.9,D, illustrates a striking example of differences in landform due directly to change in process (see also Figs. 15.19 and 15.20). A delta, with shore bars and terraces, was deposited at the foot of the Wasatch

Mountains in Lake Bonneville, a Pleistocene lake that was once 1,000 feet deep and lapped against the side of the mountains. Because the climate has changed, the region is now semiarid; Great Salt Lake is the residue of the Pleistocene lake. Stream erosion in the Wasatch Mountains now extends to the foot of the mountains, and the delta and other deposits in Lake Bonneville are now subject to erosion by streams and wind.

Changes in stream regimen and process that are attributable to climatic change also are illustrated by deep, wide glaciated valleys now occupied by streams too small to cut them; an example is Yosemite Valley in the Sierra Nevada. Other changes in stream regimen are illustrated by the alluvial deposits in many western valleys. The deposits and the arroyos they fill record a succession of episodes of downcutting alternating with valley filling.

Much or most of our landscape is the result of processes that have operated during the latter part of the Cenozoic Era. During this time, about 30 million years, there have been earth movements and changes in climates. It follows that most landforms are polygenetic. The landforms evolved while their structure was being changed and while the processes shaping them were changing in intensity or even in kind.

Contrasting the Provinces

Structure

The distribution of the mountains, plateaus, and plains in the United States (Fig. 3.2) reflects the paleogeography of the Paleozoic and Early Mesozoic (Fig. 2.7,A and B) and to a lesser extent that of the Cretaceous (Fig. 2.7, C). The Rocky Mountains formed near the axis of a Cretaceous geosyncline. The Coast Ranges and the Sierra Nevada developed on the sites of Triassic and Jurassic geosynclines. The block mountains in Nevada and the Appalachian Highlands formed along the axes of Paleozoic geosynclines. The plains, both in the interior and along the coast, are the sites of ancient shallow seas (shelf areas) in which thin beds were deposited. In a sense, therefore, the landforms attributed to structure are the product of a series of structures, each dependent upon something that preceded.

PLATEAUS

The four major plateaus in the United States are the Appalachian, Ozark, Colorado, and Columbia plateaus. In each of these physiographic provinces the rock formations are nearly horizontal and the surfaces of the plateaus have been raised high above sea level—2,000 feet in the Appalachian and Ozark plateaus, 1,500 to 4,000 feet in the Columbia Plateau, and more than 5,000 feet in the Colorado Plateau. Parts of the Colorado Plateau—the High Plateaus of Utah—are 11,000 feet above sea level and are among the highest plateaus in the world. Two other plateaus, both averaging below 1,000 feet in altitude, are the Piedmont Province and the Interior Low Plateaus.

A small plateau is known as a butte, or as a *mesa*—a Spanish term commonly used in the Southwest. The difference between a plateau and a butte or mesa is simply one of scale, not unlike the difference between a mountain and a hill.

The geologic structure of a plateau is easy to visualize, and the nearly horizontal but elevated strata can be seen along canyon walls (Fig. 3.3). In the more elevated plateaus the streams are incised deeply, like the Grand Canyon of the Colorado River, or the even deeper, though less colorful, Hell's Canyon of the Snake River along the boundary between Oregon and Idaho. Such canyons have been described as "mountains inside out."

The development of plateaus requires not only the uplift of nearly horizontal formations

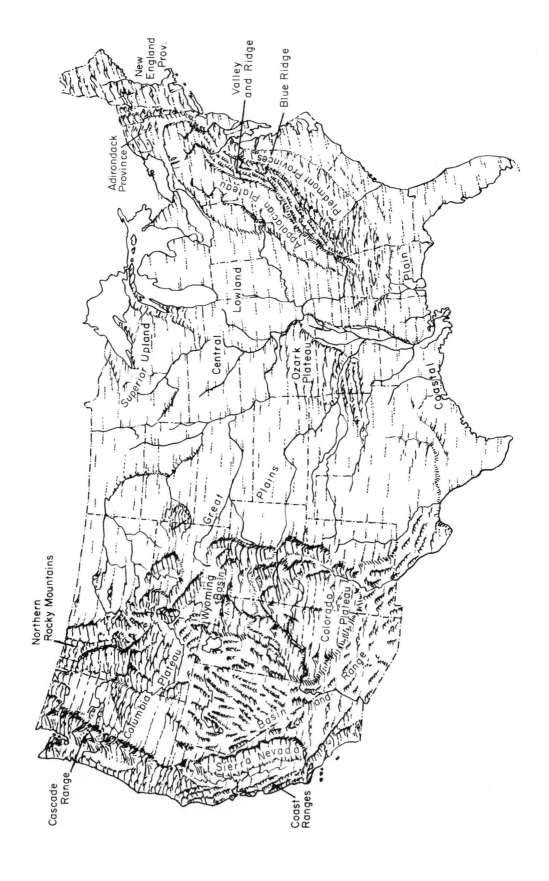

Figure 3.2 *Landform map contrasting the physiographic provinces in the United States.*

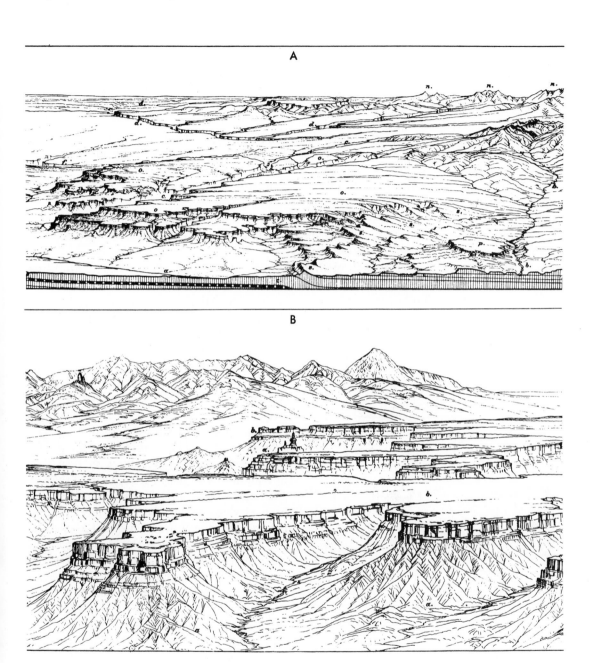

Figure 3.3 *Some plateau structures, as sketched by W. H. Holmes. (A) View north across Mesa Verde (o) to the Rio Dolores (d), La Plata Mountains (l), and San Miguel Mountains (n) in southwest Colorado. Other localities: San Juan River (a), Rio La Plata (b), Rio Mancos (c), McElmo Creek (f), hogback (s), Pinon mesa (p). (B) Closer view of the Mesa Verde: slopes (a) are shale; the caprock (b) is sandstone (Cretaceous).*

but the presence of resistant formations to maintain the upland surface. In areas where all the formations are easily eroded, the result is badland topography. Similar topography derives from weathering and erosion of homogeneous formations that are resistant enough so that joints, or cracks, in the rock become expressed in the landforms (Fig. 3.4).

Locally in the plateau provinces the formations are flexed into step folds known as *monoclines*, expressed topographically by *hogbacks*, like the one shown at *s* in Figure 3.3,A. Hogbacks, formed by the eroded, protruding edge of a steeply dipping resistant formation, are notable features on the Colorado Plateau, and form some of the spectacular scenery of that area. One, the Waterpocket Fold, is 1,000 to 1,500 feet high and 75 miles long; only at a

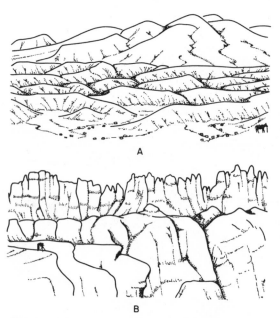

A

B

Figure 3.4 *Two kinds of badland topography. (A) Badlands developed in easily eroded, homogeneous Cretaceous shale, Henry Mountains, Utah. (B) Badlands forming The Needles, in Canyonlands National Park, Utah, are developed in Permian sandstone formations. The sandstones are resistant enough so that fractures in the rock (joints) become expressed in the topography.*

few places can its rugged cliffs be crossed, even on foot.

Where the formations dip less steeply than in a hogback, the resistant formations produce *cuestas,* which are ridges having escarpments facing updip and long, gentle slopes in the downdip direction (Fig. 3.7, section C-D). Cuestas are a characteristic feature of the Coastal Plain Province. They are also characteristic of large areas on the Colorado Plateau and the Great Plains.

PLAINS

Within the United States, there are three major plains (Fig. 3.2). One, the Coastal Plain, is along the Atlantic and Gulf coasts. Another, the largest of them all, comprises the Central Lowland and Great Plains in the Middle West. The third is the California Trough, which forms the Central Valley in California. Another major plain borders the Yukon River in Alaska (Fig. 3.9,C). The Continental Shelf along the Atlantic seaboard is part of the Coastal Plain but is still submerged.

Structurally, plains are like plateaus, for their formations are horizontal, or nearly so, but landforms on plains are less varied than on plateaus because the plains either have not been elevated much above sea level or they rise very gradually from low altitudes, as do the Great Plains, which are higher than the Appalachian Plateaus. Interstream areas on plains are but little higher than the drainage courses, and there is little topographic relief. Consequently, the plains are the most densely populated and most used parts of our land.

A different and special kind of plain is represented by the playas in the valleys separating the block mountains of the Basin and Range Province. Some of these cover thousands of square miles, as does the Great Salt Lake desert, which includes the well-known speed course at the Bonneville Salt Flats. Another large playa, the Carson Sink in Nevada, covers more than a thousand square miles.

There are many smaller ones, such as the salt-encrusted floor of Death Valley, which covers about 200 square miles.

MOUNTAINS

The most complex kinds of landforms are the mountains, which are of many different kinds, each reflecting a different kind of geologic structure. Figure 3.5 illustrates four kinds of mountains—dome, volcanic, fold, and block-fault mountains—and their structures.

Most of the volcanic mountains in the United States are along the Pacific coast, especially in the Cascade Range and Aleutian Islands. These are part of a belt of active volcanoes and numerous earthquake centers surrounding the Pacific Ocean (Fig. 3.6).

Fold mountains, represented by the Valley and Ridge Province in the Appalachian Highlands and the Ouachita Mountains in Oklahoma, have been eroded from sedimentary rock formations that were compressed into great folds; the upturned edges of the resistant formations form the mountain ridges.

A dome mountain is a special and local sort of fold mountain, and consists of a single upfold. The resistant formations turned upward around the dome form concentric ridges between the valleys cut in the more easily eroded formations. Examples of dome mountains are the Adirondacks in New York, the Black Hills in Wyoming and South Dakota, the Zuni Mountains in New Mexico, and the Henry Mountains and San Rafael Swell in Utah.

In the United States the principal area of block mountains, which are formed by faulting, is in the Basin and Range Province. The typical block mountain has an escarpment on the faulted side and a long, comparatively gentle slope away from the fault. The differences in slope on the two sides are illustrated by the profile through the Sierra Nevada (Fig. 2.17), which has been raised along a fault on the east side and tilted downward to the west.

Another important area of block mountains

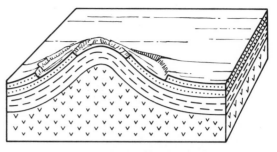

Dome mountain

Volcano

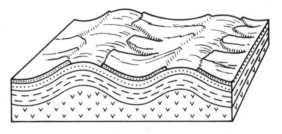

Fold mountains

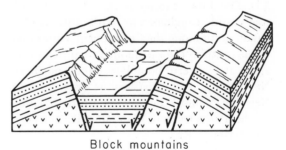

Block mountains

Figure 3.5 *Four kinds of mountains: dome mountain; volcano; fold mountain; block mountain.*

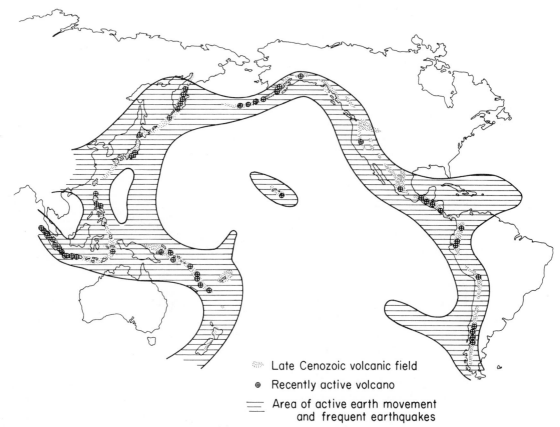

Late Cenozoic volcanic field

⊕ Recently active volcano

≡ Area of active earth movement and frequent earthquakes

Figure 3.6   *Belt of volcanic and tectonic activity surrounding the Pacific Ocean. Active earth movement is indicated by the frequent earthquakes.*

in this country is the belt of Triassic basins in the eastern part of the United States (Figs. 2.1, 3.7). The Triassic formations, mostly red sandstone and conglomerate with interbedded basalt, occur along the Connecticut Valley and to the south in the Piedmont Province, mostly along its western boundary, from northern New Jersey to North Carolina (Fig. 2.1). In New Jersey, block mountains are represented by the Palisades and Watchung Ridges (Fig. 3.7, section A-B).

Mountains composed of granite develop characteristic landforms. Because granite is both homogeneous and resistant, erosion produces topography not unlike that of badlands, but on a mountainous scale. Granitic mountains are extensive in central Idaho and in the Sierra Nevada, which is a tilted fault block of granite. Smaller granitic masses form the Black Hills, the Highlands of the Hudson, and some mountains in New England. Parts of the Rocky Mountains contain granite, notably the Front Range in Colorado, but the Rockies are complex mountains—partly fold, partly volcanic, and partly granitic.

Drainage Patterns

The structural pattern of a physiographic province becomes etched by stream erosion, and each province has its own characteristic drainage pattern. One type of pattern is branched, like a tree, and is called *dendritic.*

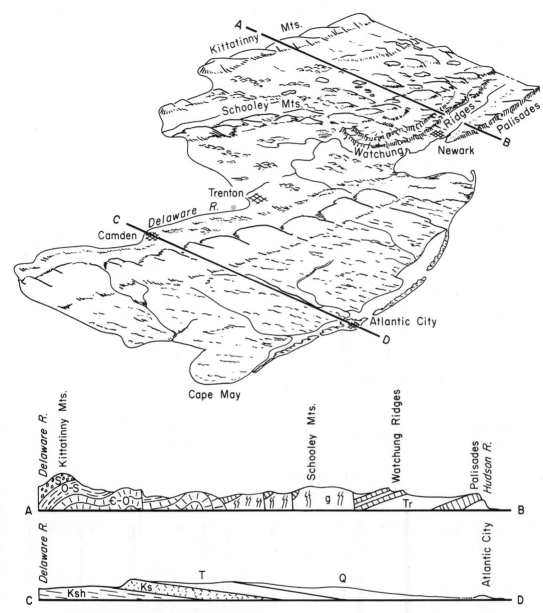

Figure 3.7 *Relief map and cross sections of New Jersey, illustrating several kinds of landforms. Southeastern New Jersey is coastal plain with Cretaceous (K), Tertiary (T), and Quaternary (Q) formations dipping gently seaward. The resistant formations form ridges (cuestas) paralleling the coast. The New Jersey turnpike follows one of the westernmost valleys. Atlantic City is on a barrier beach. The Triassic (Tr) belt of block mountains extends from Newark Bay to Trenton and westward to the Reading Prong, which is a complex (g) of granite, volcanic rocks and Paleozoic formations. To the west are the folded Cambrian (€), Ordovician (O), and Silurian (S) formations.*

Drainage systems in plateaus are likely to have this pattern. Examples are the Columbia and Snake rivers on the Columbia Plateaus and the Colorado River on the Colorado Plateau (Fig. 5.1). On plains the drainage pattern tends to be *parallel* in the direction of slope, as on the Coastal Plain and on the Great Plains (Fig. 5.1). Parallel drainage also has developed on the long western slope of the Sierra Nevada. Where the geologic structure consists of long parallel folds or faults, the drainage pattern is like a *trellis,* with long straight stretches parallel to the structures and short stretches at right angles across them, as in the Valley and Ridge Province and in the Coast Ranges of California. In isolated mountains, like the Adirondacks and the volcanoes of the Cascade Range, the drainage is *radial*. In the Southern Rocky Mountains the drainage is radial, though on a larger scale.

Although these several kinds of drainage patterns reflect the geologic structure, the history of the drainage courses is highly complex, partly because of changes in climate, partly because of stream diversions such as might be caused by glaciation, and partly because of earth movements. An example of such complexity is illustrated by the riddle of how major rivers have developed and maintained their courses across mountain ranges instead of around them. Examples are legion; seven well-known ones are:

1. Columbia River gorge through the Cascade Range (Figs. 17.11, 17.14).
2. Golden Gate, San Francisco Bay (p. 387).
3. Gorge of the Bighorn River across the Big-horn Mountains, Wyoming-Montana (p. 271).
4. Colorado River gorges at the Black Mountains, Arizona and Nevada, Uncompaghre uplift, and White River Plateau, Colorado (p. 271).
5. Royal Gorge of the Arkansas River, Colorado (Fig. 13.1, p. 270).
6. Delaware River at the Water Gap (Fig. 11.22,A).
7. Susquehanna River at Harrisburg (Fig. 11.22,B).

These features can be attributed to any of three kinds of origin, referred to as *antecedence, superposition,* or a combination of those two that has been termed *anteconsequence* (or *anteposition*) (Fig. 3.8). The process of antecedence involves uplift of a potential barrier across a drainage course at a rate slower than the rate of downcutting by the stream, thus allowing the stream course to be maintained (Fig. 3.8,A). Superposition involves development of a drainage course on a surface that covers older formations that may be folded, and when the stream cuts downward into the older rocks, the drainage course becomes superimposed on those structures. Such streams bear no relation to the buried rock structures and cut across them (Fig. 3.8,B). The processes are combined where uplift ponds the drainage, which overflows the barrier; the effect is that of antecedence downstream from the barrier and superposition upstream from it (Fig. 3.8,C).

Landforms Attributable to Deposition

The converse of erosion is sedimentation, and the conditions that favor erosion, if reversed, favor deposition of sediments. Depositional landforms may be produced by the same agents that produce the erosional ones—that is, by streams, glaciers, waves, or wind. The depositional landforms are as varied as the erosional ones, but in general they are less extensive; many are merely local.

Depositional environments are of three major kinds: (1) *continental environments*—glaciers, streams, lakes, marshes, and dunes; (2) *marine environments*—shallow seas and deep seas; and (3) *mixed continental and marine environments*—the littoral zone, tidal lagoons, estuaries, and deltas. The deposits in each of these kinds of environments have characteristic bedding. Glacial till lacks bedding.

Stream deposits, including the glaciofluvial
ones included in glacial drift, are stratified,
but the beds are discontinuous because of frequent changes in the stream position. Lake
deposits and marine deposits are, in general,
thin-bedded, and individual beds may persist
for long distances.

Among the stream-deposited features are
floodplains, deltas, alluvial fans, and talus
aprons (Fig. 3.9). Most large rivers have floodplains, even though many are narrow; along
many streams there are terraces recording old
floodplains at high levels. Three large floodplains in the United States are those along the
Mississippi River, in the central valley of California, and along the lower Yukon and Kuskokwim rivers in Alaska (Fig. 3.9,A, B, and C).
Some deltas that are well exposed for study
are in the now dry bed of Lake Bonneville
(Fig. 3.9,D). Alluvial fans may be steep and
small (Fig. 3.9,E) or may be gently sloping and
large, covering many square miles. Other kinds
of deposits include *talus,* which collects at the
foot of steep slopes as a result of rock falls
(Fig. 3.9,F), and *colluvium* (Fig. 3.9,G), which
collects on hillsides and moves slowly down
gentle slopes—a process called creep.

Glacial deposits cover most of the northern
United States (Fig. 6.1) and occur on the high
mountains in the western United States and
even in Hawaii. A few examples of the many
different landforms built by glacial deposits
are illustrated in Fig. 3.10.

At the front, or terminus, of a glacier, gravel
and sand are deposited to form a hummocky
ridge called a *terminal moraine* (Fig. 11.16).
Such ridges extend across valleys that were
occupied by mountain glaciers, and many contain lakes. Terminal moraines also formed
around the fronts of the lobes of the continental ice sheets. Examples of these are the
concentric ridges around the south end of
Lake Michigan and around the ends of Lake
Erie and Saginaw Bay (Figs. 3.10 and 12.2).

Beyond the terminal moraines are *outwash
plains* of sand and gravel deposited by meltwaters from the ice (Fig. 11.16). These plains

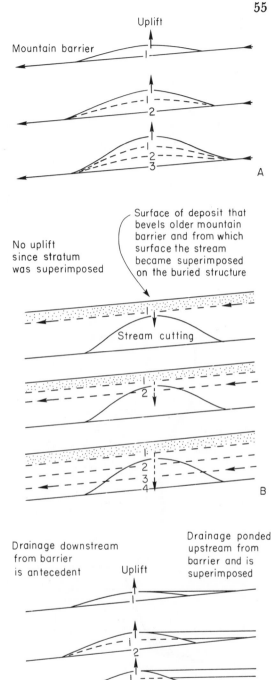

Figure 3.8 *(A) Antecedence. (B) Superposition. (C) Anteconsequence, or anteposition.
Broken lines represent positions of former
drainage after being raised structurally, from
1 (oldest) to 4 (youngest).*

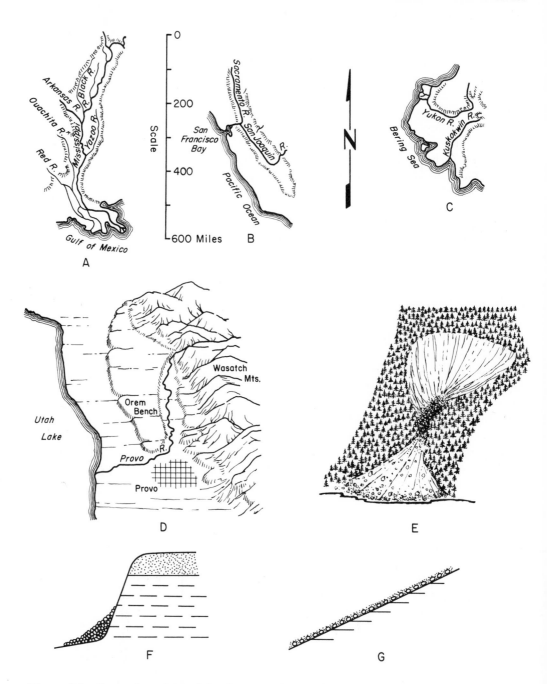

Figure 3.9 *Some depositional landforms. Floodplains of (A) Mississippi River;*
(B) Sacramento and San Joaquin rivers, California; (C) Yukon and Kuskokwim
rivers, Alaska. (D) Delta of Pleistocene Lake Bonneville forms Orem Bench near
Provo, Utah, at the foot of the Wasatch Mountains. (E) Alluvial fan, Rocky
Mountains, Colorado. (F) Talus at the foot of a cliff, a gravity rather than a
stream deposit. (G) Colluvium on a hillside.

and the moraines are hummocky, partly because deposition was torrential and irregular,
and partly because blocks of ice were deposited
with the sediments. When these blocks melted,
depressions formed, which are known as *kettle
holes;* the hillocks are referred to as *kames*
(Fig. 3.10,B). Ice readvancing over the hillocks
would reshape them like teardrops (*drumlins*),
elongating and tapering them in the direction
of the ice readvance (Fig. 3.10,C, 11.15,A,
11.17). Many of the hills about Boston, including Bunker Hill, are drumlins.

Still another example of landforms attributable to deposition by glaciers are ridges (*eskers*) formed by the channel gravels of streams
flowing on or under the glacier. When the ice
melted, the channel gravels of these streams
were deposited as meandering ridges that join
where the glacial streams joined (Fig. 3.10,D).

Other depositional landforms besides glaciers are attributable to deposition by waves,
such as barrier beaches and beach bars (Figs.
3.1, 3.7, 10.5, 10.6), spits, capes, and hooks
(Figs. 3.7, 10.21).

Depositional features attributable to wind
include dunes and loess plains. Dunes may be
arcuate or elongate and parallel. Some arcuate
dunes are concave in the windward direction,
others are concave to the leeward. The elongate dunes are parallel to the wind direction.
The kind of dune depends partly on the availability of sand, strength of wind, and presence
of vegetation, which collects and holds the
sand. Loess—wind deposited silt—blankets the
middle western plains (Fig. 6.1) and forms the
rich soil of that area. The loess dates from

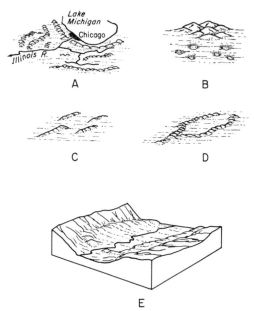

Figure 3.10 *Landforms attributable to deposition by glaciers. (A) Terminal moraines
south of Lake Michigan form a series of concentric ridges separated by till plains, outwash
plains, and lake beds. (B) Kames and kettle
holes on a till plain. (C) Drumlins. (D) Eskers.
(E) Lateral and terminal moraines deposited
by a former valley glacier.*

the glacial periods and originated as dust
blown eastward out of the great river valleys,
where it was deposited by floods caused by
melting of glacial ice.

Finally, to complete the list of depositional
features, some are built by organisms: coral
reefs, beaver ponds, peat marshes, gopher
mounds, buffalo wallows, and ant hills.

4 Climates

Climates play a major role in controlling physiography all over the world. In the United States, climates are mostly temperate, but they range from polar along the arctic coast of Alaska to tropical at the southern tip of Florida and at Puerto Rico and Hawaii. The major climatic regions are illustrated in Figure 4.1.

Polar climates have no warm season. In the severest form of polar climate, at the poles and on the high parts of mountains holding glaciers, even the warmest month averages below freezing, and snow perpetually covers the ground. In the mildest form of polar climate, the warmest month averages above freezing but below 50°F, and the growing season lasts less than about 2 months. This kind of climate

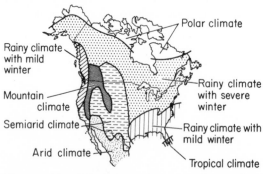

Figure 4.1 *Climatic regions in the United States and Canada.*

prevails along the arctic coasts and also at high altitudes farther south. A 1,000-foot increase in altitude is equivalent roughly to a 3° northward shift in latitude and a 3½°F drop in temperature. Thus, climates on mountain tops in the western United States are the same as those in the polar regions. A person traveling south from the arctic coast can experience polar climate, and enjoy his skiing, by climbing to 3,000 feet in the Alaska Range, 6,500 feet in the Northern Cascades, and 11,500 feet in the Sierra Nevada.

South of the polar region, there is a rainy belt with severe winters that comprises most of Alaska, most of Canada, and the eastern United States to about latitude 40°. The coldest month averages below freezing, but the warmest month averages above 50°F. The growing season increases from about 2 months at the north to about 5 months at the south.

The southeastern United States and the Pacific Coast, from San Francisco north to the Panhandle of Alaska, have rainy climates with mild winters. The coldest month averages above freezing. Annual precipitation is more than 40 inches and in some places exceeds 100. This region is divided into four parts on the basis of wet and dry seasons. The Panhandle of Alaska and the western coast of Canada have no dry season. The coast south of the state of Washington has dry summers. In the

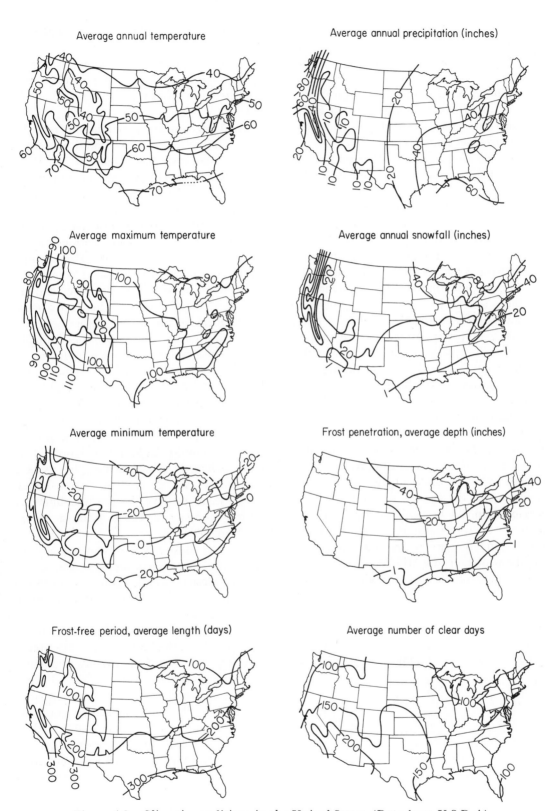

Figure 4.2 *Climatic conditions in the United States. (Data from U.S.D.A.)*

central United States summers are wet and winters dry. The Gulf and Atlantic coasts have no pronounced dry season. Tropical rainy climates prevail at the southern tip of Florida and in Hawaii and Puerto Rico. The coolest month averages more than 65°F.

From the Sierra-Cascade Province eastward to the 100th meridian, the climate is dry; evaporation exceeds precipitation, except on some of the high mountains. Part of this region is arid and desert, with annual precipitation averaging less than 8 inches. The rest is semiarid, with annual precipitation averaging between 8 and 20 inches, and treeless like the steppes of Eurasia. The difference in available or effective moisture in these two climates is even greater than indicated by the difference in precipitation, because evaporation rates in the arid regions are greater than in the semiarid ones. Permanent through-flowing streams cannot originate in these climatic regions.

Precipitation, temperature, and other climatic data for the United States are given in Figure 4.2. The average annual precipitation provides an index of moisture availability in various parts of the country, but of equal significance is the seasonal distribution of that precipitation. As brought out by Figure 4.3, most of the precipitation along the Pacific Coast (San Francisco record) takes place during the winter. In the Middle West (St. Louis record) most of the precipitation occurs dur-

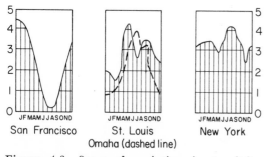

Figure 4.3 *Seasonal variation in precipitation at San Francisco, St. Louis, Omaha, and New York.*

ing the late spring and the summer. Along the Atlantic seaboard (New York record) precipitation is rather evenly spread throughout the year.

Maximum annual precipitation recorded in the United States is in Hawaii, in central Kauai, where near the summit of Mt. Waialeale (alt. 5,075 ft.) the average amount of rain is more than 450 inches. Several stations in Hawaii record more than 200 inches annually. In Alaska precipitation is heaviest along the southern coast, where some stations receive more than 150 inches annually. The Olympic Mountains near Seattle receive 140 inches of precipitation annually. At the other extreme is Death Valley, California, where the average precipitation is about 1.6 inches and the evaporation *rate* is about 150 inches annually.

Some extreme temperatures recorded in the United States are −78°F in the Yukon Valley, Alaska, −66°F at Yellowstone Park, and −65°F in parts of Montana. The highest temperature on record is 134°F in Death Valley, California. The Middle West shows the greatest variability. In St. Louis, January temperatures have been recorded as high as 74°F and as low as −22°F. The Yukon Valley, Alaska, seems to have the greatest difference between annual extremes, from a record −78°F to 100°F.

Figure 4.4 illustrates the frequency of some climatic hazards—hurricanes, tornadoes, fog, hail, and electric storms. Figure 4.5 illustrates some common cloud forms and their usual weather significance.

All these climatic conditions refer only to the *troposphere,* the lower layer of the atmosphere (Fig. 4.6). This layer extends to about 5 miles above the surface at the poles and about 10 miles above the surface at the equator. Temperatures in the troposphere gradually decrease upward to less than −40°F and to as low as −134°F. In the upper layer, the *stratosphere,* temperatures change very little with increase in height. The boundary between the two layers is called the *tropopause;* the greater its height, the lower the tempera-

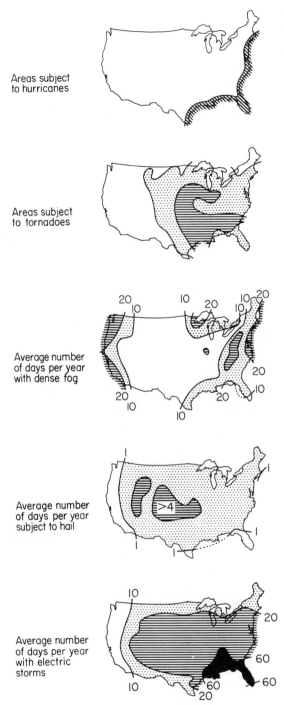

Areas subject to hurricanes

Areas subject to tornadoes

Average number of days per year with dense fog

Average number of days per year subject to hail

Average number of days per year with electric storms

Figure 4.4 *Climatic hazards. Ruled or black areas indicate where hazard is greatest; stippled areas intermediate; white areas slight.*

ture of the stratosphere. Over the equator, the upper part of the troposphere is very much colder than it is over the poles!

Climatic Factors

Some of the factors controlling climate can be illustrated by comparing the different regions.

Alaska illustrates the effect of *latitude.* At the winter solstice the sun's rays are tangent to the ground surface at the Arctic Circle, and north of the Arctic Circle there is no sun. Even in summer the sun's rays strike Alaska at a low angle, whereas they strike the southern United States almost perpendicularly. This is shown in Figure 4.7,A, which also illustrates the effect of seasons. In winter, the tilt of the earth's axis places the northern hemisphere away from the sun, and the sun's rays strike this half of the earth at low angles. Less radiation and less heat are received than in summer, and days are shorter.

St. Louis and Fort Yukon illustrate the effects of a *continental climate,* in which the annual variation in temperature is great. At St. Louis January temperatures average 32°F; July temperatures average 80°F. At Fort Yukon January temperatures average −21°F; July temperatures average 61°F. Hawaii and Puerto Rico illustrate the effect of a *marine climate,* in which the annual variation in temperature is small. At Honolulu January temperatures average 71°F; July temperatures average 77°F. At San Juan, Puerto Rico, January temperatures average 75°F; July temperatures average 80°F.

Differences between our Atlantic and Pacific coasts illustrate the effect of wind (Fig. 4.7,C). Because of the prevailing westerly winds, the Pacific Coast has a marine climate with cool summers and mild winters, whereas the Atlantic coast has a continental climate with hot summers and cold winters. Hawaii and Puerto Rico are in tropical latitudes, but are cooled by the northeast trade winds. Winds

Low clouds;
mostly below 6,500 feet.

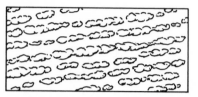

Stratocumulus. Layers or patches of small globular masses arranged in groups, lines, or waves and aligned in one or two directions; edges may join to form continuous cover. Composed of water; develops light rain or snow; associated with active fronts where weather is changing.

Clouds with vertical development;
lower parts may be as low as 1,000 feet;
tops may be above 20,000 feet.

Cumulus. Dense clouds with vertical development; upper surface dome-shaped with rounded protuberances; base nearly horizontal. Fair-weather clouds composed of water and produced by diurnal convection.

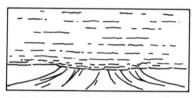

Stratus. A low, uniform layer resembling fog, but not resting on the ground. Composed of water; develops drizzle or snow flurries. When broken up into irregular shreds, the form is known as *fractostratus.*

Fractocumulus. Like cumulus, but with wispy or ragged edges because of wind.

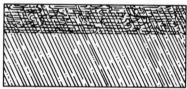

Nimbostratus. Low, amorphous, rainy layer. Dark gray, usually nearly uniform. Precipitation continuous, either rain or snow.

Cumulonimbus. Cumulus with great vertical development, the summits rising as towering masses and spreading out in shape of an anvil. Composed of water and ice; develops rain, snow, or hail; associated with thunderstorms commonly preceding warm or cold fronts.

Middle clouds;
mostly between 6,500 and 20,000 feet.

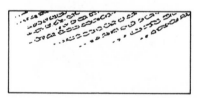

Figure 4.5 *Cloud forms. (Data from U.S. Weather Bureau.)*

Altocumulus. Similar to stratocumulus, but higher altitude, and the globular masses appear smaller. Usually composed of water. May develop light rain or snow and evolve into altostratus, which produces more precipitation.

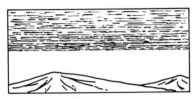

Altostratus. An amorphous sheet, striated or fibrous, gray; like a thin, high-altitude nimbostratus. Composed of water, except upper part may be ice; develops steady rain or snow and may grade into the thicker and lower nimbostratus.

High clouds;
generally above 20,000 feet; composed of ice crystals.

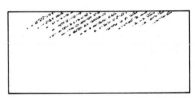

Cirrocumulus. Similar to altocumulus but higher altitude, the globular masses small and wispy with fibrous edges. Composed of ice crystals; no precipitation, but where formed in front of a warm front may be followed by thicker, lower clouds indicative of rain.

Cirrostratus. A high-altitude, thin, whitish, milky veil that does not blur the outlines of the sun or moon and usually gives rise to halos. Composed of ice crystals; no precipitation. Commonly precedes warm fronts.

Cirrus. Detached clouds of delicate, fibrous appearance, without shading; white. May be isolated tufts, or in lines branching like feathers, or in bands. Composed of ice crystals; no precipitation.

result from differences in *barometric pressure.* In the northern hemisphere winds move counterclockwise around a center of low pressure and clockwise around a center of high pressure. In winter a low-pressure center develops in the North Pacific, but it is weaker in summer; North America is a high pressure area in winter and a low pressure area in summer (Fig. 4.7,D). A scale for estimating wind velocity, developed in 1805 by Admiral Beaufort in England, is summarized in Table 4.1. This scale still has many practical uses.

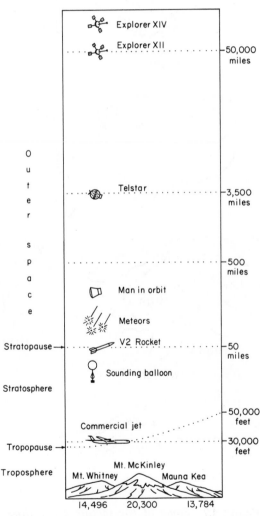

Figure 4.6 *The atmosphere and outer space. In the usual sense of the word, "climate" refers to conditions in the troposphere.*

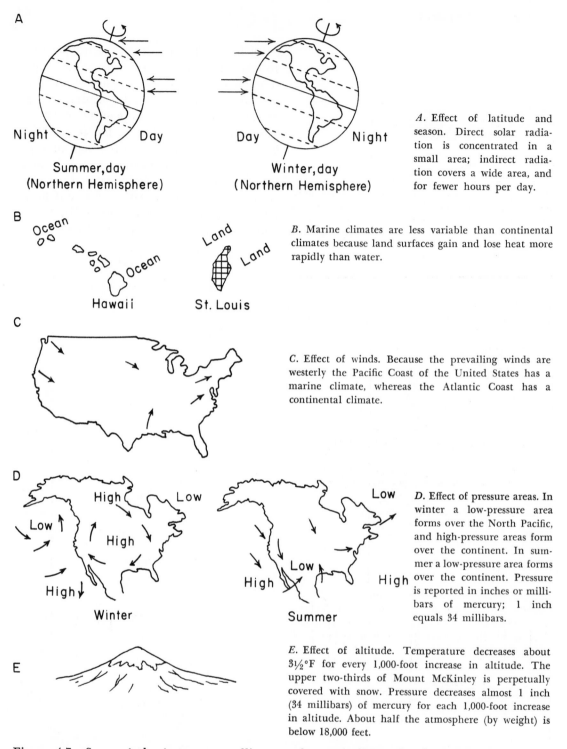

A. Effect of latitude and season. Direct solar radiation is concentrated in a small area; indirect radiation covers a wide area, and for fewer hours per day.

B. Marine climates are less variable than continental climates because land surfaces gain and lose heat more rapidly than water.

C. Effect of winds. Because the prevailing winds are westerly the Pacific Coast of the United States has a marine climate, whereas the Atlantic Coast has a continental climate.

D. Effect of pressure areas. In winter a low-pressure area forms over the North Pacific, and high-pressure areas form over the continent. In summer a low-pressure area forms over the continent. Pressure is reported in inches or millibars of mercury; 1 inch equals 34 millibars.

E. Effect of altitude. Temperature decreases about $3\frac{1}{2}°F$ for every 1,000-foot increase in altitude. The upper two-thirds of Mount McKinley is perpetually covered with snow. Pressure decreases almost 1 inch (34 millibars) of mercury for each 1,000-foot increase in altitude. About half the atmosphere (by weight) is below 18,000 feet.

Figure 4.7 *Some of the factors controlling weather and climate in the United States.*

F

Wet

Pacific
Ocean

Cascade-
Sierra Nevada

Dry

F. Effect of topography. A rain shadow extends east from the Cascade Range and the Sierra Nevada.

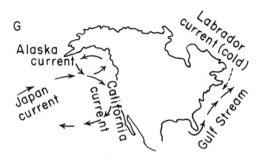

G

Alaska
current

Japan
current

California
current

Labrador
current (cold)

Gulf Stream

G. Effect of ocean currents. Our climates are influenced by the Japan Current, the Labrador Current, and the Gulf Stream.

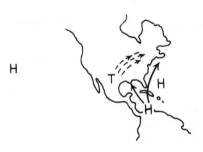

H

T

H

H

H. Hurricanes (H) develop in the Caribbean and commonly move north to the Gulf Coast or the Atlantic Coast. Tornadoes (T) are frequent in the Middle West.

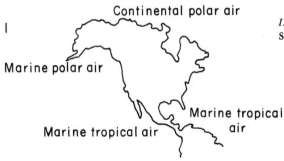

I

Continental polar air

Marine polar air

Marine tropical air

Marine tropical air

I. Sources of air masses that move into the United States.

J. Sections through a warm front and a cold front.

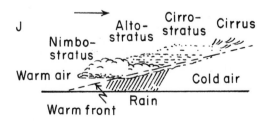

J

Nimbo-
stratus

Alto-
stratus

Cirro-
stratus

Cirrus

Warm air

Cold air

Rain

Warm front

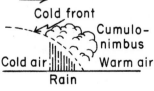

Cold front

Cumulo-
nimbus

Cold air

Warm air

Rain

TABLE 4.1   Beaufort Scale of Wind Velocity

Beaufort number	Name	Velocity (miles per hour)	Effects
0	Calm	<1	Smoke rises vertically.
1	Light	1–3	Wind directions shown by smoke but not by vanes.
2	Light	4–7	Wind felt on face; leaves rustle; vanes move.
3	Gentle	8–12	Leaves in constant motion; light flags extended.
4	Moderate	13–18	Raises dust and loose paper; small branches move.
5	Fresh	19–24	Small trees sway; wavelets on inland waters.
6	Strong	25–31	Large branches move; whistling in telegraph wires; umbrellas used with difficulty.
7	Strong	32–38	Whole trees move; difficult to walk against the wind.
8	Gale	39–46	Twigs break off trees; progress impeded.
9	Gale	47–54	Slight structural damage such as removal of slate and chiminey pots.
10	Whole gale	55–63	Considerable structural damage; trees uprooted.
11	Whole gale	64–75	Widespread damage.
12	Hurricane	>75	Widespread damage, devastation.

The effect of altitude, already discussed, is illustrated by the snow cover on Mount Mc-Kinley, for the upper two-thirds of that mountain is enveloped by snow throughout the year (Fig. 4.7,E).

The deserts east of the Sierra Nevada provide an example of how *topography* can affect climate. The moisture-laden westerly winds must rise to cross the mountains. In doing so they become chilled and drop much or most of their moisture. The dry area east of the mountains is referred to as a *rain shadow* (Fig. 4.7,F). Figure 4.8 illustrates the close relationship between topography and precipitation in the mountains, plateaus, and basins in the western United States.

A different effect of topography is the downhill drainage of cold air, which collects in valleys by displacing the lighter warm air. Valley bottoms are colder and have more frequent frosts than nearby hillsides. Most of the apple orchards of Yakima and Wenatchee, Washington, are on hillslopes; only alfalfa is grown in the valleys.

The effect of *oceanic currents* on climate is illustrated by the North Pacific currents. The Japan Current moves eastward and divides, one current turning northward and warming the south coast of Alaska, and the other turning southward and cooling (at least in summer) the coast south of Alaska (Fig. 4.7,G). On the Atlantic seaboard the warm Gulf Stream has a moderating effect as far north as Cape Cod. North of Cape Cod the effects of the cold Labrador Current are felt.

Storms that are part of our climate include

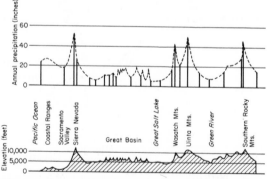

Figure 4.8 *Differences in annual precipitation in the mountains, plateaus, and basins of the western United States. The curve is very similar to the topographic profile because the precipitation varies according to altitude. (From U.S.D.A. Yearbook, 1941.)*

the *hurricanes* that occasionally move north-ward out of the Caribbean Sea to the Gulf Coast or sweep along the Atlantic seaboard, and the tornadoes that occur in the Middle West (Fig. 4.7,H). Hurricanes are the western-hemisphere equivalent of the typhoons in the western Pacific Ocean, the Willy-Willies of the southwest Pacific, and the cyclones of the Indian Ocean. Such tropical storms average about 400 miles in diameter. Barometric pressure at their centers may be less than 28 inches of mercury. As in other low-pressure areas in the northern hemisphere, the winds rotate counterclockwise and may attain velocities of 150 miles per hour. Tornadoes, which form over the land, are much smaller but far more violent. They are usually only a few hundred yards in diameter, but their wind velocities may be twice the velocity of a hurricane. In a half century more than 6,000 tornadoes have been recorded, and they have caused almost 9,000 deaths and three-quarters of a billion dollars in property loss.

Another major influence on climate is the *air masses,* which are hundreds of miles in diameter and many thousands of feet high and have fairly uniform moisture content and temperature. Air masses move into the United States from four principal regions (Fig. 4.7,I). The continental polar air masses bring cold, dry weather. The North Pacific center delivers moist, cold air. The South Pacific and Gulf centers deliver warm, moist air.

The advancing edge of a warm air mass—a warm front—moves more slowly than the advancing edge of a cold air mass, or cold front, because cold air can displace warm air more readily than warm air can displace cold air. For the same reason, cold fronts are steeper than warm fronts (Fig. 4.7,J). Along cold fronts rain and snow are likely to be heavy but of short duration; along warm fronts the cloudiness is more general and precipitation is more likely to be even and to last for a longer time. Cloudiness reduces radiation, which is one of the reasons why temperatures are less extreme in humid regions than in deserts. In deserts,

the daily temperature range commonly exceeds 30°F, which is about twice the range at inland humid stations.

Another factor affecting climate is the composition of the air. If unpolluted and dry, it consists chiefly of nitrogen (78 percent by volume) and oxygen (21 percent). The remaining 1 percent is mostly argon, but includes some carbon dioxide and traces of hydrogen, helium, neon, krypton, and xenon. Air, however, is never pure and never completely dry, for it contains varying quantities of moisture, dust, soot, and foreign gases. The climate in an industrial city blanketed with smog is different from that in the surrounding countryside. The difference can be seen in the cities and can be felt in all kinds of disagreeable ways.

The climate on and near the ground, referred to as *microclimate,* may differ greatly from the climate a few feet above the ground. The ground may be hotter or colder than the air above it, and may cause moisture to condense from air that is comparatively dry. Air at the ground surface may be almost still while the air some feet higher is in motion. The ground layers of air have more shade than the upper layers because of trees, small plants, topographic eminences, and buildings. These variations in microclimate, compounded with those that we ordinarily think of as climate, have a major influence on soil processes and on the biota. They greatly influence the use of the land and the design of highway and other foundations. Examples of the effects of microclimate may be seen by comparing the ground on the shaded north side of a house with that on the sunny south side.

Because ground is a poor conductor, the surface becomes intensely heated during the day, and conversely may cool more than the air above it at night. In deserts, the temperature of the ground surface in the sun commonly is nearly twice the air temperature; ground-surface temperatures as high as 190°F have been recorded in Death Valley.

But this surface layer of the ground that is subject to such extreme diurnal temperature changes is only skin deep. In general, the seasonal average temperature for a given locality is reached within a couple of feet of the surface, and for practical purposes the average annual temperature is reached within a few more feet. For example, the limestone caverns in Virginia, Mammoth Cave, and the Carlsbad Caverns are located approximately along the 55°F isotherm (Fig. 4.2) and the temperatures in those caves are nearly constant at about 55°F.

Climatic Changes

The differences between the climatic regions are of great importance physiographically, but of equal importance are the climates of the past, especially those of the Pleistocene Epoch. The kinds of ground in most of the country are attributable largely to conditions that prevailed under climates different from those of the present.

As recently as 20,000 years ago an ice sheet covered most of Canada and extended southward to Long Island and northern New Jersey on the east and to the Ohio and Missouri Rivers in the Middle West. The extent of the

ice mass was about equal to that of the present Antarctic ice cap. This was the most recent of four glacial stages, each of which is named for the state in which deposits of the stage are particularly well exposed (see table below).

Period	Epoch	Stages	
		Glacial	*Interglacial*
	Recent		
Quaternary	Pleistocene	Wisconsin Illinoian Kansan Nebraskan	Sangamon Yarmouth Aftonian

The physical evidence for the existence of these ancient glaciers is found in the several kinds of deposits they left behind. The area covered by the ice (Fig. 4.9) is blanketed with bouldery sand, silt, and clay (Fig. 6.1), and the boulders are of northern types of rocks that have been moved southward. The nonstratified deposits left by the ice are called *till;* the stratified deposits, formed by glacial streams on or under the ice are *glaciofluvial.* The till and the glaciofluvial deposits are referred to collectively as *drift.*

Other deposits (Figs. 4.10, 6.1) record the

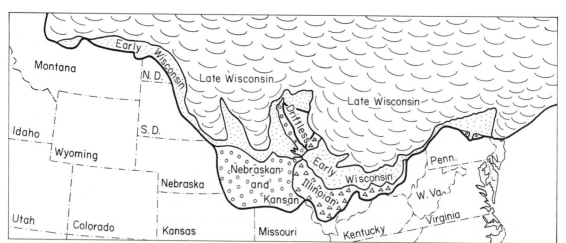

Figure 4.9 *Limits reached by the continental ice sheets from New Jersey to Montana.*

existence of at least three different kinds of lakes. One kind formed in front of the ice sheets; good examples are in Montana. A second kind formed during retreat of the ice and filled valleys that had been scoured and deepened by the ice; examples are the Finger Lakes, in New York, and the Great Lakes, which are relics of older and larger ones. A third kind flooded closed depressions in the Basin and Range Province; two large ones are Lake Bonneville, in Utah, and Lake Lahontan, in Nevada.

Still other deposits related to the glaciation are of eolian (wind) origin. Spring thaws caused rivers to flood, and the silt-laden flood waters made barren wastes of the river valleys. As floods subsided silt blown out of these valleys settled on the adjoining uplands and formed the deposits of loess that compose the rich soils of most of the Middle West farm belt (Fig. 6.1). These deposits thin and become finer grained leeward (eastward) from the valleys that were their sources.

In addition to these evidences of the glacial stages, there is the evidence provided by paleontology. The glacial deposits contain the remains of vertebrate and invertebrate animals characteristic of northern latitudes. The interglacial deposits contain the remains of faunas characteristic of temperate climates. These faunal changes are paralleled by similar changes in the flora.

Climatic changes during the Quaternary Period also affected sea level. During the glacial stages, a vast amount of water was locked in the ice sheets, and sea level stood a few

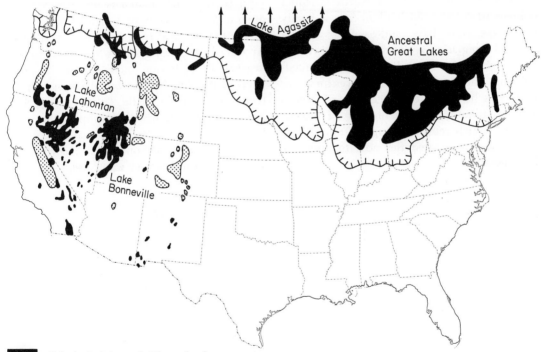

Principal lakes of Wisconsin Age

Southern limit of Wisconsin Continental Ice

Mountain glaciers

Figure 4.10 *Paleogeographic map showing distribution of principal lakes (black) of late Wisconsin age in the United States and their relation to the southern limit of Wisconsin continental ice (hachured line) and to the mountain glaciers (stippled areas).*

hundred feet lower than it does now. Furthermore, when the deglaciation was greater than at the present time, the sea stood higher—along the Atlantic Coast, probably about 35 feet higher. These *eustatic* (world-wide) changes in sea level, however, are difficult to study because crustal changes of two kinds also have been taking place. One kind, not related to the climatic changes, is illustrated by the faulting and other earth movement taking place along the coast of California. Another kind, which indirectly is the result of the climatic changes, involved downwarping of the northern United States and Canada because of the weight of ice on that part of the crust. Since that weight has been removed, that area has been uplifted. To such changes can be attributed the differences in the coastline along the Atlantic seaboard. From North Carolina to Long Island the old land surface is partly submerged, and bays and sounds occupy drowned preglacial river valleys. The rocky New England coast is still deeply submerged.

During the first half of this century the North Pole has migrated 30 feet toward Greenland, presumably because melting of Greenland ice, which removed weight from an off-center location, caused the pole to move in that direction.

The effects of the glacial and interglacial climates were felt far south of the ice fronts. In the southern and southwestern parts of the United States the glacial stages were *pluvial,* or rainy, times, and streams were larger, perhaps because of actual increase in precipitation, or perhaps because of decreased evaporation, caused, for example, by increased cloudiness. The record is clear that during the pluvial times, the effective available moisture was greatly increased. Even Death Valley contained a lake hundreds of feet deep. The Great Salt Lake desert was submerged under a thousand feet of water. The climate was different.

Moreover, the climatic changes are continuing. We seem to be in a period of thaw. Glaciers have been retreating, ground that has been permanently frozen is melting, and the areas of floating ice have decreased. From 1885 to the 1940's world temperatures rose slightly; Arctic winter temperatures rose one to two degrees. Precipitation increased in the arctic parts of this hemisphere but decreased in the temperate latitudes of the United States. This has been accompanied by a drop in the water level of such lakes as the Great Lakes and Great Salt Lake, although this record is obscured by an increase in water use.

5 Water

The Hydrologic Cycle

The hydrologic cycle begins with precipitation, in the form of rain, hail, snow, frost, or dew. Precipitation on the oceans returns to the atmosphere by evaporation. Precipitation on the land divides three ways:

1. One part, perhaps as much as half, returns to the atmosphere directly by evaporation.
2. A second part, perhaps a sixth, is returned to the atmosphere by transpiration of plants.
3. A third part, perhaps a third, joins streams or glaciers that discharge into the ocean, where it can be returned to the atmosphere.
4. The fourth part, a small but important fraction, enters the ground, but in time returns to the surface, as springs or other ground-water discharge, and from there is returned to the atmosphere.

Over the whole earth, precipitation is equal to evaporation plus transpiration; the hydrologic cycle is a balanced economy. But precipitation, evaporation, and transpiration are three variables that differ greatly from area to area. For example, in the humid parts of the country, less than half the precipitation may be lost by evaporation and transpiration, but in arid regions—for example, along the lower part of the Colorado River—as much as 95 percent may be lost by evaporation.

Surface Water

Surface water, as that term is used by hydrologists, refers to water on the surface of the land. Oceans are excluded. Surface water is mostly *stream runoff*, and it may be collected by being impounded naturally or artificially in lakes and reservoirs. Quantity of runoff is a function of the precipitation and of the *drainage basins* or *catchment areas* and is expressed in *acre-feet* (1 acre-foot is the quantity of water that would cover an acre to a depth of one foot: 43,560 cubic feet, or 325,829 gallons). Figure 5.1 shows the average annual discharge of some rivers in the United States.

The discharge of large streams may be expressed in acre-feet per unit of time. Discharge may also be expressed in gallons per minute or cubic feet per second (abbreviated to second-feet). The cubic foot per second (cfs) is the fundamental unit from which others are determined by conversion. It is the discharge of water in a channel of rectangular cross section 1 foot wide and 1 foot deep at an average

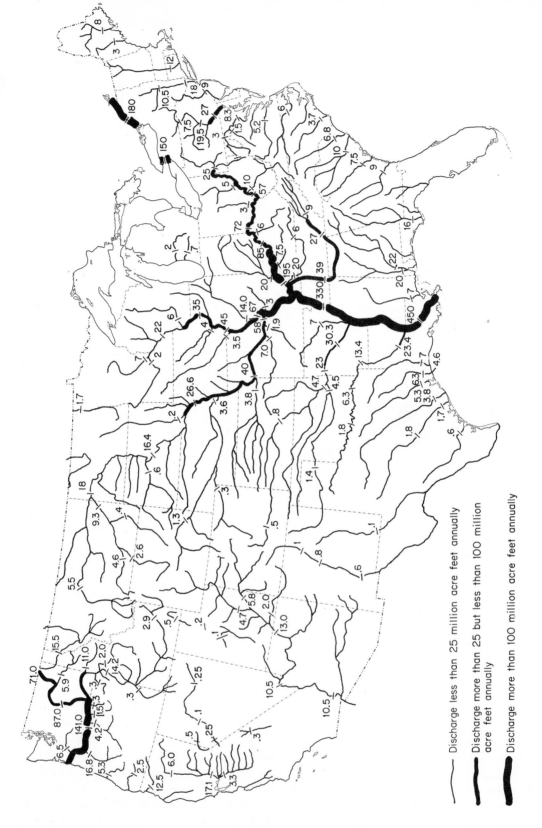

Figure 5.1 *Average annual discharge of some rivers in the United States in millions of acre-feet per year. (Data from U.S.G.S.)*

— Discharge less than 25 million acre feet annually

— Discharge more than 25 but less than 100 million acre feet annually

— Discharge more than 100 million acre feet annually

velocity of 1 foot per second. One cubic foot equals 7.48 gallons.

1 second-foot = 7.48 gallons per second
= 448.8 gallons per minute
= 1.98 acre-feet per day
= 725 acre-feet per year.

Measuring the discharge of our streams is a responsibility of the U.S. Geological Survey, although many other agencies, state and federal, collect such data in the areas of their interests. The measurements sometimes are difficult to make accurately because velocity is not uniform in different parts of a stream channel, owing to frictional drag along the bottom and sides or to extreme turbulence at times of flood. Discharge of streams with relatively uniform flow can be estimated roughly by (a) measuring the area of cross section of the channel, (b) selecting a convenient length of channel (10 feet), and (c) timing the rate of flow of a small piece of paper floating on the stream. Discharge (Q) is given by the formula

$$Q = \frac{A \times d}{t},$$

where A is the area of cross section (sq ft), d is the distance (ft), and t is the time required to flow the distance (sec). For most streams this method gives a result that is about a fifth too great, because the measured surface velocity is greater than the average velocity.

Streams may be categorized in many dif-

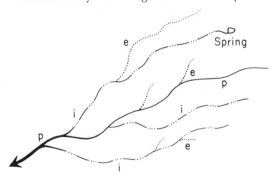

Figure 5.2 *Some categories of streams related to permanence and continuity.* p, *perennial;* i, *intermittent;* e, *ephemeral.*

ferent ways, depending on what factors one wishes to stress—drainage pattern and valley form, origin and relation to the geomorphic surface, age, size, permanence or continuity of flow, relation to groundwater, quality of the water, biota, navigability, or other possible use.

In theory natural streams contrast sharply with such artificial ones as canals, irrigation ditches, and aqueducts, but in today's world they are not distinct, because almost every stream has been modified by dams for power, flood control, or water diversion, by industrial and municipal wastes, and/or by various kinds of stream-side developments.

Streams may be classed according to permanence as *perennial, intermittent,* or *ephemeral* (Fig. 5.2). Some streams are *continuous,* others are interrupted—that is, their perennial stretches may be interrupted by intermittent or ephemeral stretches.

Impounded bodies of water also can be classified according to origin, age, size, permanence and continuity, and quality. Lakes and reservoirs are simply stream runoff in storage.

Stream runoff, including that stored in lakes and reservoirs, is the principal source of our water supply. It provides 75 percent of the water used for municipal sources and for irrigation, 90 percent of the fresh water used by industry, and nearly all the water used to generate hydroelectric power. Knowledge about fluctuations and differences in runoff in contiguous regions becomes important in order that waste and damage during flood seasons be minimized and excess flood waters stored for use when stream discharge is reduced.

Figure 5.3 shows runoff by regions. This runoff, as might be expected, correlates rather well with precipitation (compare with Fig. 4.2). It should be emphasized, too, that runoff is very much greater in urban areas than in rural areas because of the extensive paving and other surfacing. Figure 5.4, which shows months of peak runoff, illustrates the seasonal variation in discharge of some typical rivers. These variations in stream discharge are much more uniform throughout the country than is the seasonal variation in rainfall (see Fig. 4.4), probably because the discharge of so many rivers is to a considerable degree controlled by the water stored in the snow pack.

Subsurface Water

Subsurface water is derived largely from the atmosphere or from surface water. Other kinds of subsurface water, less important physiographically, include: water chemically combined in minerals, water trapped in sediments at the time of deposition, and *primitive water* —water escaping for the first time from the earth's interior or water created by the combination of primitive hydrogen with exterior oxygen.

Some of the modes in which water occurs

in the ground are shown in Figure 5.5. Water in the ground occupies voids in the soil or other overburden and in the rocks, and its occurrence and movement are controlled largely by the abundance and size of the voids (*porosity*), their shape and continuity—that is, whether the voids are connected or isolated. A rock is saturated with water when all its voids are filled, which is the condition below the water table.

The hydrologic properties of a rock depend on the size of its voids. *Capillary interstices* are small enough to cause water to rise above the water table and to be held a considerable height above it—a phenomenon illustrated by the absorption of water upward into a blotter. Larger interstices lack the property of capillarity, and water moves through them in currents. Ground, including the bedrock, is *permeable* if water can move through it— that is, if the voids are of capillary size or

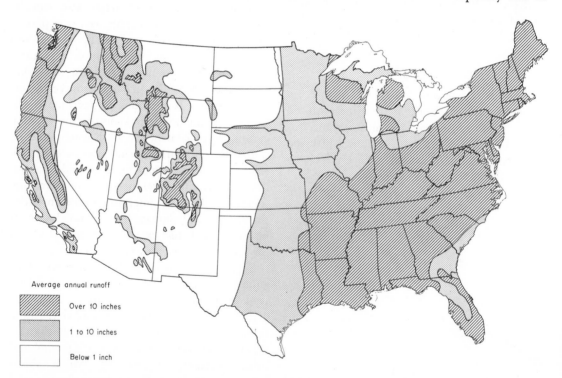

Average annual runoff

Over 10 inches

1 to 10 inches

Below 1 inch

Figure 5.3 *Average annual runoff in the United States. (After U.S.G.S.) Each inch of runoff per square mile equals about 17.4 million gallons of water.*

larger and connected. Permeability differs from porosity; some fine-grained rocks are highly porous, but the voids are subcapillary in size, and the rock is impermeable. In Alaska and in other northern states, permeable layers may become impermeable in cold seasons because the water in them freezes.

A *water table* is the upper surface of a *zone of saturation*—the upper surface of *groundwater*. Above the water table is a zone called the *capillary fringe,* where water rises from the water table by capillarity. From the capillary fringe upward to the surface is a zone that is alternately wet and dry, a zone of aeration, and its water is called *vadose, gravitational,* or *suspended* water (Fig. 5.5). A stratum that yields water is an *aquifer.* Figure 5.6 illustrates the availability of ground water in the United States.

Soil water, which is water in the surface layers, is classed according to its availability to plants. The *wilting coefficient* of a soil is the ratio of the weight of water in soil when permanent wilting begins to the weight of the soil when dry. In most soils this is less than half the moisture-holding capacity of the soil. Water in excess of the wilting coefficient is available to plants; water in lesser amounts is not available.

Despite folklore to the contrary, few hot springs discharge primitive water. Most discharge water that enters the ground, circulates deeply, becomes heated, and then rises again at the springs. In some areas the circulation need not be deep. At Yellowstone Park, for example, earth temperatures increase hundreds of degrees (fahrenheit) within a few hundred feet of the surface. At other places the temperature increase may be as small as 6°F in 1,000 feet of depth.

A water table can be represented on maps by contours. The depth one must dig or drill

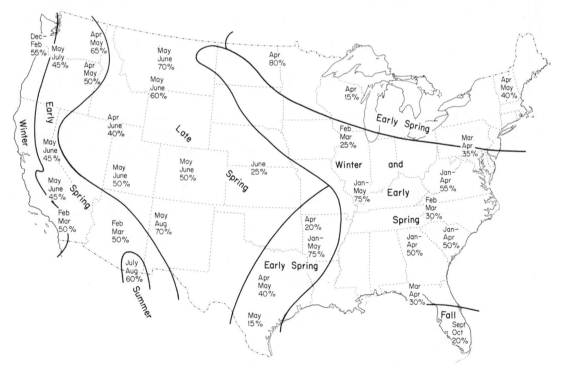

Figure 5.4 *Months and seasons of normal peak runoff, and the percent of annual flow normally discharged during the flood periods at various drainage basins in the United States. (Data from U.S.G.S.)*

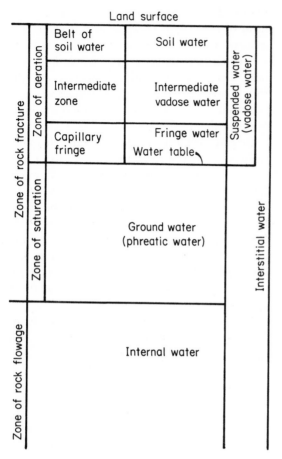

Figure 5.5 *Modes of occurrence of subsurface water. (After U.S.G.S.)*

to reach groundwater is measured by the difference in altitude between the topographic contour and the contour on the water table at a particular place.

Where the water table is a free surface, it may fluctuate daily, seasonally (Fig. 5.7), or secularly (periods of wet years alternating with periods of dry years). Commonly, though, the groundwater is confined beneath an impermeable bed, as in Figure 5.8 (bottom). In such situations the water rises in the wells because of the hydrostatic pressure. The level to which the water rises is the static level, and is called the *piezometric surface.*

Contours drawn to show the static levels in the wells in Figure 5.8 (bottom) would have altitudes lower than those of the ground surface at wells C and D, and an altitude higher than that of the ground surface at well E. The difference between the topographic contours and the contours showing the piezometric surface indicates the height to which water would have to be pumped at C and D and what the pressure head would be at the surface at E.

Where groundwater occurs above the normal water table, as it does in places where an impermeable bed prevents downward circulation, the groundwater is said to be *perched,* and the upper surface of such groundwater is called a *perched water table.* Two examples of perched water tables are illustrated in Figure 5.9. The effect of such situations on wells is illustrated in Figure 5.8 (top). A water table may resemble that shown in Figure 5.7 or those shown in Figure 5.8; in oil and gas fields a water table may be an oil-water or gas-water interface. Withdrawal of the oil or gas causes the interface to rise, and one of the problems in oil-field development is to raise the interface evenly. Overpumping causes irregular rise of the water and reduces the quantity of oil that can be recovered (Fig. 5.10).

In relation to streams, the water table may be above the stream, in which case groundwater will discharge into it, or the water table may be below the stream and receive discharge into it.

Subsurface water is cycled back to the surface or to the atmosphere in several ways. In semiarid and arid regions, most of the soil water and vadose water returns to the atmosphere by evaporation or transpiration, whereas in humid regions such water may continue downward to the water table. Groundwater may be returned to the atmosphere by evaporation, by transpiration of plants (Fig. 5.12), or by discharge into streams (Fig. 5.11), wells (Fig. 5.8), or springs (Fig. 5.9).

The relative importance of groundwater supplies in different parts of the country is illustrated in Figure 9.19,A.

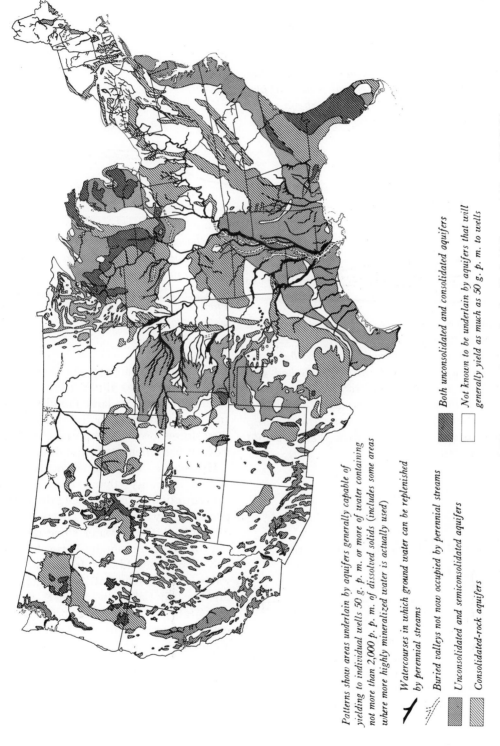

Patterns show areas underlain by aquifers generally capable of yielding to individual wells 50 g. p. m. or more of water containing not more than 2,000 p. p. m. of dissolved solids (includes some areas where more highly mineralized water is actually used)

↗ *Watercourses in which ground water can be replenished by perennial streams*

⸝⸝⸝ *Buried valleys not now occupied by perennial streams*

▨ *Unconsolidated and semiconsolidated aquifers*

▧ *Consolidated-rock aquifers*

■ *Both unconsolidated and consolidated aquifers*

☐ *Not known to be underlain by aquifers that will generally yield as much as 50 g. p. m. to wells*

Figure 5.6 *Availability of groundwater in the United States. (After U.S.G.S.)*

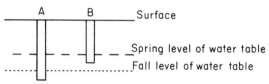

Figure 5.7 *Seasonal fluctuations of a water table. Well* A *has a perennial water supply; well* B *becomes dry seasonally. Depending on the kind of ground and recharge, the fluctuation might be 2 or 3 feet.*

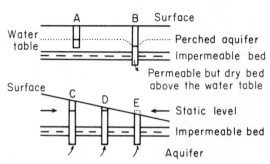

Figure 5.8 *Examples of how impermeable beds affect groundwater.* (*Top*) *An aquifer perched on an impermeable bed. The water level in well* B *driven through this bed will be lower than the water table.* (*Bottom*) *An aquifer beneath an impermeable bed. The hydrostatic pressure causes water to rise into wells driven through the bed. Well* E *would flow without pumping.*

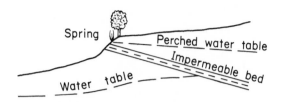

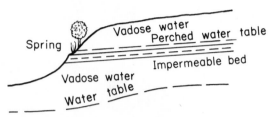

Figure 5.9 *Examples of perched water tables. The barrier formed by the impermeable bed in the upper diagram is a groundwater dam. Spring zones are commonly caused by perched water tables, and this must be determined when estimating potential water yields and water resources.*

Water in the Atmosphere and in the Oceans

Great lakes and great rivers are impressive, and of utmost importance to us, but all the surface water and groundwater on the continents amounts to little more than 0.5 percent of the earth's total water supply. A little more than 2 percent is in the atmosphere; all the remainder, more than 97 percent, is in the ocean.

Water in the atmosphere occurs as a gas (water vapor), as a liquid (tiny particles suspended in the air or large raindrops that fall), and as a solid (snow or ice). Water in any of these forms becomes important in hydrology when it has fallen as precipitation on land.

Hydrologic interest in the ocean water centers on its quality—that is to say, the kind and concentration of its dissolved salts—and on its circulation, which greatly affects the climates on the land. Ocean water along the shores of the United States contains between 3.3 and 3.6 percent of dissolved salts. In percent of the salt water these are: $NaCl$, 2.7; $MgCl_2$, 0.4; $MgSO_4$, 0.2; $CaSO_4$, 0.1; K_2SO_4, 0.1; $CaCO_3$ and $MgBr_2$, traces. These principal constituents are present in the following relative abundance (percent):

Na	30.6	Cl	55.0
K	1.1	SO_4	7.7
Mg	3.7	HCO_3	0.4
Ca	1.2	Other	0.3
			100.0

The concentration of salt water is more than twice that of the fluids in the human body, which is why ocean water does not quench thirst. Instead, the salt water, by osmosis, extracts fluids from the body! Ocean water can be desalted for drinking purposes, and used to increase water supplies, especially of coastal cities.

Quality of Water

Quality of water refers not to its biology but to its chemistry—the content of dissolved or suspended matter, mostly solids, although dissolved gases may be important locally. Purity of water pertains to its content of living organisms. Rain water contains almost no dissolved or suspended matter after the first of the fall has cleared the air of dust or smoke, but as soon as the water enters the ground or runs off the surface, it dissolves both organic matter and mineral matter.

The organic matter dissolved or suspended in surface or subsurface water consists in part of carbon dioxide, carbonic acid, and various humic compounds. This organic matter is especially important in soil water, where it is a major factor in the soil-forming processes. The humic compounds also affect the quality of some surface waters to the extent of coloring them brown, especially where drainage is sluggish, as in some ponds.

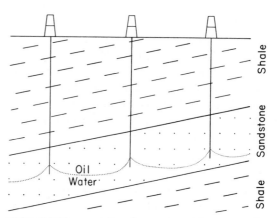

Figure 5.10 *Overpumping in oil fields causes the oil-water interface to rise in a cone at each well. This causes water to rise into the wells before the oil between the wells is recovered. A similar problem occurs in water wells drawing fresh water from a lense above salt water.*

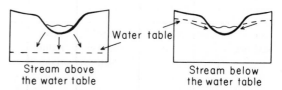

Figure 5.11 *Streams that are above the water table lose water into the ground. Streams that are below the water table receive drainage from it; at flood stage the direction of flow may be reversed.*

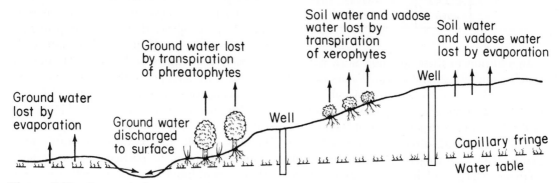

Figure 5.12 *Some of the ways subsurface water is returned to the atmosphere and to the surface.*

In most water, most of the dissolved and suspended solids is mineral matter. The quantity and proportions of various mineral constituents are controlled chiefly by the composition of the rocks forming the drainage basin or aquifer and the quality fluctuates seasonally with fluctuations in discharge. The common salts in natural waters are shown in Table 5.1. Water quality is generally described in terms of the anions (Table 5.1).

TABLE 5.1   Common Salts in Natural Waters

Cations	Anions		
	CO_3^{--} carbonate	SO_4^{--} sulfate	Cl^- chloride
Ca^{++} calcium	$CaCO_3$ limestone	$CaSO_4$ gypsum	$CaCl_2$
Mg^{++} magnesium	$MgCO_3$ magnesia	$MgSO_4$ Epsom salt	$MgCl_2$
Na^+ sodium	Na_2CO_3 soda	Na_2SO_4 Glauber salt	$NaCl$ halite (table salt)
K^+ potassium (quantity generally minor)	K_2CO_3	K_2SO_4	KCl
	Alkaline water	Saline water	

Hard water / *Soft water* (right-hand bracket labels)

In addition to these common salts, natural waters contain iron and silica. Waters become acidic chiefly because of carbonic acid (H_2CO_3), and more rarely because of sulfuric acid (H_2SO_4) or hydrochloric acid (HCl).

The common dissolved gases are carbon dioxide (CO_2), nitrogen (N), oxygen (O), methane (CH_4), and hydrogen sulfide (H_2S). Other constituents are present in minor amounts, yet these amounts may be significant,

physiologically or otherwise. Fluorine is an example; in some areas it has even been politically significant.

The content of dissolved solids in water is expressed in parts per million (ppm). One part per million is nearly the same as 1 milligram per liter; 10,000 ppm equals 1 percent. Sea water contains 33,000 to 36,000 ppm of dissolved solids. Great Salt Lake, which is saturated, contains roughly 333,000 ppm. In waters more saline than sea water it is convenient to express the salt content in percent. Most municipal water supplies contain less than 150 ppm of dissolved solids. Public Health Service standards (1962) provide for a maximum of 500 ppm of dissolved solids for drinking water. More than 1,000 ppm is considered objectionable by persons who have not spent much time in the deserts. Water containing as much as 2,500 ppm can be tolerated for short periods. Such water is suitable for stock but not for irrigation. The compositions of river waters in the United States are given in Figure 5.13.

Iron rarely is present in more than minute quantities, but even 0.2 ppm may stain clothing, enamel, and porcelain ware. Quantities above 1 ppm generally precipitate when exposed to air.

In general, waters containing less than 100 ppm of dissolved solids are soft, because, as one water chemist expressed it, where the amounts are less, even the salesmen give up trying to sell water softeners.

What is "hardness" in water? Hardness refers to the property that causes soap to form precipitates rather than to lather, and to the property that causes boiler scale. Hardness is measured in parts per million of $CaCO_3$, other salts being converted to equivalents of $CaCO_3$ for this purpose. Hardness is caused by salts of calcium and magnesium, especially the carbonates (Table 5.1). Waters containing more than 200 ppm of the particular salts are hard. Water containing more than 500 ppm commonly is saline, but may be hard too if it also contains the salts that produce hardness. Car-

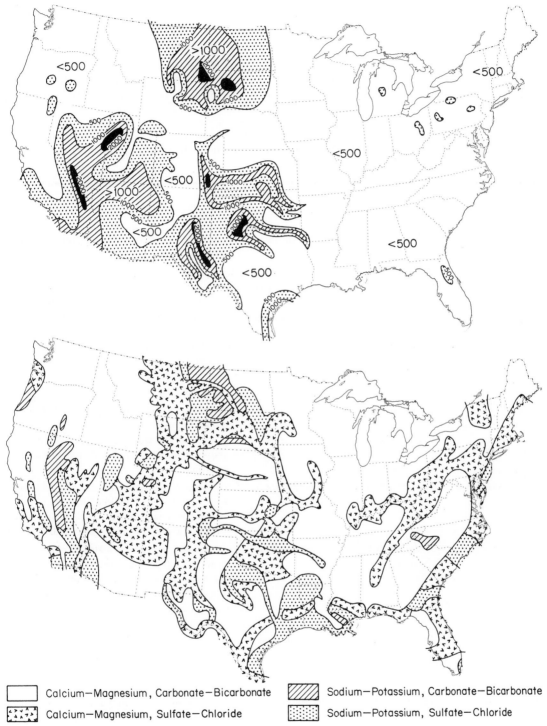

Figure 5.13 *Composition of river waters in the United States. (After U.S.G.S.)*
(Top) Prevalent total dissolved solids in rivers; figures are in parts per million.
(Bottom) Prevalent chemical types of rivers.

bonate hardness may be reduced by boiling, but noncarbonate hardness requires the addition of chemicals, such as sodium carbonate, slaked lime, or zeolites.

Subsurface water generally contains more dissolved solids than does surface water (Fig.

5.14). Streams in regions of low runoff generally contain more dissolved solids than do streams in regions of high runoff (compare Figs. 5.3 and 5.13).

Table 5.2 lists the common dissolved mineral constituents in natural water and their

TABLE 5.2   Significance of dissolved mineral constituents and physical properties of natural water. (After U.S.G.S.)

Constituent or physical property	Source or cause	Significance
Silica (SiO_2)	Dissolved from practically all rocks and soils, usually 1 to 30 ppm.	Forms hard scale in pipes and boilers and on blades of steam turbines.
Iron (Fe)	Dissolved from practically all rocks and soils; also derived from iron pipes. More than 1 or 2 ppm of soluble iron in surface water usually indicate acid wastes from mine drainage or other sources.	On exposure to air, iron in groundwater oxidizes to reddish-brown sediment. More than about 0.3 ppm stains laundry and utensils. Objectionable for food processing, Federal drinking water standards state that iron and manganese together should not exceed 0.3 ppm. Larger quantities cause unpleasant taste and favor growth of iron bacteria.
Manganese (Mn)	Not as common as iron.	Same objectionable features as iron.
Calcium (Ca) and magnesium (Mg)	Dissolved from practically all soils and rocks, but especially from limestone, dolomite, and gypsum.	Cause most of the hardness and scale-forming properties of water; (see hardness). Waters low in calcium and magnesium desired in electroplating, tanning, dyeing, and in textile manufacturing.
Sodium (Na) and potassium (K)	Dissolved from practically all rocks and soils.	Large amounts, in combination with chloride, give a salty taste. Sodium salts may cause foaming in steam boilers and a high sodium ratio may limit the use of water for irrigation.
Bicarbonate (HCO_3) and carbonate (CO_3)	Action of carbon dioxide in water on carbonate rocks.	Produce alkalinity. Bicarbonates of calcium and magnesium decompose in steam boilers and hot water facilities to form scale and release corrosive carbon-dioxide gas. In combination with calcium and magnesium cause carbonate hardness.
Sulfate (SO_4)	Dissolved from many rocks and soils.	Sulfate in water containing calcium forms hard scale in steam boilers. Federal drinking water standards recommend that the sulfate content should not exceed 250 ppm.
Chloride (Cl)	Dissolved from rocks and soils. Present in sewage and found in large amounts in ancient brines, sea water, and industrial brines.	In large amounts in combination with sodium gives salty taste. In large quantities increases the corrosiveness of water. Federal drinking water standards recommend that the chloride content should not exceed 250 ppm.

Fluoride (F)........	Dissolved in small to minute quantities from most rocks and soils.	Fluoride in drinking water reduces the incidence of tooth decay when the water is consumed during the period of enamel calcification. However, in excess it may cause mottling of the teeth.
Nitrate (NO_3).......	Decaying organic matter, sewage, and nitrates in soil.	Concentrations much greater than the local average suggest pollution.
Dissolved solids.....	Chiefly mineral constituents dissolved from rocks and soils, but includes organic matter.	Federal drinking water standards recommend that the dissolved solids should not exceed 500 ppm. Waters containing more than 1,000 ppm of dissolved solids are unsuitable for many purposes.
Hardness as $CaCO_3$	In most water, nearly all the hardness is due to calcium and magnesium.	Consumes soap before a lather will form. Deposits soap curd on bathtubs. Hard water forms scale in boilers, water heaters, and pipes. Hardness equivalent to the bicarbonate and carbonate is called carbonate hardness. Any hardness in excess of this is called noncarbonate hardness.
Acidity or alkalinity (hydrogen ion concentration, pH)	Acids, acid-generating salts, and free carbon dioxide lower the pH. Carbonates, bicarbonates, hydroxides and phosphates, silicates, and borates raise the pH.	A pH of 7.0 indicates neutrality of a solution. Values higher than 7.0 denote increasing alkalinity; values lower than 7.0 indicate increasing acidity. Corrosiveness of water generally increases with decreasing pH.
Dissolved oxygen (O_3)	Dissolved in water from air and from oxygen given off in the process of photosynthesis by aquatic plants.	Dissolved oxygen increases the palatability of water. Under average stream conditions, 4 ppm is usually necessary to maintain a varied fish fauna in good condition. For industrial uses, zero dissolved oxygen is desirable to inhibit corrosion.

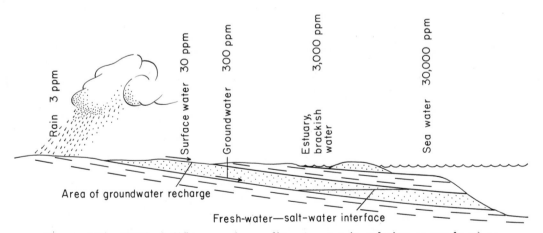

Figure 5.14 *Typical differences in quality of water in relation to mode of occurrence. In addition to the five orders of magnitude of salinity illustrated, a sixth would be saturation (10 times the salinity of sea water), as in natural salt pans along a shore, in Great Salt Lake, and in the Dead Sea.*

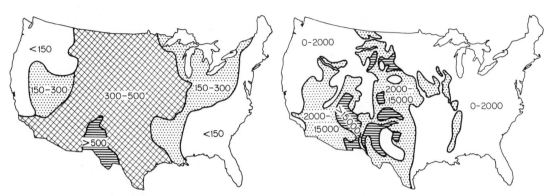

Figure 5.15   (*Left*) *Average dissolved solids in water withdrawn for public supplies. (After U.S.G.S.) (Right) Average concentration of sediment in rivers in the United States (ratio of annual load to annual stream flow). (After U.S.G.S.)*

practical effects. Figure 5.15,A, illustrates regional differences in the average quality of water used for public supplies. The amount of dissolved solids transported by our rivers to the oceans averages more than 600,000 tons daily. Probably twice this amount is transported as suspended load. Streams in the arid and semiarid regions carry high concentrations of load (Fig. 5.15,B), but the total sediment removed is less than in humid regions because runoff is less. In many of the arid and semi-arid regions the suspended loads average less than 500 tons per square mile of drainage basin, but extensive areas in the humid regions average more than 1,000 tons of sediment per square mile drained.

Surficial Deposits and Soils

6

Kinds and Distribution

Although the bedrock geology determines the structural framework and topography of the physiographic provinces, of equal importance in terms of land use are the unconsolidated surface deposits and soils. Figure 6.1 shows the principal surficial deposits in the United States.

The northern part of the United States is blanketed with glacial deposits. In hilly or mountainous areas these deposits are confined to valleys and are discontinuous. When the last of the ice sheets was retreating and stood about at the position of the Great Lakes, depressions in front of the ice were occupied by lakes, and are now marked by dry lake beds. Glacial deposits, and landforms attributable to glaciers, are also found on the lofty western mountains.

Meltwaters from the northern glaciers flooded the Mississippi Valley and deposited alluvium there. Valleys discharging meltwaters were devastated during floods, and when the floods ebbed the river flats became a source of silt and sand that was blown from the valleys onto surrounding uplands. Thus was formed the vast expanse of loess in the Central Lowlands and along the east side of the Mississippi Valley (Fig. 6.1). Farther west, similar deposits are sandy.

Two widely separated parts of the United States are characterized by deep residual deposits. One of these is the belt of metamorphic rocks forming the Piedmont Plateau east of the Appalachian Mountains; the other is the belt of high rainfall along the Pacific Coast north of San Francisco.

Examples of other surface deposits are the volcanic ash leeward from Crater Lake; the sandy and shaley deserts in Wyoming, Utah, Arizona, and New Mexico; and the valley fill in the faulted Basin and Range Province.

The Basin and Range Province consists of three kinds of ground. The ranges, which are rocky fault-block mountains without much soil, are flanked by broad gravel fans that slope from the foot of the mountains to the basins. The interiors of the basins are playas or, in the southern part of the province, broad alluvial floodplains. The extensive dry lake bed around Great Salt Lake is the remnant of Pleistocene Lake Bonneville; another in northwestern Nevada is the remnant of Pleistocene Lake Lahontan.

Some of the common soils in the United States are described in Table 6.1 and their distribution is shown in Figure 6.2. The term "soil" is used with three very different mean-

Figure 6.1 *Surficial deposits in the United States.*

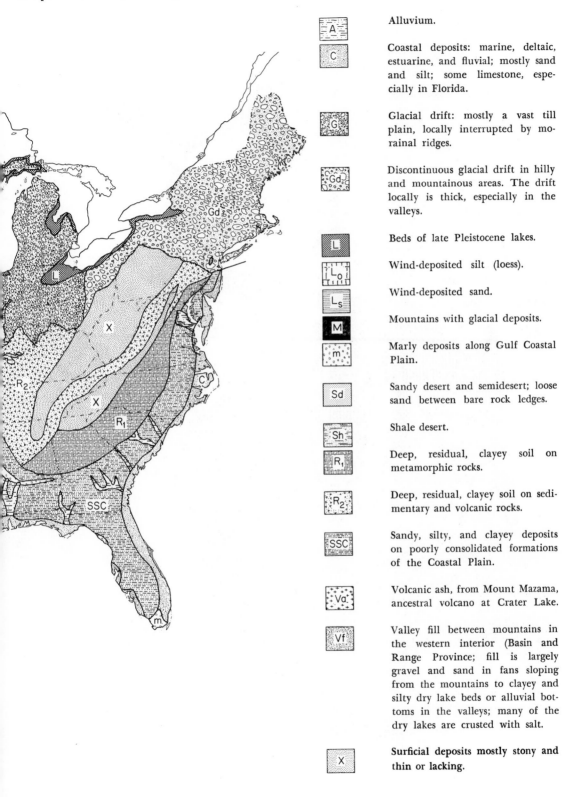

Alluvium.

Coastal deposits: marine, deltaic, estuarine, and fluvial; mostly sand and silt; some limestone, especially in Florida.

Glacial drift: mostly a vast till plain, locally interrupted by morainal ridges.

Discontinuous glacial drift in hilly and mountainous areas. The drift locally is thick, especially in the valleys.

Beds of late Pleistocene lakes.

Wind-deposited silt (loess).

Wind-deposited sand.

Mountains with glacial deposits.

Marly deposits along Gulf Coastal Plain.

Sandy desert and semidesert; loose sand between bare rock ledges.

Shale desert.

Deep, residual, clayey soil on metamorphic rocks.

Deep, residual, clayey soil on sedimentary and volcanic rocks.

Sandy, silty, and clayey deposits on poorly consolidated formations of the Coastal Plain.

Volcanic ash, from Mount Mazama, ancestral volcano at Crater Lake.

Valley fill between mountains in the western interior (Basin and Range Province; fill is largely gravel and sand in fans sloping from the mountains to clayey and silty dry lake beds or alluvial bottoms in the valleys; many of the dry lakes are crusted with salt.

Surficial deposits mostly stony and thin or lacking.

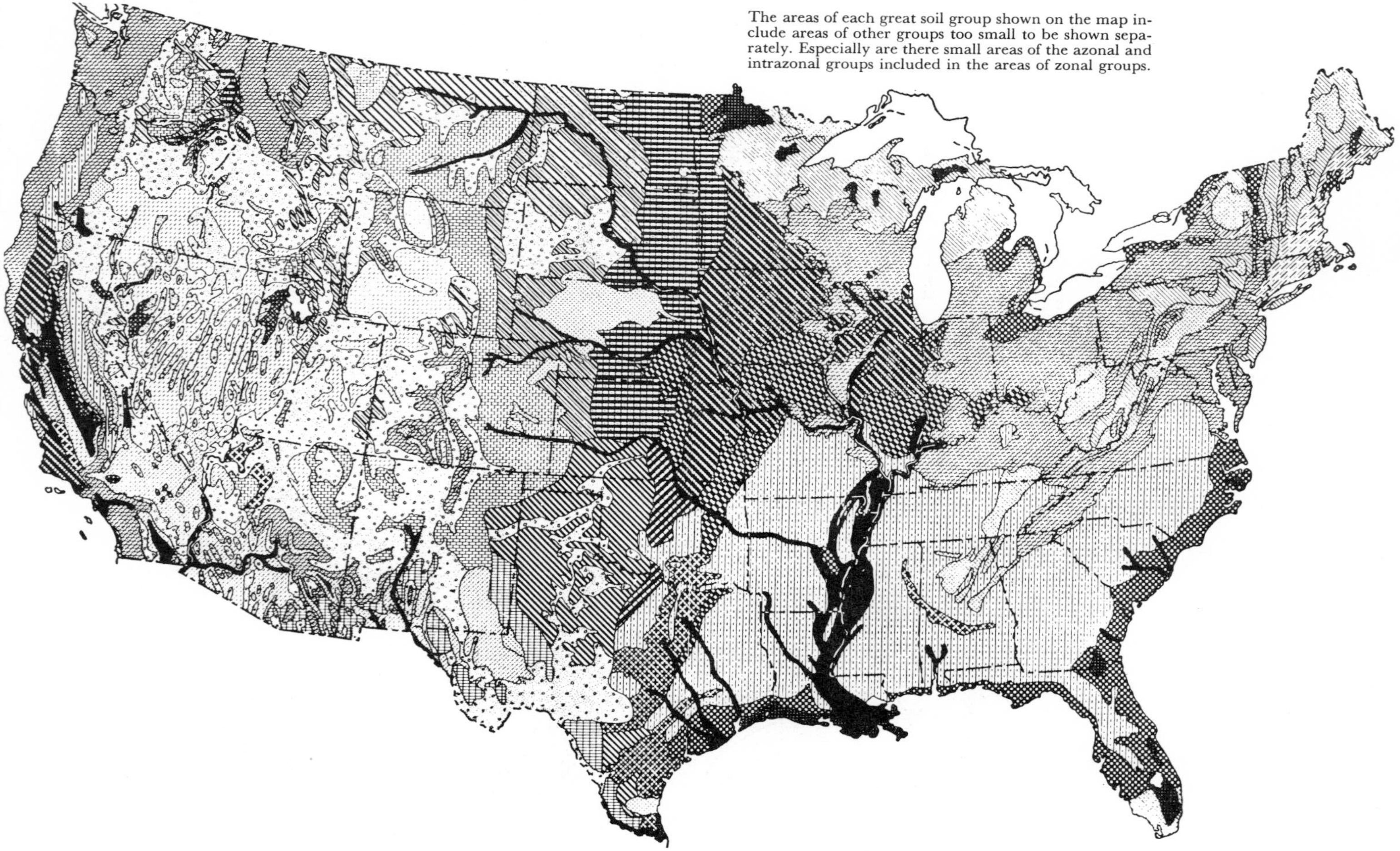

The areas of each great soil group shown on the map include areas of other groups too small to be shown separately. Especially are there small areas of the azonal and intrazonal groups included in the areas of zonal groups.

Figure 6.2 *Soil map of the United States. (Data from U.S.D.A.)*

Great groups of soils with well-developed soil characteristics, reflecting the dominating influence of climate and vegetation. (As shown on the map, many small areas of intrazonal and azonal soils are included.)

Podzol Soils
Light-colored leached soils of cool, humid forested regions.

Brown Podzolic Soils
Brown leached soils of cool-temperate, humid forested regions.

Gray-Brown Podzolic Soils
Grayish-brown leached soils of temperate, humid forested regions.

Red and Yellow Podzolic Soils
Red or yellow leached soils of warm-temperate, humid forested regions.

Prairie Soils
Very dark brown soils of cool and temperate, relatively humid grasslands.

Reddish Prairie Soils
Dark reddish-brown soils of warm-temperate, relatively humid grasslands.

Chernozem Soils
Dark-brown to nearly black soils of cool and temperate, subhumid grasslands.

Chestnut Soils
Dark-brown soils of cool and temperate, subhumid to semiarid grasslands.

Reddish Chestnut Soils
Dark reddish-brown soils of warm-temperate, semiarid regions under mixed shrub and grass vegetation.

Brown Soils
Brown soils of cool and temperate, semiarid grasslands.

Reddish Brown Soils
Reddish-brown soils of warm-temperate to hot, semiarid to arid regions, under mixed shrub and grass vegetation.

Noncalcic Brown Soils
Brown or light reddish-brown soils of warm-temperate, wet-dry, semiarid regions, under mixed forest, shrub, and grass vegetation.

Sierozem or Gray Desert Soils
Gray soils of cool to temperate, arid regions, under shrub and grass vegetation.

Red Desert Soils
Light reddish-brown soils of warm-temperate to hot, arid regions, under shrub vegetation.

INTRAZONAL

Great groups of soils with more or less well-developed soil characteristics reflecting the dominating influence of some local factor of relief, parent material, or age over the normal effect of climate and vegetation. (Many areas of these soils are included with zonal groups on the map.)

Planosols
Soils with strongly leached surface horizons over clay-pans on nearly flat land in cool to warm, humid to subhumid regions, under grass or forest vegetation.

Rendzina Soils
Dark grayish-brown to black soils developed from soft limy materials in cool to warm, humid to subhumid regions, mostly under grass vegetation.

Solonchak (1) and Solonetz (2) Soils
(1) Light-colored soils with high concentration of soluble salts, in subhumid to arid regions, under salt-loving plants.
(2) Dark-colored soils with hard prismatic subsoils, usually strongly alkaline, in subhumid or semiarid regions under grass or shrub vegetation.

Wiesenboden (1), Ground Water Podzol (2), and Half-Bog Soils (3)
(1) Dark-brown to black soils developed with poor drainage under grasses in humid and subhumid regions.
(2) Gray sandy soils with brown cemented sandy subsoils developed under forests from nearly level imperfectly drained sand in humid regions.
(3) Poorly drained, shallow, dark peaty or mucky soils underlain by gray mineral soil, in humid regions, under swamp-forests.

Bog Soils
Poorly drained dark peat or muck soils underlain by peat, mostly in humid regions, under swamp or marsh types of vegetation.

AZONAL

Soils without well-developed soil characteristics. (Many areas of these soils are included with other groups on the map.)

Lithosols and Shallow Soils (Arid-Subhumid)
Shallow soils consisting largely of an imperfectly weathered mass of rock fragments, largely but not exclusively on steep slopes.

(Humid)

Sands (Dry)
Very sandy soils.

Alluvial Soils
Soils developing from recently deposited alluvium that have had little or no modification by processes of soil formation.

TABLE 6.1 Characteristics of some common soils.

	Pedalfers
Tundra Soil	Dark-brown peaty layer over gray horizons mottled with rust; substrate permanently frozen. *Climate:* frigid, humid. *Vegetation:* lichens, mosses, herbs, shrubs. *Process:* gleization (development of organic-rich, sticky, compact, clayey layer due to excessive wetting). *Age:* Recent.
Alpine Meadow	Dark-brown organic-rich layer grading down at 1 to 2 feet to gray and rusty soil, streaked and mottled. *Climate:* cool temperate to frigid. *Vegetation:* grasses, sedges, herbs. *Process:* gleization, some calcification (deposition of calcium carbonate). *Age:* Recent.
Bog and Half-Bog	Brown, dark-brown, or black peaty material over soils of mineral matter mottled gray and rust. *Climate:* cool to tropical; generally humid. *Vegetation:* swamp, forest, sedges, or grass. *Process:* gleization. *Age:* Recent.
Podzol, Brown-Podzol, Gray-Brown Podzol	Leaf litter over a humus-rich layer over a whitish-gray to grayish-brown leached layer; B horizon clayey and brown. Acid. *Climate:* cool, temperate, humid. *Vegetation:* northern forests, coniferous and/or deciduous. *Process:* podzolization (bases—Al and Fe—leached more than silica from A horizon and accumulated in B horizon). *Age:* mostly late Pleistocene and Recent.
Red and Yellow Podzol	Thin, dark organic layer at surface over yellow-gray or gray-brown leached layer ½ to 3 feet thick, over clayey B horizon over parent material mottled red, yellow, and gray. *Climate:* warm temperate to tropical humid. *Vegetation:* coniferous forest or mixed deciduous and coniferous. *Process:* podzolization superimposed on lateritization (silica leached more than the bases). *Age:* the podzolic surface layers are late Pleistocene and Recent; the lateritic parent material is the result of much older soil processes—early Pleistocene, Tertiary, and even older.
Prairie and Reddish Prairie	Brown in the north; reddish-brown toward the south. Grades down to lighter colored parent material with no horizon of carbonate accumulation. *Climate:* cool temperate to warm temperate, humid. *Vegetation:* tall grass. *Process:* weak podzolization. *Age:* the northern facies is late Pleistocene and Recent; the reddish, southern facies may include some older soils.
	Pedocals
Chernozem	Black to gray-brown, crumbly soil to depth of 3 or 4 feet, grading through lighter color to a layer of carbonate accumulation. *Climate:* subhumid, temperate to cool. *Vegetation:* tall grass. *Process:* calcification (accumulation of carbonates in lower horizons). *Age:* late Pleistocene and Recent.
Chestnut, Brown, Reddish Chestnut, and Reddish Brown	Brown to black surface layer in north; reddish in south; lighter color at depth and grading down to layer of carbonate accumulation. Chestnut thinner than Chernozem and Brown thinner than Chestnut. *Climate:* semiarid; cool to hot. *Vegetation:* mostly short grasses in north; grasses and shrub in south. *Process:* calcification. *Age:* very commonly mixed ages with late Pleistocene and Recent weathering profiles superimposed on older Pleistocene ones.
Desert, Sierozem, Red Desert	Light gray or brown in north; reddish in south; low in organic matter; carbonate layer generally within 1 foot of the surface. *Climate:* arid, cool to hot. *Vegetation:* mostly desert shrubs. *Process:* calcification. *Age:* Late Pleistocene and Recent soils have shallow, weakly developed profiles; older Pleistocene soils are several feet thick and horizons are well developed and generally reddish.

Others	
Rendzina	Dark-gray or black, organic rich, surface layers over soft light gray or white calcareous material derived from chalk, soft limestone, or marl. *Climate:* variable. *Vegetation:* mostly grassland. *Process:* the lime in these soils is derived from the parent materials. *Age:* mostly late Pleistocene and Recent; older soils that are related develop red clay in the upper layers and are referred to as *terra rosa.*
Laterite	Thin organic layer over reddish, strongly leached soil, generally clayey and enriched in hydrous alumina or iron oxide or both; low in silica; generally many feet thick. *Climate:* tropical wet. *Vegetation:* mostly forest. *Process:* lateritization (see Red and Yellow Podzol). *Age:* early Pleistocene, Teritiary, and even older.
Saline and Alkali Soils	Soils in which salts including alkali have accumulated, generally in poorly drained areas. *Climate:* variable, but commonly arid or semiarid. *Vegetation:* salt tolerant species or lacking. *Process:* salinization or alkalization (salts deposited in soil as a result of evaporation). *Age:* mostly late Pleistocene and Recent.

ings. Agriculturalists limit the term to the surficial materials that provide a foundation and nutrient substratum for plants. Engineers use the term soil to refer to all unconsolidated materials, regardless of depth, that may be involved in foundation and excavation problems or be utilized as fill. Geologists use the term to refer to the surficial zone altered by weathering. In this book the term "soil" is used in the geologist's sense, but most terms used in the description of soils are borrowed from the nomenclature of soil scientists, who are agriculturally oriented.

Soils are layered parallel to the surface as a result of weathering (Fig. 6.3). The surface layers are rich in organic matter. The uppermost layer is a mat of leaves and other litter that is only slightly decomposed. Below this is a layer of partly decomposed leaves and other organic matter, and this grades downward into a layer of mineral matter blackened with organic matter. Below this is a light-colored layer in which there has been maximum leaching—that is, the transfer of constituents downward, by solution and by physical washing. Decomposition of organic matter in the surface layers produces acids that

are carried downward by the soil water and dissolve matter from the layer immediately below the organic-rich one. Part or all of the dissolved matter becomes deposited in the subsoil (B horizon in Fig. 6.3). Below this is the parent material.

Pedalfers, soils of the humid provinces, differ from *pedocals,* soils of the semiarid and arid provinces. Pedalfer profiles (Fig. 6.3) develop where moisture is sufficient to penetrate downward to the water table. Because soil moisture is ample, vegetation is lush and organic matter plentiful; decomposition of the organic matter renders the soils acid, and leaching is intensive. Aluminum and iron (hence the name pedalfer) and clays are leached from the A horizon and deposited in the B horizon, which is less acid and may even be neutral in chemical reaction. Since moisture is sufficient to drain downward to the water table, it also removes silica and the very soluble alkalis and alkali earths from the profile. Continued weathering of pedalfers changes the composition of the soil toward that of a clay mineral composed of aluminum and silica (kaolinite) and the hydroxides of ferric iron and aluminum.

Pedocal profiles (Fig. 6.3) develop where moisture wets only the upper layers of the ground and does not seep downward to the water table. Vegetation is sparse compared to that of humid regions; there is less organic matter in the soil, and leaching is correspondingly less. Such constituents as are leached are transported downward as far as the water penetrates and are deposited where the water evaporates as the soil dries. Carbonates, whether contributed by organic matter or by the parent material, combine with the alkalis and alkali earths to form soluble salts. The deposition of these gives rise to a B horizon containing much carbonate, especially calcium

carbonate (hence the name pedocal). Pedocal soils have lost no constituents; indeed, carbon (from the organic matter) has been added.

Figure 6.4 illustrates the changes in soil profiles that accompany changes in vegetation and climate along a transect from northeastern Canada to the southwestern United States. The northeast end of the transect is cold and wet, and the soils there are pedalfers; the southwest end is warm and dry, and the soils there are pedocals. The vegetation changes from tundra and conifer forest at the northeast, to grassland on the semiarid plains, to shrubland in the desert at the southwest.

Soils under the conifer forests are *Podzols*

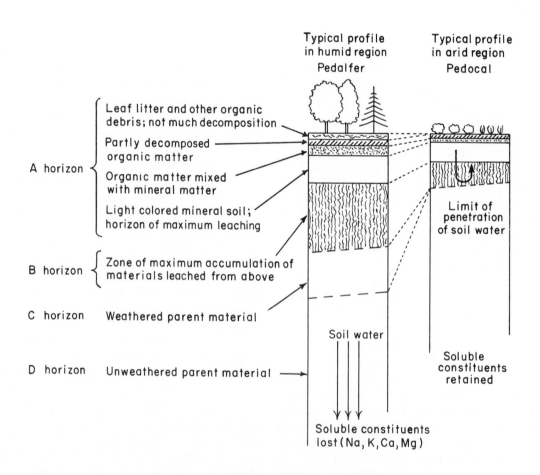

Figure 6.3 *Soil profiles, showing* horizons.

Southwest   Northeast

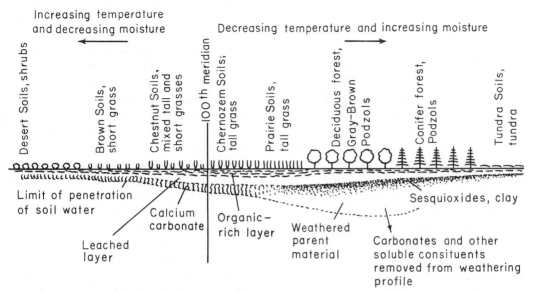

Figure 6.4 *Changes in soil profiles that accompany changes in vegetation and climate between the tundra in northern Canada and the deserts in the southwestern United States.*

characterized by a thin, ash-gray, leached horizon (A) over a dark-brown (B) horizon. Soils under the deciduous forests are *Gray-Brown Podzols* characterized by a gray-brown leached horizon (A) over a dark-brown (B) horizon. These are typical pedalfers.

Under the tall grass on the plains the A horizons become thicker. Near the 100th meridian, where the annual precipitation averages about 20 inches, the soils are typical pedocals with lime carbonate in the subsoil. Prairie soils have a deep organic layer without a lime zone. Chernozem Soils, farther west but still under deep-rooted tall grass, have a deep layer of black organic material and an underlying zone of lime accumulation. Still farther west, where rainfall is less, the grasses are short and shallow rooted. The organic layer is thinner in the Chestnut Soils and lighter in the Brown Soils; the lime zone of both is more distinct but thinner. Soils in the deserts are thin and the horizons are not well developed.

Differences between soils in the northern and southern physiographic provinces are due partly to differences in climate but chiefly to differences in the ages of the soils. The Red and Yellow Podzols south of the limit of Wisconsin glaciation owe their principal characteristics to weathering that occurred before the Wisconsin glaciation. The organic fraction is the product of Recent vegetation, which has developed a Recent profile near the surface, but the present mineralogy of the soils is largely inherited from pre-Wisconsin time, as shown by the fact that the B and lower horizons are overlapped by and therefore older than the glacial drift and other deposits of Wisconsin age. These old soils have been leached of silica and are called *lateritic soils,* or *latosols,* because of their similarity to tropical soils known as laterites.

Most of the red soils of the southwestern United States also are old soils, but the Podzols and the Gray-Brown Podzols, which are developed on glacial drift and other deposits of Wisconsin age or younger, are young.

Rock Weathering

Soils are the product of rock weathering, which involves chemical decay and physical disintegration of the rocks. Soils include grains of unaltered, resistant minerals, partly altered minerals, and new minerals composed of the chemical elements freed from the altered minerals. The rock-forming minerals differ in their susceptibility to weathering and alteration (Table 2.2). In general, their relative susceptibility is the same as the order in which they crystallize from silicate melts. The minerals that form early under conditions of high temperature and high pressure are least resistant, whereas minerals that form late are most resistant to alteration in the soil.

The factors controlling rock weathering, like the factors controlling erosion, can be considered in terms of structure, process, and stage. Differences in the structure of rocks, including their hardness, permeability, and mineral composition, give rise to differences in the soils derived from them.

The processes of weathering are controlled chiefly by four factors: organisms, climate, geologic setting, and topographic position. Acids derived from decomposition of organic matter on and in the soil are the principal causes of rock decay, and accordingly the biota determines the kind and intensity of the processes, chiefly biochemical, that alter the mineral matter. Climate affects not only the biota but the abundance and temperature of soil moisture. The geologic setting may affect the soil climate—for example, by controlling the position of the water table. Similarly, the topographic position affects soil processes by controlling surface drainage; hillsides are better drained than flat uplands or valley bottoms.

The alteration of minerals by solutions requires time, and the kind and stage of alteration are therefore partly functions of the duration of the process. This leads to still another dimension in rock weathering, mineral altera-

tion, and soil origin: geologic history. The organic fraction in soils, largely a function of the present biota, is a product of the Recent Epoch. But the Recent Epoch has not lasted long enough to affect greatly the mineral fraction of soils; the characteristics of this fraction are largely inherited from the Pleistocene and older epochs, when the climate and biota over wide areas differed greatly from those of the present. In brief, then, rock weathering, mineral alteration, and soil development are controlled by structure (parent material), process (biota, climate, topographic setting, geologic environment), and stage (time).

The chemical processes that alter minerals and cause rocks to weather involve oxygen, carbon dioxide, and moisture from the air and from the biota. The four principal processes are *carbonation, oxidation, hydration,* and *solution.*

Carbon dioxide (CO_2) is readily soluble in water (H_2O) and becomes carbonic acid (H_2CO_3), which dissolves such carbonates as calcite.

$$\underset{\text{carbonic acid}}{H_2CO_3} \quad + \quad \underset{\text{calcite}}{CaCO_3} \quad \rightarrow \quad \underset{\substack{\text{calcium carbonate} \\ \text{(soluble)}}}{H_2Ca(CO_3)_2}$$

Carbon dioxide exists in the atmosphere in quantities of about 300 ppm of air; in the soil atmosphere the CO_2 content is very much greater than in the air above ground because of the intense biochemical activity.

Oxygen, which makes up about 21 percent of the atmosphere, dissolves in rain and groundwater and combines with various bases in the process known as oxidation. The process is most notable in connection with alteration of iron-bearing minerals (dark minerals in Table 2.2); the iron becomes oxidized, and the minerals and soils become stained brown or red.

Hydration is the process by which water combines with various compounds. Hydration, together with the processes of carbonation and solution, is involved in the alteration of feldspars to clay minerals. A sodic-calcic feldspar, for example, alters to a clay mineral (kaolinite, a hydrated aluminum silicate) and to calcium and sodium bicarbonate:

$$CaAl_2Si_2O_8 \cdot 2NaAlSi_3O_8 \quad + \quad 4H_2CO_3 \quad + \quad 2(nH_2O) \rightarrow$$

sodic-calcic feldspar   carbonic   water
                 acid

$$2Al_2(OH)_2Si_4O_{10} \cdot H_2O \quad + \quad Ca(HCO_3)_2 \quad + \quad 2NaHCO_3$$

kaolinite   calcium   sodium
          bicarbonate   bicarbonate

The bicarbonates are soluble and are removed in solution; the clays remain behind. This explains why old soils tend to be enriched in clay.

The stable products of these processes of mineral alteration are the clay minerals and the hydroxides of aluminum and ferric iron. Where weathering is advanced these new minerals become mixed in the soil with the more resistant minerals surviving from the parent rock, especially quartz and muscovite. The alkalis (K, Na) and alkali earths (Ca, Mg) freed by these alterations form carbonates, sulfates, chlorides, nitrates, borates, and other highly soluble salts that can be removed in solution. Silica also is released and may be removed by groundwater; the feldspars and the dark silicates contain more silica than do the clay minerals that develop from them.

Rock weathering also involves mechanical processes of rock disintegration. Examples are frost action, splitting of rocks by plant roots, growth of salt crystals, fires, and abrasion during transport by wind, water, or glacial ice. The continental and alpine glaciers produced quantities of rock flour by grinding the rock fragments they transported. Rock disintegration greatly accelerates chemical decomposition, because susceptibility to alteration by weathering increases with increase in surface area subject to alteration. Fine-grained materials expose more surface area per unit volume and weather more rapidly than do coarse materials.

The rates of different kinds of weathering and erosion are affected by the climate, but the relationships are complex. Increased rainfall tends to accelerate both weathering and stream discharge, and so increases erosion. But the effects are partly offset by increase in vegetation, which reduces runoff. Increased temperature greatly increases the biochemical processes involved in rock weathering and soil development. The rate of chemical reactions, in general, about doubles for every 10°C rise in temperature, which is to say that, other things being equal, rocks in the southern states decompose twice as rapidly as do those in the northern states. Moreover, the increased rainfall increases the vegetation, which in turn increases the quantity of organic acids for decomposing rocks and minerals.

7 Erosion and Sedimentation

Erosion sufficient to affect land use and land values in the United States is of several kinds. In some areas, sheetflooding or wind erodes the topsoil and exposes the subsoil. In other areas, hillside runoff becomes concentrated and the ground becomes gullied. In still other areas, notably in the Colorado Plateau and in the Rocky Mountain Provinces, floodplains are subject to arroyo-cutting, and in other parts of the country stream banks are subject to severe erosion. Figure 7.1 shows the extent and relative severity of erosion in the United States.

The areas most subject to erosion in the eastern United States are those of the Red and Yellow Podzolic soils. In the Middle West, those of the loessial soils. The southern Great Plains are the "dust bowl" areas and are subject to severe wind erosion, especially when tilled.

In the Rocky Mountains and other western provinces, the kinds of ground most subject to erosion are alluvial floodplains, loessial soils, and shale deserts. The Soil Conservation Service studies methods for curbing such erosion.

Erosion of beaches is a serious problem along much of the Atlantic and Gulf Coastal Plains and along the coast of California, especially toward the south. Hurricanes cause much of the erosion along the Atlantic seaboard and the Gulf Coast, and erosion there is becoming more serious as sea level rises. A rise of as much as 6 inches has been recorded in the last 50 years (see p. 160).

In California, recent uplift along sections of the coast has developed coastal terraces, and some of these are highly unstable and subject to landsliding. Such lands, and the exposed stretches of the Atlantic Coast, obviously are more suitable for park lands than for real estate developments. We need the parks, and can do without the perennial disaster relief that is the price for settling in such areas.

Rates of Erosion

Rates of erosion vary greatly from place to place and they have varied from time to time in the geologic past as a result of structural movements and climatic changes. Erosion rates can be estimated by comparing the quantity of sediment contained in the formations in old geosynclines with the areas that were eroded and the duration of the period represented. Present-day erosion can be estimated by comparing the sediment load of streams with the areas drained. Erosion rates vary according to the topography (relief and slope), climate (amount and kind of runoff), and kind of ground (bare rock or easily eroded surficial deposits). Estimates of this kind are not very accurate, but they do provide an approximate measure of the forces involved and the times required to accomplish changes in landforms.

On lowlands and plains where slopes average no more than about 5 feet per mile the rate of lowering seems to be about a quarter of an inch in a thousand years. Where relief is considerable and slopes are steep, as on mountains and plateaus, the rate may be 10 or 20 times that amount. If we assume that the average rate is 1 inch per thousand years, the United States would be eroded to a low plain in something like 50 million years, approximately the duration of the Cenozoic Era. This has not happened, of course, because structural movements of the crust—folding, faulting, and uplift—have offset the lowering by erosion. In fact, during the Cenozoic Era land has been added to the United States, as represented by the Tertiary and Quaternary formations along both the East and West coasts.

This erosion may remove soil or other surficial deposits, or it may remove unweathered bedrock. The relative importance of these in shaping landforms is difficult to assess, but we may assume that channel cutting by streams and by glacial ice is accomplished chiefly by erosion of bedrock, whereas the retreat of hillsides and the lowering of hilltops, at least in the humid provinces, are accomplished chiefly by erosion of the products of weathering—the soil or other surficial deposits.

There is some evidence that this is a valid generalization, even though there are exceptions. In the humid provinces, where weathering is rapid, valleys are V-shaped. Hillsides are soil covered and tend to rise smoothly, though in places steeply, from valley floors. In the arid provinces, where weathering is slow, hillsides are rocky and interrupted by cliffs. Hilltops in humid provinces commonly are soil covered and rounded, but in arid provinces they are mostly bare rock and reflect the structure.

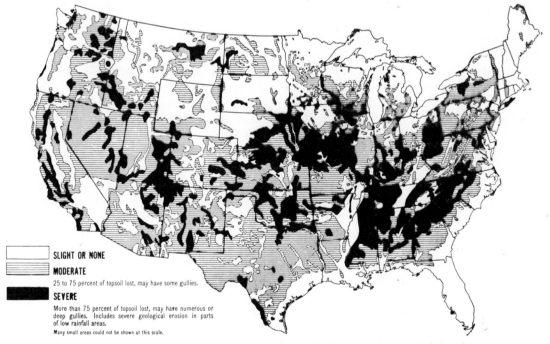

SLIGHT OR NONE

MODERATE

25 to 75 percent of topsoil lost, may have some gullies.

SEVERE

More than 75 percent of topsoil lost, may have numerous or deep gullies. Includes severe geological erosion in parts of low rainfall areas.

Many small areas could not be shown at this scale.

Figure 7.1   *Present-day erosion in the United States. (From U.S.D.A.)*

Transportation of Sediment

Particles of rocks and minerals loosened by weathering are transported from the site by gravity, water, waves, ice, or wind. Gravity transportation takes three principal forms. One involves the slow *creep* or slumping of sediments down hillsides, most commonly as a result of alternate freezing and thawing. On steeper slopes debris from landslides and rock falls, often caused by torrential rains, may accumulate in steep *colluvial* cones (Fig. 3.9,G). At the foot of cliffs rock falls accumulate as *talus*. The processes involved in gravity transportation are referred to collectively as *mass wasting*.

Running water transports sediment in *solution, suspension,* and as *bed load.* Constituents transported in *solution* include carbonates and other salts of the alkalis and alkali earths (Table 5.1), but also silica and certain salts of iron and aluminum. Even the most quietly moving water can transport vast quantities of sediment in solution (see p. 84).

Sediment transported in suspension consists mostly of the fine-grained particles, especially those of clay size. They settle to the bottom in quiet water, but water is sufficiently viscous to hold the particles in suspension where the water is turbulent. The more turbulent the water, the larger the particles that can be suspended.

The quantity of sediment transported along streambeds is difficult to measure. Bed load depends on the stream velocity, size of the particles, and roughness of the bed. Part of the load—the gravels that are too large to be lifted off the bottom by the particular current—is rolled along the bottom. A second part is moved partly by rolling and partly by suspension, a process known as *saltation.* These particles are smaller than those moved by rolling but larger than those moved solely by suspension.

With increased velocity the volume of sediment that can be transported is increased, and the fractions that are transported by suspension, saltation, and rolling are increased. Some examples of stream velocities required to transport particles of different sizes are:

Stream velocity	Sediment size that can be transported
⅙ mph	clay
⅓ mph	fine sand
1 mph	gravel up to pea size
2 mph	gravel up to thumb size
3 mph	gravel up to size of hen's egg

Wind, like running water, also can transport materials by rolling them along the ground (tumbleweed is a familiar example), saltation, suspension (does your city have smog?), and even by solution. Materials in solution are mostly salts in the water vapor or water droplets. The chloride content of the atmosphere, and of the rain and snow, decreases inland from the coasts.

Sediment transport by glacial ice is very different from that by streams. The debris transported by valley glaciers and deposited in lateral and terminal moraines (Fig. 3.10,E) is derived mostly from the hillsides above the ice, which are subject to severe freezing and thawing and develop mud flows and avalanches as a result of sudden thaws. The sediment is washed onto the ice in the valley and transported down valley by the glacier.

Other sediment moved by valley glaciers is gouged from the valley floor under the ice. Most surficial deposits, when overridden by a glacier, become incorporated in the ice and transported down valley to the terminus, where floods transport the glacial outwash away from the ice front. Although ice movement is responsible for part of the transport by glaciers, much or most of the debris is transported by streams on, in, and under the ice.

The continental glaciers of the Pleistocene derived their load of sediment chiefly from the soil and other unconsolidated deposits overridden by the glaciers, for few hills protruded above the ice to shed debris onto it, except in the northeastern United States. Glaciated areas generally are free of unconsolidated surficial deposits other than those left by the glaciers themselves. Bare rock surfaces are extensive, and these show striations and other signs of gouge caused by rocks frozen into the bottom of the ice.

8 Plant and Animal Geography

Life Zones

Along the tropical coast of Florida, one can find mangrove and alligator; around lakes in northern Minnesota, spruce and moose.

Some like it hot, and some like it cold. Each climatic region has its characteristic flora and fauna, and these regions are referred to as *life zones*. The climatic regions are completely gradational with each other and their boundaries necessarily arbitrary. The faunal zones also are gradational, but less completely so. The floral zones are still less gradational, and in many cases are set apart by surprisingly sharp boundaries.

In North America, seven transcontinental life zones can be recognized (Fig. 8.1). At the north, the *Arctic, Hudsonian,* and *Canadian Zones* constitute the *Boreal Region.* South of this region is the *Transition Zone;* still farther south are the *Upper* and *Lower Austral Zones,* which constitute the *Austral Region.* At the south is the *Tropical Zone.* The general arrangement, by latitude, evidently reflects temperature differences; a similar zonation arranged by altitude is found on mountains (Figs. 8.4, 11.18). The more northerly zones extend southward along the tops of the Appalachian, Rocky, and Cascade-Sierra mountains (Fig. 8.1). The Arctic Zone on the mountain tops is referred to as the *Alpine Zone.*

But there also are biotic differences reflecting differences in amount of moisture, especially in the Austral Region. The differences are great enough to require distinction between the Austral Zones of the humid East and those of the semiarid West, as follows:

	Semiarid West	Humid East
Austral region {	Upper Sonoran Zone	Carolinian Zone
	Lower Sonoran Zone	Austroriparian Zone

The Eastern States

The Tropical Zone, represented by a small area at the southern tip of Florida, has mangrove swamps, mostly in the shoals between the islands (keys) and the mainland and along the southern and western borders of the Everglades. Besides the mangrove there are royal palm, coconut palm, and banana. This area is the home of the alligator and a few tropical birds, such as the great white heron, everglade kite, and mangrove cuckoo. Coral grows in the warm coastal waters.

Along the Gulf Coast, from the panhandle of Florida westward to Texas, there are con-

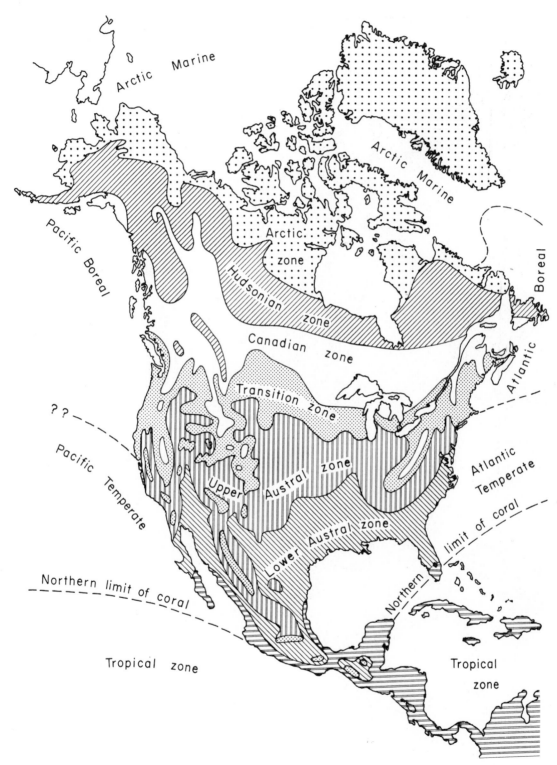

Figure 8.1 *Map of life zones in North America.*

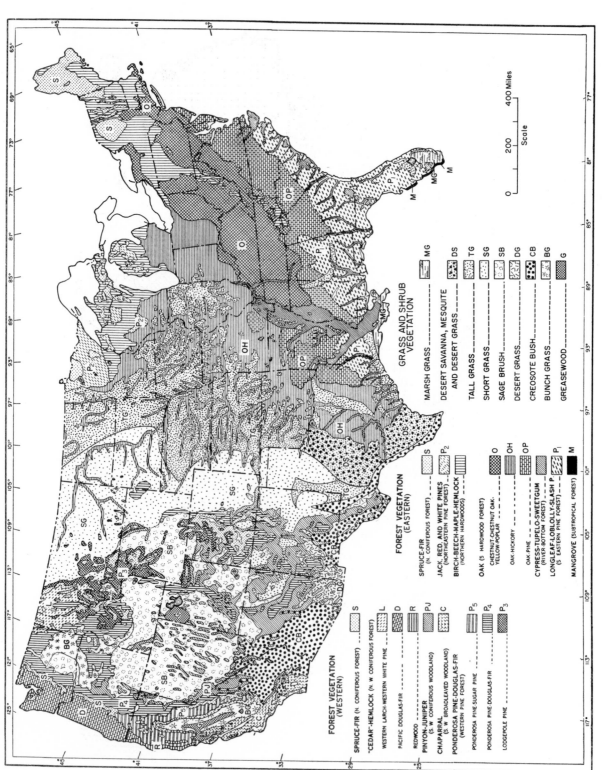

FOREST VEGETATION
(WESTERN)

SPRUCE-FIR (N. CONIFEROUS FOREST) ------------- S

"CEDAR"-HEMLOCK (N. W. CONIFEROUS FOREST) ----- L

WESTERN LARCH-WESTERN WHITE PINE ------------- D

PACIFIC DOUGLAS-FIR --------------------------- R

REDWOOD --------------------------------------- PJ

PINYON-JUNIPER
(S. W. CONIFEROUS WOODLAND) ------------------- C

CHAPARRAL
(S. W. BROADLEAVED WOODLAND)

PONDEROSA PINE-DOUGLAS-FIR
(WESTERN PINE FOREST) ------------------------- P₅

PONDEROSA PINE-SUGAR PINE --------------------- P₄

PONDEROSA PINE-DOUGLAS-FIR -------------------- P₃

LODGEPOLE PINE

FOREST VEGETATION
(EASTERN)

SPRUCE-FIR
(N. CONIFEROUS FOREST) ------------------------ S

JACK, RED, AND WHITE PINES
(NORTHEASTERN PINE FOREST) -------------------- P₂

BIRCH-BEECH-MAPLE-HEMLOCK
(NORTHERN HARDWOODS)

OAK (S. HARDWOOD FOREST) ---------------------- O

CHESTNUT-CHESTNUT OAK-
YELLOW-POPLAR --------------------------------- OH

OAK-HICKORY ----------------------------------- OP

OAK-PINE

CYPRESS-TUPELO-SWEETGUM
(RIVER BOTTOM FOREST)

LONGLEAF-LOBLOLLY-SLASH P.
(S. EASTERN PINE FOREST) ---------------------- P₁

MANGROVE (SUBTROPICAL FOREST) ----------------- M

GRASS AND SHRUB
VEGETATION

MARSH GRASS ----------------------------------- MG

DESERT SAVANNA, MESQUITE
AND DESERT GRASS ------------------------------ DS

TALL GRASS ------------------------------------ TG

SHORT GRASS ----------------------------------- SG

SAGE BRUSH ------------------------------------ SB

DESERT GRASS ---------------------------------- DG

CREOSOTE BUSH --------------------------------- CB

BUNCH GRASS ----------------------------------- BG

GREASEWOOD ------------------------------------ G

Figure 8.2 Natural vegetation in the United States. (After U.S.D.A.)

siderable areas of marsh grass. On the seaward side of these areas the water is brackish and the grass is salt tolerant (*Spartina*); on the landward side the marshes contain fresh water and are characterized by Indian rice grass (*Zizania*). In southern Louisiana this land is drained and developed for raising rice. The Gulf Coast marshes are the breeding ground for numerous species of waterfowl that migrate to the far north during the summer.

North of the coastal belt of grasses is the Southeastern Pine Forest (Figs. 8.2, 8.3), characterized by the slash, longleaf, and loblolly pines (Fig. 10.14). This is the Lower Austral (Austroriparian) Zone. Poorly drained lowlands in this zone have swamps of cypress, tupelo, and red gum. In Alabama the Southeastern Pine Forest is interrupted by a belt of tall grass that coincides with the limey soils (Rendzina, Table 6.1) on one of the Tertiary formations of the Coastal Plain (Fig. 8.10,B). some characteristic mammals of this zone are the southern woodrat, eastern harvest mouse, cotton mouse, and marsh rabbit. Birds that gather there in the nesting season include the water turkey, black vulture, ivory-billed woodpecker, yellow-throated warbler, and brownheaded nuthatch. Principal crops are cotton, corn, peanuts, sweet potatoes, and beans.

At the inner edge of the Coastal Plain and southern edge of the Appalachian Highlands, is Mixed Oak and Pine Forest. Principal oaks are the black, chestnut, post, blackjack, and Spanish oaks. The most abundant pine is the shortleaf pine. In addition, there are pignut and mockernut hickory. Principal crops are corn, wheat, cotton, oats, apples, and peaches.

The Upper Austral, or Carolinian, Zone extends north from the Tennessee River. The forests of the Carolinian Zone are referred to as the Central Hardwood Forest. As far north as the Ohio River, this forest was originally populated by chestnut, chestnut oak, and yellow poplar and is said to contain a greater number of species of trees (more than 1,000) than any other forest area in the world. North of the Ohio River, in western Ohio, Indiana, and southern Michigan, the original forest consisted of oak and hickory. The forests now have largely been cut over and the land cleared for agriculture. Principal agricultural products are livestock, fruit, and tobacco in the south, and corn, soybeans, grains, hay, and potatoes in the north. Some mammals characteristic of the Carolinian Zone are the thirteenlined squirrel, southern bog lemming, and prairie vole. Some of the birds nesting there include the Acadian flycatcher, cardinal,

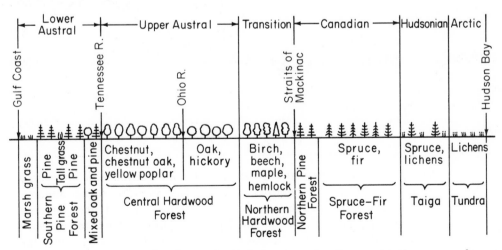

Figure 8.3 *Transect showing principal forest and other vegetation zones between the Gulf Coast and Hudson Bay.*

hooded warbler, chat, Carolina wren, and tufted titmouse.

To the north of the Upper Austral Zone is the Transition Zone, marked by the Northern Hardwood Forest and originally composed chiefly of birch, beech, maple, and hemlock. This zone marks the northern limit of several Austral species of trees and animals and the southern limit of several species of the Canadian Zone. It is the northern limit of most snakes and other reptiles, which are cold-blooded animals. The woodland jumping mouse and yellownose vole are characteristic mammals. Among the characteristic birds nesting there are the bobwhite, mourning dove, kingbird, crested flycatcher, bobolink, cowbird, meadowlark, Baltimore oriole, chipping sparrow, towhee, catbird, house wren, and wood thrush. The land is used mostly for dairy produce.

The Canadian Zone is conifer forest, consisting principally of spruce and fir but including some pine toward the south. Among the characteristic animals are the lynx, marten, porcupine, red squirrel, snowshoe hare, and

moose. Some birds that nest there include the Canada jay, spruce partridge, hawk owl, white-throated sparrow, junco, and hermit thrush.

The Hudsonian, or Taiga, Zone supports a growth of spruce and lichens. This is the northern limit of forest and northern limit for such mammals as moose, elk, wolverine, marten, and gray wolf. Characteristic birds are the rough-legged hawk, great gray owl, pine grosbeak, and northern shrike.

North of this is the Arctic, or Tundra, Zone, which is treeless except for dwarfed willows and consists of mosses, lichens, and sedges. This is home for the polar bear, musk-ox, caribou, and reindeer and for such characteristic birds as the snowy owl and snow bunting. This zone is circumpolar; most of the fauna, and to a lesser extent the flora, occurs in Eurasia as well as in North America.

The effect of altitude on the distribution of the life zones may be seen in the vegetation patterns in the Appalachian Highlands. On the high mountains the northern zones extend far south of their normal latitudinal range. Spruce-Fir Forest grows at sea level along the

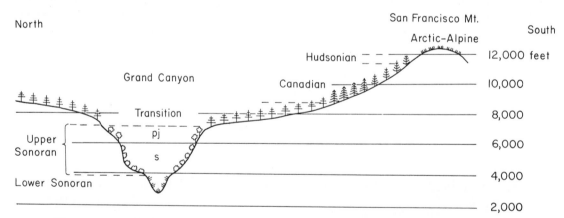

Figure 8.4 *Altitudinal zoning of vegetation in Grand Canyon and on nearby San Francisco Mountain. In the bottom of Grand Canyon is the Lower Sonoran Zone, with creosote bush, catclaw acacia, and mesquite. The Upper Sonoran Zone of sagebrush (S), pinyon and juniper (PJ) and cliffrose extends to the south rim of the canyon. The Transition Zone is characterized by yellow pine, the Canadian Zone by Douglas fir and white fir, the Hudsonian Zone by Englemann spruce and alpine fir. The Arctic-Alpine Zone has only low herbs.*

Maine coast and also in West Virginia and Maryland at altitudes of about 3,500 feet and on the Great Smoky Mountains at 6,000 feet. The boundary between the Carolinian and Transition Zones is at sea level in northern New Jersey, about 1,200 feet in western Maryland, 2,500 feet in North Carolina, and about 3,500 feet in Georgia (Fig. 11.18).

The Western States

Because of the great height of the mountains in the western states the life zones there are arranged in two patterns, one conforming to the transcontinental latitudinal zones and the other to altitudinal zones (Fig. 8.5). Both of these distribution patterns are controlled largely by temperature, probably duration of the growing season; they differ from the eastern zones chiefly in amount of moisture received, for the western states are semiarid.

At the south, in southern California, Arizona, New Mexico, and western Texas, is the Lower Sonoran Zone, characterized chiefly by the creosote bush but including stands of desert holly, mesquite, catclaw acacia, paloverde, and a variety of the picturesque yuccas and cacti. Among the more unusual animals are two large lizards, the gila monster and the chuckwalla; the sidewinder rattlesnake; a considerable population of rodents; a native pig, the peccary; badgers; foxes; coyotes; vultures; ravens; and the roadrunner. In most of the Lower Sonoran Zone annual rainfall is less than 10 inches, and the evaporation rates exceed the average rainfall by factors of 10 to 100. Moist locations, where groundwater is at shallow depths, support oases of various species of water-loving plants.

The upper altitudinal limit of the Lower Sonoran Zone is between about 2,500 and 4,000 feet (Fig. 8.4). Its most northerly extent is southernmost Nevada and the southwest corner of Utah.

The next higher and cooler zone (Upper Sonoran Zone), which covers much of the western states, is the zone of sagebrush, where annual rainfall averages slightly greater than, and evaporation rates lower than, in the Lower Sonoran Zone. Some of the distinctive stands of plants found in this zone are given in the table at the bottom of this page.

Except for the extensive pinyon-juniper woodland and the less extensive stands of the Joshua tree, the Upper Sonoran Zone is dominated by shrubs. Plants 10 feet tall are rare, and taller trees are practically nonexistent. Most of the shrubs are 1 to 3 feet high and are separated by a few feet of bare soil supporting only scattered herbaceous plants. Moist locations, where groundwater is shallow, support oases of greasewood, saltgrass, alkali sacaton, rabbitbrush, or cottonwood.

Altitudinal position in the zone	Kind of ground	Type of vegetation
Uppermost altitudes	all kinds, but commonly stony	pinyon and juniper woodland; in north may be replaced by scrub oak
Next lower altitudes	stony desert	sagebrush and grama grass
Intermediate altitudes	stony desert	shadscale and curly grass
Intermediate altitudes	sand desert	sand sagebrush
Intermediate altitudes	shale desert	mat saltbush
Low altitudes	loamy desert	blackbrush; in south replaced by live oak and grass
Low altitudes	gravel fans	Joshua tree, in south only

In southern Arizona and Nevada the upper altitudinal limit of the Upper Sonoran Zone is at about 7,500 feet. In northern Utah and Nevada it is at about 6,500 feet, and still farther north it is at about 5,000 feet.

The Upper Sonoran Zone is inhabited by antelope, coyote, gray fox, the desert rattle-snake, many lizards, kangaroo rats, packrats, and other rodents. The land is used mostly for grazing.

Next upward on the mountains, and next northward, is the Transition Zone, which in much of the west is characterized by yellow pine (*Pinus ponderosa*), and on some dry hill-sides by mountain mahogany. In the Pacific Northwest the most characteristic tree is the Douglas fir (*Pseudotsuga mucronata*). These trees form pure stands, which contrast with the deciduous forests in the eastern states, where forest stands may be composed of hundreds of different species. Toward the south, the upper limit of the Transition Zone is at about 9,000 feet; in the north it is at about 7,000 feet.

On most of the higher mountains, above the yellow-pine–Douglas-fir forest, is the blue spruce and white fir forest of the Canadian Zone; this grades upward to a belt of Engle-mann spruce and alpine fir of the Hudsonian Zone. Summits higher than about 12,000 feet are without trees and have only low-growing plants of the Alpine or Arctic Zone. Many mountain tops lower than 12,000 feet are tree-less, but this probably is because of wind (Fig. 8.9) rather than temperature.

The Transition and higher zones are sum-mer home for deer, elk, mountain lion, bear,

bighorn sheep, beaver, conies, and wildcats. The fish show altitudinal zoning. Various trout and whitefish live in the cold waters of the Transition and higher zones, and channel cat-fish, yellow perch, sunfish, black bass, walleye, and carp live in the warmer waters of the Upper Sonoran Zone. The mountain lands are used mostly for grazing, but produce lum-ber and other forest products, particularly in the Pacific Northwest.

In most places the boundary between the vegetation in adjoining altitudinal life zones is sharp, but the position of a boundary varies considerably from place to place depending on the exposure. On cool north slopes the high-altitude zones extend to lower levels than on warm south ones; moreover, the high-altitude vegetation may extend far down can-yons that drain cold air from high parts of mountains. This causes an inverted arrange-ment in which the vegetation characteristic of the high altitudes grows in the valley bottoms below the vegetation generally characteristic of low altitudes but growing on the adjoining ridges.

Changes in Vegetation from East to West

Although the life zones just described seem to be controlled largely by temperature (length of growing season?), other regional differences reflect differences in moisture. A transect from the Atlantic Coast to the Pa-cific Coast can be divided into five parts, each

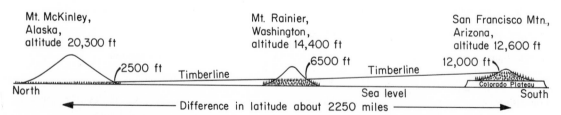

Figure 8.5 *The altitudes reached by the various life zones decrease northward. A thousand feet of altitude is roughly equivalent to 250 miles of latitude.*

with a distinct complex of vegetative types corresponding to differences in availability of moisture. For example, along the 39th parallel, which corresponds roughly with the 55° isotherm (Fig. 4.2), a transect from the Atlantic Coast first crosses the Central, or Southern Hardwood, Forest (Fig. 8.2) of the humid eastern United States. This forest extends to central Missouri. The second region, from there to the Rocky Mountains, is grassland of the subhumid and semiarid belts. The subhumid belt, east of the 100th meridian, is characterized by tall grass; the semiarid belt to the west has short grass.

A third region, described in the preceding section, takes in the Rocky Mountains and the plateaus and deserts westward to the Central Valley of California, where, at the western foot of the Sierra Nevada and eastern foot of the Coast Ranges is another semiarid belt characterized by broadleaf evergreen and broadleaf deciduous trees. The fifth region is the very wet Pacific slope of the coast ranges, location of the redwood forests. The three belts of forest—the eastern, Rocky Mountain, and Pacific Coast forests—extend northward to the northern coniferous forest of spruce, the only forest that extends from coast to coast.

Except across the Rocky Mountains, the average annual temperature along this transect is not much above or below 55°F. The differences in vegetation in the five zones are due chiefly to differences in availability of moisture.

Alaska, Hawaii, and Puerto Rico

Vegetation in Alaska, Hawaii, and Puerto Rico differs greatly from that in the rest of the United States, but also illustrates the principle that life zones are controlled by temperature and availability of moisture.

For example, at Mount McKinley, Alaska, at latitude 63°, timberline is at about 2,500 feet. At San Francisco Mountain in Arizona, at latitude 35° (Fig. 8.4), timberline is at almost 12,000 feet. Life at 2,500 feet in Alaska is comparable to that at 12,000 feet in Arizona (Fig. 8.5).

Alaska has four principal types of vegetation: hemlock-spruce forests along the southeastern coast, spruce-birch forests in the interior, grasslands on the Alaska Peninsula and Aleutian Islands, and tundra growth on the Bering and Arctic Sea slopes (Fig. 18.20).

Hawaii has an oceanic climate with much less seasonal variation than the other states. Nevertheless, along with the great relief on some of the islands are examples of altitudinal zoning of the vegetation, and the considerable differences in rainfall between the windward and leeward sides of the islands provide examples of the way vegetation reflects differences in availability of moisture.

Puerto Rico, like Hawaii, has a tropical marine climate and it too has rain forest on the wet north slopes of the mountains and dry forest on the south side. Mangrove grows in swamps along much of the coast.

Local Differences

Climatic Factors in Plant Distribution

Plant distribution, the subject of plant geography, is controlled partly by climate and partly by geology. The local variations in climate include both those of the macroclimate and microclimate; the four principal factors affecting plant growth are light, temperature, precipitation, and wind.

Some species of plants require bright light, which controls chlorophyll and photosynthesis; others live in shade. Forests contain both kinds of species (Fig. 8.6). Those that require light reach to the upper canopy, whereas those that can endure shade form the understory. A tree's shape is a result of the light it receives.

Figure 8.6 *Light affects plant distribution and plant growth. In a forest (right) shade-tolerant trees form the understory; beneath this understory grow various species of herbs, which are even more shade tolerant. Trees that demand light reach to the upper canopy, and may have live branches only at the crown, whereas in open sites (left) trees of the same species may bear live branches the entire height of the tree.*

Figure 8.7 *Wooded north slopes contrast with grassy south slopes in a semiarid environment. The vegetation on north-facing slopes commonly differs from that on south facing slopes, especially in semiarid and arid environments where small differences in temperature cause major differences in moisture retention.*

Many conifers, standing alone in the open, bear leaves and branches all the way from the ground up, but the same species in a forest may be without branches on its lower parts and bear only a small green crown.

Temperature controls the length of the growing season, and, during growth, the rate of physiological processes. Moreover, for each species there is an upper and a lower critical temperature. At northerly latitudes and at high altitudes the growing season is short, and the plants living there differ from those at southerly latitudes and low altitudes, where the growing season is long. Temperature also is a major factor in controlling the differences that are found between north and south slopes (Fig. 8.7).

Moisture availability is controlled by many factors, but the best single index is precipitation. Precipitation is important not only in terms of its annual total, but also in terms of its distribution by seasons. For example, the Pacific Coast has dry summers, whereas the Middle West has wet summers. Mountain ranges have wet slopes on the windward side, dry slopes on the leeward side (Fig. 8.8), and forests on the two sides are different. On the wet western slopes of the Cascades, for example, are found such trees as western red cedar, Pacific yew, western hemlock, red alder, maples, and oaks, whereas the dry eastern slopes have yellow pine, juniper, and quaking aspen. On the Sierra Nevada, the sequoia forests are limited to the wet western slope (Fig. 8.8). On the Coast Ranges the redwood forests are limited for the most part to the wet western slopes.

Wind affects both the distribution and the configuration of plants. The absence of trees at some exposed situations is due to wind, partly because of physical damage to anything standing upright, partly because of excessive transpiration, and partly because of the decrease in soil temperature due to the removal of the protective cover of snow. These effects are evident at wind-controlled timberlines: the trees are prostrate, both trunk and boughs are bent with the wind, and the shoots are short and mostly on the lee side, resulting in a flag-like unilateral branching (Fig. 8.9).

Ground Influences

Although the distribution of the life zones is controlled by the climate, local differences within a zone are controlled chiefly by differences in the ground conditions, especially moisture availability. This is the geologic factor in plant distribution, referred to by ecologists as the *edaphic* factor, and includes effects of the surficial soils and of the substrate beneath the soil.

Soil properties most important for plant growth are: composition and structure of the mineral fraction, the soil atmosphere and soil moisture, content of organic matter, depth, and temperature.

The mineral fraction of a soil may be hard rock, a favorite environment for some lichens. Most soils suitable for the roots of flowering plants consist of various mixtures of particles of gravel, sand, silt, and clay size, and the mineral and chemical composition of these particles determines the degree to which certain elements necessary for plant growth are available to the plants. In general, availability depends on solubility; the more soluble the element and the more soluble the form in which it occurs, the more available it is for absorption by plant roots. The proportion of the different particle sizes in soils controls pore space, which in turn affects the availability of soil moisture and soil air. Sandy soils, for example, dry more rapidly than clay soils. Clay soils are more difficult to penetrate but provide more mineral nutrients than do soils that are largely quartz sand.

The principal elements required by plants are oxygen, hydrogen, carbon, nitrogen, phosphorus, sulfur, iron, potassium, calcium, and magnesium. Excesses or deficiencies of any of these elements, or of some other minor elements, lead to specialized vegetation adapted

to that soil. Some examples are the specialized plant stands on the serpentine (magnesium rich) soils in the California Coast Ranges and the Maryland Piedmont (Fig. 8.10,A). Other examples are the belts of grassland on the lime-rich black belts of Alabama, Mississippi, and Texas (Fig. 8.10,B), and the low, mat saltbush on shale deserts (p. 105) of the Upper Somoran Zone, which contrast with the upright shrubs on adjoining sandy ground (Fig. 8.10, C).

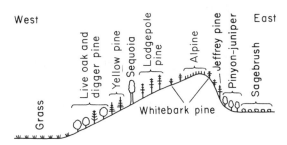

Figure 8.8 *Transect across the Sierra Nevada, illustrating contrast in vegetation on the wet windward slope (west) and the dry leeward slope. Low on the west side is grass with a belt of live oak and digger pine in the foothills. Low on the dry east side is sagebrush with a belt of pinyon and juniper woodland in the foothills. Higher on the west side are belts of yellow pine, sequoia, and lodgepole pine; on the east slope is Jeffrey pine. At high altitudes on both sides is white-bark pine and alpine forms.*

Figure 8.9 *At a wind-controlled timberline, found on many mountain summits, trees are prostrate and gnarled. The upper branches turn with the wind, forming so-called "flag trees." The wind-blasted summit supports only small herbs.*

The soil atmosphere contains more carbon dioxide and less oxygen than the atmosphere above ground, and in a clayey soil, where circulation is slowed, the oxygen necessary for roots may become depleted. Waterlogged soils may be anaerobic.

Water available for plant growth occurs in the ground either as vadose or gravitational water (Fig. 5.5) or as groundwater below the water table (Fig. 8.11). *Xerophytes*—plants that live on gravitational water—are capable of surviving periods of protracted drought. *Phreatophytes*—plants that send their roots

to the water table—have a permanent water supply, even in deserts.

The drought-resistant and the water-loving kinds of plant stands can be distinguished in every part of the United States. In the southeastern states, cypress, tupelo, and red gum live in the wet bottoms; longleaf, loblolly, and slash pine on the uplands. In the northeastern states, spruce, the dominant tree, grows with balsam, tamarack, cedar, and soft maples in swampy areas, and with hard maples, beech, and birch on the lowlands. In the more arid western states, shallow ground-

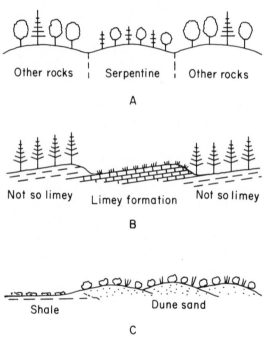

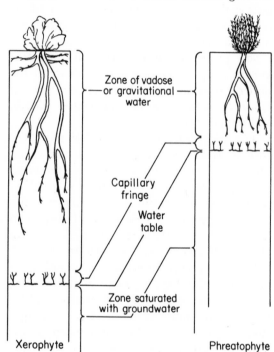

Figure 8.10 *Three examples of vegetation differences that reflect differences in soil composition and texture. On the Maryland Piedmont (A) the vegetation on serpentine formations is dwarfed and differs from that on other rocks. Limy formations in Alabama (B) support grasses in the midst of Southern Pine Forest growing on the less limy formations. On the Colorado Plateau (C) shale formations support low, mat saltbush, whereas adjoining sand dunes support grasses and upright shrubs.*

Figure 8.11 *Water in the ground is available to plant roots in two ways. The top of the zone saturated with groundwater is referred to as the water table. A capillary fringe rises upward from it. Plants that send their roots down to this zone have a permanent water supply and are known as* phreatophytes. *The zone above the capillary fringe is wet only when water seeps downward through it, following rains or floods. Plants that root in this zone must be capable of surviving droughts, and are known as* xerophytes.

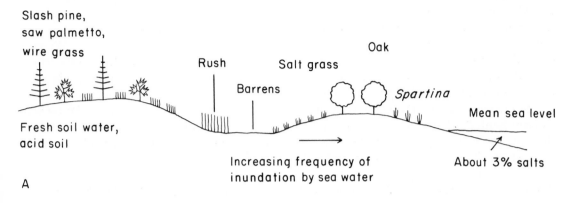

A

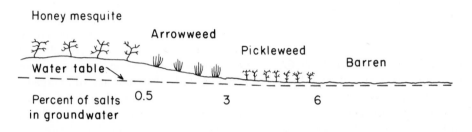

B

Figure 8.12 *Two examples of plant distribution controlled by salts dissolved in groundwaters. (A) Coast of Florida (generalized after Florida Geological Survey). (B) Edge of salt pan in Death Valley, California.*

water and springs are marked by stands of such trees as cottonwood and willow and a considerable number of shrubs and grasses that are not drought resistant.

The kind and amount of dissolved matter in groundwater also affects plant distribution, especially along coasts and along the edges of desert basins where the water is brackish or saline. Figure 8.12 gives an example from the coast of Florida and another from the edge of the salt pan in Death Valley, California.

The organic content of soils includes both the dead organic matter and the organisms living in and on the soil. The vegetative cover and the layer of litter at the surface affect soil temperature, its moisture content and chemistry, compactness, amount of light received, and air movement. Decaying organic matter

in soil is important in controlling the distribution and abundance of the living microorganisms. But the organic content of soils is largely controlled by the larger flowering plants living on it, and differs greatly among deciduous forest, conifer forest, grassland, and desert shrubland. Plants control the kind of litter that provides the habitat for the microorganisms, which in turn may be deleterious or beneficial for the growth and spread of a particular species of flowering plant. Pathogens of forest trees—viruses, fungi, or bacteria—may kill by root rot, heart rot, cankers, wilting, leaf rust, or needle blight. Parasitic insects are familiar to every gardener; some serious pests in the forests are beetles, budworms, weevils, moths, sawflies, aphids, and the all-too-familiar tent caterpillar. These insects cause damage by defoliation, boring, or suck-ing. The virtual elimination of the chestnut in the United States is perhaps the best known example of how microorganisms (and insects) affect plant distribution.

Soil depth, as a factor in plant distribution, may be controlled by depth to a water table or depth to bedrock. Vegetation growing along a stream bank or along the edge of a pond is different from that growing some distance away where the depth to the water table is greater. Examples of how depth to bedrock affects plant distribution can be seen in most mountainous areas where bare rock surfaces, supporting only lichens, are surrounded by a distinctive group of flowering plants growing where thin soil overlaps the rock, and this group, in turn, is surrounded by forest where the soil deepens.

Plant distribution also is affected by fire. Fire may burn only the layer of leaf litter, seedlings, and small trees; as a *ground fire,* it may extend into the ground and burn roots; as a *crown fire,* it may burn the tree tops. Climate is important in connection with such fires. In the eastern United States electric storms are usually accompanied by rain, and fires caused by lightning are uncommon. In the western United States, lightning is a major cause of forest fires because it is frequently accompanied by only light rain or none at all. In the western United States the fire hazard is greatest during the dry summer months; in the central and eastern United States the hazard is greatest in spring and fall—before the deciduous trees have leafed and after the leaves have fallen.

Form of Plant Growth as Controlled by Climate and Soils

Vegetation differs in many ways between one life zone and another and between one en-vironment and another within a particular life zone. For example, there are differences in the growth forms; in a given life zone the plants may be mostly trees, shrubs, grasses, mosses, or lichens. Differences between the dominant growth forms of different life zones are per-haps most striking at timberline. Western mountains have two timberlines, one where the Canadian and Hudsonian zones give way to the Arctic-Alpine Zone, and another near the foot of the mountains, where the pinyon-juniper woodland of the Upper Sonoran Zone ends downward against sagebrush or other shrubland.

In addition to the differences in growth forms, numerous conspicuously different ecolo-gical types are distinguishable. Aquatic plants, *hydrophytes,* vary according to the dis-solved oxygen, exposure to light, water tem-perature, quality of the water, its depth and movement, and the nature of the banks and bottom. Marsh plants, *helophytes,* differ from aquatic plants in having their foliage out of the water; only the roots are submerged. The important environmental factors are about the same as for aquatic plants. Some plants are adapted to moist ground that is highly acid, as in peat bogs. Other plants are adapted to moist ground that is cold, as in tundra and taiga. Still other plants are adapted to moist saline ground (*halophytes*), like some along the coasts and parts of the deserts (Fig. 8.12).

Plants adapted to dry ground may grow on bare rock (lichens), on sand and gravel (dune grasses), or on impervious, shaly ground (mat saltbush of the Upper Sonoran Zone on the Colorado Plateau) (Fig. 8.10,C). With an in-crease in moisture during the growing season, shrubs are replaced by grasses, as on the Great Plains. Most forests, whether hardwood or conifer, grow where ground conditions are neither too wet nor too dry.

Local Aspects of Zoogeography

Local factors also affect the distribution of animal life, especially of insects. Figure 8.13 illustrates some differences in stream habitats that affect the distribution of aquatic species. Figure 10.25 illustrates some variations in

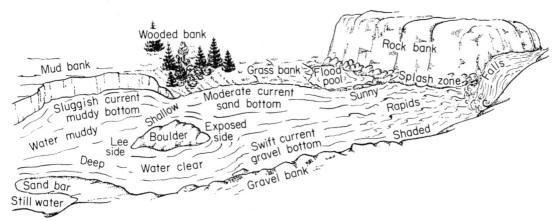

Figure 8.13 *Stream habitats. The sketch illustrates more than two dozen kinds of stream habitats, each having distinctive biotic characteristics. The major controlling factors are: kind of stream flow (swiftness, depth, continuity, and quality of the water); kind of channel and banks (rocky or muddy, straight or meandering, low or high); climate (especially temperature, nature of recharge, and seasonal effects); and the adjoining biota at each particular locality.*

littoral and marine habitats that affect the distribution of shellfish and other marine life. The differences and variations in habitats in springs, ponds, lakes, bays, and estuaries include all the kinds of features illustrated in Figures 8.13 and 10.25 and combinations of them. Other familiar examples of local aspects of zoogeography are the insects that swarm under rocks, effects of muddiness and pollution on fish distribution, and the adaptation of the pigeon, English sparrow, and starling to our cities.

Changes in Life Zones

Effects of Climatic Changes

During the Pleistocene Epoch, which ended only about 12,000 years ago, the climate was very different from that of today (p. 68). Continental ice sheets spread southward into the northern United States, and lakes formed in what are now the dry basins of the arid west. During these wet, cold stages the life zones were shifted to more southerly latitudes and, on the mountains, to lower altitudes. Figure 8.14 illustrates an interpretation of how the life zones shifted during the last glaciation.

Continued climatic change is indicated by the present-day northward migration of warm-latitude species. Spruce forest is advancing into areas of tundra. The upper part of Mount Washington has been isolated and preserves a relic fauna of arctic species of insects and mice surrounded by warm-latitude species. The marine life is migrating north, too, and mid-Atlantic species (for example, the green crab) have advanced north of Cape Cod. Along the Pacific Coast certain mollusks live 8 to 10 degrees of latitude north of their range in early Pleistocene time. In part of late Pleistocene time their range averaged a degree of latitude north of their present range, perhaps in response to an interglaciation, whereas in latest Pleistocene time their range averaged two degrees south of their present range, perhaps in response to a glaciation. But the Pacific coast evidence is of doubtful significance because of the active earth movements there; the differences cited could reflect crustal movement and not climatic change.

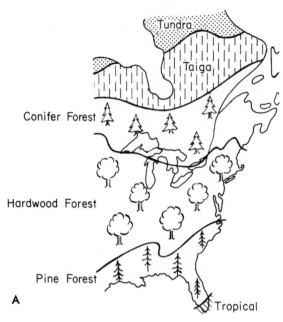

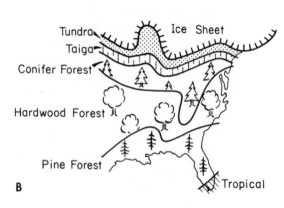

Changes Wrought by Man

Because Europeans settling this country cleared the land and removed forests, it has been widely assumed that settlement and land use have devastated our soil and vegetation. In much of the country, though, this assumption appears unwarranted. Historical accounts of the original state of the forests in the northeastern United States indicate that present forests are not very different, only less extensive. The forest always has been subject to disturbance—fires by lightning in the west, hurricane winds in the east (like the storm of 1962 in New England).

Losses as a result of forest fire make frightening statistics but they need to be viewed in the perspective of other losses. The annual loss due to fire is about half the loss caused by insects and plant disease and about 3 to 4 percent of the annual cut. Moreover, the distribution of loss by fire is regionally very uneven. By far the greatest loss is in the Southeastern Pine Forest, where as much as 1 percent of lands protected by forest agencies burn annually (Fig. 8.15), and a third of that loss is attributed to fires purposely set as part of a long-established practice (whether good or bad) to help establish new crops of pine, to improve grazing, and to reduce the fire hazard.

Figure 8.14 *Vegetation zones in eastern North America at the present time (A) and their probable distribution during the Wisconsin glaciation (B). The shift in position of the zones is continuing. According to many ecologists beech and sugar maple are moving northward into pine and spruce areas; in Alaska spruce is moving into tundra; trees are migrating westward in Nebraska; and yellow pine of the Rocky Mountains may be spreading eastward on the Great Plains.*

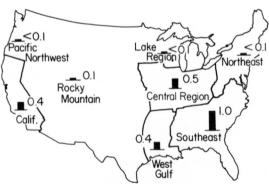

Figure 8.15 *Average annual burn (1941–45) on national forests by regions, in percent of area protected. (After U.S.D.A.)*

The high rate of burn in California probably reflects the dry summer season. In most of the country 0.1 percent or less of the protected areas are burned annually. With increased use of the forests, however, man's carelessness with fire is increasingly a problem.

Man also has caused changes by introducing new species or by contributing to the spread of others. Tamarisk, or salt cedar, introduced to the Southwest from the Mediterranean, has spread along all the rivers and irrigation ditches of that region (p. 330). Mesquite has spread along the cattle trails in Texas. Such insects as the Japanese beetle have been introduced. The horse became extinct in North America at the end of the Pleistocene, and was reintroduced by the Spanish in post-Columbian time.

Sketch of
9 the Resources

Historical Background

At the time of Columbus, the area that later became the United States was occupied by perhaps a million Indians grouped in tribes representing a half dozen linguistic families. Probably a third of the Indians lived along the coasts, and most of the rest were gathered along the interior waterways. But despite an average population density of only one person for every three or four square miles, plenty of water, no problems of strategic or critical minerals, no need for tariffs, and evident plenty for everyone, still tribes warred with one another, and the Indians were still in the stone age. A favorable environment does not by itself create good living; in 1492 ours was an underdeveloped country in need of foreign aid.

Spain and Portugal first claimed the newly discovered lands and they agreed to divide them; Spain was to have all land west of a line about 1,200 miles west of the Cape Verde Islands, and Portugal was to have all the land to the east. A good deal of today's diplomatic negotiation may seem equally absurd a few hundred years from now.

But while Spain and Portugal negotiated boundary lines on paper, the English and Dutch proceeded to settle at the harbor sites: Jamestown, 1606; Fort Nassau (Albany), 1614; Plymouth, 1620; Manhattan Island, 1623; Little Harbor (Rye, New Hampshire), 1623; Boston, 1630; St. Marys, 1634; Providence, 1636; and Wilmington, 1638.

Meanwhile, the French established outposts in the Middle West, and the Spanish moved northward from Mexico into the Southwest.

The spread of settlement and exploration from the Atlantic Coast, the Middle West, and the Southwest followed the natural routes, but the lands as acquired by the United States had arbitrary and vague boundaries, perhaps because the acquisitions were made before the lands were well known. To a considerable degree, acquisition came first, and settlement later. Our land resources, now totalling more than 3,700,000 square miles of land and water, was acquired chiefly in ten real estate deals (see also Fig. 9.1):

1. 1782–83, original territory of the United States as recognized by treaties with England (869,735 sq. miles).

2. 1803, Louisiana Purchase, exclusive of the part that extended north of the 49th parallel (909,130 sq. miles).

3. 1818, Red River Basin and Lake of the Woods drainage, south of the 49th parallel, secured by treaty with England (48,080 sq. miles).

4. 1819, East and West Florida acquired from Spain by trading to Spain about 100,000 sq. miles of land west of the Mississippi River. Value at that time appraised at about the cost of a modern Miami hotel.
5. 1845, Texas annexed (388,687 sq. miles).
6. 1846, Oregon Territory; title established by treaty with England (286,541 sq. miles).
7. 1848, Mexican cession, Treaty of Guadalupe Hidalgo (529,189 sq. miles).
8. 1853, Gadsden Purchase (29,670 sq. miles).
9. 1867, Alaska Purchase (586,400 sq. miles).
10. 1898, Hawaii, Puerto Rico, and Guam (10,144 sq. miles).

Some of the colonies had charters that granted land from ocean to ocean, for the kings had been gracious givers. These lands, which were ceded to the federal government when the colonies became states, included the Northwest Territory—the present states of Ohio, Indiana, Illinois, Michigan, Wisconsin, and part of Minnesota. Revenue from sale of the lands was used to pay the public debt, and as the lands became settled new states were created.

As our real estate grew, so did our population. By 1750 the population numbered

Figure 9.1 *Major United States land acquisitions.*

about 2,000,000. When George Washington became president the population had doubled to about 4,000,000, but only a half dozen towns had populations greater than 10,000. In another 25 years, about 1815, the population had doubled again to 8,000,000, and it doubled again during each quarter of the last century— to 16,000,000 in 1840, 32,000,000 at the time of the Civil War, and 64,000,000 in 1890. By 1925 it had doubled again to about 125,000,000, and by that time urban population exceeded the rural. In 1950, 150,000,000 of us were sharing these 3,700,000 square miles, and our population is expected to reach 200,000,000 by 1975, with 90 percent concentrated in urban areas (Fig. 9.2). As late as 1860 the center of population still was east of the Plains; today it is at the 100th meridian and continues moving west.

For comparison, the population of China in 1961 was estimated (United Nations) to be 700,000,000 and their area is only a little larger than ours, 3,850,000 square miles. Russia in 1963 had an estimated population of almost 225,000,000 and an area of almost 8,600,000 square miles.

As late as 1890 we still had frontiers. At that time 50,000,000 people, about 80 percent of the population, resided below 1,000 feet altitude in an area comprising about two-thirds of the country. Only 1,500,000 people lived in that vast area, including most of the West, that is higher than 2,000 feet in altitude. Land was plentiful, and to a large degree it was this abundance of land that assured democracy in the colonies when attempts to import nobility and to divide the population into classes failed and were replaced by democratic institutions. There was always free land a little back from the river bank or upstream for those who decided to forego their opportunity of continuing as second-class citizens.

Now, except in Alaska, our frontier days are over; cheap land is no more. Megalopolis, extending from Boston to Richmond along the Atlantic seaboard, has 37,000,000 people in about 50,000 square miles, a population

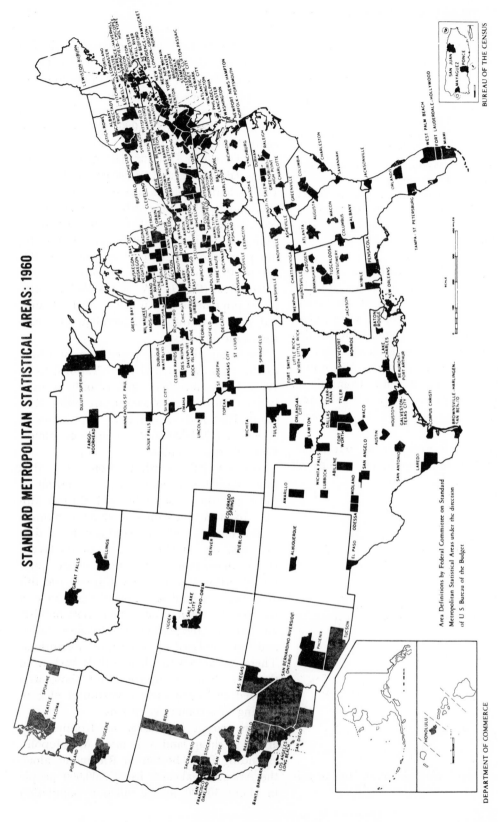

STANDARD METROPOLITAN STATISTICAL AREAS: 1960

BUREAU OF THE CENSUS

Area Definitions by Federal Committee on Standard Metropolitan Statistical Areas under the direction of U S Bureau of the Budget

DEPARTMENT OF COMMERCE

Figure 9.2   Standard metropolitan statistical areas as defined by the federal government, 1960. The map illustrates our urban sprawl, despite the fact that some areas as drawn are quite unrealistic. Few would regard the Mojave Desert and the south end of Death Valley as urban!

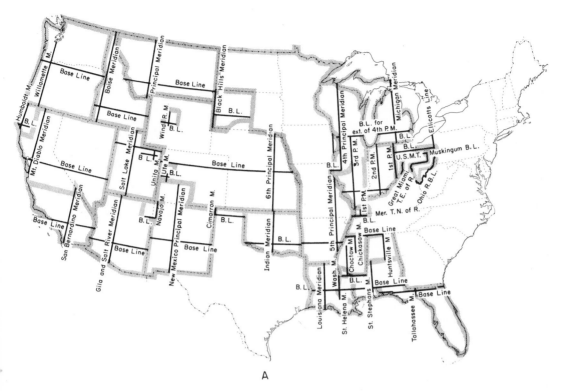

A

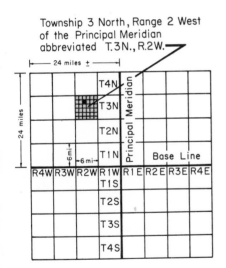

Township 3 North, Range 2 West
of the Principal Meridian
abbreviated T.3N., R.2W.

B

Section 9 Township 3 North,
Range 2 West of the
Principal Meridian
abbreviated Sec. 9,
T.3N., R.2W.

6	5	4	3	2	1
7	8	9	10	11	12
18	17	16	15	14	13
19	20	21	22	23	24
30	29	28	27	26	25
31	32	33	34	35	36

Northeast
quarter of
section 24,
abbreviated
NE 1/4 sec. 24

Sections 1 through 6 on the north
side and 7, 18, 19, 30, and 31 on the
west side are fractional sections.

C

Figure 9.3 *System of United States rectangular surveys. (A) Location of the several prime meridians and their base lines. (B) Townships are numbered according to their position north or south of a base line and east or west of a principal meridian. (C) Numbering of the sections within a township. (After U.S.D.A.)*

density approximately that of sagebrush in Nevada. As our land becomes more crowded, there is increasing need to understand its nature and its resources.

Land Surveys—The Basis for Orderly Settlement and Development of the Frontier

The basis for orderly settlement and development of the entire west was contained in the Land Ordinance of 1785, which established public land policy for the United States and provided for rectangular surveys of the public lands.

The lands are divided into townships 6 miles square numbered with reference to principal meridians and base lines (Fig. 9.3,A). The townships (Fig. 9.3,B) are divided into 36 sections (Fig. 9.3,C), each a mile square and containing 640 acres. These are divided into quarters of 160 acres, and the quarters can be further divided into 40-acre tracts (Fig. 9.3,C).

Such squares do not fit the spherical earth's surface, but this difficulty is met by introducing correction lines about every 10 townships where section and township lines are offset in order to restore full measure.

This system allows any part of the United States west of the Appalachians to be precisely identified by location and by size. An air traveler today can scarcely fail to notice the contrast between the crazyquilt pattern of roads and property lines in the Appalachian Highlands and the orderly township and section lines west of Ohio (Fig. 9.4). The flat terrain greatly favored the rectangular surveys, but they were extended later into the mountainous western states too. State boundaries west of the Mississippi are mostly rectangular; many boundaries east of the Mississippi follow natural features.

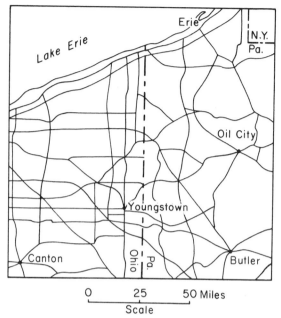

Figure 9.4 *Contrast in road patterns in northwestern Pennsylvania and northeastern Ohio. The rectangular pattern in Ohio is due chiefly to the rectangular surveys that were begun there and continued westward across the United States.*

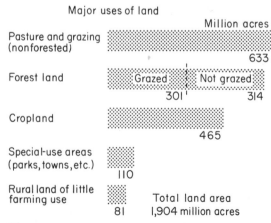

Figure 9.5 *Major economic uses of lands in the United States. (From U.S.D.A.)*

Land Use

About a third of the country, excluding Alaska, is in forest, and another third is in pasture and range. Somewhat less than a third is cropland, and less than a tenth is truly urban or in roads or wasteland (Fig. 9.5).

Figure 9.6 illustrates the major types of land use in the United States; Figure 9.7 illustrates the seasonal use of western range land.

A practical effect of the physiography is illustrated in Figure 9.8, which shows the great difference in carrying capacity of pasture and range land in different parts of the country. A few acres in the humid eastern states are as productive, on the average, as a square mile in much of the west. In the east, and along the northwest coast, the principal source of grazed

forage is provided by cultivated pastures; in the rest of the country, native plants are the principal forage.

Public Lands

Excluding Alaska, slightly more than 20 percent of the United States is federally owned land. Five percent is owned by state and local governments; 3 percent is Indian land. Seventy percent is private. Alaska still is about 90 percent federally owned land.

Of the federally owned lands, other than in Alaska, about 40 percent is forest and another 40 percent is nonforested pasture and grazing land. The remaining public lands are those having special uses—parks, wildlife refuges, public reservoirs, and military reservations.

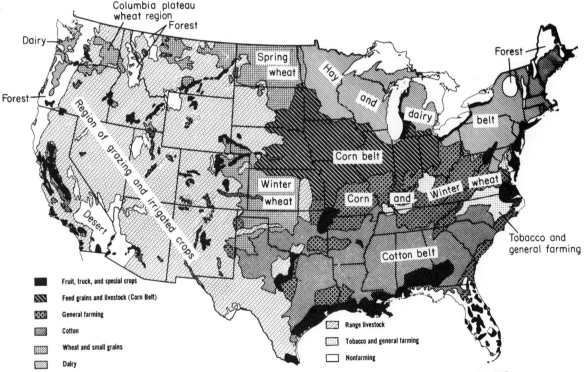

Figure 9.6　*Major types of land use in the United States. (After U.S.D.A.) The Central Lowland includes the corn belt and most of the wheat areas. Although the plains west of the 100th meridian are semiarid, much of that area produces wheat. It also produces dust.*

Agriculture

Because of its favorable physiography the United States's agricultural produce is prodigious. We overproduce practically all the necessary foods to the absurd degree that landowners are paid not to grow certain crops. Moreover, farm production by intensive methods on reduced acreage seems almost limitless, and one may reasonably wonder how much of the western United States should be developed for agriculture by irrigation.

The agricultural resource is illustrated by a series of maps (Figs. 9.9 to 9.15) showing acreage in vegetables, fruit orchards, corn, cotton, wheat (an additional 12½ million acres is planted in barley), soybeans, and hay. The productive areas are mostly in the Central Lowland, Coastal Plain, Columbia Plateau, and the valleys in the Pacific Mountain System. Much of the Valley and Ridge Province is used for orchards.

Forests

The distribution of forests is shown in Figure 9.16. Present lumber production is roughly 40 billion board feet annually, which is about 2 percent of the total reserve of more than 2,100 billion board feet. (A board foot is equivalent to a piece of wood 12 inches by 12 inches and 1 inch thick.) New growth annually adds more than 100 billion board feet; therefore, with reasonable protection and care we can enjoy an annual crop of forest products without endangering the resource. Indeed, intelligent cutting improves a forest by providing space for new growth.

More than 80 percent of the sawtimber is pine, spruce, fir, and other conifers (so-called softwoods); the remainder consists of the broadleaf trees (so-called hardwoods) such as oak, maple, hickory, elm, cottonwood, and beech. The terms "hardwood" and "softwood" are misleading, for some of the hardwoods (for example, cottonwood) are softer than some of the softwoods.

Standards for classifying stands of timber

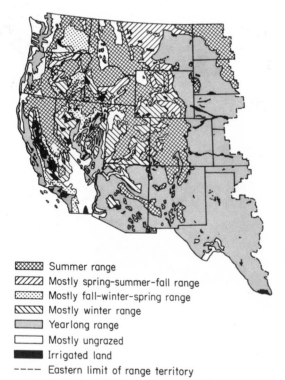

Summer range
Mostly spring-summer-fall range
Mostly fall-winter-spring range
Mostly winter range
Yearlong range
Mostly ungrazed
Irrigated land
Eastern limit of range territory

Figure 9.7 *Seasonal use of western range lands. (After U.S.D.A.)*

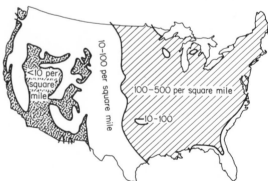

Figure 9.8 *Carrying capacity of pasture and range land in the United States, in average number of cows per square mile. (U.S.D.A.)*

Figure 9.11 Principal areas producing corn, the back-bone of United States agriculture. Corn is grown on more than half our farms; total acreage is almost 80 million, and annual production is about 3 billion bushels.

Figure 9.12 Principal areas producing cotton. A half million cotton farms, making up 20 million acres, an-nually produce about 12 million bales.

Figure 9.9 Principal areas harvesting vegetables other than sweet potatoes. The total acreage, almost 4 million, is about 1 percent of all cropland harvested. Production (1954) valued at about $645 million, which is about 5 percent of the total value of all crops sold. There are about 32,500 vegetable farms.

Figure 9.10 Principal areas in nut and fruit orchards, and vineyards. Value of the produce almost $1.2 bil-lion (1954) from 82,000 farms totaling 4 million acres.

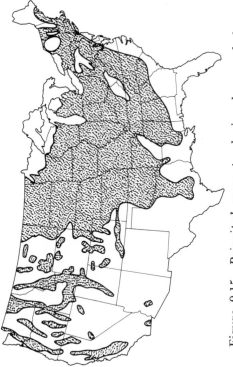

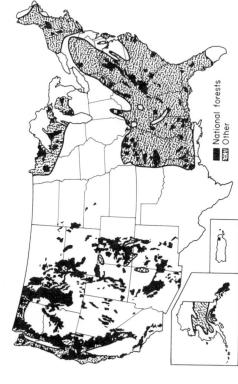

Figure 9.15 Principal areas producing hay, excluding soybean, cowpea, peanut, and sorghum hay. Generally our third most important crop. Production (1954) more than 100 million tons from 70 million acres; valued at more than $2 billion.

National forests
Other

Figure 9.16 Principal areas of forests in the United

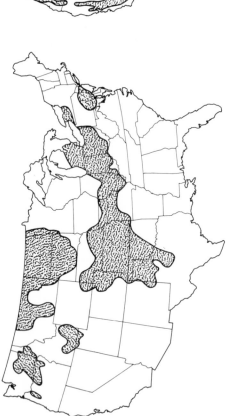

Figure 9.13 Principal areas producing wheat, our second most important crop. Production (1954) nearly 1 billion bushels from 50 million acres; valued at almost $2 billion.

Figure 9.14 Principal areas producing soybeans. Production (1954) more than 300,000 bushels from al-

have varied greatly over the years and from place to place. One set of specifications in recent use classes commercial stands as *sawtimber* if stocked 10 percent or more with trees greater than 11 inches in diameter at breast height. Stands with smaller trees are classed as *poletimber* if stocked 10 percent or more with trees greater than 5 inches in diameter at breast height.

Livestock

The livestock population on our farms and ranches is about as follows:

Cattle	Almost 100,000,000
Hogs	More than 50,000,000
Sheep	Almost 50,000,000
Chickens	About 500,000,000
Turkeys	About 10,000,000
Horses	About 10,000,000
Mules	Less than 5,000,000

Annual production totals about 20 billion pounds of beef, 20 billion pounds of pork, and 2 billion pounds of lamb and mutton. Other production includes leather goods, wool, butter, eggs, milk, and in the West, cowboys and sheepherders. Lands in the humid central and eastern United States are much more productive for livestock (see Fig. 9.8).

Fish

Total production of our saltwater fisheries each year is about 4.5 billion pounds, worth about $200 million. About 55 percent of the production comes from the Atlantic and Gulf coasts, and about 45 percent from the Pacific coast, including Alaska (15 percent). Annual production from commercial fresh-water fisheries is worth only a few million dollars in terms of its market value. The recreational value of fresh-water fisheries is impossible to measure in dollar value; however, it would undoubtedly be many times its commercial value. Millions of persons in this country annually spend many days on lakes or along streams—sometimes catching fish and sometimes not, but always catching worthwhile relaxation and enjoyment of the outdoors.

Water Resources

Annual precipitation in the United States averages about 30 inches, of which three-fourths is lost by evaporation and transpiration. The usable part totals about 7,500 gallons per person, five times the present demand. Homes use an average of about 50 gallons per day per person. Leaks in municipal systems, including leaky faucets in homes, are responsible for an average loss of about 25 gallons per day per person. Total use for all purposes, including use by the big consumers—agriculture and industry—averages about 1,300 gallons per day per person. The water that is used is consumed as follows (U.S.G.S.):

Use	Total withdrawn (millions of gallons per day)	Percent of total
Public supplies	17,000	7
Rural use	3,000	1
Irrigation	110,000	46
Delivered to farms	*81,000*	
Lost from canals	*29,000*	
Self-supplied industrial	110,000	46
Total	240,000	100

Not all water that is withdrawn from a stream, lake, or aquifer is consumed, for it may be returned without loss in quantity or important change in quality, as is true of water used by hydroelectric plants.

Our total supply of water is adequate, but we face problems of distribution, quality, pollution, floods, and dependability (Fig. 9.17). Distribution problems primarily reflect the fact that part of the country is humid and

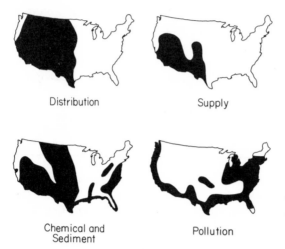

Distribution   Supply   Floods   Variability

Chemical and   Pollution
Sediment

Figure 9.17 *Areas affected by the major problems of water supply. The problems are particularly troublesome in the black areas, less so in the stippled areas, and least in the white areas.* (*After U.S.G.S.*)

part is arid or semiarid. Some parts are excessively wet and need to be drained for ordinary use (Fig. 9.18,A), like the marshes along the Atlantic and Gulf coasts and the many marshes in the Great Lakes area. In the arid and semiarid parts of the country—that is, in the West—lands need to be irrigated (Fig. 9.18,B). But even around the Great Lakes, because of dense settlement and intensive industrial development, water supplies are not adequate to meet anticipated increases in demand in the next 25 years. The same is true of most of the western United States too.

The water supplies that are consumed include substantial amounts of groundwater, especially in the arid and semiarid parts of the country (Fig. 9.19,left). Special care is needed in developing these water sources because they can be depleted by overdraft (Fig. 9.19,right), as is already happening in many parts of the country. Water uses that cause lowering of water tables need to be greatly limited.

Nonconsumptive uses of water include production of hydroelectricity, navigation, and recreation—boating, water-skiing, fishing, swimming, and other aquatic sports. Waste disposal can be considered a consumptive use if it pollutes or changes the quality of the water sufficiently to affect its use.

Dams in the United States are about evenly distributed between the humid and semiarid parts of the country (Fig. 9.20,A). Those in the East are mostly for flood control; losses because of floods in the eastern United States are considerable (Fig. 9.20,B). Dams in the West are mostly for irrigation. Whether for flood control, irrigation, or hydroelectricity, we have built more than 200 dams that are more than 200 feet high—175 of them since 1925. Some think the country has gone dam crazy. For example, water losses by evaporation from the reservoirs now exceed the amount used for public supplies in the entire country! Moreover, one can debate the wisdom of building dams for flood control that permanently flood a substantial area that previously was flooded only seasonally.

Our principal water problem, however, is self-imposed—pollution. There is hardly a community in the country that does not face this problem. When our population was small, we could get by with dumping wastes into streams—disposal by dilution—but with our greatly increased population and industrial activity we can no longer afford to do so. The economic, health, and social problems posed by water pollution are, at last, receiving attention. Although the problems are great, they

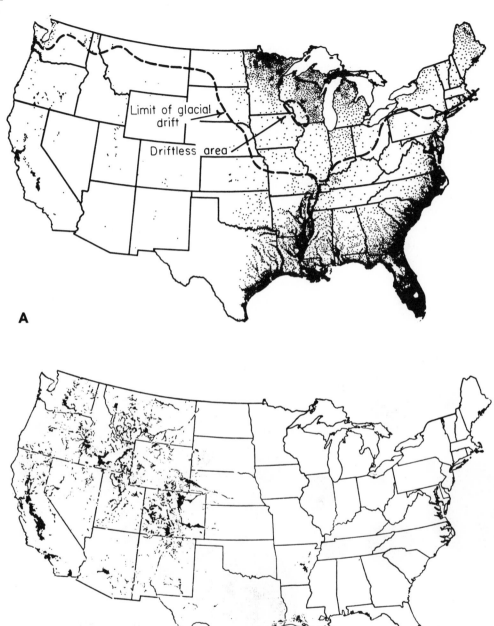

A

B

Figure 9.18 (*A*) *Wet lands in the United States occur mostly along the Atlantic and Gulf coasts and in the glaciated part of the country.* (*From U.S.D.A.*) (*B*) *Irrigated lands in the United States. In 1954 the total irrigated area was almost 30 million acres of a total cropland area of more than 400 million acres.* (*From U.S.D.A.*)

are surmountable, and if the effort is continued, we can look forward to the elimination of pollution in our lakes and rivers so that they may be pleasant for boating, swimming, and even for drinking. It is sobering to contemplate that nuclear war could contaminate our surface water, rendering it unusable and leaving us dependent on groundwater reservoirs.

Another major aspect of our water resources is their use for navigation. The Great Lakes, together with the St. Lawrence River, and Mississippi, Ohio, and Missouri rivers, provide economical transportation to and from the richly productive central states. About 15 percent of our freight moves via inland water-

ways, compared to 40 percent by railroad, 25 percent by motor vehicle, and 20 percent by pipeline.

Minerals

The United States is rich in mineral resources, both in variety and quantity; no comparably large area of the world is so richly endowed. Our mineral wealth is a major reason why the United States has attained a position of industrial pre-eminence. Although the general mineral position of the United States is excellent, we lack some minerals that are vital

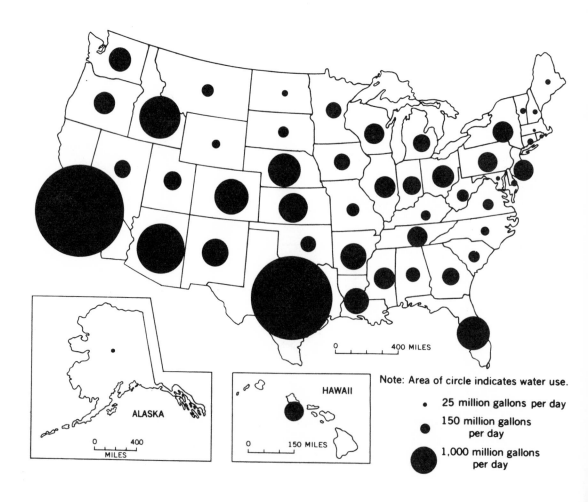

Note: Area of circle indicates water use.

- 25 million gallons per day
- 150 million gallons per day
- 1,000 million gallons per day

to industry, and our supplies of some others are only partly adequate for our needs. The mineral self-sufficiency of the United States, as reported about 1950 by the United States Geological Survey and Bureau of Mines, is summarized in the following list.

Virtual self-sufficiency assured for a long time:

Mineral fuels

bituminous coal, lignite, anthracite, natural gas

Metals

magnesium, molybdenum

Nonmetallic minerals

fluorspar (metallurgical grades), helium, magnesite, nitrates, phosphate rock, potash, salt, sulfur

Virtual self-sufficiency when technologic and economic changes permit use of known submarginal deposits:

Mineral fuels

petroleum

Metals

aluminum, copper, iron, lead, manganese, mercury, titanium, vanadium, zinc

Nonmetallic minerals

graphite, fluorspar (all grades)

Virtual dependence on foreign sources:

Metals

cobalt, chromite, ferro-grade manganese, nickel, platinum metals, tin

Nonmetallic minerals

industrial diamonds, quartz crystal, asbestos (spinning variety)

Figure 9.19 (*Facing page*) *Total use of groundwater in the United States.* (*From U.S.G.S.*) (*Above*) *Areas where significant cones of depression have been developed in the water table because of overpumping from wells.* (*From U.S.G.S.*)

A

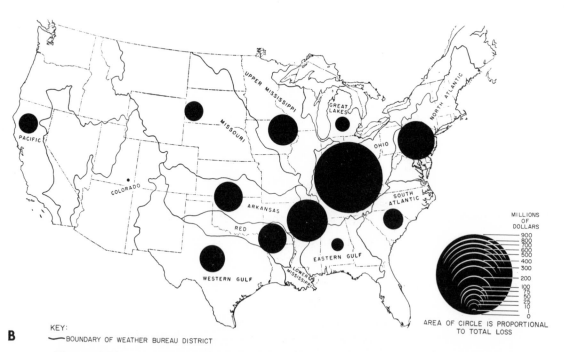

B

KEY:
— BOUNDARY OF WEATHER BUREAU DISTRICT

Figure 9.20 (A) *Major dams and reservoirs in the United States.* (B) *Distribution of flood losses by regions, 1902–1937. (From U.S.D.A.)*

Our mineral production in 1963 was valued at about $20 billion, of which $2 billion was for metals, $13½ billion for fuels, and $4½ billion for other nonmetals. The locations of some of our principal mineral deposits are shown in Figure 9.21.

To qualify as a resource mineral, a deposit must be in sufficient quantity and of high enough grade to be commercially produced, a principle illustrated in the words of a prospector who once said: "There's a million dollars in gold in that claim of mine, but there's just too darn much sand and gravel mixed with it." At a higher price for gold, his deposit may have become productive. For example, at normal peacetime prices, we import most of our mercury from foreign countries having deposits richer and, therefore, less costly to produce than ours. But during World War II, because of a considerable increase in the price of mercury, the United States produced practically all it needed. Any appraisal of the mineral resources of a country must consider the size and grade of the deposits, the

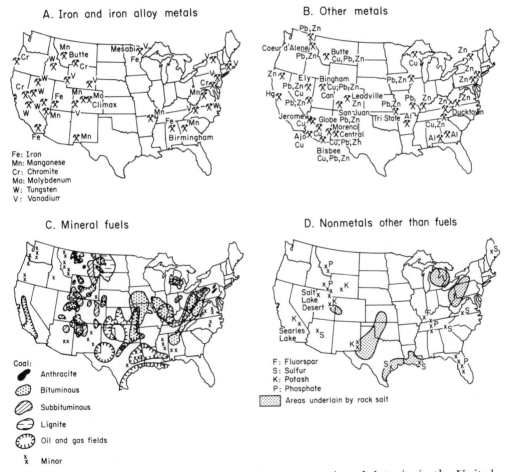

Figure 9.21 *Maps showing locations of important mineral deposits in the United States. (A) Iron and iron alloy metals. (B) Other metals. (C) Mineral fuels. Other energy sources include hydroelectricity at dams (Fig. 9.20, A) and uranium deposits, especially on the Colorado Plateau. (D) Nonmetals other than fuels.*

costs of production, and the market prices of the various products. Technological advances may affect a nation's mineral wealth, as illustrated by the changes in use of various kinds of energy sources (Fig. 9.22).

Air—A Resource Needing Protection

Air pollution is increasingly a national problem. The oxygen we need for breathing is concentrated in a thin layer at the base of the atmosphere, a layer barely reaching to the tops of high mountains. Airplanes flying in the rarefied air above that layer carry supplemental oxygen. But this layer of air is being polluted and not merely disagreeably so. In many cases the pollution has been lethal: in 1948, in Donora, Pennsylvania, 20 persons died in a smog; in 1952 some 4,000 persons died in a smog in London; a year later, in

New York, 200 deaths were charged to a local smog. Undoubtedly many other deaths in our cities and much illness can be attributed to air pollution.

One of the chief pollutants is carbon dioxide, a product of the combustion of organic fuels. The amount that has been added to the atmosphere is estimated to be enough to raise global temperatures by a degree or two. A related pollutant, carbon monoxide, results when combustion is incomplete. A thousand parts per million can kill quickly; most people are sickened if exposed for a few hours to concentrations of 100 parts per million. Concentrations about this high have been recorded in cities.

Another dangerous pollutant is sulfur dioxide, which, on contact with water, forms sulfuric acid. Normally the concentration of these pollutants is only a few parts per million, but the concentration around some industrial plants is great enough so that whole hillsides may be deforested. Sulfur dioxide and sulfuric acid are exceedingly harmful to the respiratory system.

Nitrogen compounds, also released into the air, give rise to a complex of toxic substances. So do the simple hydrocarbons, like ethylene and the aldehydes (for example, formaldehyde).

The various air pollutants become concentrated when there is little or no wind. Air chilled at the ground at night is sometimes overlain by a stratum of warm air that acts as a lid and prevents air circulation. This condition is called a thermal inversion. The confined cool layer may be only a few hundred feet thick. Smoke spreads laterally at the base of the layer of warm air and collects beneath it. The smoke and other pollutants continue to accumulate until the inversion is disrupted by wind or by heating of the ground and the lower stratum.

Cities are notoriously subject to smog because of the vast amounts of smoke and fumes released in them, and unless the pollution is brought under control the kinds of tragedies

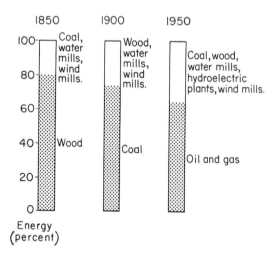

Figure 9.22 *Changes in proportions of energy supplied by different fuels or energy sources as a result of technological advances. Nuclear fuels are becoming an important source of energy.*

that have already occurred will be repeated, and with increasing frequency and severity.

Even in a remote mountain valley with one industrial plant, smog conditions can be serious. In the eastern mountains smog has been a serious problem for a long time; now, with the spread of industry in the West, some Rocky Mountain valleys have been made almost uninhabitable because of air pollution.

Resources for Outdoor Recreation

In recent years there has been a prodigious increase in the number of visitors to parks, forests, and other recreational areas. The number is expected to double by 1970 and to double again by 1980. The national parks and monuments are by far the best known, for they contain many spectacular examples of major geomorphic features, yet they account for only 10 percent of the visits. National forests account for 25 percent, and the state parks and forests account for 65 percent. Alleghany Park in New York is not widely known outside of the surrounding area, but the number of persons using it each year is nearly as great as the number visiting many of our best-known national parks.

Most of the national parks and forests are located in the West. We need these and more like them. Wilderness Areas are desirable, but most of these are in the West and, under present circumstances, are accessible chiefly to the wealthy. More parks and forests are needed in the eastern United States, where big-city congestion is greatest. The burden there is currently being carried by the comparatively modest state park and forest systems, but their attendance records, like those of Alleghany Park, prove the popularity of parks and forests near home. Development of more of the eastern mountains as parks and forests would provide recreational outlets for the cities and would help relieve poverty in Appalachia.

PART 2

Physiography
of the Provinces

10

Coastal Plain and Continental Shelf

Along the Atlantic seaboard and Gulf Coast is the Coastal Plain, which is 100 to 200 miles wide and makes up almost 10 percent of the United States (Fig. 10.1). This plain continues seaward as the Continental Shelf, which extends another 100 to 200 miles offshore to a depth of 500 to 600 feet below sea level. At the outer margin of the Continental Shelf the ocean bottom plunges downward, forming the steep *continental slope,* which descends to depths of more than 2 miles.

Outstanding features of the Coastal Plain are given in the following list.

1. The Coastal Plain is an elevated sea bottom with low topographic relief and extensive marshy tracts.
2. With minor exceptions, altitudes are below 500 feet; more than half the plain is below 100 feet.
3. The geologic formations—Cretaceous, Tertiary, and Quaternary—are sedimentary deposits representing various onshore, nearshore, and offshore environments; since the beginning of Cretaceous time the shoreline has receded as the Coastal Plain has been elevated.
4. The formations dip gently seaward and crop out in belts forming cuestas and valleys roughly parallel to the inner and outer edges of the plain; the Cretaceous System forms an inland belt, the Tertiary an intermediate belt, and the Quaternary a coastal belt.
5. The surface of the plain slopes northward, and the valleys in the northern part are drowned to form Chesapeake, Delaware, and New York bays and Long Island Sound; northeast of Cape Cod the entire surface is submerged.
6. The shore, more than 3,000 miles long, consists of sandy beaches, several set aside as national seashores; back of some of the beaches are swamps, like the Dismal Swamp in North Carolina and Virginia; there are mud flats at the delta of the Mississippi River, and coral banks at the southern tip of Florida.
7. The climate is rainy, except at the southwest, and the winters are mild, except at the northeast.
8. The Gulf Coastal Plain is subject to a high frequency of tornadoes; the Gulf and Atlantic coasts are both subject to fog and hurricanes.
9. Natural resources are varied and of great value. These include:

   A. The Southeastern Pine Forest, which is one of the two principal lumber-producing forests in the United States, the other being in the Pacific Northwest.
   B. Agricultural products, which include vegetables in the north; cotton, tobacco,

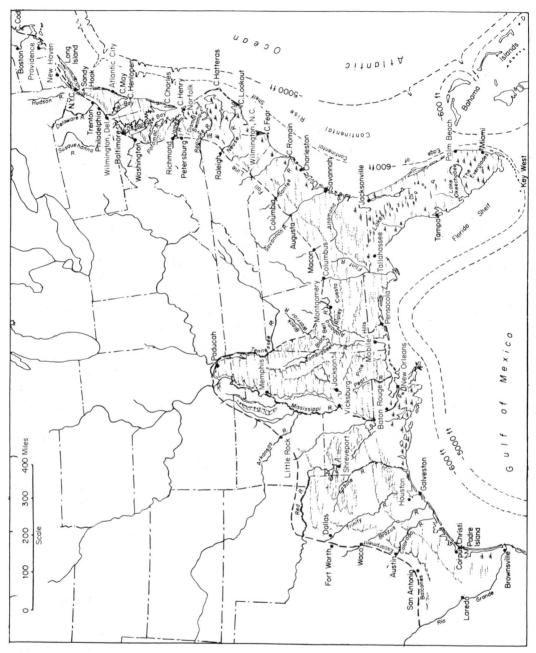

Figure 10.1 *Physiographic map of the Coastal Plain and Continental Shelf.*

and peanuts in the south; and fruits in Florida and southern Texas.

C. Fisheries, which provide about half the United States total.

D. Mineral products, which include oil and gas from the Gulf Coast; also sulfur, salt, and special-use clays, and in Florida, phosphate (for fertilizer).

E. Resort and recreational areas: the Atlantic coast beaches in summer and the Florida and Gulf coasts in winter; an inland waterway that enables small craft to travel safely almost the entire length of the coast.

A notable problem in the southeastern part of the Coastal Plain is the underdeveloped human resource. Despite rich and varied resources, Alabama, Mississippi, and Louisiana share the dubious distinction of having the highest illiteracy rate in the country. Even Puerto Rico, crowded and lacking resources, is no worse. Good physical environment favors mankind, but does not determine his destiny.

The physiography has controlled both settlement and development of the Coastal Plain. From Long Island south to Cape Lookout, drowned valleys form the bays and harbors that favored early settlement of these parts of the Atlantic seaboard. The bays and harbors are still important; in fact, about one person in five in the United States lives within commuting distance of them.

From New Jersey to southern Virginia, tidewater extends inland to a line of falls, called the Fall Line, where the Coastal Plain borders the Piedmont Province. Most of the seaboard cities—Trenton, Philadelphia, Wilmington, Baltimore, Washington, Richmond, and Petersburg—are located along the Fall Line. The growth of these cities was favored partly because each is situated at a head of navigation and partly because they are the most easterly places at which the rivers could be crossed easily (Fig. 10.2). East of the Fall Line the rivers are broad, and twentieth-century technology was required to bridge or to tunnel

under such bodies of water as the Hudson River, Delaware Bay, and Chesapeake Bay. The early colonists did not have the 100,000 miles of wire necessary for spinning cables to support suspension bridges across the rivers. Even the Brooklyn Bridge, a small structure by today's standards, was not built until 1883. Early wagon roads connecting the Fall Line cities—and later the turnpikes and railroads —followed routes near the inner edge of the Coastal Plain, and at each river the roads turned westward to the falls.

South of the region of drowned valleys, the principal cities are located either along the coast (Norfolk, Wilmington, Charleston, Savannah, Jacksonville, Miami, Tampa, Mobile, Galveston, Corpus Christi, and Brownsville) or along the inner edge of the Coastal Plain (Raleigh, Columbia, Augusta, Macon, Montgomery, Little Rock, Dallas, Waco, Austin, and San Antonio). Few cities are located *within* the Coastal Plain; Houston, an exception, has joined itself by canal to the sea. New Orleans, Memphis, and other cities along the Mississippi are joined to the sea by that river.

Some of the physiographic features of the Coastal Plain may be seen in national and state parks and beaches. National Sea Shores have been created at Cape Cod, Massachusetts; Fire Island, New York; Assoteague Island, Maryland; Cape Hatteras, North Carolina; and at Padre Island, Texas. New York has developed public beaches along the barrier bars on the south side of Long Island. Florida has the Everglades National Park and a recently established marine park off the southern tip of the peninsula, where visitors may observe the ocean bottom and the offshore biota.

Structure, Boundaries, and Subdivisions

The geologic formations of the Coastal Plain and Continental Shelf are listed and briefly described in Table 10.1. Figure 10.3 illustrates

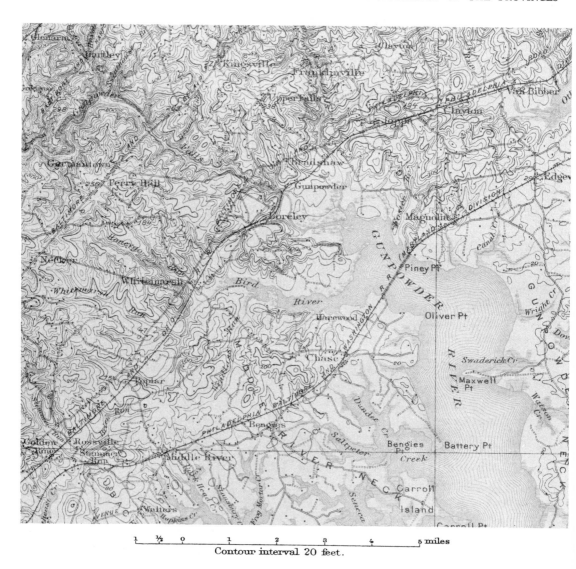

Contour interval 20 feet.

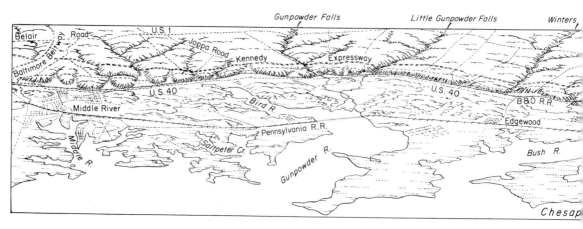

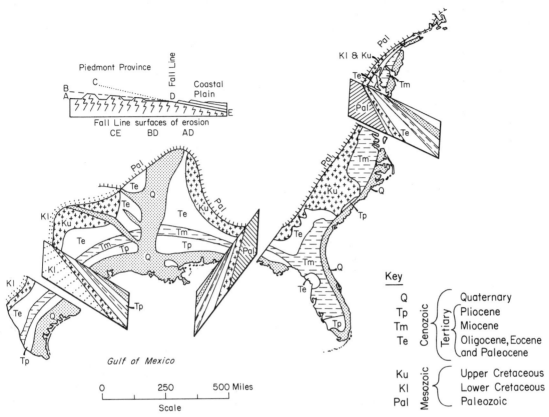

Figure 10.3 *Structural framework of the Coastal Plain.*

Figure 10.2 *Topographic map and diagram of the Fall Line along the north-west part of Chesapeake Bay. The Fall Line is the escarpment at the Baltimore and Ohio Railroad. To the northwest is the hilly Piedmont Province; to the southeast is the low-lying Coastal Plain with the drowned valleys and tidewater extending to the Fall Line. (From U.S.G.S. Tolchester, Md., sheet, 1908.)*

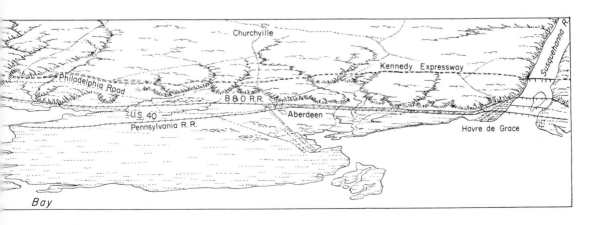

TABLE 10.1 Geologic formations on the Coastal Plain.

QUATERNARY	RECENT AND PLEISTOCENE	Coastal and estuarine sand and gravel; alluvium; in Florida, marine limestone; loess along the east side of the Mississippi River Alluvial Plain.			
TERTIARY	PLIOCENE	Mostly river and estuarine terrace deposits of gravel, sand, and clay; some sinkhole deposits; marine shell marl and phosphate deposits in Florida and in South Carolina.			
	MIOCENE	Yorktown Formation: marine sand, sandy clay, and marl. St. Mary's Formation: marine clay and sand. (Cohansey sandstone in New Jersey equivalent to St. Mary's and Choptank.) Choptank Formation: marine sand, clay, and marl. (Called Alum Bluff Group in eastern Gulf Coast; Hawthorne Limestone in Florida.) Calvert Formation: marine sand, clay, marl, and diatomaceous earth; includes Tampa Limestone in Florida.			
	OLIGOCENE	Vicksburg Group: mostly marine limestone; some bentonite (volcanic ash); includes Ocala Limestone in Florida.			
	EOCENE AND PALEOCENE?	Jackson Group: marine limestone and nonmarine lignitic clay and sand; some volcanic ash. Claiborne Group: clay, siliceous clay, and clayey sandstone; brown iron ore, limy sandy clay, and clayey sand; phosphatic greensand. Wilcox Group: marine and estuarine sand; clay; some lignite. Midway Group: marine limestone, clay, limy clay, varicolored sand.			

CRETACEOUS — UPPER

	Western Gulf	*Eastern Gulf*	*South Atlantic*	*North Atlantic*
	Navarro Formation: clay, chalk, sand, some volcanic ash.	Ripley Formation and Selma Chalk: chalk grades east and west into clay and sand.	Peedee Formation: sand and clay.	Monmouth Formation: sand.
	Taylor Marl: clay and marl; some volcanic ash.	Eutaw Formation: limy and phosphatic beds; volcanic ash.	Black Creek Formation: lignitic clay and sand.	Matawan Formation: dark, micaceous, sandy clay. Magothy Formation: lignitic sand and clay.
	Austin Chalk; impure chalk. Eagle Ford Formation: bituminous clay. Woodbine Sandstone: iron-stained sand and clay.	Tuscaloosa Formation: sand, gravel, clay.	Middendorf Formation: clay, sand.	Raritan Formation: sand, clay.

CRETACEOUS — LOWER

	Washita Group: limy, but more shaly and sandy than next older formation. Fredricksburg Group: clay, limestone, chalk, marl. Trinity Group: mostly sand, some thin beds of limestone.	Potomac Group: Patapsco Formation: nonmarine clay and sand. Arundel Formation: clay, lignite, bog iron ores; nonmarine. Patuxent Formation: sand, gravel; nonmarine.

their general structure. The basement rocks on which formations rest are of three kinds. Along the Atlantic seaboard the basement rocks are like those of the Piedmont Province, mostly metamorphic rocks but including some Triassic sedimentary rocks (Figs. 2.1, 2.2). Under the Mississippi Valley, the basement rocks are folded Paleozoic formations like those in the Valley and Ridge and Ouachita provinces. In Texas, the basement is taken arbitrarily at the top of the Lower Cretaceous formations, which in turn rest on Jurassic and folded Paleozoic formations.

The basement rocks form the greater part of the earth's crust, and this crust thins seaward under the Coastal Plain and Continental Shelf (Fig. 2.20). Near the inner edge of the Coastal Plain the base of the crust is about 35 kilometers below sea level; under the shelf it rises to about 25 kilometers below sea level.

Along the inner boundary of the Coastal Plain the top of the basement rocks rises landward from beneath the Cretaceous and Tertiary formations and forms the line of rapids and falls—the Fall Line—where the rivers tumble off the Piedmont Province onto the Coastal Plain. The boundary is similar and equally distinct along each side of the Mississippi Valley. In Texas, the Lower Cretaceous formations are excluded from the Coastal Plain because they are much faulted and uplifted, and form a dissected plateau—the Edwards Plateau.

The Coastal Plain is divided into seven sections (Fig. 10.4):

1. Embayed Section, where the Coastal Plain and Continental Shelf slope north from the Cape Fear Arch.
2. Cape Fear Arch.
3. Sea Islands Downwarp.
4. Peninsular Arch, in Florida.
5. East Gulf Coastal Plain.
6. Mississippi River Alluvial Plain.
7. West Gulf Coastal Plain.

These sections differ in their surface and subsurface geologic structure, geomorphology, soils, hydrology, and economies.

Embayed Section

The Embayed Section extends from Cape Cod to about the Neuse River in North Carolina. At the north end, east of the Hudson River, all but the highest parts of the Coastal Plain are submerged and joined with the Continental Shelf. Cape Cod, Nantucket Island, Martha's Vineyard, Block Island, and Long Island are the tops of ridges formed by Coastal Plain formations and capped by glacial drift (Fig. 10.5). The north end of the Embayed Section, including small areas west of the Hudson River at Staten Island and in northern New Jersey, is the only part of the Coastal Plain that was glaciated. Two terminal moraines form ridges of gravel and sand extending the length of Long Island; these ridges form the "fishtail" extensions at the east end of the Island.

Barrier beaches extend almost the entire length of Long Island and New Jersey. These are popular resort areas, and along the south side of Long Island extensive stretches have wisely been set aside as state parks. Some of the bars have closed the mouths of small bays and converted them into ponds.

The southern part of the Embayed Section (Fig. 10.6) also is characterized by barrier beaches, but only the lowermost parts of the

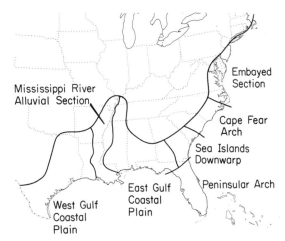

Figure 10.4 *Sections of the Coastal Plain.*

valleys are drowned; upstream, as far west as the Fall Line, there are stretches of swampy alluvial flats.

The formations in this part of the Embayed Section dip east, but against the north flank of the Cape Fear Arch (Fig. 10.2) the younger formations extend landward and unconformably overlap the older ones. At the Fall Line in Delaware and Maryland, Lower Cretaceous

formations overlie the crystalline rocks of the Piedmont Province (too thin to be shown in Fig. 10.2), and the Lower Cretaceous is overlain by Upper Cretaceous formations and these, in turn, by Eocene formations. Near the Potomac River the Eocene formations extend unconformably across the Upper Cretaceous and rest on the Lower Cretaceous. South of the Potomac River, the Eocene formations un-

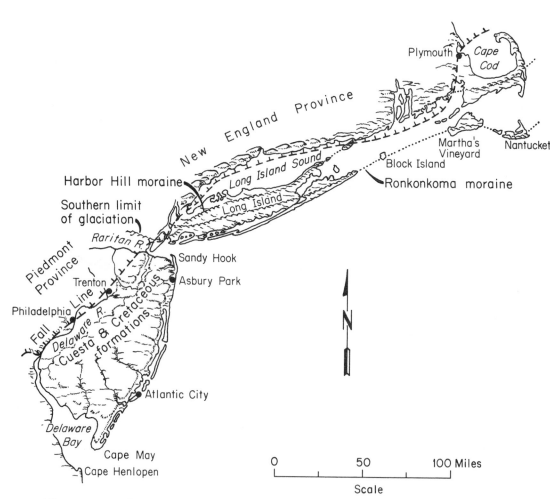

Figure 10.5 *Physiographic diagram of the north end of the Embayed Section of the Coastal Plain. East of the Hudson River all but the highest parts of the Coastal Plain are submerged. Long Island and the islands to the east are ridges of Coastal Plain formations capped by glacial deposits.*

conformably overlap the Lower Cretaceous and extend onto the crystalline rocks of the Piedmont Province. South of the Rappahannock River, Miocene formations overlap the Eocene and extend onto the crystalline rocks of the Piedmont Province. These unconformable overlaps are very important in interpreting the geologic history and the subsurface structure because they record structural movements that took place while the formations were being deposited.

North of the Rappahannock River the boundary between the Coastal Plain and the Piedmont Province is marked by an escarpment, and tidewater extends to the Fall Line. South of that river the boundary is not very distinct topographically, being marked chiefly by a difference in kind of topography and soil without much difference in altitude across the boundary, and tidewater does not reach to the Fall Line.

Cape Fear Arch

Structural uplift at the Cape Fear Arch amounts to about 2500 feet. Cretaceous formations are exposed at the surface across most of the arch (Fig. 10.2), but to the north and south these are overlain by Tertiary formations. Along the coast, between the Quaternary and the Cretaceous, is a narrow outcrop of marine Pliocene deposits.

The boundary between the Coastal Plain and the Piedmont Province at the edge of this section is a well-defined contact between the Cretaceous formations and the crystalline rocks of the Piedmont Province. There is little topographic relief across this boundary, but the valleys deepen as they enter the Coastal Plain from the Piedmont and are marked by falls. Hills at the Fall Line are sandy. Columbia, South Carolina, is the principal Fall Line city in this section.

The northern boundary of the Cape Fear Arch is taken arbitrarily at about the Neuse River, and the south boundary near the Santee

River. Near these rivers the Miocene formations extend far inland and unconformably overlap the Cretaceous formations.

The Cape Fear Section has a distinctive coast line, being marked by three large, smooth scallops between Capes Hatteras, Lookout, Fear, and Romain. The scallops are being eroded and the debris transported to the capes. The smoothness of the scallops and the fact

Figure 10.6 *Physiographic diagram of the southern part of the Embayed Section of the Coastal Plain.*

that they are being eroded suggests an emergent, smooth sea floor, as if uplift were continuing.

Sea Islands Downwarp

In Georgia the Coastal Plain formations are folded into a syncline, the Sea Islands Downwarp, between the Cape Fear Arch and the Peninsular Arch in Florida. The inner edge of the Coastal Plain continues to be marked by a line of falls; Augusta, Macon, and Columbus, Georgia, are the principal Fall Line cities. The coastline is marked by many islands, which is a belt about 7 miles wide. Much of the land is salt marsh, but the outermost edges of many islands are bordered with firm sandy beaches. In places there are dunes, some of which are moving inland. That the islands are due to very recent downwarping, or rise of sea level, is indicated by the presence of stumps of live oak on beaches where they are covered by high tide. Some tidal marshes have encroached a quarter mile onto dry land in the last half century.

Peninsular Arch

Florida is the emerged, highest part of an anticlinal ridge known as the Peninsular Arch. Its boundaries with the neighboring sections on the Coastal Plain are arbitrary. The Bahama Shelf southeast of Florida, the Continental Shelf east of Florida, and the Florida Shelf to the west are all part of the arch. The submerged part of the Arch is twice as long and three times as wide as Florida (Fig. 10.7). Between Florida and the Bahama Islands the arch is broken by a transverse trough through which the Gulf stream flows.

The arch is underlain by Cretaceous limestone and shale more than 10,000 feet thick under the central and southern part of the peninsula. The formations thin northward toward the Fall Line in Georgia. Resting on the Cretaceous formations are comparatively thin deposits of Eocene, Miocene, and Pliocene age. During Cretaceous time the site of Florida was a basin in which sediments 2 miles or more thick were deposited. Since the beginning of Tertiary time, Florida has been a shallow shelf area, and part of the time, as now, elevated above sea level.

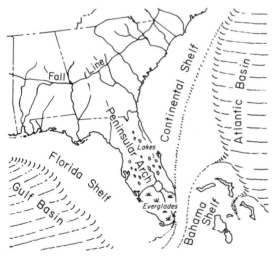

Figure 10.7 *Florida is the highest, emerged part of the Peninsular Arch, which extends southeastward between the Atlantic and Gulf basins.*

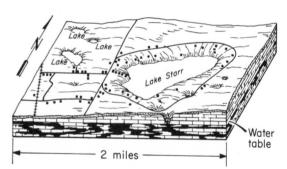

Figure 10.8 *Limestone sinks in Florida. The lake country in Florida is underlain by cavernous limestone (Miocene), and the surface is dotted with sinks that are due to solution of the limestone and to collapse of cavern roofs. Sinks that are deeper than the water table contain lakes; shallower ones (southeast of Lake Starr) are dry. The Florida lakes are much used for recreation and for homesites.*

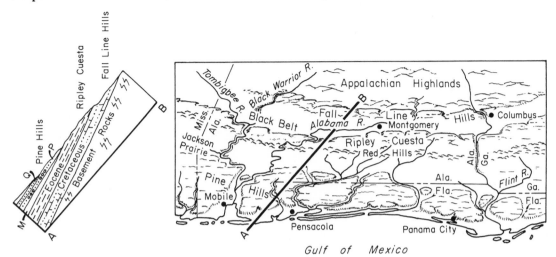

Figure 10.9 *Diagrammatic view and cross section of the East Gulf Coastal Plain. Upper Cretaceous formations form the Fall Line Hills (Tuscaloosa and Eutaw Formations), Black Belt (Selma Chalk), and Ripley Cuesta (Ripley Formation). Eocene formations (Midway Formation, Wilcox and Claiborne Groups, and Jackson Formation) extend from there to the Pine Hills. Pliocene deposits (P, Citronelle Formation) form the Pine Hills and unconformably overlie the Miocene (M). Along the coast are Quaternary (Q) deposits.*

Florida is a land of lakes, many of which occupy sinkholes dissolved in the uplifted limestone formations (Fig. 10.8). Southern Florida is the site of the Everglades. Lake Okeechobe, about 18 feet above sea level and covering about 750 square miles, has a maximum depth of only about 15 feet.

The peninsula has a varied coastline, with barrier beaches along the Atlantic Coast, coral reefs and mangrove swamp around the south end of the peninsula, and rocky stretches between bays protected by barrier beaches along the west coast. The eastern keys are elongate islands of Pleistocene coral reef flanked by modern coral; the western keys are irregular islands of marine-deposited limestone.

Gulf Coast Sections

Along the Gulf Coast the formations are much thicker than those along the Atlantic Coast—about three times as thick. But like the formations along the Atlantic Coast they thin landward and form belts parallel to the coast; the resistant formations form the ridges, or cuestas, and the easily eroded ones form the valleys (Fig. 10.9).

The East Gulf Coastal Plain is separated from the West Gulf Coastal Plain by the Mississippi Alluvial Plain. In the East Gulf Coastal Plain, the Fall Line swings westward around the south end of the Piedmont, Valley and Ridge, and Appalachian Plateau provinces. In a sense, the Fall Line ends in central Alabama, because the streams farther west have no falls where they flow from the Appalachian Highlands to the Coastal Plain formations. Moreover, there is no abrupt change in topography between the highlands and the Fall Line Hills of the Coastal Plain (Fig. 10.9), despite the change in geologic formations and kind of ground.

The Fall Line Hills are sandy ground formed by the Tuscaloosa and Eutaw Formations of Upper Cretaceous age. South of the Fall Line Hills is a lowland, the Black Belt, named for its characteristic black soil, developed on the Selma Chalk, and one of the most fertile areas in the region.

South of the Black Belt is a ridge, the Ripley Cuesta. South of this ridge is a lowland that is developed on the formations of the Midway Group (basal Eocene), and then another belt of hills formed by beds of the Wilcox and Claiborne groups, also of Eocene age. South of these hills, in eastern Alabama and Georgia, is a plain developed on the uppermost Eocene and dotted with sinkholes. Much of the drainage is underground. South of this plain are the Pine Hills, a sandy area developed on the Citronelle Formation of Pliocene age. Along the coast is a lowland developed on Quaternary deposits, mostly sand along the present beaches. The string of low bluffs paralleling the beach apparently marks the site of an elevated former shoreline.

The structure and general topography of the West Gulf Coastal Plain are similar to those in the East Gulf Coastal Plain (Fig. 10.10). The escarpments are less well developed, but the barrier beaches are especially well developed. One of these, Padre Island (Fig. 10.1), extends 125 miles north from the mouth of the Rio Grande. The West Gulf Coastal Plain ends inland at the escarpment formed by the Balcones fault zone, which marks the edge of the Edwards Plateau.

The Mississippi River Alluvial Plain, which is 500 miles long and 50 to 100 miles wide (Fig. 10.11), has a southward slope averaging less than 8 inches per mile. At the junction of the Ohio and Mississippi rivers the altitude is about 275 feet. Midway from there to the coast, near northern Louisiana, the altitude is 100 feet; in the last 250 miles the slope averages less than 6 inches per mile, and because the river follows a meandering course

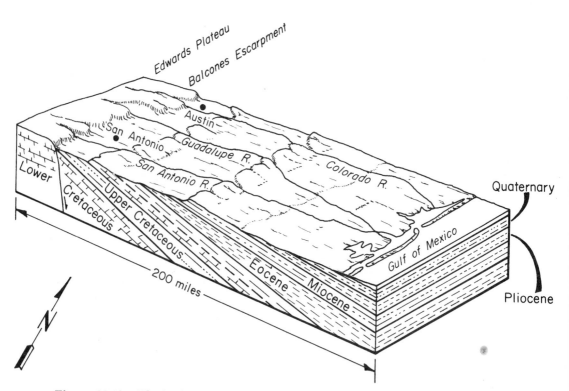

Figure 10.10 *Block diagam illustrating the relation of escarpments and cuestas to the structural geology of part of the West Gulf Coastal Plain.*

its gradient is only about half that. This is the land of oxbow lakes—the cutoff meanders. According to Mark Twain, cutting off the meanders would so shorten the Mississippi River that Cairo, Illinois, would soon be joined to New Orleans.

The alluvial fill unconformably overlies and conceals the Coastal Plain formations, which in turn overlie and conceal the Paleozoic and other ancient rock formations.

The Mississippi Alluvial Plain is divided into five basins. In Louisiana, on the delta west of the river, is the Atchafalaya Basin, which was the site of the Mississippi River

delta some hundreds of years ago. West of the river, between Natchez and Vicksburg, is the Tensas Basin. On the east side, above Vicksburg is the Yazoo Basin. Farther upstream, in northeastern Arkansas, there are two basins, those of the St. Francis and Black rivers. Parts of each of the five basins are lower than the Mississippi River, which is an aggrading stream. For example, the Mississippi River at 100 feet above sea level is 50 feet higher than the Ouachita River due west in the Tensas Basin. For emergency flood control purposes, these basins can be backfilled with flood waters from the Mississippi. The basins probably are due in part to irregular deposition by the Mississippi River and in part to downfaulting or downfolding of the Coastal Plain formations and basement rocks that underlie the alluvial fill.

The Cretaceous and Tertiary formations in the East and West Gulf Coastal Plains, and beneath the Mississippi River Alluvial Plain are not only thicker than those along the Atlantic Plain but are more folded and faulted. The principal structural features are illustrated in Figure 10.12. Most of these structural features lie in two belts, one near the inner edge of the Coastal Plain and another along the coast and extending offshore. Some of the folds form broad upwarps, like the Sabine Uplift and Jackson Dome; others form structural basins. The folds are accompanied by faults that trend parallel to the general strike of the formations. Most of the fault blocks are downthrown toward the coast.

Associated structures are formed by salt plugs—masses of salt a mile or more wide that have been plastically squeezed upward from salt beds that probably lie 4 or 5 miles below the surface. As Figure 10.13 shows, the formations penetrated by the salt plugs are dragged upward, and the younger, near-surface formations are domed. Many salt plugs have reached the surface, where they are reflected in the topography and vegetation. The plugs, which consist chiefly of rock salt, are usually capped with gypsum; some are capped with sulfur.

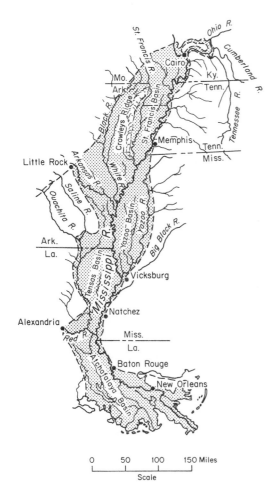

Figure 10.11 *Drainage system of the Mississippi River Alluvial Section.*

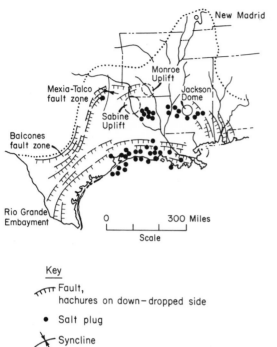

Key

┬┬┬ Fault,
         hachures on down—dropped side

•   Salt plug

✕   Syncline

Figure 10.12 *Major structural features of the Gulf Coast sections.*

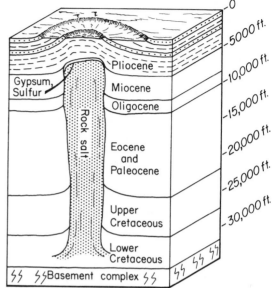

Figure 10.13 *Block diagram of salt plug and dome.*

Much of the oil produced along the outer part of the Coastal Plain (p. 159) has been obtained from the flanks of the structural domes formed by the plugs. The plugs are also a major source of the world's sulfur and salt.

Earthquakes provide historical evidence about the instability of parts of the Coastal Plain. The head of the Mississippi River Alluvial Plain was the site of one of the most severe earthquakes recorded in the United States—the New Madrid, Missouri, earthquake, which occurred in 1811 and 1812. Damage was slight only because the region was sparsely settled. The occurrence of a similar earthquake today would be disastrous.

Another major earthquake virtually destroyed Charleston, South Carolina, in 1886. This quake damaged practically every building in Charleston, bent railroad tracks, and produced fissures and depressions.

Climate

Most of the Coastal Plain Province has a rainy climate, with mild winters, but the southwestern part is semiarid, and the northeastern part, although rainy, has severe winters.

The maximum average annual temperature, 75°F, has been recorded at the southern tip of Florida. The 70° isotherm extends across northern Florida to New Orleans, Galveston, and San Antonio. The 60° isotherm extends from about Norfolk to near the head of the Mississippi River Alluvial Section. The 50° isotherm passes through Long Island and other parts of the north end of the Embayed Section. An effect of proximity to the ocean is shown by the maximum and minimum temperatures that have been recorded. The maxima, between 100 and 110°F, are only 5° to 10° above the average annual maximum temperatures. The minima are only about 10° below the average annual minimum.

The average length of the frost-free period is about 180 days at the north end of the Coastal Plain. The number of frost-free days increases southward to more than 300 along the Gulf Coast (Fig. 4.2). The average depth of frost penetration decreases southward from almost 20 inches on Long Island to less than 1 inch along the Gulf Coast (Fig. 4.2).

Across the West Gulf Coastal Plain precipitation increases from an annual average of 20 inches along the Rio Grande to 60 inches in southern Louisiana and southern Florida. Along most of the Atlantic Coast it is between 40 and 50 inches. This precipitation is distributed rather evenly throughout the year. Annual precipitation has never been less than 20 inches except in the western half of the West Gulf Coastal Plain, where precipitation has been less than 20 inches for 50 percent of the years for which weather records are available. A high evaporation rate contributes to the aridity in that part of the province.

Excessive precipitation can be as devastating as drought. Every part of the Coastal Plain has experienced storms that have dumped 2.5 inches or more of rain in an hour. Four inches or more of rain in an hour has been recorded at several places from Virginia southward along the Atlantic Coast and westward across the Gulf Coast to Galveston. Average annual snowfall is 30 inches on Long Island, 10 inches in Virginia, and less than 1 inch along the Gulf Coast and southernmost part of the Atlantic Coast (Fig. 4.2).

Tornadoes are most common in the Mississippi River Alluvial Section and in the adjoining parts of the East and West Gulf Coastal Plains. During the 30-year period ending in 1950 every 50-mile square of this area was struck by about a dozen tornadoes, and in the whole of that area more than 2,000 persons were killed. During the same period the Embayed Section of the Coastal Plain was struck by about 5 tornadoes per 50-mile square and about 75 persons were killed. Tornado frequency in the Gulf sections of the Coastal Plain is greatest between October and April,

and greatest during the afternoon and evening.

Hurricanes that strike at our Coastal Plain form over the Caribbean Sea, mostly in late summer and fall. They first move westward with the trade winds, but then curve northward around the west side of the high pressure areas that prevail over the central Atlantic Ocean. They lose their force as they move inland or to middle latitudes. In an average year the coast is struck by about 5 hurricanes.

The effects of past climates on the Coastal Plain are manifest chiefly in the loessial deposits east of the Mississippi River (Fig. 6.1; p. 85), the Red and Yellow Podzolic soils (p. 155), and the rise in sea level attributed to melting of the glaciers (p. 160).

Vegetation, Agriculture

Most of the Coastal Plain is covered by the Southeastern Pine Forest, which extends from eastern Texas to North Carolina. This forest is bounded on the north by the Mixed Oak and Pine Forest that is transitional northward to the Hardwood Forests (Figs. 8.2; 8.3). The distribution and distinguishing leaf and cone characteristics of six common pine trees in these parts of the Coastal Plain are shown in Figure 10.14.

Shortleaf, loblolly, longleaf, and slash pine are important timber trees that provide about a third of the total timber production of the United States. Longleaf and slash pine provide about two-thirds of the world's production of turpentine and rosin, products known as "naval stores" because in the early days tar and pitch were produced chiefly for sailing vessels. This industry figured prominently in our early industrial history. Tar and pitch were needed for the British navy; a bounty was paid for production of naval stores, and their export other than to Britain was prohibited by the Navigation Acts.

The pines grow principally on sandy uplands. The principal other trees on the up-

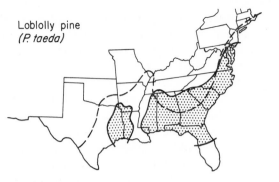

Loblolly pine
(P. taeda)

3 needles, 6—9 inches long; cones 2–3 inches
with stiff prickles

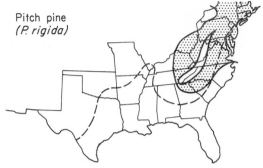

Pitch pine
(P. rigida)

3 needles, 3–7 inches long, twisted; cones short,
broad, 2–3 inches, small prickles

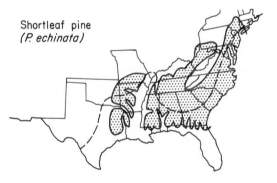

Shortleaf pine
(P. echinata)

2 or 3 needles, 3–5 inches long; cone 2 inches
with fine prickles

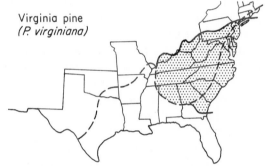

Virginia pine
(P. virginiana)

2 needles, 2–3 inches long, twisted; cones
2–3 inches, very prickly

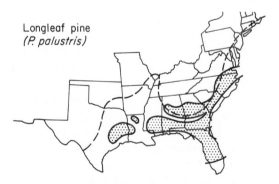

Longleaf pine
(P. palustris)

3 needles, 8–18 inches long; cones 6–10
inches with prickles

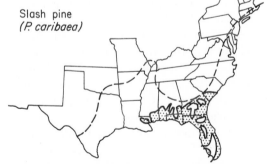

Slash pine
(P. caribaea)

2 or 3 needles, 3–5 inches long; cone shiney,
3–5 inches with prickles

Figure 10.14   *Distribution of six Coastal Plain pine trees.*

lands, in order of their importance or abundance, are, according to the U.S. Forest Service:

Southern red, black, post, laurel, cherrybark, and willow oaks
Sweetgum
Winged, American, and cedar elms
Black, red, sand, and pignut hickories
Eastern and southern red cedars
Basswoods

The principal trees on alluvial bottoms and swamps are:

Sweetgum and tupelo
Water, laurel, live, overcup, Texas, and swamp white oaks
Southern cypress
Pecan, water, and swamp hickories
Beech, river birch, ash
Red and silver maples
Cottonwoods and willows
Sycamore, hackberry, honeylocust, and holly
Red bay and sweet bay
Southern magnolia
Pond and spruce pines
Atlantic white cedar

Northward the Southeastern Pine Forest grades into the Central Hardwood Forest and the pines are mixed with hardwoods, notably oaks. The Mixed Oak and Pine Forest extends northeastward from Texas to the Embayed Section of the Coastal Plain (Fig. 8.2). In the Embayed Section, the shortleaf, pitch, and scrub pines are mixed with white, chestnut, and red oaks, and some hickories.

Southernmost Florida has subtropical forest with mangrove, royal and thatch palms, and Florida yew. The hardwood trees are small evergreens. The forest is small; it probably covers less than 800 square miles. Other subtropical forest grows along the coast of southernmost Texas.

Other quite different vegetation on the Coastal Plain grows in the semiarid part of Texas. Annual rainfall there may be as much as 30 inches, but the evaporation rate is high. The principal tree is mesquite. With it grow thorn bushes, cacti, curly grass, buffalo grass, and various shrubs.

The Coastal Plain is bordered in many places along its shores by salt marshes and fresh-water marshes. The fresh-water marshes are characterized by Indian ricegrass, cattail, and tule, and in Florida, sawgrass. The salt marshes are characterized by marsh grass, *Spartina*. A transect across one of the marsh areas in Florida is illustrated in Figure 8.12,A.

Figure 10.15 illustrates an example of the relationship of vegetation to ground con-

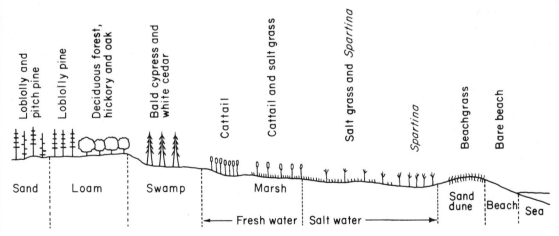

Figure 10.15 *Diagrammatic transect showing relationship between ground conditions and some kinds of plant stands on the Coastal Plain of Maryland.*

ditions on the Coastal Plain in Maryland. Landward from the shore are found a succession of different environments, each with a distinctive flora. Beachgrass grows on dry dunes along the beaches. Back of these are salt marshes with salt-tolerant grasses, species of *Spartina* in pure stands in the most salty ground, and *Spartina* mixed with salt grass where the salt content is less. These grade into less brackish marshes with salt grass and rush, and then into fresh-water marshes with cattail. Farther inland, along streams, are fresh-water marshes and swamps, the latter with bald cypress and white cedar. On the dry uplands, where the ground is loam, the forests are coniferous or deciduous. The coniferous forests consist of loblolly pine mixed with sweet gum, white oak, Spanish oak, and red maple. The deciduous forests are mockernut, pignut, and bitternut hickory with black oak and Spanish oak. Sandy uplands support loblolly and pitch pine.

Agricultural production on the Coastal Plain, other than forest crops, also is zoned from north to south as follows:

1. The Embayed Section produces garden crops, dairy and poultry products for supplying the large northeastern cities.
2. The south end of the Embayed Section produces peanuts and tobacco. Here and southward to South Carolina is the principal area of tobacco production.
3. Cotton, corn, peanuts, and oats are produced in the southern part of the Atlantic Coastal Plain westward across the Mississippi River Alluvial Plain to Texas.
4. Along the coast of Louisiana and Texas, rice and sugar cane are grown.
5. In Florida, and along the Rio Grande in Texas, citrus fruits and vegetables are the chief crops.

These crops are produced from less than a third of the land. Almost two-thirds of the Coastal Plain is in forest or wooded pasture, which is a higher ratio of the land than was asked for by William Penn, who stated in his Charter of Rights (1681): "Leave one acre of trees for every five acres cleared." The forests provide not only timber and other wood products but watershed protection and parklands for recreation.

Hogs are raised in all parts of the Coastal Plain, but the number is small compared to the number raised in the corn belt in the Central Lowland. The Coastal Plain in Texas, however, is one of the country's major cattle-raising areas.

Surficial Deposits and Soils

Surficial deposits on the Coastal Plain include alluvium in the floodplains of the rivers, especially along the Mississippi River; loessial deposits east of the Mississippi River valley; sand and gravel deposits on uplands; and beach sand, dune sand, peat, muck, and marsh deposits along the coasts. The coastal deposits are mostly Recent in age and they are not deeply weathered. Soils on these deposits are weakly developed. The alluvium includes older Pleistocene deposits, but much of this land is subject to flooding and the upper layers of these deposits are mostly Recent. These deposits are highly productive despite the weak soil development. In the Mississippi Valley well-drained areas produce cotton and corn; poorly drained areas are used for pasture or left in forest.

Recent deposits of peat and muck are extensive along the Atlantic seaboard from Maryland south to Florida. The peat may be woody and derived from the stumps and logs of the cypress-tupelo-gum swamps, or it may be fibrous and derived chiefly from grasses and sedges. The coastal marshes contain fibrous peat deposits, and these grade from fresh-water inland to salt-water near the coast (Fig. 10.15). Depending on the geologic history of the location, either the woody or the fibrous peat may contain muds washed in with the organic mat-

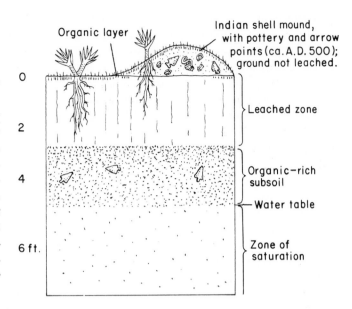

Figure 10.16 *Diagrammatic section of Ground Water Podzol, in Florida. Indian shell mounds consisting of unleached debris, and containing pottery and arrow points, overlie the Ground Water Podzols. These mounds range in age from historic time back to about A.D. 500. The Ground Water Podzols predate the mounds, but seem younger than some earlier, prepottery archeological remains that occur in the subsoil down to the water table.*

ter. The lands are used chiefly for timber production and for wildlife refuges. The largest areas are at the Everglades in Florida, the Okefenokee Swamp in southern Georgia, and the Dismal Swamp in Virginia and North Carolina.

Next older of the Coastal Plain soils is a group known as Ground Water Podzols, developed on sandy Quaternary formations or on older formations that lie at low elevations and are poorly drained (Figs. 10.16, 10.17,B). The soils have a thin, ashy, organic-rich surface layer over a light-gray, leached layer about 2½ feet thick. Below this is 6 to 20 inches of organic-rich and iron-rich hardpan, generally mottled brown and yellow, but dark brown in some soils. Below the hardpan is the water table. The soils are not very productive and most are left in pasture or in forest. Many or most of the Ground Water Podzols date from earliest Recent or late Pleistocene time. They are more than 2,000 years old, for they antedate archeological remains of that age. (Figs. 10.16, 10.17,B).

On most of the Coastal Plain the surficial deposits or older formations are deeply weathered. This weathering is older than the last

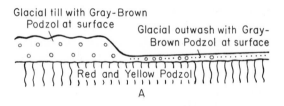

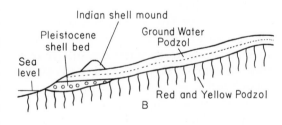

Figure 10.17 *Diagrammatic sections illustrating stratigraphic ages of soils on the Coastal Plain. (A) In the north, the Red and Yellow Podzols are overlain by glacial till and glacial outwash of the Wisconsin stage of glaciation; Gray-Brown Podzols are developed on the glacial deposits. (B) Southward to Florida the Red and Yellow Podzols are overlain by Pleistocene shell beds that are 15 to 25 feet above present sea level; Ground Water Podzols are developed on the shell bed.*

(Wisconsin stage) glaciation, because northward the weathered layers, called *residuum* or *saprolite,* extend under and are overlapped by the terminal moraines and outwash of that ice sheet (Fig. 10.17,A). Moreover, along the coast the residuum extends under and is overlapped by elevated shell beds of Pleistocene age (Fig. 10.17,B). The soils developed on the residuum are classed as Red and Yellow Podzols.

The Red and Yellow Podzols and underlying residuum are deeply and strongly leached, acidic, and low in organic matter and mineral plant nutrients. The near-surface layers, to a depth of 1 to 3 feet, are light in color; the deeper layers are clayey and mottled red and yellow. These soils, related to the laterites, are sometimes referred to as latosols. Leaching has removed alkalis, alkali earths, and silica, leaving behind an excess of iron and alumina. Most of the Red and Yellow Podzols on the Coastal Plain have developed on the Cretaceous and Tertiary formations, but some are developed on the loess deposits east of the Mississippi River Alluvial Plain (Fig. 6.1).

Near the Mississippi River this loess is 100 to 200 feet thick, but it thins eastward. The loessial soils are fine grained throughout and are leached to a depth of 10 to 20 feet. Below that depth, however, they are still limy in some locations. The southern part of this loessial belt is used mostly for raising cotton; the northern part, for corn.

Another kind of soil, known as Rendzina Soil (Table 6.1), has developed on chalk or marl under native grasses. The soils are black because, in the presence of so much lime, humic colloids coagulate and the organic matter is retained. The parent material still dominates the soil profile (Fig. 8.10,B). The soils sometimes are referred to as immature, but may be as old as the neighboring Red and Yellow Podzols. They are highly productive of corn, cotton, and alfalfa.

In the Embayed Section of the Coastal Plain some of the soils are Gray-Brown Podzols. Related soils on very sandy ground in southeastern New Jersey and on Long Island support scrubby oak and pine. Cranberries are cultivated to some extent in boggy areas, but agriculturally these soils are among the poorest in the United States.

Long Island is covered with glacial till and glacial outwash of Wisconsin age, and the soils on them are younger than the Red and Yellow Podzols farther south. The soils closely reflect the texture and composition of the parent materials, and are of four kinds: (1) gravelly, or even bouldery, soils on the terminal moraines and till-covered area to the north; (2) coarse sandy loam on the outwash plain just south of the moraines; (3) fine sandy loam farther south on the outwash plain; and (4) clayey loam on the transition zone between the outwash plains and the salt marshes. Native vegetation of the outwash plain is pitch pine and scrub oak.

At the opposite end of the Coastal Plain, in southern Texas, the soils are Pedocals, for that region is semiarid.

Soil erosion on the Coastal Plain is most serious on the east side of the Mississippi River; deep ravines have been cut into the fine-grained and much-farmed loessial soils. The Red and Yellow Podzols and residuum are moderately subject to erosion. These, too, are productive, fine-grained soils, but they are clayey, and the general relief is less than in the loessial belt. Elsewhere on the Coastal Plain erosion is slight, because the lands are low lying. Along the valleys the lands are subject to flooding and deposition of muds on the soils.

Water Resources

Water supplies along the Atlantic seaboard are adequate for present demand and are believed to be adequate for the demand expected about 1980, but by the end of the century the water supplies for the West Gulf Coastal Plain may be inadequate (Fig. 9.17). It seems likely, however, that by that time satisfactory methods will have been discovered for desalting sea water, and the low altitudes on the Coastal Plain would favor use of such a source.

In the Embayed Section of the Coastal Plain, not much surface water is available for use because brackish water extends up the rivers to the Fall Line. The Fall Line cities are supplied chiefly from surface-water sources on the Piedmont Province or other parts of the Appalachian Highlands. East of the Fall Line, however, much use is made of groundwater, and most municipal water systems are supplied by wells. Many of the Coastal Plain formations are important aquifers and yield large supplies of water of good quality, but at depths of about 1,000 feet in some areas the fresh water changes to salt water, and it is necessary to avoid overpumping to avoid mixing the waters. Heavy drafts on the groundwater supply, particularly on Long Island, have caused the fresh-water–salt-water interface to rise and thereby introduced salt water into the aquifers.

Despite the fact that the municipal water supplies in the Embayed Section are largely underground, the waters are soft by comparison with most other parts of the country. The waters average less than 100 ppm of dissolved solids (Fig. 10.18). At some locations, such as Cambridge, Maryland, the content of dissolved solids is high, yet the waters are soft because they contain sodium rather than calcium or magnesium salts.

Along the inner edge of the Coastal Plain the surface waters contain carbonate and bicarbonate, as do those of the Piedmont and other bordering provinces. Toward the coast the waters change to sulfate-chloride types. Along the West Gulf Coastal Plain and parts of the Georgia and South Carolina coasts the surface waters are soft; elsewhere the surface waters contain calcium and magnesium and are hard.

In Texas, as in the Embayed Section, the content of dissolved solids in the surface water is about the same as in the groundwater, but from the East Gulf Coastal Plain northward

to the Embayed Section, the content of dissolved solids is higher in the groundwater than in the surface water—in some places by a factor of 3 to 10.

On the Florida limestone peninsula, the raw waters are hard, averaging perhaps 150 to 200 ppm of $CaCO_3$ equivalent (p. 80), but the waters are treated, and the delivered water is considerably softened. In some parts of Texas —Houston, for example—the water contains sodium, and the hardness is only moderate, even though the content of dissolved solids is considerable. Some water wells in Houston are a half mile deep, and becoming saltier.

A remarkable series of large springs that issue from the Balcones fault zone along the west edge of the West Gulf Coastal Plain (Fig. 10.19) supply much of the water for the cities there, notably San Antonio. The springs are large enough to feed some of the rivers. The water flows from beds of limestone and is hard.

Considerable hydroelectric power is produced at the Fall Line and at falls farther inland, but the Coastal Plain has very little power potential because of the low stream gradients. The rise and fall of tides, however, have been used on estuaries to turn the water wheels of grinding mills.

Stream pollution is a problem on the Coastal Plain, as it is in so much of the country. Disposal of sewage, detergents, and industrial wastes plague most American communities. In recent years, vast numbers of fish in the lower Mississippi River have been killed by industrial wastes and by pesticides washed into the water from the farmed lands upstream. The tragedy is that none of this is necessary.

Mineral Resources

The mineral industry in the United States was started on the Coastal Plain in 1608 when the Jamestown settlers attempted to manufacture glass, probably using sand from the Mio-

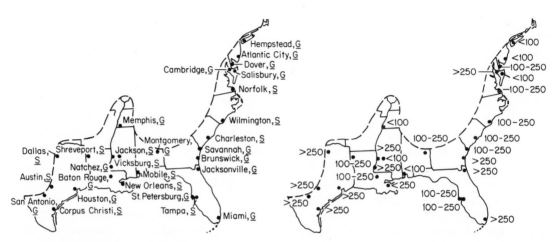

A. Municipalities and principal sources
of supply (S, surface water; G, groundwater).

B. Total dissolved solids in the principal
source.

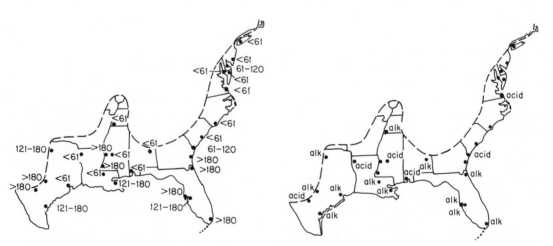

C. Hardness of the untreated water.

D. Acid and alkaline sources.

Figure 10.18   Examples of different kinds of water in municipal systems on the
Coastal Plain. Total dissolved solids are generally high in waters on the Peninsular Arch and West Gulf Coastal Plain. Because of the limestone source rocks
on the Peninsular Arch and inner edge of the West Gulf Coastal Plain, waters
in those areas are hard, and, except at San Antonio, they are alkaline. Water supplies along the Atlantic seaboard are generally soft.

cene formations which crop out upstream from the settlement. In 1619 an iron foundry was established on the James River below Richmond. In 1674 iron ore was produced at Shrewsbury, New Jersey. On the Coastal Plain, iron has been deposited in bogs, and also occurs as nodules, called concretions, in the Coastal Plain formations. Such deposits were widely developed by the colonists throughout the Embayed Section.

Today the most important mineral resource on the Coastal Plain is the petroleum along the Gulf Coast, especially in Texas and Louisiana. There are two belts of quite different kinds of oil fields, one along the coast and extending offshore, and the other inland.

The oil fields along the coast are small but numerous and highly productive. Production has come from domes, many of which have been formed by salt plugs (Fig. 10.13). The inland oil fields are few in number but large; the East Texas field one of the world's large oil fields, comprises more than 25,000 wells. At this field, a sandstone (Woodbine Sandstone) thins out against the flank of the Sabine uplift (Fig. 10.12) and is overlapped by a chalk (Austin Chalk) which extends up the flank unconformably onto the older formations. Oil has been trapped in the thinned edges of the sandstone (Fig. 10.20).

Increasingly, natural gas is being produced at the oil fields. Oil and gas together have accounted for about 95 percent of the half billion dollars worth of minerals annually produced from the Coastal Plain. Practically all the remaining 5 percent is from nonmetals.

The salt domes and formations associated with them in the West Gulf Coastal Plain supply about 75 percent of the nation's sulfur. Common salt is produced at the salt domes, for both industrial and table use. Moreover, chemical industries have been favored by the occurrence together of sulfur and salt along with nearby sources of oil and gas for hydrocarbon products and fuel.

About 70 percent of the nation's phosphate

is produced in Florida. The deposits occur in the weathered upper part of a phosphatic Pliocene formation. This weathered layer, an ancient phosphatic soil related to the Red and Yellow Podzols (Fig. 10.23,B), is a near-surface blanket deposit that can be mined by open-pit methods.

Another major resource of the Coastal Plain is the clay deposits, which include bleaching clay and aluminous, or bauxitic, clay. Bleaching clay, mostly the clay mineral montmorillonite, is known as fuller's earth because it was originally used to remove grease from woolen cloth in a process known as fulling; today, a major use of bleaching clays is for decolorizing mineral oils.

The clay deposits are widespread in formations of the Gulf Coast sections, but prin-

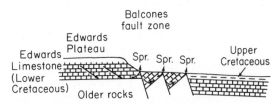

Figure 10.19 *Diagram illustrating springs at the Balcones fault zone. On the Edwards Plateau water seeps into the limestone and emerges in springs at the faults.*

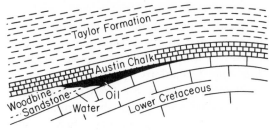

Figure 10.20 *Diagrammatic section through the East Texas oil field, showing the thinned edge of the productive formation (Woodbine Sandstone) where it is overlapped by nonproductive ones (Austin Chalk and Taylor Formation). Oil is trapped in the sandstone by the impermeability of the chalk. (After Internat. Geol. Cong.)*

cipal production has been from the Hawthorne Formation in Florida and Georgia, from Eocene formations at the head of the Mississippi River Alluvial Plain in Illinois, and from Texas. These areas have supplied about 80 percent of the United States total.

Ceramic clays are of many kinds, such as kaolin (china clay), refractory clay, and pottery and brick clay. Kaolin from the Tuscaloosa Formation in South Carolina and Georgia has been used for making firebrick and for filler in rubber; this formation was formerly a major source of the clay required for manufacturing coated papers. These two states have accounted for about 90 percent of the United States production of kaolin. Pottery or brick clays are omnipresent in the Coastal Plain formations and have been widely produced. Bauxite and bauxitic clays that might be a source of alumina are abundant in Arkansas, which has supplied 97 percent of the bauxite produced in the United States.

Few Coastal Plain formations are well enough cemented to serve as building stone, but a gray sandstone quarried from a Cretaceous formation at Aquia, Virginia, was used in 1795 in constructing the White House (painted white) and the central part of the Capitol in Washington, D.C. Among the buildings in Washington, these two are unique for their building stone as well as in other, more familiar ways.

About 5 percent of the Portland cement manufactured in the United States has been produced from Upper Cretaceous chalk or limestone formations in Texas.

In many parts of the Coastal Plain roads are metalled with oyster shells, quarried in large part from prehistoric Indian shell mounds. Sand is plentiful on the Coastal Plain, but gravel is less abundant, and stone for riprap to control beach erosion must be imported. Other potentially important deposits include the heavy sands (placer deposits) containing monazite, a phosphate of the rare earths containing cerium and thorium. These occur as beach deposits along the Atlantic Coast south of Cape Hatteras; deposits in Florida have yielded concentrates of titanium.

The Shore and Continental Shelf

Differences in the kinds of shoreline along the Coastal Plain depend chiefly on whether there has been recent submergence or emergence. The Embayed Section and the Sea Island Downwarp evidently are being submerged; the Mississippi Delta is being extended seaward by deposition. The Cape Fear Arch may be emergent. Sea level records for numerous stations along the Atlantic and Gulf coasts indicate an average rise of about 6 inches during the last half century. Sea-level measurements are difficult to make, partly because exact low tide and exact high tide levels are necessarily arbitrary, and partly because tidal fluctuations vary greatly along the coasts. The tidal range—the difference between high and low tide—is only a foot or two in parts of Florida but more than 20 feet in parts of New England.

The submergence is attributed chiefly to a world-wide rise in sea level resulting from the melting of ice caps, but there may also be some crustal movement; and in some places, such as the Mississippi River delta, land may be settling due to compaction of the deposits. Shore features resulting from submergence include the drowned valleys, sea cliffs at truncated headlands, barrier beaches, spits, and the small sandy islands along the Georgia and South Carolina coasts. Sandy Hook (Fig. 10.21) is an example of a shore feature that has developed as a result of a recent rise in sea level. The spit has been built by shore currents that have cut off headlands and transported sediments northward.

But there are also features of emergence along the shores of the Coastal Plain, such as shell beds and beach bars 15 to 25 feet above sea level (Fig. 10.17,B). These date from Pleistocene time, and record stages—probably interglacial stages—during which sea level was that much higher than it is today. The Cape Fear Arch may be rising.

The waves and currents that build a beach are illustrated in Figure 10.22. The maximum height reached by the uprush of water on a beach is usually 2 or 3 times the height of the waves. The slope of a beach is controlled partly by the coarseness of the sediment; fine sand may slope 3 degrees or less, whereas pebbles may slope as much as 15 to 20 degrees. As ocean waves enter shallow water, both their velocity and wavelength decrease, but their height increases. They drag bottom and begin to break when the depth is half the wavelength. As in streams, sediment is moved by rolling along the bottom, by saltation, and by suspension.

Where waves break at an angle to the shore, as is usual, there is a longshore component. The waves transport sediment onshore; the longshore currents transport sediment along the shore; rip currents transport sediment offshore. These processes are reflected in the distribution of spits in the Embayed Section, for the spits are at the south sides of the mouths of the bays—at Sandy Hook, Cape Henlopen, and Cape Henry. Shoreline differences reflecting different exposure to the waves and different composition of materials being eroded are illustrated by contrasts between the Connecticut coast and the north and south sides of Long Island (Fig. 10.23).

The sediments on beaches and the shelf illustrate how the sources of sediments can be identified by studying the proportions of different minerals in the deposits. Different streams transport different sediments. All the streams transport sediments composed chiefly of quartz sand and clay, but the other minerals, though minor in amount, account for the differences. Beaches built by sands brought by the rivers draining from the Piedmont Province contain minerals characteristic of

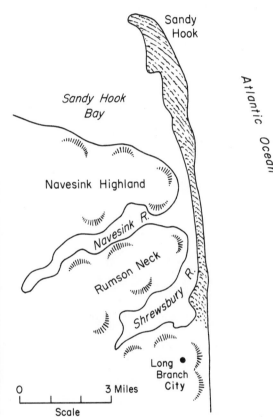

Figure 10.21 *Topography at Sandy Hook, New Jersey. Sediments eroded by longshore currents from cliffs along the shore at Long Branch City have been transported northward and deposited to form the bar and cape. Headlands at Rumson Neck and Navesink Highlands also were eroded as Sandy Hook was built. The hook curves into the bay because it is exposed to the westward sweep of wind and waves from the ocean. Shrewsbury and Navesink rivers are drowned valleys.*

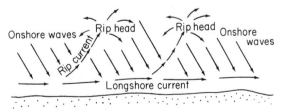

Figure 10.22 *Plan of onshore, longshore, and rip currents along a beach.*

metamorphic rocks. Beaches along the Texas coast are built of sands brought by rivers draining sedimentary rocks. Sands on Florida beaches also are from sedimentary rocks, but many contain a high percentage of siliceous sponge spicules as well as much carbonate. Beaches on Long Island contain sands derived from glacial deposits brought from New England.

The Continental Shelf and Coastal Plain together maintain a fairly constant width of about 200 miles from Georgia north to Cape Cod. As the Coastal Plain narrows northward from Cape Hatteras, the Continental Shelf widens. In Cretaceous time the Coastal Plain was submerged and was part of the shelf (Fig.

10.24). In Eocene time, most of the Coastal Plain still was submerged, but the Cape Fear Arch had started forming and that area was coastal plain. During Miocene time the Coastal Plain was about half its present width. Even as late as Pleistocene time, parts of the Coastal Plain were still submerged. The present shoreline has developed since the last glacial period. In a sense, Florida is our youngest state, for it did not emerge until very late Tertiary time.

We still cannot be sure about the origin of the Continental Shelf and of the steep break at its outer edge, which has been described as the "world's greatest slope." The shelf probably is some kind of structural unit separated

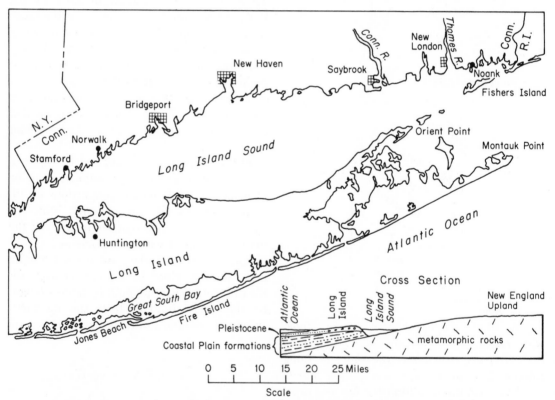

Figure 10.23 *Contrasts in shorelines reflecting differences in process and struc-ture. The south side of Long Island, mostly nonbouldery glacial outwash and exposed to the ocean, has long beach bars and straight, eroded headlands. The north side, composed of bouldery glacial drift and protected from ocean waves, is irregular. The Connecticut coast is rocky with irregular headlands, irregular inlets, and short bars, spits, and narrow beaches.*

Cretaceous

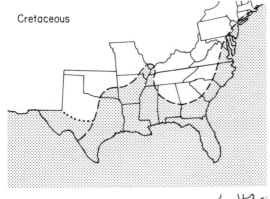

Eocene

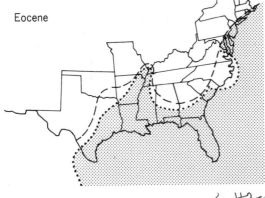

Miocene

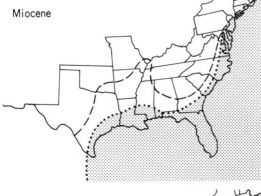

Pleistocene

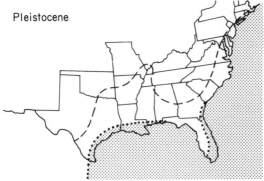

from the abyss and hinged to it by a belt of faulting or folding. But the surface and the steep slope at the edge have been modified by sedimentation and erosion, including, at least in the shallow parts, alternate submergence and emergence.

Marine Environments; Fisheries

Environments in the sea reflect differences in the water, the sea bottom, and the marine climate. The water varies in depth, temperature, turbulence, salinity, and biological content; bottoms vary depending on the texture of the bottom sediments, rockiness, and topography; and marine climates vary with latitude, exposure, depth, and currents. Figure 10.25,A, illustrates some differences in littoral environments.

The principal environments reflecting differences in depth are illustrated in Figure 10.25,B. Differences in depth are accompanied by differences in temperature and illumination. Temperatures in the abyssal zone are as low as 40°F. Depths greater than about 300 feet have little or no illumination. Turbulence is an important environmental factor in the shallow-water zones, and perhaps along the continental rise, where there is evidence of submarine sliding and submarine currents capable of transporting sediment. Variations in salinity are greatest in the inner neritic and intertidal, or littoral, zone, where there is complete gradation from sea water (15,000 ppm to about 35,000 ppm of salts), through brackish water (500 to 15,000 ppm), to fresh water (less than about 500 ppm). In Chesapeake Bay, for example, the salinity decreases from 30,000 ppm at the mouth of the bay to

Figure 10.24 *Extent of the Coastal Plain during the Cretaceous, Eocene, Miocene, and Pleistocene. Submerged areas stippled. Compare Figures 2.1 and 10.2.*

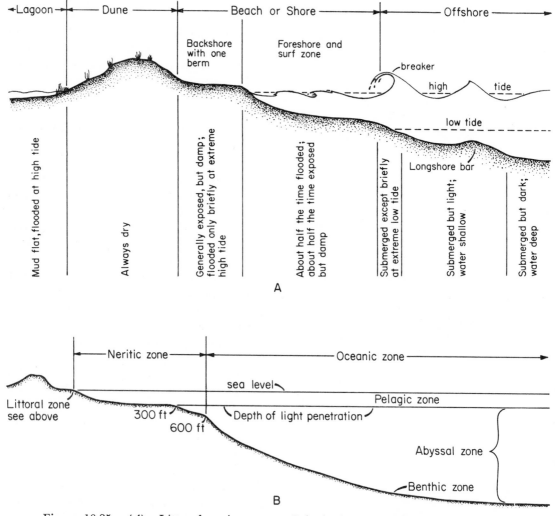

Figure 10.25 *(A) Littoral environments. Principal controlling factors are: frequency and depth of submergence, salinity of the water, exposure to surf, and rockiness, sandiness, or muddiness of the beach. (B) Marine environments vary chiefly according to depth of water and depth of light penetration.*

15,000 ppm half way up the bay, and to 5,000 ppm at Baltimore near the head of the bay. In lagoons, however, where there is considerable evaporation without much inflow of fresh water, salinities may exceed the salinity of sea water. An example is Laguna Madre, along the south coast of Texas, where salinites are much greater than the salinity of sea water.

The biota faithfully reflects these differences in environment. Some animals live at-

tached to the bottom, like the oyster. Others are bottom feeders but move about, like the crab and some fish—for example, cod and haddock. Still other animals float on the surface, such as the various forms of *plankton,* exemplified along the Atlantic Coast by the unwelcome sea nettles. Many or most of the fish, like birds, are migratory, and each species has its own habits. Some, like the striped bass, winter off the southern coast and migrate northward for the summer. The summer flounder spends its summer near shore but migrates to deeper water for the winter. Alewife and shad migrate to fresh water to spawn; the eel migrates to the deep warm water.

There are two patterns of zoning of marine life along and near coasts, one arranged according to latitude and reflecting differences in temperature of the water, and the other arranged from land to sea and reflecting differences in such factors as salinity, frequency of wetting, and depth of water (compare Figs. 10.25 and 10.26).

Fish, including shellfish, are one of America's chief resources, and fishing was the earliest industry. Even before the first settlements had been established, French Portuguese, Spanish, and English fishing boats crossed the Atlantic and took cod from the banks off Newfoundland. About half our present production of commercial fisheries is from the Atlantic and Gulf coasts, and about half is from the Pacific Coast including Alaska. About a third of the production is canned, a third is sold fresh or frozen, and a third is used for fish meal and oils.

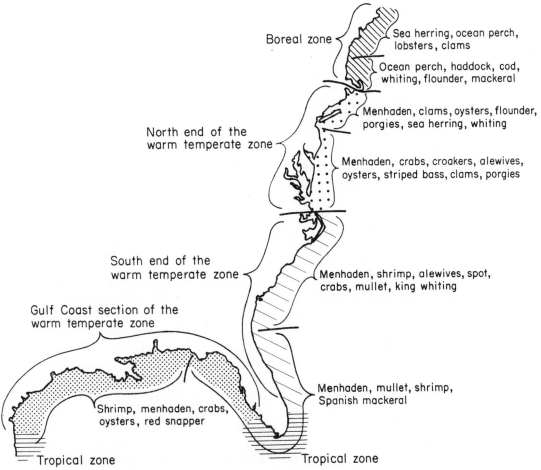

Boreal zone — Sea herring, ocean perch, lobsters, clams

Ocean perch, haddock, cod, whiting, flounder, mackerel

Menhaden, clams, oysters, flounder, porgies, sea herring, whiting

North end of the warm temperate zone

Menhaden, crabs, croakers, alewives, oysters, striped bass, clams, porgies

South end of the warm temperate zone

Menhaden, shrimp, alewives, spot, crabs, mullet, king whiting

Gulf Coast section of the warm temperate zone

Menhaden, mullet, shrimp, Spanish mackerel

Shrimp, menhaden, crabs, oysters, red snapper

Tropical zone   Tropical zone

Figure 10.26 *Latitudinal zoning of fish along the Atlantic and Gulf coasts, as illustrated by the production of some commercial fish. For each stretch of coast, the fish are listed in the order of their weight of commercial production. (Compiled from U.S. Dept. of Commerce statistics.)*

11

Appalachian Highlands

The Appalachian Highlands, the mountainous part of the eastern United States, include the Piedmont, Blue Ridge, Valley and Ridge, Appalachian Plateaus, Adirondack, and New England provinces, and the St. Lawrence Lowland (Fig. 11.1). This physiographic division covers an area about equal to that of the Coastal Plain and separates the plain of the eastern seaboard from the low-lying valleys of the Ohio and Mississippi rivers.

In the central part of the Appalachian Highlands, fold mountains form the Valley and Ridge Province. In the Piedmont Province, which lies to the east, the rock structures are also those of fold mountains, but much faulted. The formations have been truncated, however, and are so reduced in height that the landforms are not mountainous except in parts of New England and in a narrow strip formed by the Blue Ridge Province. West of the fold mountains are the Appalachian Plateaus. Here the rock formations are nearly horizontal, a typical plateau structure, but the formations are so elevated and dissected that the landforms are in large part mountainous. Thus, the Appalachian Plateaus are mountainous with a plateau structure, whereas the Piedmont Province is a low plateau with the kind of structures that generally produce mountains. The Adirondack Province consists of a mountainous structural dome with Precambrian rocks at the core.

The differences between the provinces of the Appalachian Highlands were fully recognized in early American atlases. One, the Carey and Lea Atlas, 1823, distinguished four belts of country along the seaboard. "The first, extending from the sea-coast to the termination of tide water . . . is low and flat . . . The next division extends from the head of tide water to the Blue Ridge . . . The third division is the valley between the Blue Ridge and . . . Allegheny mountains . . . The fourth . . . extends from the Allegheny mountains to the Ohio River and is wild and broken. . . ."

During the Paleozoic Era the site of the Appalachian Highlands was a geosyncline occupied by a mediterranean sea in which sediments accumulated to a thickness of about 40,000 feet. The sea was never that deep: the trough sank gradually during the Paleozoic, and the eight miles of sinking and comparable rise of the mountains to the east, from which the sediments were derived, could have been accomplished by earth movements averaging only a foot in 10,000 years. Some of the earth movements that occurred repeatedly during the Paleozoic are recorded by unconformities between formations, quite like those that separate some of the Coastal Plain formations and record the rise of the Cape Fear Arch (p. 145). The hinge line between the crustal area being uplifted and the area that was sinking seems to have shifted gradually westward. In early

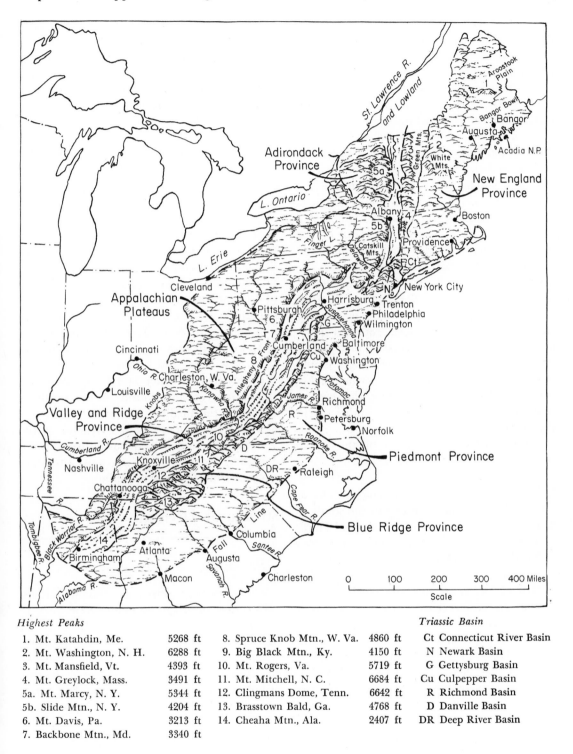

Figure 11.1 *Physiographic map of the Appalachian Highlands.*

Highest Peaks				Triassic Basin
1. Mt. Katahdin, Me.	5268 ft	8. Spruce Knob Mtn., W. Va.	4860 ft	Ct Connecticut River Basin
2. Mt. Washington, N. H.	6288 ft	9. Big Black Mtn., Ky.	4150 ft	N Newark Basin
3. Mt. Mansfield, Vt.	4393 ft	10. Mt. Rogers, Va.	5719 ft	G Gettysburg Basin
4. Mt. Greylock, Mass.	3491 ft	11. Mt. Mitchell, N. C.	6684 ft	Cu Culpepper Basin
5a. Mt. Marcy, N. Y.	5344 ft	12. Clingmans Dome, Tenn.	6642 ft	R Richmond Basin
5b. Slide Mtn., N. Y.	4204 ft	13. Brasstown Bald, Ga.	4768 ft	D Danville Basin
6. Mt. Davis, Pa.	3213 ft	14. Cheaha Mtn., Ala.	2407 ft	DR Deep River Basin
7. Backbone Mtn., Md.	3340 ft			

Paleozoic time the Piedmont Province was part of the geosyncline, but by late Paleozoic time it became part of the mountain area supplying sediments westward.

At the end of Paleozoic time, the earth movements reversed, and the sedimentary formations in the geosyncline were folded and uplifted. During the ensuing 200 million years, the uplifted formations have been subject to erosion, and the Appalachian Mountains have not been submerged again beneath the sea. Erosion of the mountains supplied the sediments that make up the Coastal Plain formations, which have buried the roots of the Paleozoic mountains that had supplied sediments to the Appalachian geosyncline.

Compared to the Rocky Mountains, the Appalachians are not high. They are more humid, however, and as a consequence the weathering and erosion have produced rounded landforms. The Appalachians lack the sharply angular profiles so common in the western mountains. Fifteen of the highest peaks in the Appalachian Highlands, including the highest peaks in 14 of the states, are indicated in Figure 11.1.

Other outstanding features of the Appalachian Highlands are listed below.

1. The climate is humid, with cold winters in the north and mild winters in the south.
2. Forests consist mostly of the Central Hardwood Forest but grade northward into Northeastern Hardwood and Spruce-Fir forests.
3. Glacial features formed during the Pleistocene glaciation characterize the northern part of the highlands.
4. Surficial deposits and soils are of four principal kinds: glacial drift in the north, with young (late Pleistocene and Recent) podzolic soils; ancient and deep residual soils in the Piedmont Province and in some of the valleys of the Valley and Ridge Province; alluvium and alluvial terraces on floodplains; colluvium with weakly developed soils in the mountains.

5. Rivers are numerous and large, and lakes abound in the glaciated areas; these provide water supplies considered adequate to meet anticipated increases in demand during the next quarter century. These lakes and rivers provided the basis for the country's first transportation boom—the development of shipping by canal—and provided the water power that was the basis for early industry and is the source of much of today's hydroelectric power.
6. Minerals are a major resource of the highlands, especially the mineral fuels. The abundance of coal, oil, and gas led to intensive industrialization. Other important resources are limestone for cement, building stone, sand for glass-making, salt, mica, copper, and zinc.
7. Other basic resources include fish and dairy produce in New England, potatoes in Maine, wine-growing in New York, dairies in New York and Pennsylvania, fruit orchards in the Valley and Ridge Province, and tobacco and cotton in the southern part of the Piedmont Province.
8. The Appalachian Trail, a symbol of the important recreational possibilities of this region, extends along various mountain crests from Georgia to Maine.

Structural Divisions

Piedmont Province

The Piedmont Province extends almost 1,000 miles from southernmost New York to Alabama and has a maximum width of about 125 miles. To the south, where the province is widest, altitudes range from about 500 feet at the Fall Line to about 1,000 feet at the foot of the mountains to the west. Like the Coastal Plain, the Piedmont Province slopes northward and is between 100 and 500 feet in altitude in Pennsylvania and New Jersey.

The rocks are mostly metamorphic with complex structures that, with local exceptions noted later, are truncated by the plateau surface. The landforms therefore only locally reflect the subsurface structures. The boundary between the Piedmont Province and the Coastal Plain is at the Fall Line, where the metamorphic rocks of Paleozoic age extend under the Cretaceous formations. By definition the physiographic boundary is at the contact between the Cretaceous and the metamorphic rocks (Fig. 11.2).

The boundary between the Piedmont and the more mountainous province to the west is almost as sharp. To the south, where the Piedmont Province adjoins the Valley and Ridge Province, the boundary follows an overthrust fault (Cartersville fault), along which the metamorphic rocks have been thrust westward onto folded Paleozoic rocks (Fig. 11.3). The boundary between the Piedmont Province and the mountainous Blue Ridge Province is approximately where the metamorphic

rocks of the Piedmont end against upthrust Precambrian formations, most of which are highly metamorphosed but, in places, very little altered, especially toward the north.

Most of the rocks in the Piedmont Province are gneiss and schist, with some marble and quartzite, and were derived by metamorphism of older sedimentary and volcanic rocks. There are many mineralogical varieties of these rocks; altogether they cover about half the province. In Pennsylvania and Maryland the belts of marble form valleys and are the sites of reservoirs; the gneiss, schist, quartzite, and granite form uplands.

Some less intensively metamorphosed rocks, including considerable slate, occur along the eastern part of the province from southern Virginia to Georgia. This area, called the Carolina slate belt, makes up about 20 percent of the province (Fig. 11.3). The rocks in the slate belt are somewhat less resistant to erosion

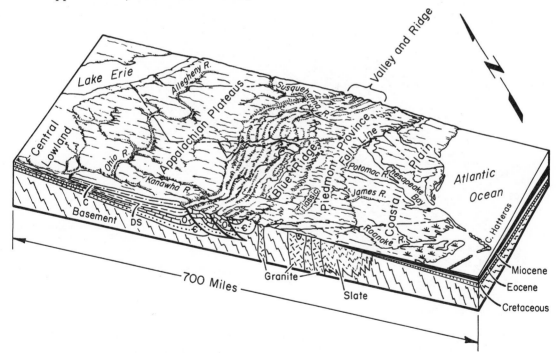

Figure 11.2 *Structural framework of the Appalachian Plateaus, Valley and Ridge, Blue Ridge, and Piedmont Provinces.* €, *Cambrian;* O, *Ordovician;* DS, *Devonian, Silurian;* C, *Carboniferous (Mississippian, Pennsylvanian, and Permian).*

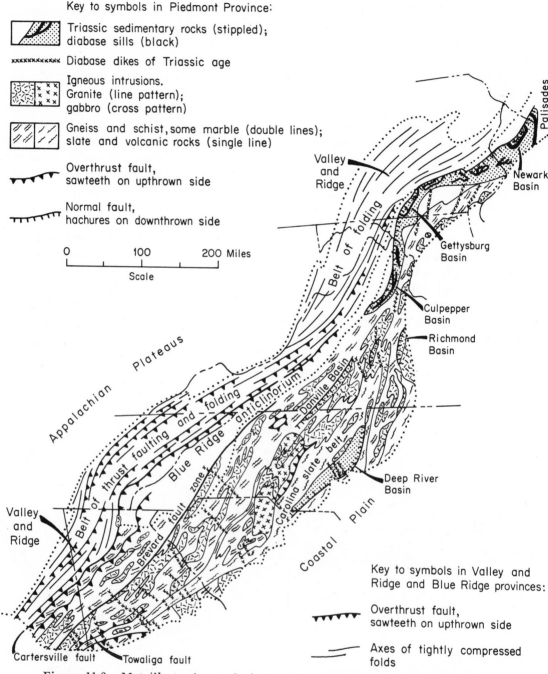

Key to symbols in Piedmont Province:

Triassic sedimentary rocks (stippled); diabase sills (black)

Diabase dikes of Triassic age

Igneous intrusions. Granite (line pattern); gabbro (cross pattern)

Gneiss and schist, some marble (double lines); slate and volcanic rocks (single line)

Overthrust fault, sawteeth on upthrown side

Normal fault, hachures on downthrown side

0   100   200 Miles
Scale

Key to symbols in Valley and Ridge and Blue Ridge provinces:

Overthrust fault, sawteeth on upthrown side

Axes of tightly compressed folds

Figure 11.3 *Map illustrating geologic structure of the Piedmont, Blue Ridge, and Valley and Ridge provinces. Distribution of the principal rock types is indicated in the Piedmont Province. The rocks in the Blue Ridge upthrust, shown without pattern, are mostly Precambrian metamorphic rocks. The rocks in the Valley and Ridge Province are limestone, sandstone, and shale of Paleozoic age. (Generalized from Tectonic Map of U.S. by U.S.G.S. and A.A.P.G.)*

than are the neighboring formations, and they form slightly lower ground with wider valleys. Consequently, the slate belt was favored for reservoir sites on the Saluda River above Columbia, South Carolina, and on the Savannah River above Augusta, Georgia.

Another 20 percent of the Piedmont Province is granite, or the metamorphic equivalent, granite gneiss. The granites tend to form uplands, and some form striking, isolated, domical hills (Fig. 11.4).

Other intrusions in this Province consist of gabbro and related rocks with abundant dark minerals. Some of these, especially in Pennsylvania and Maryland, are altered to serpentine, a hydrous magnesium silicate that develops a characteristic and poor soil supporting a distinctive, dwarfed vegetation (Fig. 8.10,A).

In addition to the igneous and metamorphic

Figure 11.4 *Stone Mountain, Georgia, near Atlanta, is a domical hill of granite about 1½ miles in diameter and 650 feet high.*

rocks, about 5 percent of the Piedmont Province consists of unmetamorphosed rocks of Triassic age that have been downfaulted into the older metamorphic and igneous formations (Fig. 11.5). The Triassic formations are mostly red beds of sandstone, conglomerate,

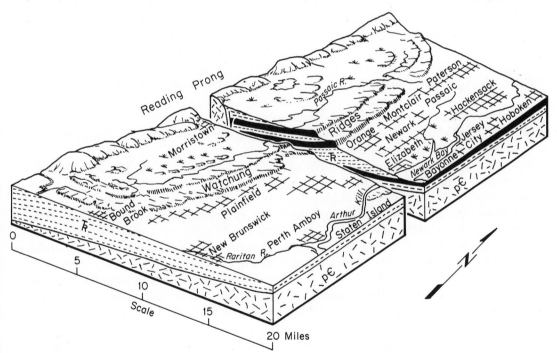

Figure 11.5 *Part of the Newark Basin, showing the topographic expression of the Watchung Ridges, which are sills of diabase (black) that intrude the Triassic (Tr) red beds of sandstone, shale, and conglomerate that dip westward into a structural basin centering under Morristown. The Triassic formations have been downfaulted against the metamorphic rocks of the Reading Prong; other metamorphic rocks underlie the Triassic formations.*

and silt, but include dikes and sills of diabase. The principal Triassic basins are (see also Fig. 11.3):

1. The Newark Basin (Fig. 11.5), which extends from the Hudson River southwest to the Schuylkill River;
2. The Gettysburg Basin, which extends from the Schuylkill River to Maryland;
3. The Culpepper Basin, which extends from the Potomac River south to Culpepper, Virginia;
4. The Richmond Basin, located a few miles west of Richmond, Virginia;
5. Danville Basin, southern Virginia;
6. Deep River Basin, North Carolina.

In New England another basin extends along the Connecticut River from New Haven northward almost to the northern boundary of Massachusetts (Fig. 11.13).

Cemetery Ridge, at Gettysburg, is a ridge of diabase similar to the Watchung Ridges (Fig. 11.5) but less regular.

Blue Ridge Province

The Blue Ridge Province extends from Georgia to Pennsylvania, and ranges from 5 miles to more than 50 miles in width. In places it is a single ridge; elsewhere a complex of closely spaced ridges. The province is the easternmost ridge of the Appalachian Highlands, and overlooks the Piedmont Province on the east, rising 1,000 to 5,000 feet above it. It is higher in the south than in the north, and reaches 6,684 feet at Mount Mitchell in North Carolina.

The rocks that make up the province include Precambrian granite and gneiss that formed the basement of the geosyncline in which the Paleozoic formations of the Appalachian Highlands were deposited. The Paleozoic formations of the Valley and Ridge Province are thickest near the Blue Ridge Province, which must therefore be at or near what was the deepest part of the Paleozoic geosyncline. Thus, not only has the Blue

Ridge Province the highest peaks in the Appalachian Highlands, but it has been uplifted more than any other part of the highlands.

In addition to the basement complex of granite and gneiss, the rocks in the southern part of the Blue Ridge Province include a thick series of late Precambrian sedimentary rocks (Ocoee Series, 20,000 feet thick) consisting of poorly sorted siltstone, sandstone, and conglomerate that grades upward into the Cambrian formations. These late Precambrian formations are metamorphosed, but less so than the formations in the Piedmont Province. Northward, in Virginia, their place is taken by metamorphosed volcanic rocks of late Precambrian age.

Along the western edge of the Blue Ridge Province, the lower Paleozoic formations of the Valley and Ridge Province are turned up steeply at the contact with the uplifted Precambrian rocks. In places this is a fault contact and provides a sharp structural boundary between the two provinces (Fig. 11.6). Valleys west of the Blue Ridge are only slightly higher than the Piedmont Province.

Valley and Ridge Province

The Valley and Ridge Province extends the entire length of the Appalachian Highlands. It is divided into three sections: a very narrow one, only 25 miles wide, with much shale at the north along the Hudson River; a second, 75 miles wide, with varied kinds of rocks in Pennsylvania, Maryland, and northern Virginia; and a third, about 50 miles wide, which is like the second but more faulted, extending from southern Virginia to the south end of the highlands in Alabama.

The Valley and Ridge Province is world famous for its fold mountains. (Figs. 11.7, 11.8), which are made up of Paleozoic sedimentary formations 40,000 feet in thickness. The sediments that formed these rocks were derived from a mountain mass that lay to the east, the roots of which are now buried under the Coastal Plain and the Atlantic Ocean. The composition of the formations changes away from the source of the sediments. Sandstone and shale formations in the east tend to grade westward into shale and limestone. The well-known limestone caverns of Virginia are developed in lower Paleozoic limestone formations in the valley west of the Blue Ridge (Fig. 11.6).

Toward the end of Paleozoic time the geosyncline in which the formations of the Appalachian Highlands were deposited became filled with sediments faster than it was sinking, and deposits like those on the Coastal Plain spread westward across the top of the older marine formations. This coastal plain contained swamps, probably not unlike the Dismal Swamp and others along the present Atlantic seaboard, except that the woody plants were tree-like ferns rather than today's broadleaf and conifer trees. The accumulation of this woody material in the swamps produced the coal beds that are found in the anthracite fields in the Valley and Ridge Province and in the bituminous coalfields of the Appalachian Plateaus farther west.

At the end of Paleozoic time the part of the crust now represented by the Piedmont and Blue Ridge provinces was pushed westward against the side of the geosynclinal trough, and this squeezed the formations in the trough into great linear folds. In the southern section of the Valley and Ridge Province, there was thrust faulting westward as well as folding; in the central section there was folding without much thrust faulting (Fig. 11.3). In the Blue Ridge Province also there is more thrust faulting in the south than in the north. The northern section, along the Hudson River Valley, seems to have been even more compressed than the southern section of the province.

A representative stratigraphic section of these Paleozoic formations is given in Table 11.1, which describes the principal formations in the Valley and Ridge Province and Appalachian Plateaus in Pennsylvania. Figure 11.8 shows the structural pattern of those formations.

Appalachian Plateaus

The Appalachian Plateaus, approximately equal in area to the Piedmont, Blue Ridge, and Valley and Ridge provinces combined, are an elevated tract of nearly horizontal or gently folded strata.

Altitudes range from about 1,000 feet along the western edge to somewhat more than 3,000 feet at the Allegheny Front, which is a southeast-facing escarpment overlooking the Valley and Ridge Province and forming the boundary between the two provinces. The Allegheny Front and its extensions form one of the most persistent and most striking topographic breaks in the country. From Alabama to northern Pennsylvania, a distance of 700 miles, the escarpment is 500 to 1,000 feet high. Its extension along the Hudson River Valley, at the eastern front of the Catskill Mountains, is more than 3,000 feet high.

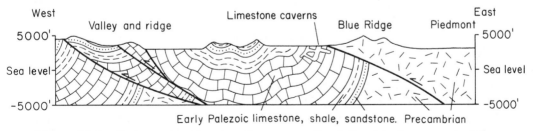

Figure 11.6 *Cross section showing the structural relationship between the Blue Ridge and the Valley and Ridge provinces in Virginia. (After Virginia Geol. Survey.)*

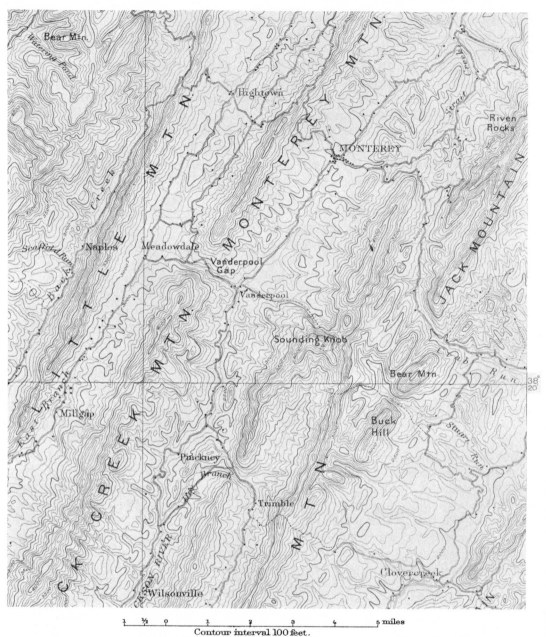

Figure 11.7 *Topographic map (above) and geologic map with cross sections (facing page), illustrating some relationships between the topography and the structural geology in the Valley and Ridge Province. The topographic grain reflects the parallel folds. The ridges have developed along the formations that are resistant to erosion whether these be at crests of such anticlines as Jack Mountain north of Crab Run or along the flanks of such folds as Little Mtn. The valleys are in the easily eroded formations, whether they form anticlines, like East Branch; synclines, like Jackson River; or the flanks of folds, like Back Creek. (From U.S.G.S.)*

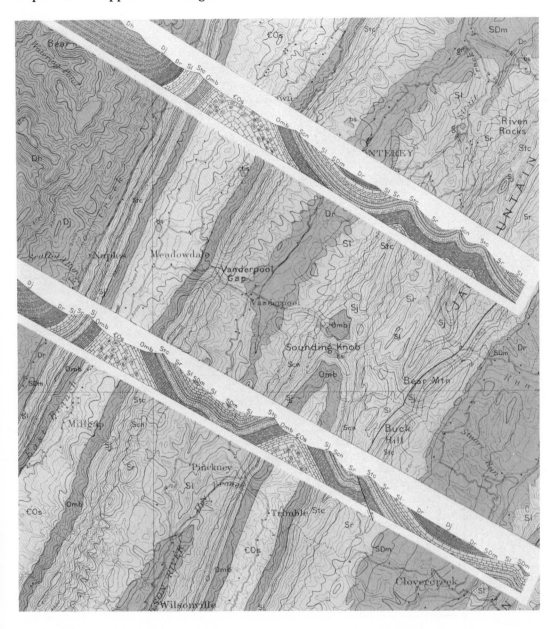

Structurally the Appalachian Plateaus are a basin in which each formation has the shape of a saucer (Fig. 11.9). The deepest part of the structural basin is in southwestern Pennsylvania and West Virginia, which is one of the highest and roughest parts of the plateau. The formations are described in Table 11.1.

The Appalachian Plateaus can be divided into several sections on the basis of differences in structure and on the basis of the processes of erosion. At the north, in New York State and northernmost Pennsylvania and Ohio, the plateaus, formed of Devonian formations, were glaciated and exhibit such glacial features as the Finger Lakes (Fig. 11.17), but otherwise this part of the province differs little from other parts of the province in terms of structure and degree of dissection. At the Catskill

TABLE 11.1. Paleozoic formations or groups of formations in the Valley
and Ridge Province and Appalachian Plateaus in Pennsylvania.

System		Formation or Group	Lithology, Thickness
Permian		Dunkard Group	Chiefly shale and shaley sandstone over sandy shale and coarse sandstone; some coal and limestone; 1,200 feet thick.
Pennsylvanian		Monongahela Group	Shale, sandstone, and thick limestone; Pittsburgh Coal bed at base; other workable coal beds; one of the highly productive coal measures; 300 to 460 feet thick.
		Conemaugh Group	Chiefly variegated shale and thick, coarse standstone; thin coal beds; some limestone; 450 to 900 feet thick.
		Allegheny Group	Shale and sandstone, several workable coal beds including the Kittanning and Freeport Coal beds; some ironstone and limestone; one of the highly productive coal measures; 300 feet thick.
		Pottsville Group	Chiefly coarse sandstone, conglomerate, irregular shale beds, thin coal beds; thickens southwestward to 1,800 feet.
Mississippian		Mauch Chunk Formation	In east, mostly lumpy red and green shale with green sandstone; in west, mostly limestone; as much as 3,000 feet thick in places.
		Pocono Formation	Chiefly thick-bedded coarse-gray sandstone and conglomerate; some red shale toward base; 700 to 1,000 feet thick.
Devonian	Upper	Catskill Formation	Chiefly red sandstone and shale; thickens eastward to 7,500 feet.
		Chemung Group	Chiefly gray sandy shale and blocky sandstone; 1,800 feet thick.
		Portage Group	Dark- to light-gray platy shale; thin beds of sandstone; 1,000 feet thick.
		Genesee Group	Black carbonaceous shale; some limestone; 150 feet thick.
	Middle	Hamilton Group	Very fossiliferous sandy shale and sandstone; 400 to 2,200 feet thick.
		Marcellus Group	Mostly dark shale, some limestone; 175 feet thick.
		Onondaga Group	Sandstone, grit, cherty limestone; 250 feet or less.
	Lower	Oriskany Sandstone	Chiefly pure granular sandstone suitable for glass sand; 20 to 200 feet thick.
		Helderberg Group	Mostly limestone and limey shale; 200 feet thick.

Silurian	Cayuga Group	Finely laminated limestone and limey shale; 50 to 600 feet thick.
	Clinton Group	Green fossiliferous shale weathers buff; rusty fossiliferous sandstone; hematite iron ore; 250 to 1,300 feet thick.
	Tuscarora Sandstone	Thick-bedded white sandstone; suitable for ganister and sand; 100 to 1,000 feet thick.
	Juniata Formation	Red shale and shaley sandstone; 500 to 1,600 feet thick.
	Oswego Group	Gray sandstone with some conglomerate; hard, ridge former; 75 to 1,300 feet thick.
Ordovician	Martinsburg Shale	Dark gray shale; 1,000 to 3,000 feet thick.
	Trenton Group	Black limestone, becomes shaley eastward; 300 to 400 feet thick.
	Black River and Lowville Groups	Limestone; 1,000 feet thick.
	Beekmantown Limestone	Impure, thick-bedded dolomitic limestone; cherty and sandy; 1,000 to 2,300 feet thick.
	Conococheague Limestone	900 to 2,000 feet thick.
Cambrian	Elbrook Limestone	Bluish-gray magnesian limestone, some shale; cherty; thickness 2,000 to 3,000 feet.
	Waynsboro Formation	Gray sandy limestone; red and purple shale at top; 1,000 feet thick.
	Tomstown Group	Mostly dolomite, some interbedded shale; 1,600 feet thick.
	Antietam Sandstone	The oldest fossiliferous formation; 300 feet thick.
Precambrian	Harpers Formation	Partly metamorphosed shale and sandstone; 2,000 feet thick.
	Weverton Quartzite	250 feet.
	Loudoun Formation	Tuffaceous slate, arkosic quartzite, and conglomerate; 300 feet thick.
	Metamorphic	Basement rocks.

Mountains the relief is mountainous and is greater than in any other part of the Appalachian Plateaus. In New York State the Devonian formations form an escarpment overlooking Silurian and Ordovician formations along the Hudson River and along the Mohawk Valley from Albany westward to Lake Erie. Where the Silurian and Ordovician formations extend northward from under the Devonian, they are turned up around the south and west flanks of the structural dome that forms the Adirondack Mountains. This area, referred to as the Mohawk Section, consists of a series of cuestas with steep slopes facing the dome and long gentle slopes away from it (Fig. 11.11).

In Ohio, Kentucky, and southward into Tennessee and Alabama, the western edge of the plateaus is an escarpment of Mississippian formations capped by Pennsylvanian formations. This escarpment is dissected to form scattered buttes and promontories, and is locally referred to by the colorful and descriptive term, "Knob Belt" (Fig. 12.12).

On the east, from Pennsylvania southward between the Allegheny Front and the trough of the basin under the Appalachian Plateaus, is a series of open folds parallel to those in the Valley and Ridge Province. This belt of country provides a structural transition from the plateaus to the Valley and Ridge Province. Westward the folds become lower and less steep. Topographically, this belt is part of the plateaus because the folds are not deeply

dissected like those in the Valley and Ridge Province.

In Alabama the plateaus slope southwestward and pass under the Coastal Plain formations at an altitude of less than 500 feet at Tuscaloosa on the Black Warrior River. That the rock formations and structures of the Appalachian Highlands long antedate the Coastal Plain formations is shown by the unconformable overlap of the Cretaceous and other Coastal Plain formations across those of the highlands (p. 28).

In addition to these sectional differences, which are attributable to differences in the structure of the rocks or of the process of erosion, other local variations of the landforms within the sections are attributable to differences in stage, or degree, of dissection. Some areas are deeply dissected with closely spaced valleys between narrow ridges (Fig. 11.10,A);

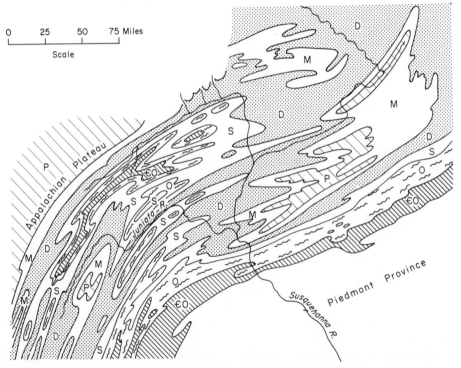

Figure 11.8   *Geologic map showing the structural pattern of the Paleozoic formations in the Valley and Ridge Province in Pennsylvania. €O, Cambrian and Lower Ordovician; O, Upper Ordovician; S, Silurian; D, Devonian; M, Mississippian; P, Pennsylvanian. (Generalized from Geologic Map of Pennsylvania.)*

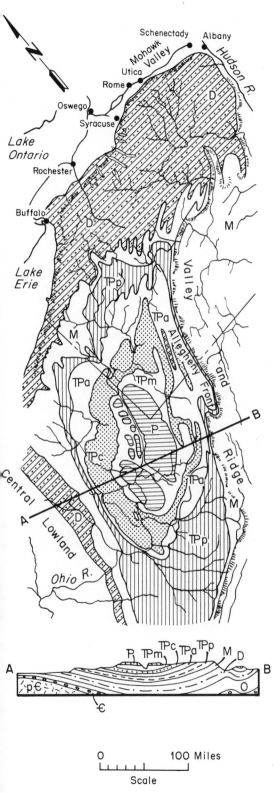

A

0   100 Miles

Scale

others may be equally deeply dissected but by widely spaced valleys that are separated by broad, open uplands (Fig. 11.10,B).

Adirondack Province

The Adirondack Mountains, in northern New York State, are a nearly circular structural dome, more than 100 miles in diameter (Fig. 11.11). At the center is a core of Precambrian rocks, and the highest peak, Mount Marcy, is at an altitude of 5,344 feet. Around the base of the dome, at altitudes around 500 feet, the Precambrian core is overlapped by early Paleozoic sedimentary formations that dip away from the dome in all directions; they form cuestas with steep slopes facing the uplift and gentle slopes away from it. The Precambrian rocks forming the core of the dome have been uplifted 2 miles or more.

Some important geologic principles are well illustrated by the structural geology of the Adirondacks. The oldest formations are those near the dome, and the formations get progressively younger away from it. This arrangement is opposite to that of a structural basin, as can be seen by comparing Figure 11.11 with Figure 11.9. In a structural basin the formations are progressively younger toward the center of the basin. Around a structural dome, the cuestas face inward; around a structural basin they face outward.

Figure 11.9 *Geologic map and cross section of the structural basin under the Appalachian Plateaus. The basin centers under the Permian Dunkard Group (*P*), which is underlain successively by the Monongahela Group (*Pm*,*) Conemaugh Group (*ℙc*), Allegheny Group (*ℙa*), and the Pottsville Group (*ℙp*) of Pennsylvanian age. Under the Pennsylvanian is the Mississippian (*M*) and Devonian (*D*). In the cross section the Silurian is included with the Devonian. Under this is Ordovician (*O*), Cambrian (*C*), and Precambrian (*p*C*). (Geology generalized from U.S.G.S. Geologic Map of the United States.)*

Particularly well illustrated by the structural geology around the Adirondack dome are the successive episodes of uplift, which occurred at numerous stages during the Paleozoic while the sedimentary formations were being deposited around it. This is recorded in the way the formations are cut off unconformably around the flanks of the dome (see Fig. 11.12).

At the south, the Cambrian is cut out by the Lower Ordovician, which overlaps it. On the southwest, both the Cambrian and Lower Ordovician are overlapped and cut off by the Middle Ordovician, and the Lower Silurian cuts off the Upper Ordovician. The Lower and Middle Silurian are in turn cut off by the Upper Silurian, which is cut off where the

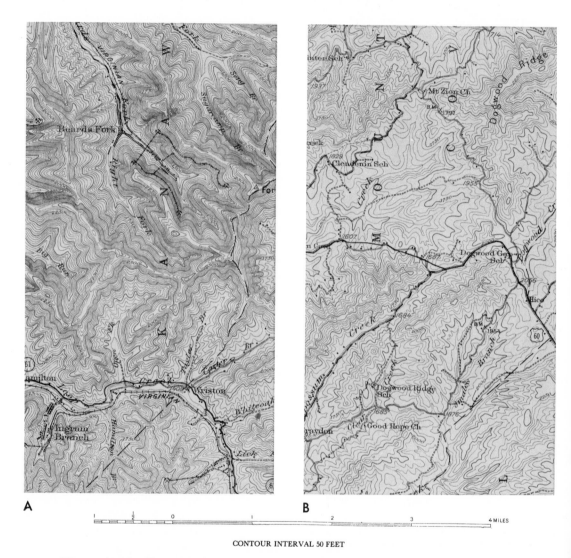

A   **B**

CONTOUR INTERVAL 50 FEET

Figure 11.10 *Topographic maps illustrating landforms on the Appalachian Plateaus, where some valleys are closely spaced between narrow, sharp-crested ridges (A) and other valleys are widely spaced and separated by broad, open uplands (B). (From U.S.G.S. Fayetteville, W. Va., quadrangle.)*

Devonian overlaps onto the Middle Ordovician. This is illustrated in Figure 11.12.

The Adirondacks are related topographically and structurally both to the Appalachian Highlands and to the Laurentian Upland of Canada. If the province is limited to the Precambrian terrain, it would relate most closely to the Laurentian Upland. If the Lower Paleozoic formations around the base of the dome are included, the province would relate most closely to the Appalachian Highlands.

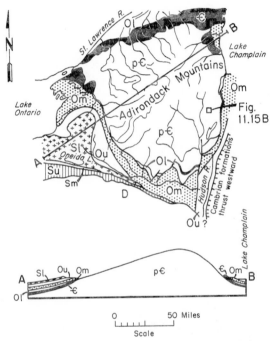

Figure 11.11 *Geologic map and cross section showing the structure of the dome at the Adirondack Mountains, New York.* p∈, *Precambrian rocks, mostly granite and gneiss, some schist, and some gabbro and other dark rocks. The Paleozoic sedimentary formations overlapping the Precambrian are:* ∈ *Cambrian;* Ol, *Lower Ordovician;* Om, *Middle Ordovician;* Ou, *Upper Ordovician;* Sl, *Lower Silurian;* Su, *Upper Silurian; and* D, *Devonian. The Paleozoic formations crop out at altitudes of around 500 feet; high point on the mountains is 5,344 feet. (Generalized from U.S.G.S. Geologic Map of the United States.)*

New England Province

Structurally, New England resembles the Piedmont Province, but the relief is very much greater—as much as 6,000 feet—and the topography is controlled by the structural features to a considerable degree. The distribution of the principal structural members is shown in

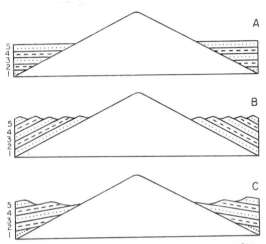

Figure 11.12 *The structural history of uplifts can be read by the pattern of the formations on the flanks. (A) Around uplifts that are older than the formations overlapping the flanks, the younger formations extend progressively farther onto the uplift and bury the older formations. (B) Around uplifts that are younger than the formations on the flanks, the dips are away from the uplift, and progressively older formations are exposed toward the uplift. (C) Around uplifts that were raised in stages while the flanking sedimentary formations were being deposited, as at the Adirondacks, combinations of the A and B situations are found. In C there was uplift after Bed 1 was deposited but before Bed 2 was deposited, because the upturned edges of Bed 1 are overlapped by Bed 2. The resulting hill survived without further uplift while Beds 2 and 3 were being deposited, because Bed 3 extends farther onto the flank than does Bed 2. Uplift occurred again after Bed 5 was deposited, because it has been tilted.*

Fig. 11.13. One of the principal mountain-forming members consists of gneissic rocks of Precambrian age. These form the cores of the Green Mountains in western Vermont, the Hoosac Mountains in western Massachusetts, the highlands along the Hudson River and the Reading Prong, which extends from the highlands southwestward across New Jersey to Reading, Pennsylvania. These highland ridges are uplifts of Precambrian rocks, much like those of the Blue Ridge. To the west of them are folded Paleozoic formations in the Valley and Ridge Province. To the east are folded and faulted metamorphosed Paleozoic formations with block-faulted Triassic formations much like those in the Piedmont Province (Fig. 11.5).

Granitic and other rocks intrusive into the metamorphic rocks in New England are extensive in a belt 75 miles wide between the Connecticut Valley and the coast. These rocks form uplands and, in places, mountains, such

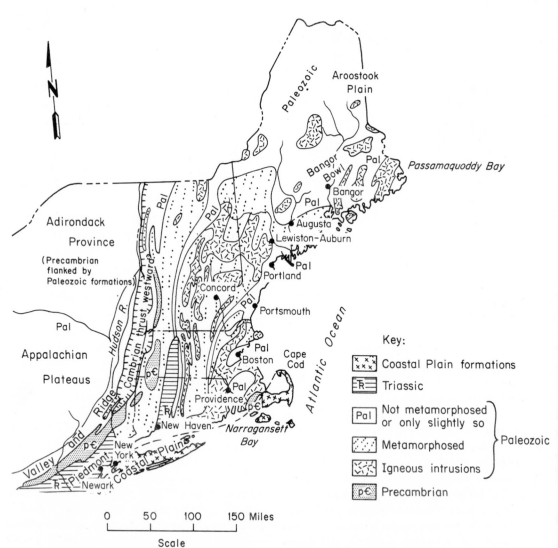

Figure 11.13 *Geologic map showing the structural pattern of the New England Province. (Generalized from Tectonic Map of the U.S. by U.S.G.S. and A.A.P.G.)*

as the White Mountains in east-central New Hampshire and southwest Maine. Isolated mountains that rise above the general level of the surrounding country are called *monadnocks,* named for Mount Monadnock in southern New Hampshire. Many or most of the isolated mountains in New England are granitic, but Mount Monadnock is composed of schist that is not obviously harder than the rocks around it.

The greater part of New England is underlain by metamorphosed rocks thought to be of Paleozoic age. In much of the region these rocks form a surface lower than the ridges of Precambrian gneiss and granite, but higher than the areas of Paleozoic rocks that are not metamorphosed or only slightly so. The unmetamorphosed Paleozoic rocks form basins. Among them are the Narragansett Basin at Providence, Rhode Island. Narragansett Bay is the drowned portion of this structural basin. Another partly drowned structural basin is at Boston. Still a third is along the New Hampshire coast and adjoining part of the coast of Maine. Other lowlands in these formations in Maine are the Bangor Bowl and the Aroostook Plain.

In New England, as in the Piedmont Province, the Triassic formations form topographic, as well as structural, basins. The structures, and even the ridges formed by diabase sills, are quite like those in the Piedmont, except that in the Connecticut Basin the Triassic rocks are downfaulted on the east and dip east. In the Piedmont Province most of the Triassic Basins are downfaulted on the west and dip west.

Another structural unit is at the western edge of the New England Province and is represented by the Taconic Mountains along the east side of the Hudson River and Lake Champlain Valley. These mountains consist of Cambrian formations (and some Ordovician formations) that form the upper plate of a westward-directed overthrust fault. The lower plate, consisting of folded rocks of Ordovician age, has been eroded to form the valleys.

One of the most characteristic features of the New England Province is the rocky coast (Fig. 11.14), which is quite unlike that of the Coastal Plain. The formations that are equivalent to those of the Coastal Plain are submerged and form the Continental Shelf. The ocean extends inland to the highlands, and the rocky valleys there are drowned. Landward, the valleys, which are cut into bedrock, are partly filled with glacial till, glacial outwash, and other fill. This fill generally is more than 100 feet thick, and in some valleys (Narragansett and Passamaquoddy bays) is 350 to 400 feet thick. The bedrock floors of some of the drowned valleys along the Connecticut coast and at Boston are 200 to 250 feet below sea level. Some of this erosion may have occurred below sea level as a result of glacial erosion, but much of it may be attributed to stream erosion that took place when sea level was lower (or the land higher).

Glacial Effects

All the New England, Adirondack, and other northern structural units in the Appalachian Highlands have been greatly modified by Pleistocene glaciation. Figure 11.15 gives two examples of the glacial features. Ice sheets of the last (Wisconsin) stage of Pleistocene glaciation covered the Appalachian Highlands as far south as northern Pennsylvania and northern New Jersey (Figs. 4.9, 6.1). The structural geology of the glaciated area is greatly masked because of ice scour and burial by glacial deposits. In places the land has been roughened by the glacial action; elsewhere it has been smoothed. The glacial effects are manifested also in regional structural upwarping caused by the ice load that once rested on that part of the crust. The crust was pressed downward under the burden of ice and has risen differentially since the load was removed.

The southern limit of the ice is marked by a terminal moraine, a hummocky ridge of till

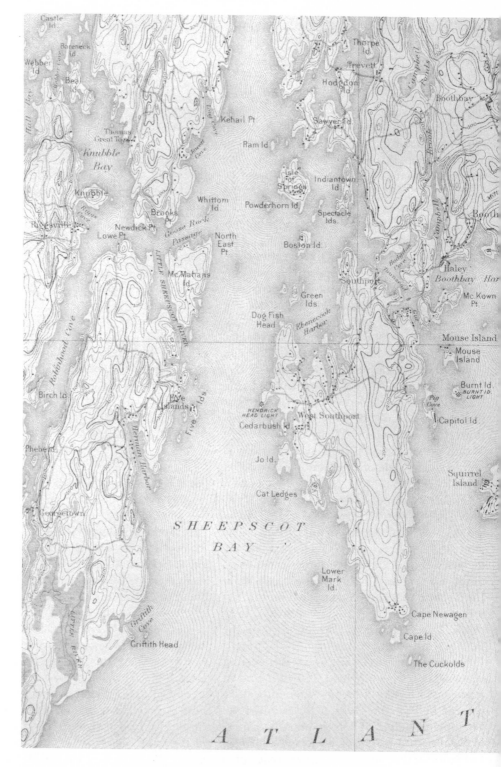

Figure 11.14 *Map illustrates the rocky coast of New England. Northeast tilting of this part of the continent submerged the coastal plain and caused the ocean to advance inland. The valleys are drowned like those in the Embayed Section of*

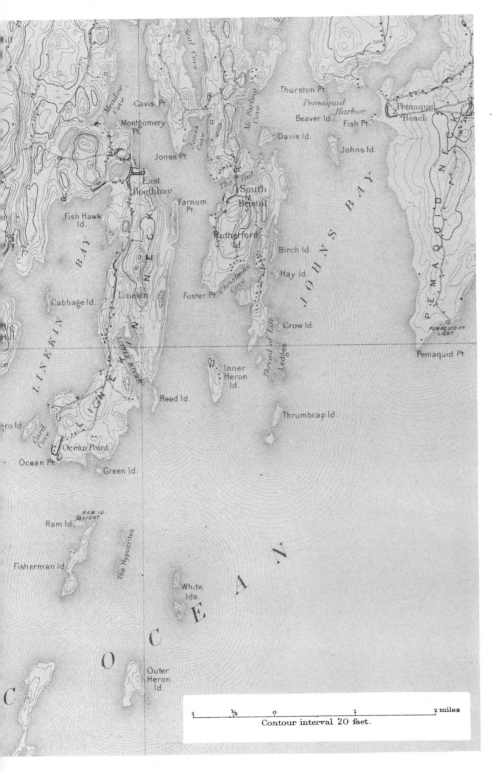

the Coastal Plain, but because of differences in rock structure the hills are much more irregular, which results in numerous islands. (From U.S.G.S. Boothbay, Me., sheet, 1908.)

composed of boulders, gravel, sand, and finely ground rock flour. Blocks of ice deposited with the moraine melted and left depressions known as *kettle holes,* many of which now are ponds or small lakes. South of the moraine is a smooth plain built of outwash deposited by meltwater streams (Fig. 11.16).

The center from which this glacial ice spread was in Labrador. The directions in which the ice moved from its center can be determined in at least three ways, and the course of the ice traced from its limits back to its source. One method is to map the directions of glacial striae, the scratches left on bare rock surfaces by rocks dragged along the bottom

of the ice. The second method is to note the direction of trains of boulders extending from hills having distinctive types of rock that can be identified in the till. Many such boulder trains have been mapped in New England. The third method is to map the axes of drumlins (Fig. 11.15, B), which are parallel to the direction of ice movement. Drumlins are numerous and conspicuous on the lowland bordering Lake Ontario (Fig. 11.17). Another group forms many of the hills in the Boston Basin, including the well-known Bunker Hill.

Probably the most distinctive feature of the glaciated part of the highlands is the abundance of lakes. From the terminal moraine

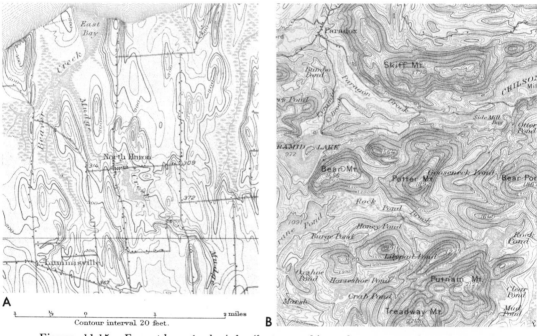

Figure 11.15 *Examples of glacial effects masking the structural geology. (A) South of Lake Ontario, hills of glacially deposited gravels (drumlins) became elongated in the direction of the ice movement when the ice advanced over them. Subsequently, along the shore, waves have cut off the north ends of the drumlins and have built small bars across the mouths of valleys. For location see Figure 11.17. (From U.S.G.S. Sodus Bay and Clyde, N.Y., sheets, 1908.) (B) Lakes characterize the glaciated part of the Appalachian Highlands from Maine to the Finger Lakes in New York. Some lakes occupy valleys deepened by glacial scour; others occupy valleys dammed by glacial deposits. These lakes are in the Adirondacks (see Fig. 11.11). (From U.S.G.S. Paradox Lake, N.Y., sheet, 1908).*

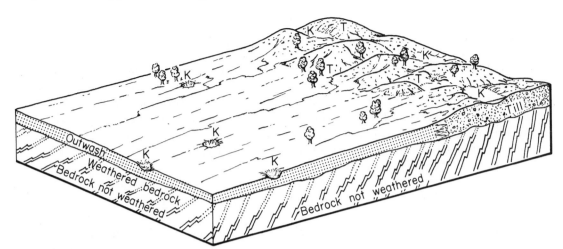

Figure 11.16 *Diagram showing relationship of outwash plain to terminal moraine (T) Both are pitted by kettle holes (K), some containing ponds. Preglacial soils and weathered bedrock commonly are preserved under the stream-deposited outwash, but the till that forms the moraine generally rests on unweathered bedrock because soils there were removed by the ice.*

north, they are counted by the thousands; south of the moraine, lakes are rare. The lakes were formed in many ways. Reference has already been made to ponds and small lakes in kettle holes. Larger lakes formed where preglacial valleys were dammed by morainal ridges. Chains of lakes developed in some preglacial valleys in which the irregular deposition of till blocked certain stretches along the valley. Still other lakes, like the Finger Lakes in central New York (Fig. 11.17), fill valleys that were deepened by ice scour. The bottoms of Cayuga and Seneca lakes are below sea level, and the fill beneath them is hundreds of feet thick. The bottom of Lake Ontario is more than 500 feet below sea level. The bottom of the Hudson River is also below sea level, and is underlain by several hundred feet of fill. Valley fill in the Connecticut River Valley extends more than 200 feet below sea level.

Most of the lakes that remain today are shallower than they were during the ice age. Other lakes that are now dry formed in front of the glaciers wherever northward drainage was dammed by the ice. For example in northern New Jersey, a broad lake, known as Lake Passaic, was formed back of the Watchung Ridges when the Passaic River near Paterson (Fig. 11.5) was dammed.

Preglacial streams became diverted by the glacial deposits. The tributaries of the Ohio River formerly drained north toward Lake Erie. The course of the Ohio River is comparatively young and was eroded by glacial meltwaters escaping to the Mississippi along the front of the ice. The Connecticut River formerly flowed southward in a broad valley to New Haven, but at Hartford it now turns out of the broad valley into a gorge through the eastern Connecticut hills. As a result of such stream diversions, drainage patterns in the glaciated region are highly irregular and haphazard as compared to the drainage patterns in the unglaciated regions.

Although U-shaped valleys were eroded by the ice, the bare rock surfaces in the glaciated region tend to be smoothed and show striae as a result of polishing by the ice. South of the glacial border rock surfaces are still rough.

Constructional features built of glacial deposits are of several kinds. In addition to the terminal moraine at the southern limit of the ice, other morainal ridges mark stands of the ice during its retreat. These are recessional moraines (Fig. 11.17); topographically, they are quite like the terminal moraine.

Mention has already been made of drumlins. In addition, in many glaciated valleys, there are irregular hills, called *kames,* composed of stratified glacial drift. They formed where streams on the ice discharged into crevasses or other openings along one side of the ice or within it. When the ice melted, the courses of some streams on or under the ice became marked by long ridges of gravel and sand called *eskers* (Fig. 3.10). These ridges, commonly only a hundred feet or so wide, extend for many miles. Some in eastern Maine

have been traced for almost 50 miles. Eskers branch in the same way that the streams did.

Glacial erratics, the boulders of hard rock carried southward by the ice, are strewn over the New England landscape. Now gathered in neat stone walls, they are characteristic of that region. The ice that covered New England moved across a rough topography having many ridges of hard rock from which the boulders could be plucked. By contrast, erratics are not common in the glaciated parts of the Appalachian Plateaus or Central Lowlands, for those areas lack the ridges of hard rock that could supply boulders.

At the time of the ice maximum, sea level was lower than it is now because so much water was withdrawn from the oceans to form the ice caps. But the weight of the ice caused the crust to sink; how much is not known. When the ice melted sea level rose. And as the load of ice was removed in the north the crust there again rose, but apparently not to its original height. Evidence of these structural movements is found in tilted shorelines of lakes that formed during the ice retreat. When the crust was pressed downward the Hudson River formed a strait connecting the ocean off Long Island with a bay that flooded the St. Lawrence Valley as far as Lake Ontario. Crustal movements of these sorts probably account for the fact that many lake bottoms in the glaciated areas are lower than sea level.

The glacial effects extended far south of the limits of the ice sheet. There must have been snow fields on the mountain summits far to the south, and the effects of freezing and thawing must have been very much more severe then than now, especially in a *periglacial* belt near the ice front and at high altitudes farther south. Accelerated mass wasting (p. 98) in this periglacial zone probably accounts for the huge boulder fields that occur along many mountain sides south of the glaciated area. The physical geology suggests that there was more effective moisture during the glacial stages than now, and in addition to accelerated mass wasting, there may have been accelerated

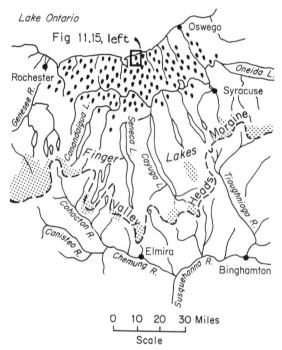

Figure 11.17 *Some glacial features in the Finger Lake country. Bordering Lake Ontario is a lowland belt of drumlins (black; size exaggerated, trends approximate) and buried valleys. South of this is the upland belt of Finger Lakes, which drain northward. At the heads of the valleys is a recessional moraine of late Wisconsin age. South of the valley heads is the drainage basin of the Susquehanna River.*

underground solution of the limestone formations, opening or enlarging the caverns that are so numerous in the limestone formations of the Valley and Ridge Province.

Climate

Present-day climates in the Appalachian Highlands vary greatly from one part to another, much more so than on the Coastal Plain, partly because of distance from the ocean and partly because of the 6,000-foot range in altitude. As on the Coastal Plain there is about a 14° range of latitude, from Alabama to Maine.

Average annual temperatures range from below 40°F in northern New England and on the Adirondacks to about 65°F on the southern part of the highlands, where the formations of the highlands pass under the Coastal Plain. Average annual precipitation is between 30 and 50 inches in most parts of the highlands, but reaches a maximum of about 80 inches in the Great Smoky Mountains in the southern part of the Blue Ridge Province. Southeast- and south-facing slopes are notably warmer and drier than northwest- and north-facing slopes, because they face the sun and are on the lee side of the ridges. A practical effect of this is a greater frequency of forest fires on south facing slopes.

The precipitation is distributed rather uniformly throughout the year. In those parts of the Highlands that receive an average of about 40 inches of precipitation per year, the averages for the ten driest and the ten wettest years (40-year record) are 30 and 50 inches, respectively. Except for two small areas, one in the lower Muskingum Valley in Ohio and another at the north end of Lake Champlain, no part of the Highlands has recorded less than 20 inches of precipitation in a year.

Maximum precipitation in a 24-hour period on the Appalachian Highlands is only about half that on the Coastal Plain. Maximum precipitation recorded in an hour is less than 2½

inches, and in northern New England is less than 2 inches.

Average annual snowfall is more than 100 inches in northern New England and northern New York, but decreases southward along the mountains to about 30 inches in the Great Smoky Mountains. In northern New England and northern New York the average annual number of days with more than 1 inch of snow cover exceeds 120.

The average length of the frost-free period is about 100 days on the mountains in the north, and about 220 days on the low, southern parts of the Appalachian Highlands. In most of the Piedmont Province frost penetrates to depths of 6 inches to 1 foot; northward, and onto the mountains, frost penetrates to greater depths. In northern New England, land cleared of snow may freeze to a depth of 6 feet; under snow, however, the depth of freezing may be no more than a foot.

Climatic hazards include thunderstorms, tornadoes, hurricanes, fog, and smoke. Thunderstorm frequency is greatest in the Great Smoky Mountains, but decreases northward and is least along the New England coast. Hail storms occur, on the average, only about two days a year. The New England coast is in the hurricane belt and every few years it experiences a lashing by hard winds, heavy rains, and high waves.

Tornadoes are less frequent in the Appalachian Highlands than in the southern part of the Coastal Plain and in the Central Lowland (Fig. 4.4), but nevertheless there have been highly destructive ones. One of the major tornadoes of the century, in terms of destructiveness, struck Worcester, Massachusetts, on June 9, 1953, killing 90 people, injuring more than 1,200 others, and causing more than $50,000,000 in property damage. During the last 50 years Pennsylvania and West Virginia, which have a combined area of about 70,000 square miles, have experienced 50 major tornadoes—major in terms of property damage. This seems to be about the average frequency for the Appalachian Highlands.

The New England coast and much of the mountain areas are subject to frequent, dense fogs. In the eastern part of the Appalachian Plateaus frequency of fog is considerable (Fig. 4.4), and about half the days each year there are cloudy—a frequency half again as great as on the Coastal Plain.

In the mountain areas, especially in narrow valleys, air inversions (such as cold air trapped under warm air) hold smoke and fumes in the valleys—a condition familiarly known as smog. Practically every community in the Appalachian Mountains is troubled to some degree by smog, and where there is much industry and other settlement, conditions have become acute. There have been occasions when fumes accumulated in valleys in lethal quantities and remained there until winds cleaned out the air, as at Donora, Pennsylvania (p. 132). Such communities become like a garage kept closed with the car motor running (Fig. 11.31).

Forests and Agriculture

Forest vegetation in the Appalachian Highlands is divided into five major forest regions. From north to south these are (Fig. 8.2):

1. Spruce–Fir Forest,
2. Northeastern Hardwood Forest,
3. Central Hardwood Forest,
4. Mixed Oak and Pine,
5. Southeastern Pine Forest.

In addition, above timberline on Mount Washington, there is tundra-like growth.

The Spruce-Fir Forest is part of a transcontinental forest that extends from the coast of Maine westward across Canada to the Pacific Coast. Three different forests extend from it southward into the United States—the Appalachian forests, the Rocky Mountain forests, and the Pacific Coast forests. In addition to the Spruce-Fir Forest in Maine, there are outliers of the forest in the Green and Adirondack Mountains and southward along the high part of the Appalachians to the Great Smoky Mountains. The altitudes of these forests rise southward from sea level on the Maine coast, to 500 to 1,000 feet in the Adirondacks, 3,000 feet in Maryland and West Virginia, and nearly 6,000 feet in the Great Smoky Mountains (Fig. 11.18). Despite the differences in latitude and length of day, the vegetation is similar at these different altitudes, and the growing conditions are evidently similar.

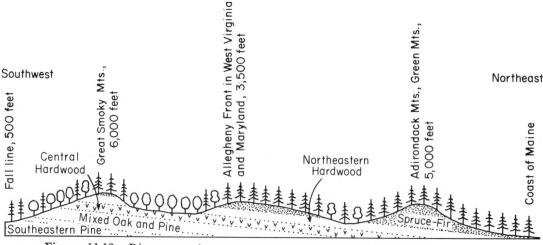

Figure 11.18 *Diagrammatic transect along the Appalachian Highlands showing the northward slope of the five forest regions.*

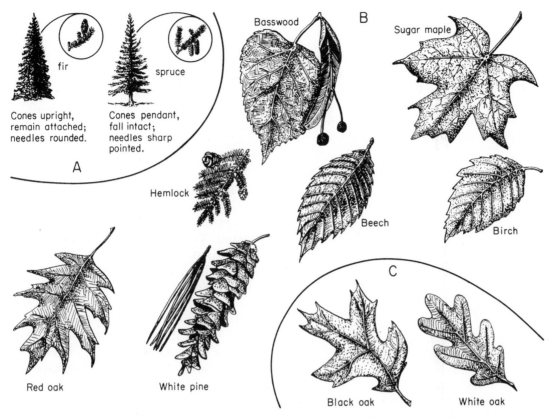

Figure 11.19 *Some trees of the Spruce-Fir Forest (A), Northeastern Hardwood Forest (B), and Central Hardwood Forest (C).*

The Spruce-Fir Forest grows on swamp ground and on well-drained uplands. In the swamps the principal trees are spruce, balsam fir, tamarack, cedar, and soft maples. On the better-drained ground between the swamps, white pine, hemlock, and birch grow with the spruce and fir. On the still drier, mountainous slopes, these several species are mixed with hardwood maples, beech, and cherry. The characteristic trees of this forest are, of course, the spruce and fir (Fig. 11.19,A). The spruce, particularly the red spruce, is much used as a source for paper pulp. The balsam fir is a favorite for Christmas trees.

The Northeastern Hardwood Forest has many more kinds of trees than the Spruce-Fir Forest. The principal trees are birch, beech, maple, hemlock, white pine, elm, red oak, and basswood (Fig. 11.19,B). White pine, hemlock, hardwood maples, elm, and basswood are important lumber trees. The sugar maple is renowned for its syrup.

The Central Hardwood Forest is chiefly an oak forest, with the white oak and black oak groups (Fig. 11.19,C) each represented by a dozen important species. The white oak group is characterized by leaves having rounded ends and by acorns that mature at the end of the first season, whereas the black oak group is characterized by leaf tips that are pointed and by acorns that mature after two seasons (Fig. 11.19,C). About a thousand different kinds of trees grow in this forest. Chestnut formerly was abundant, but a blight has destroyed most of that species. In addition to the oaks, there are poplar, hemlock, basswood, birch, ash, buckeye, hickory, black gum, dogwood, white pine, and shortleaf pine.

In the southern part of the Appalachian Highlands the mixed Oak and Pine Forest and the Southeastern Pine Forest resemble their counterparts on the Coastal Plain.

The principal uses of a few of the more important forest trees in the Appalachian Highlands may be summarized briefly:

Softwoods

Balsam fir: source of Canada balsam; wood used chiefly for pulp.

Hemlock: bark used in tanning; wood useful chiefly for coarse work, such as lathing.

White pine: of major importance as a timber tree.

Spruce: pulpwood, sounding boards, and light construction.

Hardwoods

Ash: handles, furniture.

Basswood: light construction, boxes.

Beech: boxing, flooring.

Birch: handles, millwork.

Cherry: furniture.

Elm: handles, furniture.

Hickory: one of the strongest woods; all kinds of construction.

Maple: furniture; syrup.

Oak: one of the strongest woods; all kinds of construction.

Poplar: pulp.

Agriculturally the Appalachian Highlands are used chiefly for dairying and general farming, with small areas used for special crops. Very little of the Spruce-Fir Forest is used for farming; an important exception is the potato-growing area in northernmost Maine. Dairying and poultry farming are the principal agricultural activities in the northern half of the Appalachian Highlands. The chief crops in the Piedmont Province south of the Potomac River are: in Virginia, livestock and tobacco; in North Carolina, tobacco; in South Carolina and westward across the south end of the Appalachian Highlands, cotton; in mountain areas west of the southern Piedmont, chiefly fruit, livestock, and general farming.

Surficial Deposits and Soils

The four principal kinds of surficial deposits in the Appalachian Highlands, as already noted (p. 168), are the glacial deposits, alluvium, colluvium, and the deep residuum, or saprolite. Each gives rise to characteristic soils.

Soils on the glacial drift are mostly Gray-Brown Podzols. In common with those to the south, they contain fresh, unweathered rock, even in their upper layers. As a consequence, the Gray-Brown Podzols differ from place to place in response to differences in the parent materials. For example, where the parent material includes much limestone, the soils are limy to within a few feet of the surface. The drift in New England is bouldery; that in New York State is much less so, and the New York soils are correspondingly less stoney.

The Brown Podzols, which occur in southern New England (Fig. 11.20), are even less well developed. The Podzols, which have well-developed but shallow profiles, are most extensive under coniferous forest. The Podzols, Brown Podzols, and Gray-Brown Podzols differ chiefly in the composition and distribution of their organic matter and in the degree of leaching of sesquioxides. The processes that developed these soils involved very little chemical alteration of the mineral fraction of the soils.

The alluvium and the soils developed on it are not unlike the alluvial deposits and soils on the Coastal Plain. Podzolic soils have developed on Pleistocene alluvium, but except where the alluvium has been subject to Recent flooding the soils are weakly developed and shallow.

The colluvium is mostly late Pleistocene and Recent, and much of it is subject to mass wasting at the present time. Where the wasting has taken place slowly, Gray-Brown Podzols have developed.

Saprolite is extensive in the Piedmont Province and in some of the broad valleys of the Valley and Ridge Province. These residual

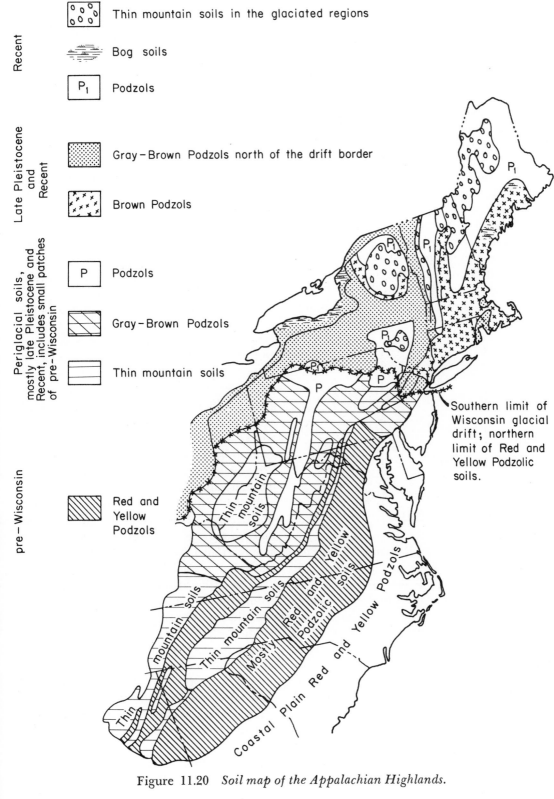

Legend (left column):

Recent
- Thin mountain soils in the glaciated regions
- Bog soils
- P_1 Podzols

Late Pleistocene and Recent
- Gray-Brown Podzols north of the drift border
- Brown Podzols

Periglacial soils, mostly late Pleistocene and Recent; includes small patches of pre-Wisconsin
- P Podzols
- Gray-Brown Podzols
- Thin mountain soils

pre-Wisconsin
- Red and Yellow Podzols

Map labels:

P_1

Southern limit of Wisconsin glacial drift; northern limit of Red and Yellow Podzolic soils.

Thin mountain soils

Mostly Red and Yellow Podzolic soils

Red and Yellow Podzols

Coastal Plain Red and Yellow Podzols

Thin mountain soils

Figure 11.20 *Soil map of the Appalachian Highlands.*

deposits are the parent material for the Red and Yellow Podzols. Where saprolite has developed on the metamorphic rocks of the Piedmont Province, it is more than a hundred feet deep in places. At the base of the saprolite is weathered rock (Fig. 11.21), which grades downward into fresh, unweathered rock. Above the zone of weathered rock is another in which the original appearance of the rock and its structures are perfectly preserved even though the rock has been reduced to clay and to oxides of iron and aluminum (sesquioxides). The density of the original rock has been reduced by 30 or even 40 percent, and the saprolite can be cut by a knife or squeezed between the fingers. In this zone the saprolite is clay that looks like rock!

Above the structured zone the saprolite

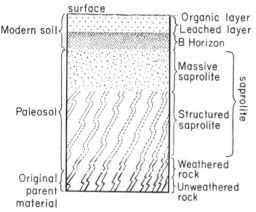

Figure 11.21 *Profile of Red and Yellow Podzol (modern soil) and underlying saprolite. At the surface is an organic layer, commonly no more than an inch thick. The leached layer, about 18 inches thick, is light in color. The illuviated layer, about 2½ feet thick, is more clayey, darker brown, and more mottled than the leached layer. It grades downward to the underlying saprolite, which may be tens of scores of feet deep. The saprolite is composed of clay and sesquioxides. The upper part is structureless; the lower part faithfully preserves the structure of the original rock. At the base is a thin zone of weathered rock that grades downward into unweathered rock.*

consists of massive clay. By some process—perhaps by frost heaving during Pleistocene time—the upper layers of the saprolite have been churned and the original structure destroyed.

The mineral fraction of the Red and Yellow Podzols that have developed on this saprolite is inherited, and is not the product of late Pleistocene or Recent weathering. The effects of late Pleistocene and Recent weathering are confined to the upper 3 or 4 feet, which (from top to bottom) consist of (1) an organic-rich layer 1 to 2 inches thick; (2) a slightly leached layer that is light in color and extends to depths of 1 to 2 feet; and (3) a clayey, illuviated layer (B horizon) about 2 to 3 feet thick. Below the B horizon is saprolite.

Traced northward, the Red and Yellow Podzols and their parent material are overlapped by glacial outwash or till, as shown in Figures 10.17,A and 11.16. Traced across the Coastal Plain, they extend under Pleistocene shell beds (Fig. 10.17,B). They are not found on glacial drift or glacial outwash of Wisconsin age, for they date from pre-Wisconsin time. Some can be dated as early Pleistocene, others seem to be Tertiary, and some are older than Cretaceous formations that overlap them at the Fall Line.

Probably the saprolite covered the entire Appalachian Highlands in pre-Wisconsin time. In the glaciated area it would have been largely eroded by the ice. In the mountains south of the glacial border, where slopes are steep and the altitude favors intensive frost action, the old soils were largely eroded. Small remnants are preserved, notably on the Cumberland Plateau. Some remnants are overlapped by younger alluvial or colluvial deposits containing unweathered rocks even in the upper layers; the soils on these young deposits are classed as Gray-Brown Podzols.

In general therefore, the soils of the Appalachian Highlands form two distinct groups. In one group, chemical decomposition of the mineral fraction is highly advanced and extends to great depths; in the other, chemical decomposition is of little or no consequence. The difference is conspicuous in the contrast between the road cuts in the saprolite along the Kennedy Expressway near Baltimore and those in the hard rocks or bouldery glacial drift along the Connecticut Thruway. The parent rocks may be alike, and there is no gradation between these extremes of weathering. The highly decomposed soils are relics from past climates, but the climatic conditions under which they formed are not known. The climatic and other environmental factors that have operated since the Wisconsin glacial maximum have not been such as to cause much chemical decomposition of the mineral fraction of the younger soils. The contrast in degree of mineral alteration in the soils commonly is attributed to the difference in their ages, but this is an oversimplified explanation. The degree of difference, and the lack of gradation between the extremes, probably reflects some major differences in the environments under which the soils formed.

Soil erosion in the Appalachian Highlands is severe, or potentially severe, wherever the Red and Yellow Podzols form the surface, and is particularly severe in the southern part of the Piedmont Province. An explanation that probably accounts, at least in part, for the high susceptibility of these soils to erosion is that they formed in an environmental regimen that no longer exists, and are now out of equilibrium with the environment. The younger soils in the Appalachian Highlands are subject to much less erosion, even in the mountainous areas where slopes are steep.

Peneplains

The term peneplain (etymologically, "almost a plain") has special meanings in plant ecology and geology. In plant ecology, the term has been used to refer to regions where variations in local climate are minor; in geology, peneplains are considered to be the ultimate

or penultimate product of stream erosion: a plain graded to sea level and surface worn down by the subaerial erosion of mountainous or hilly terrain composed of rocks varying in structure and resistance. The part of the Piedmont Province that forms the surface at Harrisburg and extends from there to the Fall Line is a dissected plain and has been called the Harrisburg Peneplain (Fig. 11.24). The erosion surface covers thousands of square miles, and its local relief generally is less than 300 feet. A few isolated monadnocks (p. 183) rise above it.

The erosion surface at Harrisburg, and a similarly dissected one in New England, forms low plateaus whose surfaces truncate structurally complex igneous, sedimentary, and metamorphic rocks. Planation occurred after

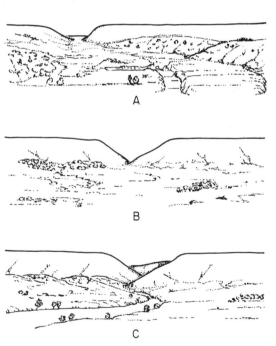

Figure 11.22 *Accordant levels of mountain summits on either side of water gaps in the Appalachian Mountains have been interpreted as the surface of an ancient peneplain. (A) Delaware River water gap. (B) Water gap at Harrisburg, Pennsylvania. (C) Water gap at Cumberland, Maryland.*

Triassic time, because Triassic formations are among those truncated. Parts of the Harrisburg Peneplain were eroded and weathered to saprolite before Cretaceous time, because Cretaceous formations locally overlap the surface and the saprolite west of the Fall Line.

In addition to the theory of peneplanation by streams, another theory attributes the erosion surface at Harrisburg to wave action at a time when sea level may have been relatively higher and the ocean may have extended to the Blue Ridge. By either theory the present hills and valleys would be the result of later erosion as a result of uplift since planation. The irregularities on the surface seem to be caused by differences in rock hardness, and this forms the basis of a third theory that assumes that the area has always been dissected and has always had about the same relief as now and that the whole area was gradually lowered. Suffice it to say that the erosional history is obscure.

West of the Piedmont Province, many ridges appear to rise to accordant heights (Figs.

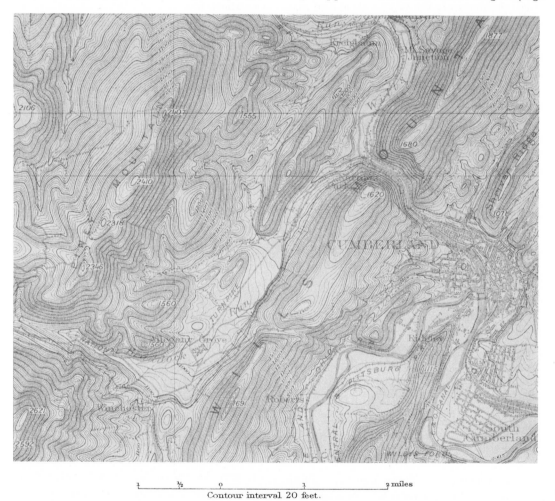

Contour interval 20 feet.

Figure 11.23 *Map illustrates water gaps at Wills Creek above Cumberland, Maryland. The gap east of Allegany Grove, referred to as a wind gap, is the former course of Braddock Run; it was captured and turned northward to Wills Creek. (From U.S.G.S. Frostburg sheet, 1908.)*

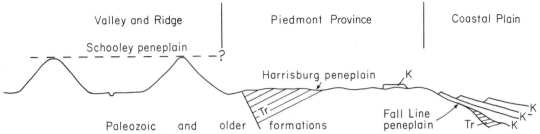

Figure 11.24 *Some interpretations of erosion surfaces (peneplains) along the Piedmont Province. Both the Harrisburg and Fall Line erosion surfaces cut across Triassic (Tr) as well as older formations and are overlapped by Cretaceous (K). They may be the same surface bent by folding, or developed at different slopes by different processes. The higher Schooley Peneplain has been postulated on the basis of accordant heights of ridges, but there is dispute about the degree of accordance; some regard the ridges as monadnocks.*

11.22, 11.23), and have been interpreted as remnants of an older erosion surface that has been called the Schooley Peneplain. Fig. 11.24 illustrates some interpretations of these old erosion surfaces.

Rivers and Canals

Rivers in the Appalachian Highlands are short, only about a fifth as long as those draining the Southern Rocky Mountains (Fig. 5.1), but they are much more numerous and larger in terms of discharge. Nearly a dozen rivers draining the Appalachian Highlands have discharges equal to or greater than the combined discharges of the vastly longer Colorado River and Rio Grande. The rivers provide bountiful water supplies, are a major source of hydroelectric power, and have played a major part in United States transportation history. Unhappily, their potential for recreational uses has been impaired by pollution.

Our first transportation boom was based on use of the rivers and led to an era of canal building. In 1800 transportation in the Appalachian Highlands was accomplished largely by pack animals. A loaded pack train with eight animals might transport a ton. This led to development of roads and the Conestoga wagon, which could transport 4 to 6 tons with four to six horses. Canal boats, a later development, were pulled by only one or two horses and could transport 40 to 80 tons. Both the automation represented by the Conestoga wagon and the government support of roads necessary for them were protested by the packers. In turn, the wagoners protested the automation represented by canal boats and the government support for construction of canals. Later, it became the canal men's turn to protest competition by the railroads, and, still later, the railroads protested competition by airlines, trucklines, and pipelines.

The canal systems constructed in the eastern United States between 1800 and 1850 are illustrated in Fig. 11.25 and listed below. Most of the dates refer to completion of work.

New England canals
   1. Sebago-Portland Canal; Maine, 1830.
   2. Middlesex Canal; Merrimac River to Boston, 1803.
   3. Blackstone Canal; Worcester, Mass., to Providence, Rhode Island, 1828.
   4. Hampshire and Hampden Canal; Northhampton, Mass., to New Haven, Conn., along Farmington River, 1835.

Erie Canal and its tributaries

5. Erie Canal; Albany to Lake Erie, 1824.

6. Champlain Canal, 1819.

7. Black River Canal, connecting the Erie Canal and Lake Ontario; authorized 1836, completed 1855.

8. Oswego Canal, connecting Oneida Lake and Lake Ontario; 1828.

9. Genesee Valley Canal, from Lake Ontario to the Genesee Valley; authorized 1836, completed ca. 1850.

10. Cayuga and Seneca Canal, ca. 1828.

11. Chemung Canal; connecting Seneca Lake with Susquehanna River, ca. 1830.

12. Chenango Canal; authorized 1833, completed after 1863.

Other Atlantic seaboard canals

13. Delaware and Hudson Canal, 1826.

14. Morris Canal; from Newark Bay to Paterson and the Delaware River at Easton, 1826.

15. Delaware and Raritan Canal, 1834.

16. Lehigh Canal (1827) and Delaware Division (1832); from the anthracite coal fields to Trenton.

Figure 11.25 *Map of the northeastern United States, showing the pattern of the early canals built to connect or to extend the navigable waterways. Numbers refer to list (pp. 197–198).*

17. Schuylkill Navigation Canal; from anthracite fields at Pottsville to Philadelphia, 1825. First tunnel in the United States.

18. Union Canal; Harrisburg to Reading, 1828. Second tunnel.

19. North Branch Canal; along the Susquehanna River, ca. 1833.

20. West Branch Canal; along West Branch of the Susquehanna River; completed to Williamsport, 1834.

21. Main Line Canal; from Harrisburg via the Juniata River, across the Allegheny Front by the Portage Railway, and down the Conemaugh River to the Ohio River at Pittsburgh, ca. 1829.

22. Susquehanna and Tidewater Canal, 1840.

23. Chesapeake and Delaware Canal, 1829.

24. Chesapeake and Ohio Canal; Washington, D.C., to Cumberland; begun 1828, completed 1850.

25. James River Canal; constructed around falls at Richmond, 1795; completed to Lynchburg, 1840; extended to Lexington and Buchanan, 1851.

26. Dismal Swamp Canal; one of the earliest. Completed for small craft, 1794; completed for flat boats, 1807. Chesapeake Bay to Albemarle and Pamlico Sounds.

27. Santee Canal; from Charleston, South Carolina, to Santee River, 1800.

Canals in the Northwest Territory

28. Ohio and Erie Canal; Cleveland to Portsmouth, Ohio, 1833.

29. Hocking Valley Branch; to coal fields, 1838.

30. Ohio and Pennsylvania Canal; from the Ohio and Erie at Akron to Newcastle and Pittsburgh, 1840.

31. Sandy and Beaver Canal; from the Ohio and Erie to Beaver River and Pittsburgh, 1840.

32. Walhonding Branch Canal, ca. 1836.

33. Muskingum Canal; to Marietta, ca. 1836.

34. Miami and Erie Canal; from Cincinnati to Dayton (ca. 1831); Maumee and Toledo section completed 1843.

35. Warren County Canal, ca. 1836.

36. White Water Canal, 1846.

37. Wabash and Erie Canal; completed from junction with Miami and Erie to Lafayette, Indiana, 1843; to Evansville, ca. 1855.

38. Illinois and Michigan Canal, 1848.

In most parts of the Appalachian Highlands, the river valleys are the favored routes for travel, and a transportation map showing railroads and highways as well as canals has the same pattern as the drainage. An exception is the Pennsylvania Turnpike, which tunnels through the fold mountains of the Valley and Ridge Province. In a few parts of the Appalachian Plateaus, especially toward the east, the uplands are broad and the valleys narrow. In those places the travel routes are on the uplands, but they parallel the drainage.

Water Supply and Water Power

Water supplies in the Appalachian Highlands are adequate for present needs and are estimated to be adequate to meet all demands anticipated by the end of the century. The water problems in this region relate not to insufficient supply but to floods and pollution.

The average annual runoff exceeds 10 inches. The months of maximum runoff and greatest flood frequency are February and March in the south, March and April in the central part, and April and May in New England. Towns in the mountain valleys may be inundated by floods where the rivers are not controlled. Figure 11.26 illustrates the network of dams along the Tennessee River; these dams control floods, produce power, and provide recreation.

But dams are not always a blessing, for some have failed, with disastrous results. One such tragedy occurred in the Appalachian Plateau at Johnstown, Pennsylvania, in May 1889. A dam 700 feet long and 100 feet high on a branch of the Conemaugh River about 12 miles above Johnstown gave way during a period of flooding, and released a flood that was 20 feet high as it swept through the city. Other towns and villages in the path of the flood were also swept away. Two thousand persons lost their lives.

Water power resources of the Appalachian

Highlands are about a third of the total for the country. Some unused capacity remains in New York and northern Pennsylvania, but in other parts of the Highlands the potential is almost fully developed. The growth of New England as a factory area after the American Revolution was due in large part to the ready availability of water power.

Pollution of water supplies by industrial wastes, sewage, and household detergents is a major problem throughout the Appalachian Highlands. The rivers and creeks have been used for disposal of wastes to such a degree that many are discolored and unpleasant to look at, some are unpleasant to smell, and more than a few have to be posted "Stay away —Typhoid!" Floating feces or other waste do not make a pretty sight, nor does the sudsy detergent foam that collects around leaves where branches reach to the water surface. The water in some rivers is so lacking in oxygen that, it is said, nails will not rust. Is all of this really necessary? Not if enough people insist otherwise.

Most municipalities use surface water, because it is plentiful; a few use groundwater. Examples of variations in water quality as a result of mixing of streams having different sources are illustrated in Figure 11.27; examples of the differences in quality of waters in municipal systems are given in Figure 11.28.

Municipal water supplies in New England average less than 100 ppm of dissolved solids.

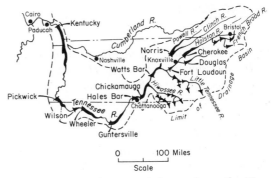

Figure 11.26 *System of dams along the Tennessee River and its tributaries.*

The hardness (noncarbonate hardness attributable to calcium) is correspondingly low. Municipal water supplies of cities in the Piedmont Province come mostly from rivers and are equally good. In both regions, groundwater contains, on the average, more dissolved solids and has greater hardness.

Water supplies of cities in the Appalachian Plateaus are variable in quality (Fig. 11.28). Many contain more than 200 ppm of dissolved solids, and these waters are of two kinds. In the north, mostly in New York State, the surface water and groundwater are hard because of their high content of carbonates and cal-

cium. In the bituminous coalfields the total dissolved solids in the surface waters commonly exceeds 200 ppm, but they are not correspondingly hard because they contain sulfate and very little calcium.

Mineral Resources

Almost one and a quarter billion dollars worth of minerals are produced annually in the Appalachian Highlands. Of this amount, coal, referred to by Emerson as the portable climate, accounts for 60 percent, oil and gas 20 percent, nonmetals 15 percent, and metals 5 percent. The Appalachian Highlands are, par excellence, the place to learn about coal.

Bituminous coalfields are almost coextensive with the Appalachian Plateaus, exclusive of the part in New York. Anthracite coal occurs in the Valley and Ridge Province in Pennsylvania. These deposits of bituminous and anthracite coal are in formations of Pennsylvanian age; in addition, there is coal in Triassic formations in Virginia and North Carolina.

The coal beds represent the woody matter that accumulated in swamps. These were coastal swamps probably not unlike the present swamps on the Coastal Plain except that the trees were related to the ferns and club mosses. Decomposition of plant matter in swamps evolves carbon dioxide (CO_2), carbon monoxide (CO), and marsh gas (methane, CH_4). As these and other gases escape, there is an increase in the concentration of carbon in the decayed wood, and it turns brown and then black. After burial by younger sediments, more volatiles escape. As the carbon content increases, the material changes successively from peat to lignite, to bituminous coal, to anthracite coal, and finally to pure carbon, graphite.

The heat value of coal lies in its content of volatile matter, and this is about 25 percent greater in bituminous coal than in anthracite.

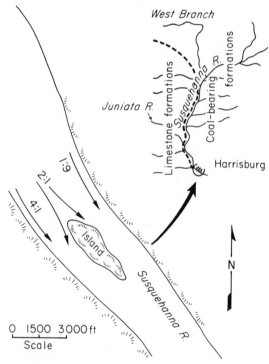

Figure 11.27 *Ratio of bicarbonate to sulfate in the Susquehanna River at Harrisburg, Pa. Water flowing along the west bank is like the water in the western tributaries, which drain limestone formations, and contains a high proportion (4:1) of bicarbonate as compared to sulfate. Water along the east bank is like the water draining the eastern tributaries, and contains a low proportion (1:9) of bicarbonate as compared to sulfate. (Data from U.S.G.S.)*

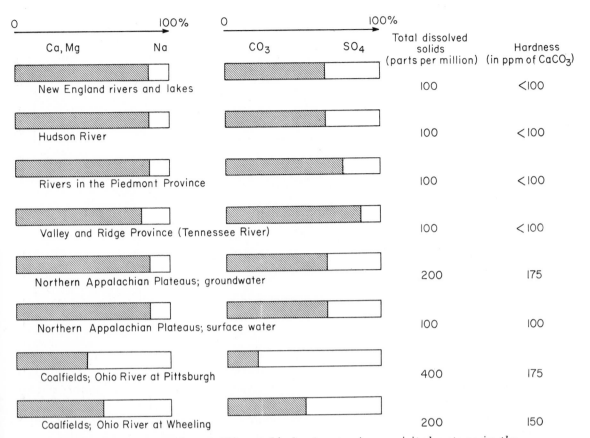

Figure 11.28 *Examples of different kinds of water in municipal systems in the Appalachian Highlands.*

It is still greater in lignite, which combusts spontaneously. But the heating value of lignite is less than bituminous coal because it retains so much moisture. Bituminous coal is favored for industry because of its efficiency; anthracite was favored for household use because of its relative cleanliness.

From east to west across the highlands, there is an orderly change in the form in which coal occurs (Fig. 11.29). Owing to the westward decrease in folding and other deformation the content of volatile constituents increases in that direction. In the highly deformed Narragansett Basin in New England, there is nearly pure carbon—graphite. In the Valley and Ridge Province there is anthracite. In the eastern part of the plateaus there is bi-

tuminous coal with a low content of volatiles; farther west there is bituminous coal with a high content of volatiles.

The earliest coal mines (1750) were in Triassic formations near Richmond, Virginia. Anthracite in Pennsylvania had been discovered before 1803 but was regarded as too difficult to burn and fit only for surfacing roads or walks. Deposits of anthracite, altered almost to graphite, were mined in Rhode Island as early as 1808, but the foundries along the Atlantic seaboard used bituminous coal imported from England, until the war of 1812 cut off that supply. Thereafter, anthracite was used and found satisfactory under forced draft.

Bituminous coal beds in the Appalachian Plateaus are 8 to 10 feet thick. They are nearly

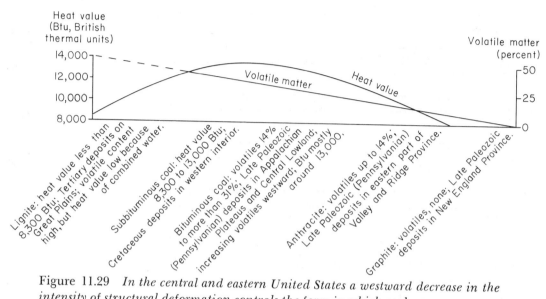

Figure 11.29 *In the central and eastern United States a westward decrease in the intensity of structural deformation controls the form in which coal occurs.*

horizontal and can be mined by stripping (turning back the overburden by shovel), or by horizontal workings—tunnels, rooms, and adits. The anthracite coal occurs in the folded rocks of the Valley and Ridge Province, and is mined mostly by vertical or inclined shafts.

Coal yields many by-products. Coke is made by heating coal in ovens without air, and the gases are driven off without burning the coal. The carbon product, coke, is a firm, porous material that can be used in blast furnaces. The gases are collected and distilled to yield more than a thousand useful materials.

Coal mine explosions, one of the major hazards of the industry, are of at least three kinds: explosions of mine gas, explosions of dust, and rock bursts. A combustible solid like coal is explosive when in the form of dust and mixed with the right proportion of air. Rock bursts result from removal of support from a bed that is under tremendous confining pressure; removal of the support may allow the rock to burst into the opened space.

Just as there is an eastward change from bituminous coal to anthracite and graphite, there is an eastward change in the distribu-

tion of oil and gas. The oil occurs in the central and western parts of the Appalachian Plateaus. The gas fields extend farther east but barely to the Valley and Ridge Province. The more eastern parts of the highlands, the Piedmont Province and New England, are too severely deformed and metamorphosed to retain oil or gas.

The petroleum industry had its beginnings in northern Pennsylvania, where oil had been encountered in wells drilled for salt brine. It was first used for medicinal purposes and sold under the name Seneca Oil. Before the Civil War supplies of sperm oil and whale oil declined, and in 1859 E. L. Drake drilled a well 69 feet deep for the purpose of producing oil. This was the first well drilled specifically for oil, and it brought in a well that produced 25 barrels a day. Both the production of oil and the development of drilling equipment began with the salt industry.

Gas was first obtained by distillation of bituminous coal, and as early as the year 1802, gas had been obtained from coal in quantities and by methods that made it feasible to consider using gas on a large scale for lighting.

Baltimore began using gas for street lights in 1817; New York adopted gas in 1823. By 1900 the nightly round of the street lighter had become a part of urban culture.

Other mineral products and important reserves of the Appalachian Highlands are:

1. Bauxite and highly aluminous clay: From Pennsylvania southward.
2. Building stones such as slate, granite, marble, and flagstone: Widespread in the Piedmont Province and New England.
3. Cement: A major industry in the limestone belt of the Valley and Ridge Province.
4. Chromite: Minor deposits in the Piedmont Province in Pennsylvania, Maryland, and North Carolina.
5. Cobalt: Reserves at Cornwall, Pennsylvania.
6. Copper: Ducktown, Tennessee, and Cornwall, Pennsylvania.
7. Gold: Piedmont Province in North Carolina; mostly of historic interest.
8. Glass sand: Sandstone formations in the Valley and Ridge Province.
9. Graphite: Low-grade deposits in Rhode Island, New York, Pennsylvania, and Alabama.
10. Iron: Hematite and limonite deposits in Silurian formations in the Valley and Ridge Province; especially productive in Alabama. Magnetite in metamorphic formations of the Piedmont Province in Pennsylvania and New Jersey, and in the Adirondack Province.
11. Manganese: Numerous small deposits in the Valley and Ridge Province and the western part of the Piedmont Province from Virginia southward.
12. Mica: Important deposits in the southern Piedmont and in New England.
13. Molybdenum: Reserves in North Carolina at the eastern edge of the Piedmont Province.
14. Salt: beds and brines underlie the Appalachian Plateaus in West Virginia, northern Pennsylvania, New York, and Virginia.
15. Sulfur: Reserves at Ducktown, Tennessee, and in Maine.
16. Talc, from serpentine masses: Piedmont Province.
17. Titanium: Reserves in the Adirondacks and in the Piedmont Province.
18. Tungsten: Reserves in the Piedmont Province in North Carolina and Virginia.
19. Vanadium: In titaniferous magnetite in the Adirondacks, northern New Jersey, and parts of the Piedmont Province.
20. Zinc: Valley and Ridge Province in Tennessee and Virginia, in Piedmont Province in Pennsylvania, in Reading Prong in northern New Jersey; and in the Adirondacks.

Forests, Parks, and Rivers— The Underdeveloped Resources

The forested mountains, broad rivers, and (in the north) the lakes of the Appalachian Highlands, represent a largely undeveloped major resource that could serve as vacationland. Half of the population of the United States lives within a day's drive of the Appalachian Trail (Fig. 11.30), and as the population increases, the recreational importance of the highlands increases. More land should be set aside, protected from unsightly development including billboards and reserved for camping and other recreational use.

Empty land areas that exist in northern Maine and New Hampshire, the Adirondacks, and plateaus in north-central Pennsylvania should be saved now, for they are far more suited for multipurpose forests and recreational use than for farming or for industry.

Farther south is Appalachia, a depressed area. Perhaps this area is depressed because we have used it without regard for its total physiographic setting. Valleys there are not suited for heavy industry, because of the atmospheric condition that frequently prevents escape of smoke and fumes (Fig. 11.31). The evidence is plain for all to see—deforested mountainsides leeward from industrial stacks, and smog over every city and town and even over the isolated factories. The air at best is

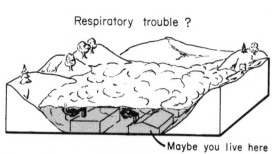

Figure 11.31 *Smog—a major problem in the Appalachian Highlands.*

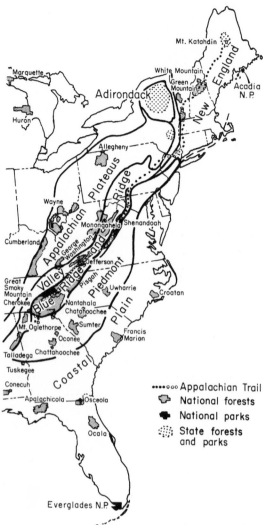

Figure 11.30 *The Appalachian Trail, and larger forests and parks in the eastern United States, and their relation to the physiographic provinces.*

disagreeably smelly and grimy, and at worst is lethal (witness Donora). Lakes and streams also are contaminated with wastes to the point of making them unsafe and unpleasant. These conditions, which arose as an inevitable result of long-term industrial growth, can be corrected and the area restored when enough people recognize that man does not exist to serve industry but that industry exists to serve man.

It would be to our advantage as a nation if most or all of the rougher parts of the Appalachian Highlands were state or national forests, and the land developed for camping, boating, hiking, swimming, golf, tennis, fishing, skiing, and other sports, even including quiet motoring at safe and reasonable speeds. At least 60 million people would be better off! A program of rural renewal should be established that would protect the areas that are still unsettled, reduce the population in the areas already settled, and provide for exporting the products of the forests and mines rather than refining or consuming them there.

The Central
12   United States

The central United States, between the Appalachian Plateaus and the Rocky Mountains, is mostly a vast plain, but there are some highlands, including both plateaus and fold mountains. Several physiographic provinces are included in the region (Fig. 12.1). The largest, and lowest, is the Central Lowland. North of it is the Superior Upland. To the south are the Interior Low Plateaus, Ozark Plateaus, and Ouachita Province. To the west are the Great Plains. These provinces are distinguished chiefly on the basis of their geologic structure and geologic history, but, in part, on the basis of climatic differences.

Structural Divisions

Central Lowland

The largest of the physiographic provinces is the Central Lowland. At its eastern edge, where it joins the Appalachians, the elevation of this lowland, and plain, is about 1,000 feet. It slopes westward to an altitude of about 500 feet along the Mississippi River, a distance of about 400 miles, and it rises again farther west to an altitude of about 2,000 feet at the 100th meridian, which is approximately the western boundary of this province.

The Central Lowland covers 585,000 square miles in 16 states, an area about equal to that of Alaska and twice the size of Texas—more than 15 percent of the United States. The low altitude and lack of much local relief results in scenery that is as plain as the plain is extensive. Scenery in the Central Lowland has a great deal of sameness and plainness, and only a few small tracts have been set aside as parks illustrating the physiography, as at Clifty Falls State Park on the Ohio River in Indiana, and Starved Rock State Park on the Illinois River in Illinois.

Outstanding features of the Central Lowland are its

1. Great extent.
2. Low altitude and slight local relief.
3. Continental climate.
4. Great lakes and great rivers.
5. Mantle of glacial deposits that smooth the ground surface and conceal the underlying rock formations.
6. Subsurface structure of broadly warped sedimentary rock formations that are thin by comparison with the same formations under the bordering mountain provinces.
7. Rich economy, well balanced between agriculture, minerals, manufacturing, and transportation.

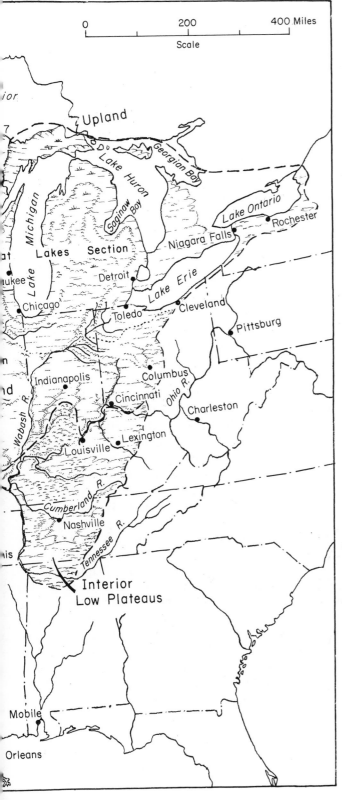

Figure 12.1 *Physiographic map
of the central United States.*

Most of the Central Lowland Province was glaciated, and the sections of the province are distinguished chiefly on the basis of differences in their glacial histories.

At the north is the Great Lakes Section, a plain of glacial till attributable to the Wisconsin glaciation. This plain is interrupted by morainal ridges, mostly about 50 feet high, arranged in concentric arcs around the rounded ends of the lakes (Fig. 12.2). Valleys between the morainal ridges are several miles wide. Parts of the till plains are hummocky with knobs and kettle holes containing lakes, ponds, or swamps (Fig. 12.3).

South of the Great Lakes Section is the Till Plain Section, an area without knob and kettle topography, but consisting of broad level uplands between valleys that have steep sides and broad floodplains (Fig. 12.4). The drainage is integrated, and there are few lakes or ponds. Most of this section lies south of the late Wisconsin moraines. It includes some early Wisconsin moraines, but much of it is on Illinoian till and is of pre-Wisconsin age. The difference in age of the tills accounts in part

for the difference in landforms; the young deposits at the north form a rough surface with a drainage system that is not integrated. West of the Mississippi River the still older Kansan till forms a plain that is correspondingly more dissected. The valleys are more closely spaced and the uplands more rounded than they are east of the river. Present relief is 100 to 300 feet.

The differences between the several till plains are in part attributable to differences in the time available for the drainage to become established and in part to differences in the modes of deposition of the till. Differences in landforms built of glacially deposited gravel, sand, and clay may reflect differences in the rates of retreat of the ice. Ice that melted back quickly left deposits differing from those that formed in front of ice that melted back slowly. Other differences depend on whether the rates of melting and retreat were uniform or intermittent, and on the direction and amount of slope of the land surface in front of the ice.

The dissected till plains east and west of the Mississippi River are mantled with loess that commonly is more than 30 feet thick. In all ways this blanket of wind-deposited silt resembles that along the east side of the Mississippi Alluvial Section in the Coastal Plain and was deposited in the same way—by winds sweeping eastward across the floodplains of large rivers, where mud was deposited from floodwaters resulting from melting glaciers. The loess thins eastward away from the river beds, which were their source. All these loess-covered areas are subject to severe soil erosion.

The Small Lakes Section in the northwestern part of the Central Lowland (Fig. 12.1) is a plain with hummocky moraines of Wisconsin till. Much of the surface is knob and kettle topography, not unlike that farther east around the Great Lakes (Fig. 12.3) except that the ponds and marshes are smaller and fewer, probably because the annual rainfall here is only about 20 inches whereas it is 30 inches or more farther east. In this part of the Central

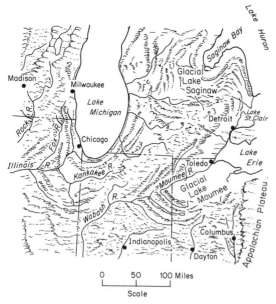

Figure 12.2 *Map illustrating morainal ridges that curve around the ends of the Great Lakes.*

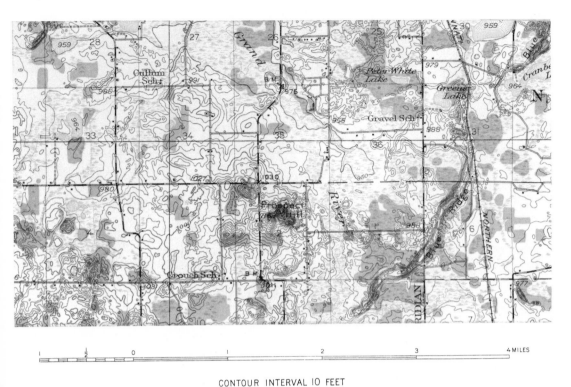

Figure 12.3 *Map of knob-and-kettle topography in the Great Lakes Section of the Central Lowland. Blue Ridge is an esker. (From U.S.G.S. Jackson, Michigan, quadrangle map.)*

Lowland the valleys are parallel to each other and to the former position of the ice front. These valleys are former outwash channels of the retreating ice (Fig. 12.5).

Along the Red River, on the boundary between Minnesota and North Dakota, is the southern part of the bed of glacial Lake Agassiz. This lake was once 700 feet deep, 700 miles long, and 250 miles wide. It occupied an area greater than that of all the Great Lakes combined. It was by far the largest of all the glacial lakes. Most of this lake was in what is now Canada; only a small part extended into the United States. Lakes Winnipeg, Winnipegosis, Manitoba, and Lake of the Woods are remnants of it. Lake Agassiz formed when the ice had retreated northward into Canada but still blocked the valleys draining into Hudson Bay. The overflow drained southeast-

ward via an outlet channel that was eroded to a depth of 100 to 220 feet and to a width of one mile. This big channel is now occupied by the Minnesota River, a small stream in an oversized valley that obviously was once oc-

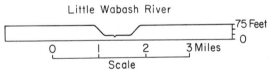

Figure 12.4 *Profile across the Little Wabash River near Effingham, Illinois. In the southeastern part of the Central Lowland the uplands are broad and level; the valleys are steep-sided but have broad floodplains. These landforms are developed on glacial deposits that are much older than those bordering the Great Lakes. (Vertical scale is exaggerated about twenty-five times.)*

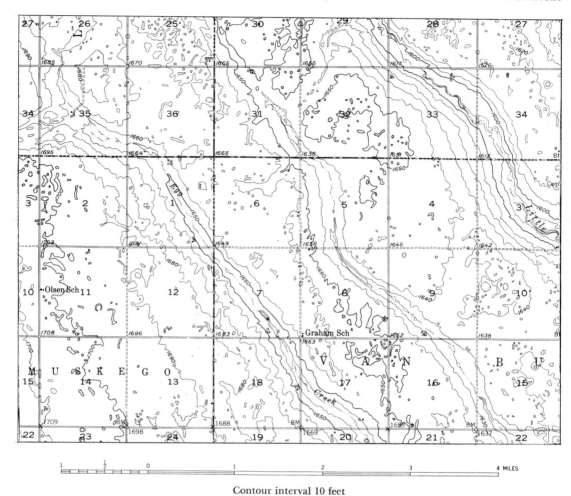

Contour interval 10 feet

Figure 12.5 *Till plain with knob-and-kettle topography interrupted by parallel valleys representing outwash channels that formed along the ice front as it retreated northeastward. (From U.S.G.S. Lansford, North Dakota, quadrangle.)*

cupied by a large, vigorous river. As the ice retreated farther northward, Lake Agassiz also discharged into the north side of Lake Superior.

A measure of the extent of poorly drained land in these glaciated areas is provided by Figure 9.18,A. Only the low parts of the Coastal Plain have comparably extensive wet areas.

Two parts of the Central Lowland were not glaciated. One of these, the Driftless Section (Fig. 12.1), comprises the southwestern quarter of Wisconsin and the adjoining 250-mile

stretch of the Mississippi River Valley. Not only is this area without glacial deposits and without glacial striae, but it preserves small, fragile landforms, such as natural bridges, arches, buttes, and rock towers (Fig. 12.6), that could not have survived being overridden by glacial ice. The valleys, of course, contain deposits of streams that discharged glacial meltwaters, and there are deposits of loess.

The Driftless Section escaped glaciation because of its topographic situation midway between the deep valleys occupied by Lake Superior and Lake Michigan, and because it is on the lee (south) side of the ridges in the Superior Upland. The glacial lobes became concentrated in the valleys and diverted to either side of the Driftless Section. The northern and southwestern edges of the Driftless Section, however, were covered by one of the pre-Wisconsin glaciers, and those areas contain deposits of deeply weathered till. But the Driftless Section was missed by the ice of the Wisconsin stage, and only about a third was covered by the earlier glaciers.

The other part of the Central Lowland that escaped glaciation is the Osage Plain (Fig. 12.1), which lies south of the limit reached by the ice. This section, beginning at the Kansas and Missouri rivers and extending southwestward to central Texas, is underlain by late Paleozoic formations that dip gently westward. In southeastern Kansas these are mostly shale and limestone, and the more resistant beds, the limestones, form low cuestas facing east. Southward, in Oklahoma, the formations contain less limestone, and the cuestas there are mostly sandstone.

In the southern part of the Osage Plains, the plains form uplands in which the rivers are trenched in gorges a few hundred feet deep. These rivers have sandy beds, and some, notably the Cimarron and Canadian Rivers, are bordered on the lee (northeast) side by sand dunes in belts 10 to 15 miles wide.

Superior Upland

The Superior Upland (Fig. 12.7), like the Central Lowland, was glaciated, but it differs in being an upwarp of Precambrian rocks, a part of the Precambrian Shield of Canada; the United States portion covers less than 100,000 square miles. This province is structurally very different from the Central Lowland, but the differences are partly masked by the effects of the Pleistocene glaciation. An anticlinal uplift trending southwestward into the United States has elevated the Precambrian rocks and has turned up the Paleozoic formations, which

underlie the glacial drift in the Central Lowland, in a series of cuestas facing the Upland and sloping away from it (Figs. 12.8, 12.9). One of these, the Niagara Escarpment defines the arcuate north shores of Lake Michigan and Huron and extends to Niagara Falls (Fig.

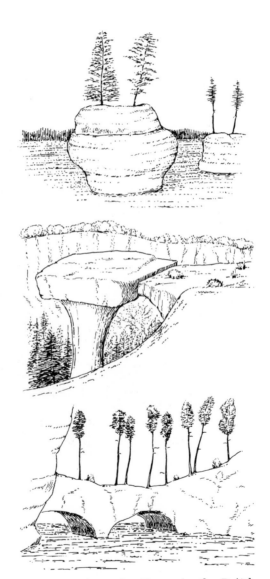

Figure 12.6 *Some landforms in the Driftless Section that would not have survived being overridden by glacial ice.*

12.9) and eastward across central New York.

The Precambrian rocks are much deformed and metamorphosed. Their structures are complex, but the structures were truncated by erosion before the Cambrian formations were deposited. As a result of subsequent uplift the Cambrian and later Paleozoic formations have been stripped from the Superior Upland and

the Precambrian rocks again exposed. The present relief, about 1,500 feet, results from later erosion by streams and glaciers that cut deeply into the less resistant of the Precambrian formations. The more resistant formations have again been etched into relief, and control the trend of many of the ranges, peninsulas, and bays of Lake Superior. Gravity and

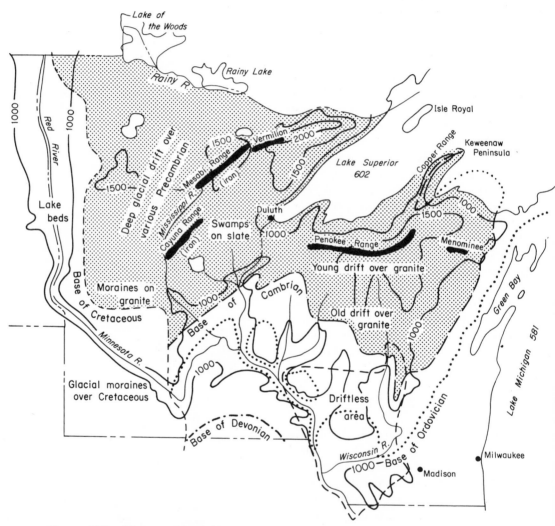

Figure 12.7 *Map of the Superior Upland (stippled area), an anticlinal upwarp. Paleozoic formations on the east and south flanks dip away from the upland and form a series of cuestas. Green Bay lies between two cuestas. On the west, Cretaceous formations overlap the Precambrian rocks and the cuestas of Paleozoic formations south of the upland. Principal ranges are shown in black. Most of the upland is deeply mantled with glacial drift, which obscures the older rocks.*

magnetic surveys indicate that the structures continue southwestward beneath the younger formations that bury the Precambrian in that direction.

On the west side of the Upland the Cretaceous formations extend unconformably onto the Precambrian and onto the south-dipping Paleozoic formations in the cuestas south of the Upland.

The Precambrian formations of the Superior Upland and the principal events that they record are listed in Table 12.1. The next important event in shaping the land surface

and resources of the Superior Upland, that of the Pleistocene glaciation, occurred 600 million years later—a mere few hundred thousand years ago. The advance of the ice caused the land to sink, but when the ice melted, the land surface rose, as is recorded by the tilting of beaches along late Pleistocene lakes. The rebounding rise, however, probably has been much less than the original sinking, for the bottom of Lake Superior is more than 700 feet below sea level—a depth that seems too great to be attributed wholly to glacial erosion.

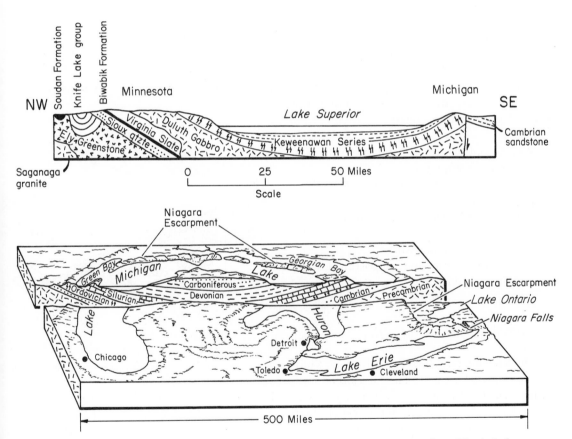

Figure 12.8 *Differences in geologic structure under the Great Lakes. (Top) Lake Lake Superior occupies a synclical basin. (Bottom) Lakes Michigan and Huron occupy strike valleys between cuestas. They are in back of the Niagara Escarpment and flank the structural basin under Michigan. Green Bay and Georgian Bay also occupy strike valleys between cuestas; they are in front of the Escarpment.*

One of the major effects of the mantle of glacial drift is the hummocky topography that made Minnesota "the land of 10,000 lakes." Many of the springs in the Superior Upland are fed by groundwater seeping through the glacial drift, moving laterally on the underlying bedrock, and discharging on the sides of valleys.

Minnesota resembles the glaciated part of the Appalachian Highlands to the degree that the bedrock formations stand high enough to form monadnocks and to express their structural forms topographically. Moreover, the hills are glacially rounded. The morainal ground between them is hummocky. The depressions are occupied by lakes and swamps; the hillocks are kames, eskers, and drumlins. The outline of Lake Superior both in general and in detail reflects the bedrock structure.

Other features of the Superior Upland are dealt with later. Among the outstanding features of the province are its

1. Rainy, continental climate with cold winters and hot summers.
2. Podzol Soils, with extensive deposits of peat.
3. Conifer forest, which consists in large part of spruce and fir.
4. Iron and copper deposits.
5. The many lakes and opportunities for camping and boating.

Interior Low Plateaus

The Interior Low Plateaus, which lie south of the glaciated area, are part of a broad anticline, referred to as the Cincinnati Arch, which forms the west flank of the Appalachian geosyncline and forms the east flank of the broad shallow structural basins under southern Illinois and the Mississippi River Alluvial Section. The axis of the arch approximately parallels the Appalachian Highlands and extends 600 miles from northwestern Alabama

to northwestern Ohio. North of the Ohio River these arched Paleozoic formations have been glaciated, and the structure is obscure. The nonglaciated parts of the arch, mostly south of the Ohio River but extending into southern Indiana, reflect the geologic structure and constitute the Interior Low Plateaus (Figs. 12.1 and 12.10), an area less than 100,000 square miles.

The Lexington Plain, Kentucky's area of bluegrass, and the Nashville Basin are on structural domes where Ordovician formations, mostly limestone, are exposed at the surface. These limestone formations are cavernous, and the land surface is pitted with sinkholes where caverns have collapsed. Much of the drainage enters the ground and is discharged in underground rivers. The surface streams are entrenched in steep-walled valleys.

Both the Lexington Plain and Nashville Basins are surrounded by infacing escarp-

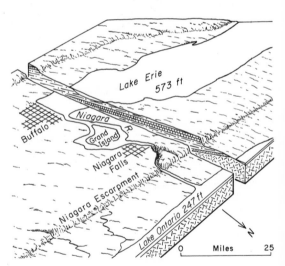

Figure 12.9 *Niagara Falls, view southwest. Niagara River, flowing from Lake Erie, divides at Grand Island, goes over falls almost 200 feet high at the Niagara Escarpment, and discharges in a gorge to Lake Ontario. The escarpment south of Lake Erie is the northern edge of the Appalachian Plateau, here composed of Devonian formations.*

TABLE 12.1 Precambrian deposits and Precambrian history of the Superior Upland.

Formation or Event	Description
Flooding by Cambrian Sea	Deposition of marine sediments. Estimated to have begun 600 million years ago.
Erosion	Truncation of Precambrian structures.
Intrusion of Duluth Gabbro	Gabbro intruded at base of Keeweenawan Series and as sills in the Keeweenawan; in part granite.
Keeweenawan Series	Deposition of lavas, about 3,000 feet thick; some sandstone and conglomerate interbedded with the lavas.
Animikie Series	Virginia Slate deposited as a clayey mud in the Animikie seaway; 2,000 to 3,000 feet thick.
	Deposition of Biwabik Formation, an iron-bearing deposit of silica and carbonates. This is the iron formation of the Mesabi Range.
	Deposition of Sioux Quartzite, a sandstone derived from basalt.
Erosion	Truncation of fold structures developed during Algoman orogeny.
Algoman Orogeny	Folding and volcanism; intrusion of granites at the Vermilion and Mesabi ranges.
Knife Lake Group	Slate, quartzite, conglomerate, iron formations, and volcanic tuff and agglomerate; at least 11,000 feet thick.
Erosion	Truncation of fold structures developed during the Laurentian orogeny.
Laurentian Orogeny	Uplift with folding and intrusion of granite.
Soudan Formation	Jasper and slate a few hundred feet thick. Subsequent weathering and leaching of the silica have left a deposit enriched in iron—the high-grade Vermilion iron ore that has been mined almost continuously since 1884.
Ely Greenstone	Lavas representing flows that accumulated under water; several thousand feet thick. Estimated 2 billion years old.

ments, or cuestas, as much as 400 feet high; they are topographic basins on the structural domes (Fig. 12.11). The surfaces that slope away from the escarpments make up the Highland Rim. Eastward, the Highland Rim slopes toward the Appalachian Plateaus; westward, it slopes toward the Tennessee and Mississippi rivers. East of the Lexington Plain the Highland Rim coincides with the west-facing escarpment at the edge of the Appalachian Plateaus, a hilly belt referred to as The Knobs (Fig. 12.12). East of the Nashville Basin the Highland Rim is deeply dissected by valleys, some with steep head walls attributable to solution.

The dissected plateaus west of the Lexington Plain and Nashville Basin slope slightly westward, but the slope of the surface is less steep than the dip of the formations. As a result, the coal-bearing Pennsylvanian formations, which occur high in the Appalachian Plateaus east of the Cincinnati Arch, reappear at altitudes around 500 feet in western Kentucky. These form the western Kentucky coalfield and the coalfield in the southern Illinois structural basin.

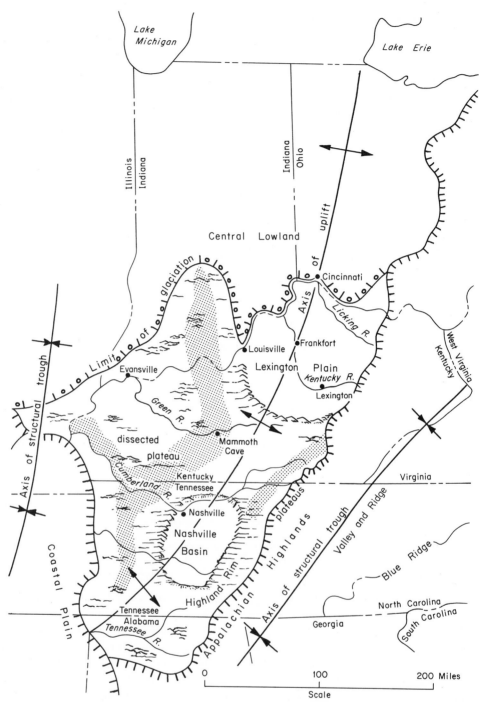

Figure 12.10 *Interior Low Plateaus Province, which lies south of the limit of glaciation and along the axis of the Cincinnati Arch. The Province is divided into four sections. North is the Lexington Plain, corresponding to the bluegrass area of Kentucky. South is the Nashville Basin; the Plateaus around it make up the Highland Rim. The remainder of the province is low, dissected plateau. Areas of limestone sinks (karst topography) on the Highland Rim and dissected plateau are indicated by stippling.*

Rivers crossing this dissected plateau are meandering and deeply entrenched. Some have meanders that are being vigorously eroded laterally to produce *undercut walls, slip-off slopes,* and *cut-off meanders* (Fig. 12.13). Much of the plateau is on cavernous limestone and exhibits karst topography with limestone sinks. Mammoth Cave (Fig. 12.10) is in this karst area.

Other features of the Interior Low Plateaus:

1. Temperate continental climate with rainy summer season.
2. Hardwood forests.
3. Residual deposits and Red and Yellow Podzol Soils.
4. Water supplies, which appear adequate to meet anticipated increases in demand during the next quarter century.
5. Tobacco, corn, coal, bourbon, and Kentucky Colonels.

Ouachita Province and Ozark Plateaus

Two other highland areas south of the glacial border are the Ouachita Province and the Ozark Plateaus, which together cover less than 100,000 square miles (Fig. 12.1). They resemble the Appalachian Highlands and Interior Low Plateaus in many ways. The Ouachita Mountains are fold mountains of thick Paleozoic formations that were deposited in a geosyncline. The folds and the mountains trend east-west (Fig. 12.14). Northward under the Arkansas River Valley the formations thin in a structural basin containing coal measures of Pennsylvanian age, somewhat like those in the Appalachian Plateaus but more folded. North of this basin is a broad upwarp, the Ozark Plateaus, exposing early Paleozoic formations like those in the Cincinnati Arch and some Precambrian rocks. North of the Ozark Plateaus is the Illinois coal basin, which extends southeastward into Kentucky on the flank of the Cincinnati Arch.

Altitudes and local relief in the Ouachita Mountains and Ozark Plateaus average lower than in the Appalachian Mountains, but the landforms are similar. The Ouachita Mountains are composed of linear ridges and valleys (Fig. 12.15). They reach a maximum altitude of about 2,600 feet, and the mountain summits are about 1,500 feet higher than the adjoining valleys.

The Ozark Plateaus resemble the Appalachian Plateaus both topographically (Fig. 12.16) and structurally, but they consist of limestone rather than coal-bearing formations. Altitudes reach to 2,000 feet in the south in an area referred to as the Boston Mountains, and to about 1,700 feet in the north. Between the Ozark Plateaus and the Ouachita Mountains is the valley of the Arkansas River, which lies at an altitude of less than 500 feet.

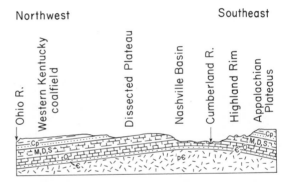

Figure 12.11 *Cross section of the Cincinnati Arch.* p€, *Precambrian;* €, *Cambrian;* O, *Ordovician;* M, D, S: *Mississippian, Devonian, and Silurian;* Cp, *Pennsylvanian. Section length c. 225 miles.*

Figure 12.12 *The knobs in eastern Kentucky, along the boundary between the Lexington Plain (back of the observer) and the Appalachian Plateaus (distant skyline).*

As in the Valley and Ridge Province, the sediments in the geosyncline under the Ouachita Province were derived from what is now the seaward side of the geosyncline. What was once the mountainous source of the sediments now lies buried under the Coastal Plain and Continental Shelf. In the Valley and Ridge and Ouachita provinces the thrust that folded and faulted the formations was directed toward the old Precambrian shield area in the interior of the continent, represented in the United States by the Superior UpIand.

The Paleozoic history of the geosyncline began with deposition of sands at the edges of

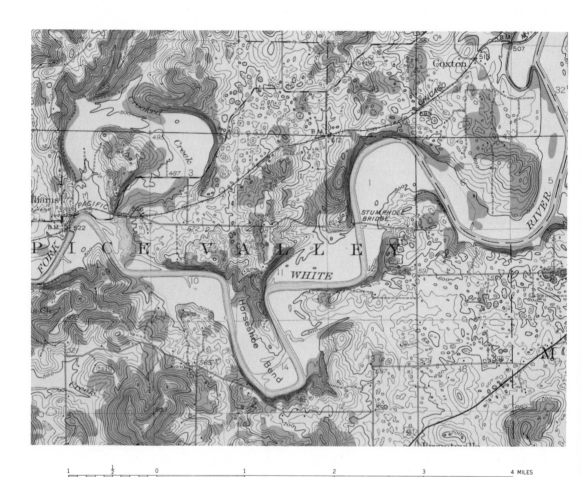

CONTOUR INTERVAL 20 FEET

Figure 12.13 *Dissected plateau in southern Indiana. Meandering streams are entrenched 100 to 300 feet into the plateau. Along the outside of the meanders the valley walls are steep, for they are undercut by the back and forth swing of the meander. Conversely, slopes along the inside are gentle slip-off slopes. Crooked Creek is in a cut-off meander. The plateau surface about 100 feet above the river is limestone and is pitted with sinkholes; hills rising above this part of the surface are shale and sandstone and are smoothly rounded. (From U.S.G.S. Oolitic quadrangle, Indiana.)*

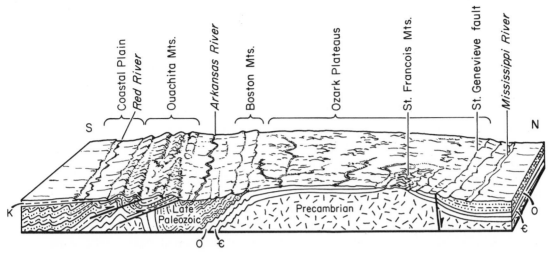

Figure 12.14 *Diagram of the Ouachita Mountains and Ozark Plateaus. The cross section extends from the Coastal Plain in north Texas to the Mississippi River below St. Louis, a distance of about 300 miles. The Ouachita Mountains, composed of Paleozoic formations in folds broken by thrust faults directed northward, developed over a Paleozoic geosyncline where the formations are very thick, as in the Valley and Ridge Province in the Appalachian Highlands. The south flank of the geosynclinal belt is buried under Coastal Plain formations of Cretaceous age (K). Northward under the Arkansas River the Paleozoic formations thin and form a broad basin containing coal measures of Pennsylvanian age. The Ozark Plateaus, a structural dome resembling the Cincinnati Arch, consist of early Paleozoic formations (O, Ordovician; Є, Cambrian) and, in the St. Francois Mountains, Precambrian rocks.*

the Cambrian sea. The resulting sandstones are found in the Arbuckle and Ouachita mountains, and they overlap the Precambrian rocks in the St. Francois Mountains (Fig. 12.14) and Lake Superior region. In the fold mountains of southern Oklahoma these sandstones are overlain by a Cambro-Ordovician limestone formation (Arbuckle Limestone) that is a mile thick; correlative limestone, with some sandstone, in the upper Mississippi Valley (Prairie de Chien Group and St. Peter Sandstone) is about 250 feet thick. In the geosyncline this limestone is overlain by two younger Ordovician limestone formations (Simpson Formation and Viola Limestone), which together are 3,000 feet thick; correlative formations of limestone and shale in the upper Mississippi Valley (Platteville Limestone,

Decorah Shale, Galena Dolomite, Maquoketa Shale) are about 500 feet thick.

Silurian and Devonian formations in the middle west do not vary in composition or thickness as much as either the earlier or later Paleozoic formations. Both in the geosynclinal areas and on the shelf to the north these rocks are mostly shale and limestone and together make up a thickness of a few hundred feet.

In Mississippian time, however, sinking of the geosyncline appears to have accelerated again. In the north, on the shelf area, shale and limestone is less than 1,000 feet thick, but in southeastern Oklahoma and adjoining areas in Arkansas, the Mississippian System is mostly shale and sandstone (Stanley Shale and Jackfork Sandstone) and is 16,000 feet thick. The Pennsylvanian similarly is much thicker in the south than in the north; in southeastern Oklahoma it consists of 15,000 feet of beds. The generalized section is given in Table 12.2.

The tremendous thickness of Pennsylvanian formations in the south does not include the upper Pennsylvanian, which is not represented there. In the north, the entire Pennsylvanian System is only about 2,000 feet thick and only the lower half of it correlates with the 15,000-foot section in the geosyncline. These Pennsylvanian formations have supplied much of the Middle West's coal.

The Permian is not well represented, but at the end of the Paleozoic, at the time the Appalachian Mountains were folded, the rocks that now form the Ouachita, Wichita and Arbuckle Mountains also were folded.

Other features of the Ouachita Province and Ozark Plateaus include their

1. Continental climate.
2. Red and Yellow Podzol Soils.
3. Hardwood forests.
4. Lack of many metropolitan areas.
5. Mules.

Great Plains Province

The Great Plains Province, covering about 450,000 square miles, which is about 12 percent of the United States, is the semiarid part of the Interior Plains. The plains slope eastward from about 5,500 feet at the foot of the

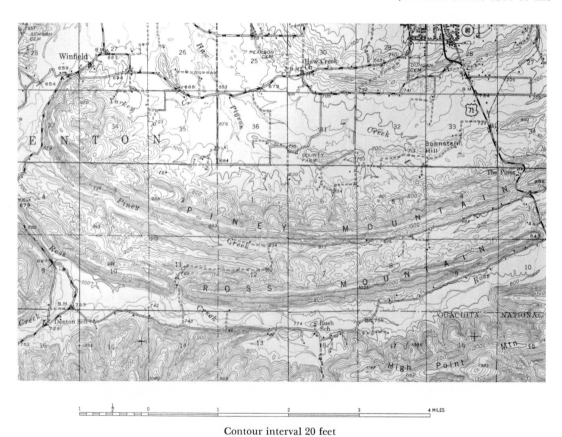

Contour interval 20 feet

Figure 12.15 *Topography in the Ouachita Mountains is like that of the Valley and Ridge Province. (From U.S.G.S. Waldron, Arkansas, quadrangle.)*

Rocky Mountains to about 2,000 feet at the eastern boundary, which is gradational with the Central Lowland. This eastern boundary approximately coincides with the 100th meridian, the 2,000-foot contour, the 20-inch rainfall line, the boundary between tall grass and short grass, and the eastern limit of the Tertiary formations that contain the sediments eroded from the Rocky Mountains and washed eastward onto the plains. The boundary also is parallel to, although a little west of, the boundary between the pedalfer and pedocal soils.

Drainage on the plains is parallel, and the

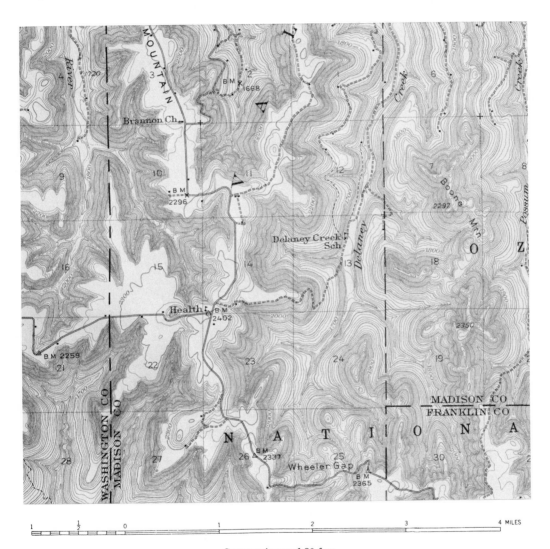

Contour interval 20 feet

Figure 12.16 *The Ozark Plateaus have a dendritic drainage pattern like that of the Appalachian Plateaus. In places the uplands are broad flats (western part of the map), but most of the divides are narrow, irregular ridges (eastern part of map). (From U.S.G.S. St. Paul, Arkansas, quadrangle.)*

streams flow eastward from the Rocky Mountains to the Missouri and Mississippi rivers. The valleys are broad, steep sided, and shallow. Few are deeper than about 150 feet; the valley walls, although not high, generally are too steep to hold soil and are formed by the outcrop of the geological formations. Between the valleys are smooth uplands, nearly flat plains. Trees are largely confined to the valleys; the almost treeless uplands, originally grassland, now are plowed fields or pasture.

Average rainfall is about 15 inches, and in dry times the plowed fields become dust bowls. The difference in climate between the Great Plains and Central Lowland is critical in terms of land use and productivity.

The structural geology of the Great Plains differs only in detail from that of the Central Lowland. The formations are nearly flat lying, mostly Mesozoic and Cenozoic overlying slightly warped Paleozoic formations. In the north, the surface of the plains is interrupted by dome mountains, such as the Black Hills (Fig. 12.17) and some of the smaller mountains in northern Montana, which are due to doming by laccolithic or other intrusions (Fig. 12.18). The boundary between the Great Plains and Central Lowland is along a low, east-facing escarpment at the eroded east edge of Cenozoic formations.

The Cenozoic formations consist of sediments washed eastward onto the plains from the Rocky Mountains. Their volume provides a minimal measure of the lowering of the Rocky Mountains by erosion during Cenozoic time. Since these sediments roughly equal the

TABLE 12.2 Formations of Pennsylvanian age in southeastern Oklahoma and western Arkansas.

Formation	Description
Thurman Sandstone	Sandstone with conglomerate and shale; top formation of the coal measures; 200 feet.
Boggy Shale	Alternating beds of shale and sandstone, with coal beds; 3,000 feet.
Savanna Sandstone	Mostly sandstone, some shale; 1,150 feet.
McAlester Shale	Shale and sandstone, with coal beds; 2,000 feet.
Hartshorne Sandstone	Sandstone; 200 feet.
Atoka Formation	Alternating beds of sandstone and shale; basal formation of the coal measures; 7,000 feet.
Wapanucka Limestone	Limestone; 200 feet.
Caney Shale	Upper part only; 250 feet?
Caney Shale	Lower part, and other Mississippian formations.

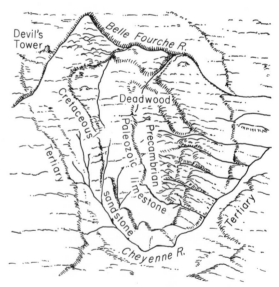

Figure 12.17 *Diagram of the Black Hills dome. At the center, Precambrian rocks are exposed at altitudes of more than 7,000 feet. Surrounding this is a series of cuestas composed of Paleozoic limestone, Cretaceous sandstone, and Tertiary sandstone. The Cheyenne River south of the dome and the Belle Fourche River north of it are at altitudes of about 4,000 feet. Width of diagram about 130 miles.*

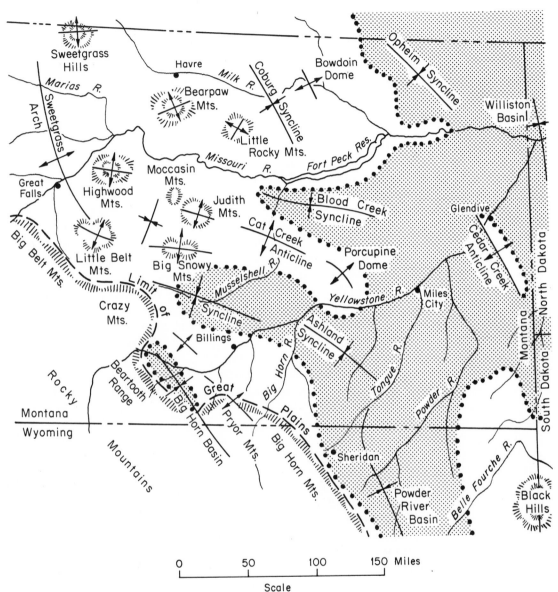

Figure 12.18 *Structural map of the northern part of the Great Plains. Dome mountains on the plains are shown by hachures. Lines indicate the trends of the principal fold axes, and cross-arrows indicate whether dips are toward the axes (synclinal) or away from them (anticlinal). Area covered by Tertiary formations is shown stippled. Except in the mountains, most of the white area is Cretaceous. Older rocks together with some intrusive rocks are exposed in the dome mountains. The youngest formations, those of Tertiary age, occupy the basins and synclines. (Data from U.S.G.S.)*

volume of the mountains that remain, we might conclude that the Rocky Mountains are at least half gone.

Most of the Mesozoic formations that underlie the Cenozoic ones originated as marine sediments deposited in a broad shallow geosyncline of Upper Cretaceous age. The axis of this geosyncline was located at about the position of the western edge of the Great Plains, and the mediterranean sea that occupied it connected the Gulf of Mexico with the Arctic Ocean. The Upper Cretaceous formations are about 10,000 feet thick in the central part of the geosyncline. They thin eastward under the Great Plains but extend to the western edge of the Superior Upland (Fig. 2.7).

Cenozoic, Mesozoic, and Paleozoic formations extend westward under the Great Plains to the foot of the Rocky Mountains, where they are turned up along the base of that uplift, which formed in late Cretaceous and early Tertiary time. The formations are listed in Table 13.1. The newly formed Rocky Mountains shed sediments eastward onto the Great Plains. The first formations, of Paleocene and Eocene age (Lance, Fort Union, and Wasatch Formations), included much volcanic debris and were deposited across the northern part of the Great Plains north of the Black Hills. The next formation, of Oligocene age (White River Formation), was deposited south of the Black Hills. The next younger formations, of Miocene age (Ogallala and Arikaree Formations), were deposited in the central parts of the Great Plains, in the area roughly corresponding to Nebraska, Kansas, and northern Oklahoma. In Pliocene time the principal area of deposition was in southern Oklahoma and Texas (Blanco Formation). From Paleocene through Pliocene time, deposition progressed southward. Moreover, southward on the Great Plains, these Tertiary formations were laid down on an erosion surface that cut across about 10,000 feet of Cretaceous formations and extended onto Paleozoic formations (Fig. 2.1), which indicates that uplift in the

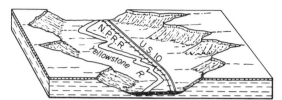

Figure 12.19 *Diagram of Yellowstone River Valley west of Billings, Montana.*

southern Great Plains has been two miles greater than in the north, despite the fact that these areas now are at about the same altitude.

These differences in the Cenozoic formations and history from north to south control the differences in landforms on the Great Plains and provide the basis for dividing the province into the sections shown in Fig. 12.1. At the north is the Missouri Plateau Section, the northern part of which was glaciated. Local relief on the Missouri Plateau is greater than in most of the Great Plains. Rivers are entrenched a few hundreds of feet into the plateau (Fig. 12.18) and numerous dome mountains rise 1,500 to 2,000 feet above it (Fig. 12.19). Largest and highest of them are the Black Hills, properly a separate section. The Black Hills are a domal uplift consisting of Precambrian rocks at the center surrounded by a series of inward-facing cuestas formed by formations that are progressively younger away from the dome (Fig. 12.17). Northwest of the Black Hills is a prominent volcanic neck about 1,000 feet high, Devils Tower, a National Monument (Fig. 2.4). A number of the other dome mountains—the Sweetgrass Hills, and the Bearpaw, Little Rocky, Highwood, Moccasin, and Judith mountains—are due to laccolithic intrusions.

Between the dome mountains are broad anticlines and synclines (Fig. 12.18), all well expressed topographically. The anticlines are surrounded by cuestas that face inward, like those in the Black Hills, the synclines are surrounded by cuestas facing outward like those in the Michigan Basin (Fig. 12.8). Where the formations are shale, there are badlands, examples of which may be seen at Badlands National Monument and Theodore Roosevelt National Memorial Park in the Dakotas.

The Tertiary formations contain abundant beds of lignite. Many of these have ignited spontaneously and have burned at their outcrops, baking the overlying shale to red clinker. This clinker is extensive on the Missouri Plateau and is one of its distinctive features.

South of the Missouri Plateau is the High Plains Section (Fig. 12.20), with a land surface

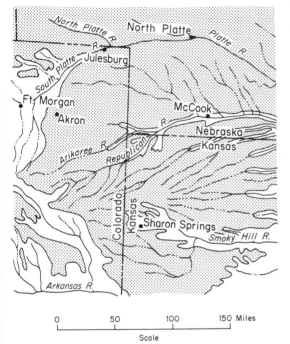

Figure 12.20 *Part of the High Plains Section of the Great Plains Province. Area covered by Tertiary formations, mostly Miocene, is shown stippled. White areas are Cretaceous. The main streams have cut through the Tertiary formations to the underlying Cretaceous. The interstream surfaces are approximately accordant with the top of the Tertiary formations, and are depositional surfaces. The Tertiary formations are relatively permeable, the Cretaceous formations relatively impermeable. Streams on the Tertiary formations are intermittent; on the Cretaceous, mostly perennial.*

approximately accordant with the top of the Miocene formations, and, therefore, a depositional rather than erosional surface. Toward the east, such streams as the Republican and Smoky Hill Rivers are incised into the Miocene formations and have exposed the underlying Cretaceous formations. This belt of country constitutes the Plains Border Section and grades into the Central Lowland. On the west, the High Plains are separated from the Rocky Mountains by a structural and topographic basin that forms the Colorado Piedmont Section. To the south is the Raton Section, which is unique among the sections of the Great Plains in having high mesas or plateaus capped by lava flows (Tertiary). Some of these mesas are 6,000 to 7,000 feet in altitude.

Parts of the High Plains Section are sandy, with extensive dunes. One such area lies southeast of Akron, Colorado—an area shown without drainage in Figure 12.20. The prevailing wind direction is toward the southeast, and the dunes are aligned in that direction. Another even more extensive sand area is in western Nebraska (Fig. 12.1). Still another area of dunes is along the south side of the Arkansas River at the big bend in Kansas.

In southeastern New Mexico and the Panhandle of Texas are the Staked Plains, the Llano Estacado, one of the most nearly level parts of the United States. This section is a nearly featureless plain, lacking even slight landmarks. The name is supposed to indicate that stakes had to be driven into the ground to mark the trails that crossed the prairie and those that lead to water. The surface is dotted with shallow depressions, buffalo wallows, where rain water is sometimes ponded. But for these in wet season, water is scarce, and there are no hills to guide the traveler. Today there are windmills. These plains, covering about 50,000 square miles, slope southeastward from a maximum altitude of about 5,500 feet to about 2,500 feet at the escarpment overlooking the Osage Plains. The Staked Plains end westward at a west-facing escarpment overlooking the Pecos Valley, a wide erosional valley from which the Tertiary cover has been stripped, exposing the Paleozoic formations.

The southern end of the Great Plains is an area of thick, Lower Cretaceous limestone, forming the Edwards Plateau in Texas. This plateau extends northward under the cover of Tertiary sediments on the Great Plains, but along the eastern and southern borders is an escarpment—the Balcones fault zone, overlooking the West Gulf Coastal Plain. Surface streams are few on the Edwards Plateau; drainage is mostly underground and discharges from the springs along the Balcones fault zone that supply the cities along that edge of the Coastal Plain. North of the Edwards Plateau, and slightly lower, is the Central Texas uplift, a broad, low structural dome exposing early Paleozoic and Precambrian rocks.

Climate

Compared to other parts of the country the climate of the central United States is continental. Temperature differences between seasons are extreme: winters are cold and blizzards frequent; summers are hot and subject to tornadoes. Yet compared to the plains of eastern Europe and western Asia, the climate in the central United States is mild, for our winters are much less severe. Also, except on the Great Plains, we are favored with more rainfall, and it is better distributed during the growing season.

The climates in the central United States are semiarid in the west and humid in the east. Average annual precipitation in the Great Plains is about 15 inches. This increases eastward to about 20 inches near the 100th meridian, to 40 inches in Ohio, and to 50 inches in Tennessee. Moreover, most of this precipitation takes place during the growing season, which largely explains the tremendous agricultural productivity of this region.

Average annual temperatures range from 40°F in the north to somewhat more than 60°F in the south. Average annual temperatures, however, are not very meaningful, because the climate is continental, with extreme seasonal differences. For example, in central Minnesota and the adjoining parts of North and South Dakota, the *average* January temperature is 10°F, whereas the *average* July temperature is 70°F. In that same area, the average annual minimum temperature is −40°F, as contrasted with an average annual maximum of more than 100°F. These extremes are about twice the range of those for equivalent latitudes along the Atlantic and Pacific coasts, where the climates are tempered by the oceans. The great difference between cold-season and warm-season temperatures in the central United States decreases southward. In southern Oklahoma the difference between average minimum and average maximum temperatures is less than 100°F.

The average length of the frost-free period is about 100 days in northern Minnesota, but increases southward to about 225 days in southern Oklahoma (Fig. 12.21). Near the Great Lakes, especially on the leeward shores, the frost-free period is longer than away from them, a result of the temporizing effect of the water. The northward increase in coldness affects the average depth of frost penetration—in southwestern Texas it is about one inch; at the Canadian border the depth of freezing in ground that is not snow covered may be more than four feet. Under snow the depth of freezing is much less. The northward increase in coldness also affects the natural vegetation, soils, kind of agricultural activity, transportation, engineering problems concerned with foundations, and sales of heavy underwear.

A major climatic hazard in the central United States are the "twisters," the tornadoes, which have wind velocities estimated to be as great as 500 miles per hour. Where they touch the ground, tornadoes commonly are about 1,000 feet wide. They extend upward into a funnel-shaped cloud darkened with dust sucked upward, and may reach to 20,000 feet. The storms move at speeds ranging from 5 to 60 miles per hour, and their tracks along the ground extend on the average for about a dozen miles. One tornado left a track more than 100 miles long.

Tornadoes are most frequent in Kansas and Iowa (Fig. 4.4), but the property damage and deaths from tornadoes in those states are less than in some of the more populous states where tornado frequency is less. Although tornadoes may occur in any month of the year, they occur most frequently in spring and early summer. The earliest spring tornadoes generally strike the Gulf Coast; as the season advances, tornadoes strike farther north. The storms may occur at any hour of the day, but usually occur in late afternoon and early evening.

The causes of tornadoes are not very well understood other than that they are associated with the turbulence accompanying weather fronts. They form in the upper air, commonly between altitudes of 10,000 and 20,000 feet. The whirling column, likened to that of water running out of a bathtub, but inverted, extends itself downward as a lower stratum of air is sucked upward.

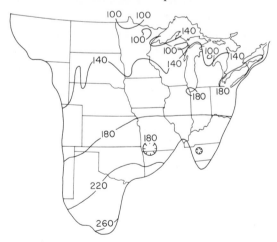

Figure 12.21 *Average length of frost-free period (days) in the central United States. (Generalized from U.S.D.A.)*

The effects of past climates on the present physiography are perhaps more striking in the central United States than in any other large segment of the country. The direct topographic effects of the deposits left by the glaciers have already been described. In addition, these deposits and the ice are responsible for the great rivers (p. 231), the Great Lakes (p. 235), the fertile loessial deposits (p. 230), and the soils (p. 229). An effect of the present climate on population distribution is illustrated by the following:

State	Average annual precipitation	Population density, per square mile
Indiana	35	130
Iowa	30	48
Nebraska	20	18
Wyoming (plains part)	15	10

For every 20,000 square miles, Indiana has 22 towns with populations more than 10,000, Iowa has 8, Nebraska has 3, and Wyoming has 1.

Vegetation

Much of the Central Lowland and almost all of the Great Plains Province was grassland when first settled. East of the 100th meridian, where the annual rainfall averages more than 20 inches, the grasses are tall and deep rooted. West of the 100th meridian, in the semiarid Great Plains, the grasses are short and shallow rooted (Fig. 12.22). Bluestem, which grows to about 4 feet, and needle grass, which grows to about 3 feet, are common tall grasses; blue gramma grass, about 18 inches tall, is one of the common short grasses.

In this region most trees grow in the valleys. In the area of short grass the valleys support cottonwood; in the area of tall grass the

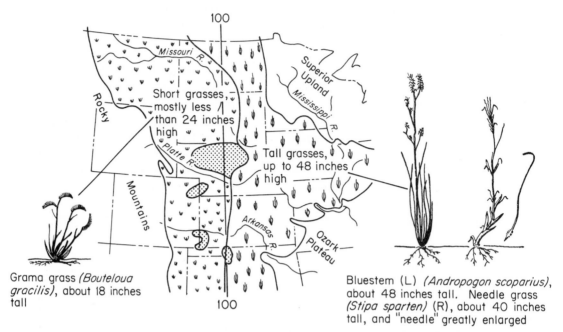

Grama grass *(Bouteloua gracilis),* about 18 inches tall

Bluestem (L) *(Andropogon scoparius),* about 48 inches tall. Needle grass *(Stipa sparten)* (R), about 40 inches tall, and "needle" greatly enlarged

Figure 12.22 *The 100th meridian is the approximate boundary between the deep-rooted, tall grasses with large leaves and the shallow-rooted, short grasses with small leaves. Bluestem and needle grass, the characteristic grasses east of the boundary, and grama grass, the characteristic grass west of the boundary, are not confined to the areas indicated here. The stippling indicates sand, covered mostly with tall grasses and shrubs.*

bottoms support oak, hickory, ash, black walnut, elm, and box elder—representatives of the Central Hardwood Forests. The hardwoods increase eastward and extend across some of the uplands near the Mississippi River. Among the common trees are:

Eastern red cedar	Sassafras
Butternut	Witch hazel
Black walnut	Sycamore
Pecan	Choke cherry
Hickories—bitternut, shag-	Black cherry
bark, mockernut, pignut	Redbud
Hop hornbean	Honey locust
River birch	Maples—sugar, black,
Beech	silver, red
Oaks—pin, scarlet, black,	Buckeye
blackjack, shingle, white	Basswood
post, bur, swamp white	Black gum
Elm	Dogwood
Mulberry	Persimmon
Ash	

The Superior Upland and the adjoining part of the Central Lowland support four kinds of forests. In the north and on the highlands is the Spruce-Fir Forest, populated by black and white spruce and balsam fir. This is bordered on the south by a mixed pine forest—the Northeastern Pine Forest—composed of jack pine, red pine, northern white pine, and aspen. This grades southward into the Northeastern Hardwood Forest of birch (yellow birch and paper birch), beech, maple (striped, sugar, and red maples), and hemlock, and this in turn gives way farther south to the Central Hardwood Forest, characterized by oaks and hickories.

Although in these northern forests the average annual burn by forest fires is low compared to other forested areas, they have been the scene of three of the most disastrous fires in the history of the United States.

The worst, in terms of casualties, occurred on October 9, 1871, at Peshtigo, Wisconsin, where more than 1,200 persons perished in a forest fire that broke out after a protracted drought and raced uncontrolled through the forests west of Green Bay. This fire received little notice in the nation because the telegraph lines had been destroyed, and the news that did reach the rest of the country was submerged by news of the great Chicago fire, which had occurred the day before. Yet the Chicago fire took only a fifth as many casualties.

Two other major forest fires, both in Minnesota near the tip of Lake Superior, occurred in September 1894, at Hinckley, and in October 1918, at Cloquet. Each of these fires killed about 400 persons.

Such fires create a climate all their own: They exhaust the oxygen to the degree that one may be suffocated without being burned. Warnings by Smoky the Bear are well based— "Everybody loses when there is a forest fire."

Yellow pine forest grows on high parts of the Great Plains, such as the Raton section, the divide between the Arkansas and South Platte Rivers, the Black Hills, and the high parts of the Missouri Plateau. The mountains on the Missouri Plateau in Montana are forested with lodgepole pine.

Surficial Deposits and Soils

Surficial deposits in the central United States include the glacial drift; shore and bottom deposits of the Pleistocene lakes; alluvium along the rivers and streams; colluvium where the land is hilly; eolian deposits, the vast blanket of loess and the dune sand; and clayey residual deposits where the sedimentary formations are deeply weathered, especially the limestone formations in the Interior Low Plateaus and Ozark Plateaus.

These differences are reflected in the soils. For example, the clayey residual deposits where the formations are deeply weathered are parent material for Red and Yellow Podzols. These are ancient soils like those in the Appalachian Highlands, and they end northward where they are overlapped by the glacial drift, glacial outwash, or loess of the Wisconsin stage of glaciation. These ancient soils are most noticeable where they are developed on the Paleozoic formations, but have formed on pre-Wisconsin glacial drift and loess too.

Soils in the central United States also reflect the climatic zones, and in the same way and to the same degree as does the vegetation. In the conifer forests of the Superior Upland the soils are mostly Podzols. Under the hardwood forest the soils are mostly Gray-Brown Podzols. The eastern part of the tall-grass belt has Prairie Soils, and these grade westward to the Chernozem Soils. The eastern part of the short-grass belt has Chestnut soils, and the western part, near the foot of the Rocky Mountains, has Brown Soils. The changes in soil profile across these belts (Fig. 6.4) are gradual and clearly reflect the decreasing availability of moisture southwestward from the Superior Upland. These soils are of Recent or late Pleistocene age.

Another group of distinctive soils, the Planosols, which have a clay pan 2 to 3 feet below the surface, have developed on nearly level, poorly drained areas that are most extensive on the loess-covered, pre-Wisconsin drift in southern Illinois, southern Iowa, and northern Missouri (Figs. 6.1, 6.2). Similar soils on the Osage Plains have developed on shale and sandstone formations, and in Nebraska on loess-covered plains.

The red color of soils south of the Arkansas River commonly is attributed to the increasingly warm climate southward. This is only partly true: Reddish Prairie Soils and the eastern series of the Reddish Chestnut Soils developed in large part from formations that are red, and much or most of their color probably is inherited. Among the western series of Reddish Chestnut Soils and the Reddish Brown Soils are some soils that are older than the last glaciation. Their properties, including their color, may be inherited from the ancient climates under which they formed, and may have little or no relationship to the present climate. An example of three very different kinds of soil of three different ages in the Great Plains is given in Figure 12.23.

Probably the most important single factor contributing to the composition and fertility of the soils in central United States is the blanket of loess and related deposits covering that region (Fig. 6.1). The loess immediately east of the Mississippi and Missouri rivers is tens of feet thick and covers most of the land. Other thick and extensive deposits cover both sides of the Platte River in Nebraska and extend across Iowa. Along the eastern and southern limits of these deposits the loess is less than 2 feet thick and covers no more than about a third of the land. The eolian deposits in the Great Plains Province are in large part sandy, and some of that area is covered by dunes.

These loessial soils are subject to severe erosion, and sediment load of streams in the loessial areas is about 10 times greater than that of streams northwest and east of the loess. Soils on the southern half of the Great Plains and west of the 100th meridian—the dust bowl—are subject not only to washing but to severe wind erosion. The soils are nutritional enough, but droughts are frequent and the soils are blown off lands where the grass cover has been removed. During the droughts in the 1930's dust was carried eastward to the cities along the Atlantic seaboard. Suitability of these lands for farming is controlled chiefly by climate and topography, and not by the fertility of the soils.

The northern half of the Great Plains has little loess and is less subject to erosion, as is suggested by photographic records covering the last 50 years. The stands of yellow pine growing on the Great Plains have spread, and except in cultivated areas the desirable grasses and shrubs there are maintaining themselves against grazing and other land use. The difference in soil erosion between the northern and southern Great Plains is in large part a function of the difference in the geology of the soils—specifically, occurrence of loess.

Soils in the central United States provide some examples of how soil texture and the availability to plants of chemical elements in the soil affect soil fertility. Some soils contain too little of certain elements necessary for plant growth; others may contain the element

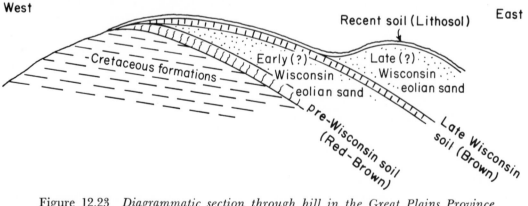

Figure 12.23 *Diagrammatic section through hill in the Great Plains Province showing eolian sand deposited on the east (lee) side of the hill and soils of three kinds and of three different ages interbedded with the sand. The oldest soil is a Red Brown Soil of pre-Wisconsin age. This is buried by a bed of wind-deposited sand of Early (?) Wisconsin age. A Brown Soil developed on this deposit is buried by a sand of Late (?) Wisconsin age, and the Recent soil on this sand is so feebly developed it could be classed as a lithosol.*

in an insoluble form not available for plant use. Some elements are toxic in small quantities; others may be essential in small quantities and become toxic if present in excessive amounts. The Chernozem and Chestnut Soils contain about twice as much phosphorus as do the Red Chestnut Soils, which commonly are deficient in this element. The Red Chestnut and other red soils obviously contain much iron, but evidently not in a very soluble form, because some plants, notably sorghums, show signs of iron deficiency when grown on the red soils. Selenium occurs in toxic quantities in soils developed on some shales of Cretaceous age, and in places selenium poisoning is serious enough to warrant fencing off the affected areas. Such lands can be used for growing fiber or seed crops, but not for growing food.

Great Rivers

The central United States, characterized by great rivers and Great Lakes, drains in three directions—to the Mississippi River, to the St. Lawrence River, and to Hudson Bay. The annual discharge averages substantially more than a half billion acre feet. Most of the region drains into the Mississippi River, which is one of the world's great rivers, both in length and annual discharge (Fig. 12.24). Its major tributaries are the Tennessee, Ohio, Missouri, and Arkansas rivers. The Great Lakes drain into the St. Lawrence. The Souris River, the Red River (of the north), and the Rainy River drain into Hudson Bay. In all three systems the drainage pattern is dendritic. Some contrasts in the rivers are illustrated in Figure 12.25.

The divide between the drainage to Hudson Bay and to the Gulf of Mexico crosses North Dakota and northern Minnesota, but in preglacial time the divide seems to have been at least 400 miles farther south. Drainage was turned southward by the glacial ice; the south-

ward course of the Missouri River across the Dakotas is a result of drainage diversion.

The valley along this stretch of the Missouri River is a deep, narrow trench, quite unlike the broad, open valley upstream in Montana and downstream in Nebraska and Iowa. The plains slope east, but the river flows south. The several large tributaries along this stretch of the river are all from the west, and occupy open valleys rather than deep trenches. Figure 12.26,A, illustrates the probable courses of the streams prior to their diversion.

Other examples of major changes in drainage caused by glaciation are illustrated in Figure 12.26. The Mississippi River drained southeastward to what is now the Illinois River until a glacial advance pushed it westward to its present position (Fig. 12.26,B); a preglacial river may have crossed Iowa to join what is now the Des Moines River.

Still another major drainage change occurred along the Missouri River in Montana

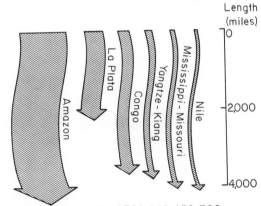

Figure 12.24 *Length and discharge of the Mississippi-Missouri River compared to some other great rivers in the world. The discharge is greater than that of the slightly longer Nile River, but less than that of the Yangtze Kiang, and very much less than that of the Congo, the comparatively short La Plata, and the Amazon Rivers.*

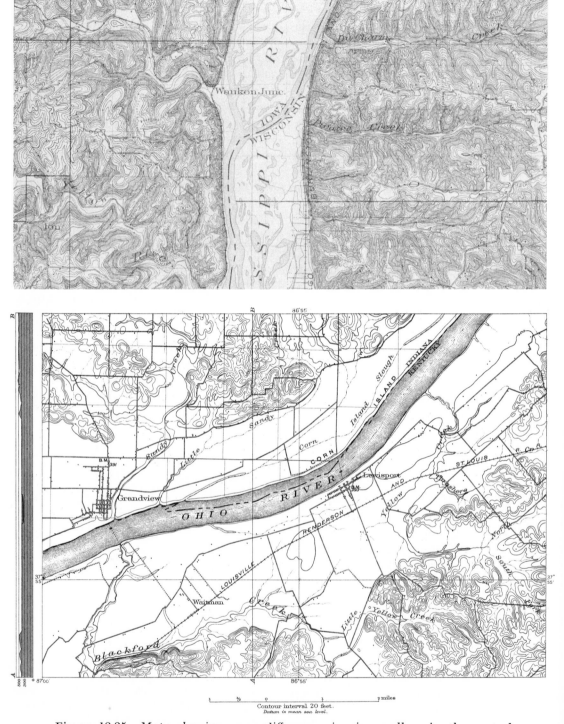

Figure 12.25 *Maps showing some differences in river valleys in the central United States. All maps date from about 1900, before modifications for flood control were made. (Top left) Mississippi River in the southern part of the Driftless Section has a braided pattern on a floodplain 2 miles wide between bluffs several hundred feet high. (From U.S.G.S. Waukon, Iowa-Wis., sheet.) (Bottom left) Ohio River is a well-defined channel on a floodplain 3 miles wide where it enters the west Kentucky coalfield between bluffs 100 feet high. (From*

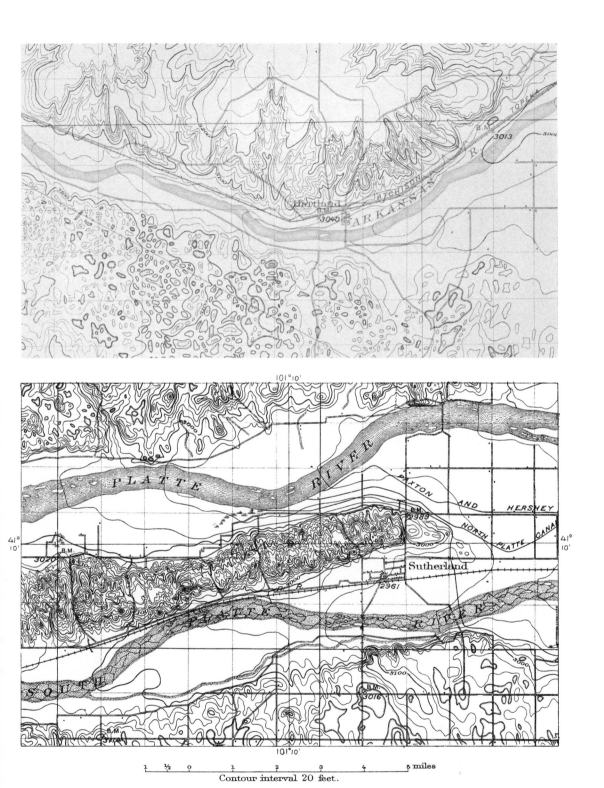

U.S.G.S. Tell City, Ky.-Ind., sheet.) (Top right) Arkansas River at the eastern edge of the Great Plains is bordered by bluffs on the north side and by sand dunes on the south. (From U.S.G.S. Lakin, Kansas, sheet.) (Bottom right) Platte River and South Platte River on the Great Plains in western Nebraska. Both streams are on broad floodplains between bluffs marked by sandy loess. The South Platte River has a choked, braided channel. (From U.S.G.S. Paxton, Nebr., sheet.) (Note: Above scale holds for map at top left and for maps on this page.)

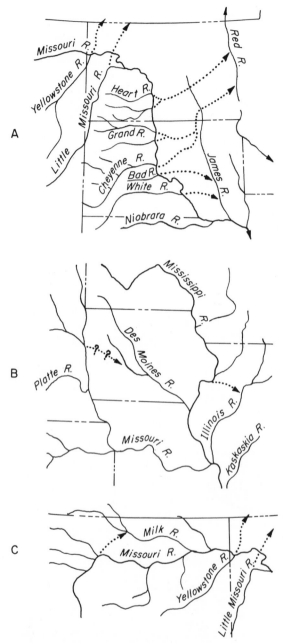

(Fig. 12.26,C). The river formerly flowed around the north side of the Bearpaw Mountains (Fig. 12.18) and along the course of the present Milk River. The advance of the glaciers to a position south of the Bearpaw and Little Rocky Mountains diverted the Missouri to its present source.

There have been drainage changes on the High Plains too, but these are not attributable directly to glaciation. For example, the Tertiary formations shown in Figure 12.20 were deposited by streams flowing eastward onto the High Plains from the Rocky Mountains. But the old drainage courses have been cut off in the Colorado Piedmont section by the South Platte River and by a tributary of the Arkansas River, both of which have eroded valleys around and below the western edge of the Tertiary formations (Fig. 2.1).

An unusually fine example of incipient diversion can be seen at Red Lodge, Montana, where the Rock River leaves the mountains and flows onto the plains (Fig. 12.27). A minor tributary, Bear Creek, rising on the plains in front of the mountains, is eroding the soft

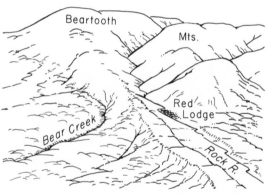

Figure 12.26 *Examples of drainage changes attributable to glaciation on the Interior Plains. Present drainage shown by solid lines; supposed former courses, dotted. (A) Drainage changes along the Missouri Trench in North and South Dakota. (B) Drainage changes along the Mississippi River. (C) Drainage changes along the Missouri River in Montana.*

Figure 12.27 *Threatened capture of Rock River by Bear Creek at the foot of the Beartooth Mountains. The head of Bear Creek is without gravel and is about 750 feet lower than Rock River. The divide is narrow, although still about 200 feet high. When the divide is breached Bear Creek will become a dumping ground for the gravel being transported by Rock River.*

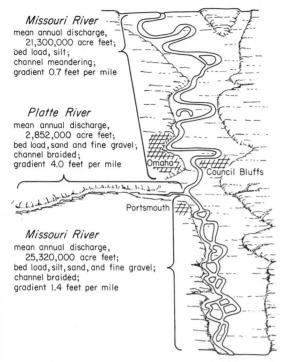

Missouri River ---
mean annual discharge,
21,300,000 acre feet;
bed load, silt;
channel meandering;
gradient 0.7 feet per mile

Platte River
mean annual discharge,
2,852,000 acre feet;
bed load, sand and fine gravel;
channel braided;
gradient 4.0 feet per mile

Omaha
Council Bluffs
Portsmouth

Missouri River
mean annual discharge,
25,320,000 acre feet;
bed load, silt, sand, and fine gravel;
channel braided;
gradient 1.4 feet per mile

Figure 12.28 *Change in channel and gradient of the Missouri River where it is joined by the Platte River. The Platte River is small compared to the Missouri but transports coarse sediment. The Missouri, below the Platte, has steepened its gradient and is braided.*

Cretaceous formations, and its channel is 750 feet lower than the channel of Rock River. A narrow divide keeps Rock River on its perched course and when that is breached, the valley of Bear Creek will receive the gravel being transported by Rock River. Other examples of this process are found on the Colorado Plateau, where every stage, including incipient and recent diversion, is represented.

An example of the differences in gradient of streams transporting gravel as compared with those transporting sand or silt is illustrated by the change in gradient of the Missouri River where it is joined by the Platte, which introduces coarse sediment to the Missouri (Fig. 12.28). Above this junction the Missouri River has a meandering channel and a gradient of 0.7 feet per mile. Although the Platte is

only a tenth as large as the Missouri, the coarse sediment it carries into the main stream causes the Missouri to double its gradient, and the channel is braided.

Another drainage curiosity is the course of the Arkansas River. It flows east from Colorado to central Kansas, where it makes a big bend to the north, as if to join the Smoky Hill and Kansas rivers. But then it turns south again and leaves the plains in a broad valley that crosses the Ouachita Province. The gradient of the Arkansas River across the Ouachita Province is no greater than that of the Mississippi River, which the Arkansas joins.

Equally curious is the course of the Tennessee River, with headwaters in the Valley and Ridge Province. A "sensible" river would continue its course southwestward and join one of the rivers on the East Gulf Coastal Plain, but not the Tennessee. It turns out of the big valleys into a gorge through the Appalachian Plateaus and then turns north around the west side of the Cincinnati Arch to join the Ohio and Mississippi rivers, a course that is about 700 miles longer than the direct one.

The great rivers have facilitated settlement and trade. Even today, the tonnage handled at river ports above Memphis, Tennessee, exceeds that of any coastal port except New York. Also, about 2 percent of our national fish production comes from these rivers—carp, buffalo fish, catfish, and mussel.

Great Lakes

We look next at the Great Lakes, which, for size, are unique not only in this country but in the world. Moreover, they are only a part of a belt of lakes that extends northwest across Canada and includes such additional large ones as Lake Winnipeg, Lake Athabasca, Great Slave Lake, and Great Bear Lake, in addition to countless smaller ones, especially in Michigan, Wisconsin, Minnesota, and Canada (Fig. 12.29).

Figure 12.29 *The Great Lakes and Minnesota's 10,000 lakes are at the southern end of a vast lake region covering more than half of Canada.*

Altitudes and maximum depths of the Great Lakes are summarized below.

Lake	Altitude of water surface	Maximum depth
Superior	602	1333
Michigan	580	923
Huron	580	750
Erie	572	210
Ontario	246	778

Average annual discharge from the Great Lakes is 150 million acre feet at Niagara Falls and 180 million acre feet where Lake Ontario empties into the St. Lawrence River.

Low divides between the heads of the tributaries of the Great Lakes and of the Ohio and Mississippi rivers facilitated French exploration of the Middle West. Easy portages could be made from the tributaries of Lake Erie to the Ohio River, and from the tributaries of Lake Michigan to the Mississippi River. One could travel by canoe from Quebec to New Orleans; canals were later dug along the portage routes followed by early travelers.

The Great Lakes were formed when the Pleistocene glaciers retreated from that area, and several have rounded ends reflecting their glacial history. Figure 12.30 illustrates four stages in the development of the lakes and of the river channels by which they overflowed. The dried parts of the lake beds form some of our best agricultural land, like that of Lake Maumee at the west end of Lake Erie and of glacial Lake Saginaw at the head of Saginaw Bay in Michigan. Between these lacustrine plains is morainal topography.

Niagara Falls came into existence when the retreat of glacial ice caused the level of lake water in the Ontario Basin to fall below the limestone rim at Lewiston. Thereafter, Lake Erie drained into Lake Ontario via Niagara River and Falls. Because of the undercutting of the shale below the limestone (Fig. 12.9) the falls have receded, at about 4 feet per year, a distance of 7 miles upstream from Lewiston. The rate of retreat, however, has not been constant; part of the time Lake Huron and other lakes to the west drained to the Mississippi River, and the Niagara River drained only the basin of Lake Erie.

When the ice sheet extended across the site of the Great Lakes, the weight of ice caused the region to be depressed. When the ice receded, the part of the crust formerly covered by ice rose differentially because of the release of load on it. These earth movements are recorded today by the tilt of the shorelines of the ancestral Great Lakes. Such movements are, in fact, still going on; the north shores of Lake Superior and Lake Ontario are tilting southward at the rate of 6 to 12 inches per 100 miles per century.

Shipping at lake ports has been as important as shipping at coastal ports, despite the fact that they are frozen and closed to shipping much of the winter. In 1959, canals were deepened and the St. Lawrence Seaway became opened to all but the largest ocean-going vessels. About 80 percent of the world's ships can now go as far as Duluth—more than 2,300 miles inland. However, the lake levels need to be maintained to accommodate the ships. At this writing lake levels are 2 to 3 feet below average; and at such low stages, when water levels drop an inch, an 18,000-ton ship loses 80 tons of cargo space.

The lakes are important too for hydroelectric power and for fisheries (they provide about 2 percent of the country's production, mostly lake herring, whitefish, lake trout, perch, and pike). Chicago withdraws more than 1¼ million gallons a minute for domestic use and to flush its sewage (after treatment) down the Illinois River to the Mississippi.

Water Supplies

Water in the central United States is obtained from six sources:
1. Great lakes,
2. Major rivers, excluding the Arkansas,
3. Small rivers and lakes,
4. Groundwater from glacial drift,
5. Groundwater from shallow bedrock (less than 500 feet),
6. Groundwater from deep bedrock (more than 500 feet).

East of the 100th meridian, except around the Great Lakes, the water supplies are adequate to meet present needs and appear ade-

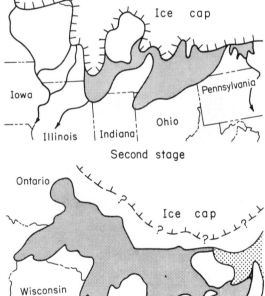

Figure 12.30 *Maps showing four stages in development of the Great Lakes and of the rivers by which they discharged. (After U.S.G.S.)*

quate to meet anticipated needs in the next 35 years. Around the Great Lakes and west of the 100th meridian, however, the water supplies are not adequate to meet the anticipated increase in demands. A comparison of water uses and water losses in the central United States east and west of the 100th meridian is given in Figure 12.31.

East of the 100th meridian, where annual precipitation exceeds 20 inches, the average annual runoff is more than 1 inch. Where the average annual rainfall is about 40 inches or more, the average annual runoff is more than 10 inches. Runoff on the Great Plains averages less than 1 inch. Streams crossing the Great Plains lose water by seepage and evaporation, and the losses exceed the gains.

Waters from the six major sources show directional variations in quality. Water in the

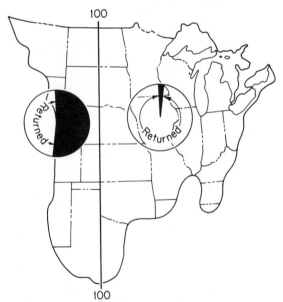

Figure 12.31 *Water withdrawn for irrigation on the Great Plains west of the 100th meridian roughly equals the quantity withdrawn for industrial use in the Central Lowland east of the 100th meridian (quantities represented by areas of circles). Over half the water withdrawn for irrigation is consumed (black); only a small fraction of the water withdrawn for industrial use is consumed.*

Great Lakes is carbonate water, and from Lake Superior to Lake Ontario, there is a progressive increase in total dissolved solids (tds) and in the proportion of sulfate (Fig. 12.32,A).

Waters in the three major rivers, the Mississippi, Ohio, and Missouri, differ greatly in quality. The Mississippi River, which carries about 200 ppm tds, begins as a carbonate water and becomes increasingly sulfate downstream to Alton (Fig. 12.32,B). The Ohio River at Pittsburgh has 500 ppm tds and is a sulfate water. Downstream the total dissolved solids decrease to less than 200 ppm and the proportion of sulfate progressively decreases (Fig. 12.32,C). The Yellowstone River, a branch of the Missouri in Montana, enters the Great Plains east of Livingston, Montana, with 140 ppm and a hardness of 65. Downstream this river crosses the lignite fields, and the tds increases to 240 ppm at Billings with hardness 140 and to 500 ppm at Miles City with hardness 230. The proportion of sulfate in the water progressively increases downstream (Fig. 12.32,D). The Missouri River below the mouth of the Yellowstone has 250 or more ppm tds and is a sulfo-carbonate water.

Quality of water supplies from the small rivers and lakes in the central United States is illustrated in Fig. 12.32,E. The content of total dissolved solids and, consequently, hardness, is least in the Superior Upland, intermediate in the eastern part of the Central Lowland, and greatest in the western part of the Central Lowland. Groundwater from the glacial drift is similar.

Groundwater from the bedrock formations generally contains more than 400 ppm tds, even in the Superior Upland, where the formations are Precambrian. Farther south, where the groundwater comes from sedimentary rocks of Paleozoic age, the tds is 800 ppm at shallow depths and exceeds 1,000 ppm in deep wells, those 500 feet deep or more. Water in the deep wells has a high content of chlorides and sulfates. To the west, groundwater is obtained from an Upper Cretaceous sandstone formation. Water enters the formation where it is

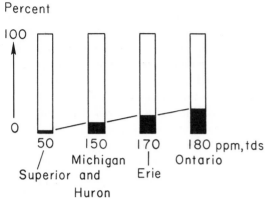

A. Great Lakes

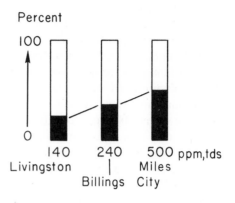

D. Yellowstone River

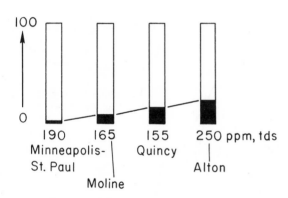

B. Mississippi River

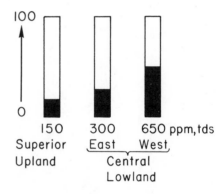

E. Small rivers and lakes

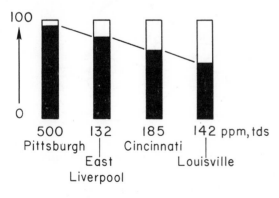

C. Ohio River

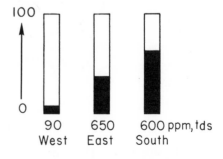

F. Municipal supplies in the west (foot of Rocky Mountains), east and south parts of the Great Plains

Figure 12.32 *Some variations in quality of water in the central United States (white = carbonate; black = sulfate).*

exposed in the uplifts at the Black Hills and Rocky Mountains and seeps eastward under the plains, where it supplies some flowing wells and numerous pumped wells. This water, like other deep groundwater in the central United States, is highly mineralized.

Cities along the western edge of the Great Plains obtain their water from the Rocky Mountains, and these waters commonly contain less than 100 ppm of dissolved solids, mostly carbonates. Eastward and southward, on the Great Plains, the content of dissolved solids increases and the proportion of sulfates and chlorides increases (Fig. 12.32,F).

Floods are a major problem in the Central Lowland. The floodplains are rich farmland and have been extensively settled, but high water inundates this land. An extensive set of dams and levees is being constructed along the rivers, as is illustrated by the network of dams in the Missouri River Basin (Fig. 12.33).

Another major water development program is planned for the Arkansas River, one of America's muddiest rivers. The development plans provide for a channel 9 feet deep and more than 150 feet wide with 18 locks to control the 400-foot drop along the lower 500 miles of the river, from near Tulsa to the junction with the Mississippi. Some opponents of this development contend that it would be

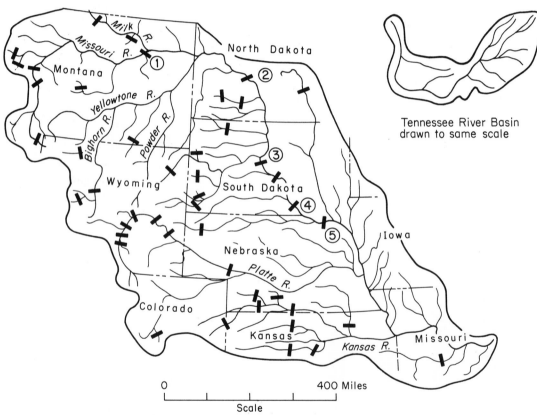

Tennessee River Basin drawn to same scale

Figure 12.33 *Dams in the Missouri River Basin. Some of these dams, especially those upstream, are multipurpose and provide for irrigation and power, but the system as a whole was designed primarily for flood control. Large dams along the main stem of the Missouri are Fort Peck Dam (1), Garrison Dam (2), Oahe Dam (3) and Big Bend Dam next downstream, Fort Randall Dam (4), and Gavins Point Dam (5).*

cheaper to build a double track railroad and to operate it free.

Water power resources in the central United States east of the Mississippi River have been developed almost to capacity. In the Missouri River Basin perhaps a quarter of the capacity remains to be developed, but the potential there is small compared to the western United States and Appalachian Highlands.

Agriculture

The Interior Plains, richest of the world's agricultural regions, are favored by a hot and rainy growing season, by rich loessial soils, and by flat land. Production is so lush that some state highway departments collect and bale hay from the highway right-of-ways. It is because of the Interior Plains that so many Americans face the problem of a bulging waistline.

The lake region specializes mostly in hay and dairying. The northern part of the Central Lowland westward onto the Great Plains is the corn and hog belt; parallel to this on the south is a belt used principally for corn and winter wheat. The two highland areas in the South and the southern part of the Great Plains are in the cotton belt. The central part of the Great Plains is used for winter wheat and the northern part for spring wheat. Lake Michigan provides an example of how local climate influences agricultural practice: fruit can be raised along the leeward (east) side of the lake, but the west side is not suitable.

By 1840 corn was raised in substantial quantities as far west as Missouri and Arkansas, but it was not until the 1870's that Iowa, Illinois, and central Indiana became the heart of the corn belt. About 1890 the pattern of production of wheat in the Plains and Prairie states began to appear as it does today.

The Middle West's impressive growth in agriculture can be illustrated in numerous examples. The center of wheat production began in New York. In 1850 the center had moved to central Ohio. By 1860 it was in Indiana, in 1870 in Illinois, in 1900 in Iowa, and today it is in Kansas. The increase in agriculture was both the cause and the effect of advances in farm machinery. Iron ploughs were not in general use until after 1842. By 1900 large farms used machinery that ploughed, harrowed, and sowed in a single operation. In 1830, 64 hours of labor were needed to produce an acre of wheat; by 1900, only 3 hours of labor were needed. In 1850 the United States had 1,500,000 farms aggregating 300 million acres; soon after 1900 there were 6,000,000 farms with a billion acres. Today there are 3,700,000 farms aggregating 1.1 billion acres. Agriculture today has become big business.

Minerals

Mineral production in the central United States, like agricultural production, involves a limited number of commodities produced in tremendous quantities. In terms of importance to the national economy, the chief products are the mineral fuels (coal, oil, gas), iron ore, lead and zinc ore, bauxite (aluminum ore), gold, fluorspar, and potash. In addition there are valuable deposits of copper, mercury, and salt.

Mineral fuels are abundant in the central United States and have been produced in great quantity. About a fifth of the United States coal production has been from formations of Pennsylvanian age in the structural basins bordering the Ozark Plateau and in the Ouachita Mountains. The coal is mostly bituminous, but the folded formations in the Ouachita Mountains contain anthracite. Where the coal is flat-lying, as in the broad structural basins, the mining is done mostly by huge steam shovels operating in open pits—strip-mining methods.

Cretaceous formations on the Great Plains contain beds of subbituminous coal; the Paleocene and Eocene formations in the northern Great Plains contain vast tonnages of lignite (brown coal). Lignite, a resource for the future, is little used at the present time, but the deposits are vast and can be produced inexpensively by strip mining and can be transported by pipeline or used at the mines to generate electricity.

Oil and gas have been produced from three major areas in the central United States. Greatest production has been from Paleozoic formations in the Mid-Continent region in Kansas, Oklahoma, and Texas, and is about one-sixth the value of the entire mineral production of the United States. A second important producing area is the Illinois Basin; a third is at the western edge of the Great Plains from New Mexico to Montana. Recently a new productive area has been discovered in the Williston Basin of North Dakota.

The United States annually produces about 100 million tons of iron, 85 percent of which is from mines in the Superior Upland. The ore occurs in Precambrian rocks as hematite (red iron oxide) in iron-rich cherts, carbonates, slates, and schists. Ore in the deposits mined thus far contains more than 50 percent iron.

Production of iron in the Lake Superior region began in 1854 but was slow in developing because the rich copper deposits in that region were more attractive to miners until after the Civil War. The building of the railroads boomed the iron industry, but the railroads grew faster than the iron mines and steel mills, and a good deal of the trackage had to be imported from England. Steel production began with the development of the Bessemer process in 1855.

The Precambrian rocks in the Lake Superior region, especially in the Keeweenaw Peninsula, also contain important deposits of copper. Native copper had been mined there by the Indians, but—to understate the matter—

their workings have since been considerably deepened; the Calumet and Hecla Mine, opened in 1846, is now more than a mile deep.

The copper deposits were discovered in 1830, and mining began in 1844. For some years this was one of the leading copper-producing districts in the world, production reaching 80,000 tons during 1900. Since then, however, the relative importance of the district has decreased because of production from the porphyry copper ores in the Basin and Range Province (p. 345).

The principal deposits of lead and zinc are in southwestern Missouri and adjoining corners of Oklahoma and Kansas—the Tri-State district. Other deposits are in southeastern Missouri, the Illinois-Kentucky district, and the Upper Mississippi Valley district. These were all discovered early. Those in the Upper Mississippi Valley were productive before 1700. The deposits in southeastern Missouri were discovered in 1715, when St. Genevieve was founded. After the Louisiana Purchase the Congress, in 1807, reserved all government lands containing lead ores and provided for leasing them at a royalty.

These ores are found in steeply dipping fissures, along bedding planes, and as irregular pockets in Paleozoic limestone. The lead occurs as a sulfide (galena) and as a carbonate (cerussite); the zinc occurs as a sulfide (sphalerite), a carbonate (smithsonite), and a silicate (calamine). The Tri-State district produces about a quarter of the total zinc mined annually in the United States and between 5 and 10 percent of the lead. The southeast Missouri district produces 40 percent of this country's lead.

One of the principal gold-producing areas in the United States is in the Black Hills Section of the Great Plains. The deposits occur in Precambrian slate associated with granitic intrusions in the central part of the domal uplift. The gold occurs free; that is, it is not contained in other minerals. The ores are rich and the mines are a half mile deep. The Black

Hills had been set aside by treaty in 1867 as permanent reservation for the Dakota, Kiowa, and Sioux Indian tribes, but the discovery in 1874 of rich gold placer deposits was too much of a temptation, and the treaty was violated. The Indians fought back as best they could; the massacre of Custer and his troops in 1876 was part of the Indian war that ensued. By 1877 the Indians had been punished for fighting for their rights and the lands were secured. Since then more than 20 million fine ounces of gold have been produced, and about half that amount still remains to be recovered.

When the United States entered World War II, demands made by the aircraft industry caused a sixfold increase in the production of aluminum. This strong, light-weight metal is one of the most abundant metallic elements in the earth's crust—by weight, half again as abundant as iron. But ores are few. At the present time, Arkansas bauxite (aluminum hydroxide) is this country's most important source, and more than 90 percent of the country's production is from there. We have no other known large deposits of bauxite, but in many parts of the country there are immense deposits of lower-grade ores such as high-alumina clay, aluminous rock known as anorthosite, and alunite (aluminum and potassium sulfate) that could become productive if technological advances reduce production costs. There is no shortage of these low-grade sources (p. 129).

Fluorspar deposits in Paleozoic limestone in southern Illinois and western Kentucky have been the chief source of fluorite in the United States, and until 1898 they were the only domestic source. Fluorite is used for flux in the steel industry, and for making hydrofluoric acid.

Until World War I the United States had to import potash, but in 1913 potash brines were discovered in wells drilled for oil in southeastern New Mexico and west Texas. This was followed by systematic exploration of the area, and such enormous deposits were found that the country is now self-sufficient; 85 percent of United States production comes from a few mines in southeastern New Mexico.

Other mineral resources in the central United States include manganese at Batesville, Arkansas. Important nonmetallic deposits include: high-grade ceramic clays in Ohio, Illinois, Missouri, Nebraska, and Colorado; gypsum (calcium sulfate), used in large part for plaster, near Grand Rapids, Michigan, Fort Dodge, Iowa, and in Kansas; salt in brines at Hutchinson, Kansas, and in rock-salt formations that are mined at Kanapolis, Lyons, and Kingman in central and southeastern Michigan; building stone in numerous formations, but notably the Sioux Quartzite at Sioux Falls, South Dakota, and limestone from Indiana and Iowa; novaculite, an abrasive useful for whetstones, in Arkansas. A soft stone, used by the Indians for making pipes, is obtained in southwestern Minnesota, and the quarry has been set aside as Pipestone National Monument.

A Misused Resource—
The Great Plains

Not quite a hundred years ago John Wesley Powell called attention to the unpleasant fact that lands west of the 100th meridian are not suited for the same kinds of uses as are the lands farther east, because the rainfall in dry years is inadequate to maintain water supplies. The Great Plains have three times the combined areas of Indiana, Illinois, and Iowa, but their effective moisture and total water supply is less than half that for those three Central Lowland states. We still have not faced the dry fact that the Great Plains are semiarid and quite unlike the Central Lowland and should not be used in the same way.

Water supplies on the Great Plains are inadequate to meet demands expected in the next two or three decades. Because irrigation consumes water, only half the water that is used is returned (Fig. 12.31). In the western panhandle of Texas and southeastern New Mexico groundwater withdrawals are depleting the storage.

What constitutes sensible use of the Great Plains remains an unanswered question. A start has been made by creating national grasslands, analogous to the national forests. More such steps are needed, for either we find another use for that vast area—a use that preserves its surface when the *inevitable, repeated,* and *protracted* droughts recur—or we must be ready with subsidies and relief programs of one kind or another when droughts convert it to a disaster area.

Rocky Mountains and Wyoming Basin

13

The Rocky Mountains (Fig. 13.1) are but a short segment of the backbone of the Americas that extends 10,000 miles from Alaska to Patagonia. The part that lies within the United States constitutes a north-south barrier—the continental divide—separating the Interior Plains from the Intermontane Plateaus and the Pacific Mountain System. The Rocky Mountains comprise three provinces, each with distinctive landforms: the Northern, Middle, and Southern Rocky Mountains. These, together with the Wyoming Basin, cover about 180,000 square miles, which is between 5 and 10 percent of the United States, an area less than that of the Appalachian Highlands.

The outstanding features of the Rocky Mountain System are its

1. High peaks, many of which are above 14,000 feet.
2. Great relief; the summits of many or most of the ranges are 5,000 to 7,000 feet higher than their bases.
3. Ruggedness, which far exceeds that of the Appalachians.
4. Rocks of igneous, metamorphic, and sedimentary origins in diverse kinds of structural uplifts and basins.
5. Shallow soils and extensive areas of bare rock.
6. Forests, which are extensive but much less varied than those of the Appalachians and consisting mostly of conifers.
7. Water supplies; this area is the principal source of water for a quarter of the United States, including the semiarid Great Plains east of the mountains and the deserts to the west.
8. Mineral wealth, which is considerable and varied.
9. Scenery—great vistas showing spectacular landforms with colorful rocks and forests.

Most of the mountains are in national forests. There are five large national parks (Glacier, Yellowstone, Grand Teton, and Rocky Mountain, and Dinosaur National Monument). Several other large national parks are in the Canadian portion of the Northern Rocky Mountains; these include Waterton Lakes, Mount Ravelstoke, Glacier, Kootenay, Yoho, and Banff National Parks.

Southern Rocky Mountains

The Southern Rocky Mountains (Fig. 13.1) form the principal barrier to travel, for they may be crossed only through high passes, all above 9,000 feet in altitude and some above

NATIONAL PARKS AND MONUMENTS

a, Glacier Nat. Park; b, Yellowstone Nat. Park; c, Grand Teton Nat. Park; cc, Craters of the Moon Nat. Mon.; d, Dinosaur Nat. Mon.; e, Rocky Mountain Nat. Park; f, Great Sand Dunes Nat. Mon.; g, Black Canyon of the Gunnison Nat. Mon.; h, Mesa Verde Nat. Park

RIVERS AND LAKES

Southern Rocky Mountains: er, Eagle River; rf, Roaring Fork; ar, Animas River; rg, Royal Gorge

Wyoming Basin and Middle Rocky Mountains: swr, Sweetwater River, bf, Blacks Fork; sc, Sandy Creek; jl, Jackson Lake; sl, Seminoe Res.; pl₁, Pathfinder Res.; pl₂, Palisade Res.; bl, Buffalo Bill Res.; sr, Shoshone River; lr, Laramie River

Northern Rocky Mountains: jr, Jefferson River; gr, Gallatin River; fl, Flathead Lake; kr, Kootenai River; po, Pend Oreille River; sr₁, Spokane River; sr₂, Sanpoil River; or, Okanogan River; cr, Clearwater River; hc, Hells Canyon

MOUNTAIN RANGES

Southern Rocky Mountains: 1, Medicine Bow Mts.; 2, Gore Range; 3, White River Plateau; 4, Mosquito Range; 5, Wet Mts.; 6, Jemez Mts.

Middle Rocky Mountains: 7, Absaroka Mts.

Northern Rocky Mountains: 8, Gallatin Range; 9, Tobacco Mts.; 10, Ruby Range; 11, Centennial Range; 12, Pioneer Mts.; 13, Deer Lodge Mts.; 14, Garnet Range; 15, Mission Range; 16, Whitefish Range; 17, Salish Mts.; 18, Purcell Mts.; 19, Selkirk Mts.; 20, Kettle Mts.; 21, Okanogan Range; 22, Pend Oreille Mts.; 23, Seven Devils Mts.; 24, Sawtooth Mts.; 25, Pioneer Mts.; 26, Lost River Range; 27, Lemhi Range

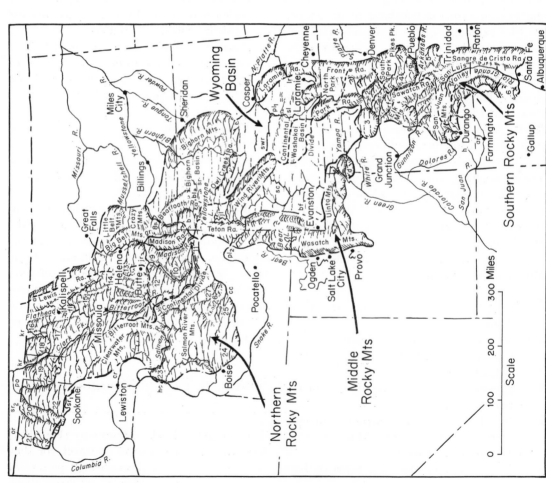

Figure 13.1 *Physiographic map of the Rocky Mountains and Wyoming Basin.*

11,000 feet. As a consequence, the emigrant trails to the west followed routes around the northern and southern ends of these mountains. One railroad, the Denver and Rio Grande, crosses the heart of the mountains along a spectacularly scenic route. The railroad's slogan is "Through the Rockies, not around them."

The Southern Rocky Mountains consist of a series of ranges, each with distinctive landforms and scenery reflecting the geologic structure of the ranges. The principal ranges along the eastern slope are the Laramie Range, Front Range, Wet Mountains, and Sangre de Cristo Range (Fig. 13.1). The principal ranges along the western slope are the Park Range, Gore Range, Sawatch Range, Elk Mountains, San Juan Mountains, and Jemez Mountains. The two groups of ranges are separated at the north by the basin of the North Platte River, North Park, the valley of the Arkansas River and South Park, and at the south by the broad San Luis Valley and the trough of the Rio Grande.

The continental divide follows the crest of the Park Range. At the south side of North Park it swings east around the head of the Colorado River to the Front Range, and then west again around the head of the Arkansas River to the Sawatch Range. It swings far west on the San Juan Mountains around the head of the Rio Grande and extends into the San Juan Basin between the heads of the San Juan and Chama rivers. Two-thirds of the Southern Rocky Mountains drains eastward.

By contrast, about four-fifths of the Northern Rocky Mountains drains to the Pacific Ocean (Fig. 13.2). The Middle Rocky Mountains and Wyoming Basin are about equally divided between drainage to the east and to the west.

Most cities are located along the foot of the mountains, where the climate is semiarid but where water can be obtained from the higher country. The population residing along the eastern foot of the Southern Rocky Mountains numbers about 1.5 million, mostly in Colorado along the foot of the Front Range. Only about a tenth as many people live along the western foot of the mountains; the population there is about 150,000. A few towns are located within the mountains, but none is large, and the total permanent population in the mountains probably is only a little more than 50,000.

Although the population is small, the private lands are, of course, the most accessible. As a consequence, the extensive and scenic public lands are nearly surrounded by private lands posted with signs warning, "No Trespassing." Colorado's mountains belong to all of us and are needed for national purposes—watershed protection, multiple-use forests, wilderness areas, and parks. It would seem in the national interest to purchase much of the acreage now held privately and to return it to the public land system.

Structural Framework and Geologic History

The Rocky Mountains began forming at the beginning of Cenozoic time. Before that, during the Cretaceous Period, a mediterranean sea that connected the Gulf of Mexico with the Arctic Ocean extended across all of what is now the Southern and Middle Rocky Mountains, and it covered at least the eastern half of the site of the Northern Rocky Mountains. The sea was a thousand miles wide, and its eastern shore lay in what is now the Central Lowland. To the west, in what is now the Basin and Range Province, mountains were shedding sediments into this sea.

The crustal movements that had built the Cretaceous mountains in the west progressed eastward. By middle Cretaceous time the area in western Utah that had been a coastal plain began to be uplifted, and the western shore moved eastward. By the end of Cretaceous time the folding and uplift of the Rocky Mountains had finally expelled the sea from the area they now occupy.

But all of Cenozoic time was required for the mountains to develop their present aspect. During the early part of the Tertiary Period, in Paleocene and Eocene time, the summits of the newly formed mountains may have been a mile or more high, but the bases of the mountains remained near sea level. A large lake, Greenriver Lake, occupied the Wyoming and Uinta Basins; east of the Rocky Mountains coastal plain deposits (Lance and Fort Union Formations) were laid down between the mountains and a remnant of the former mediterranean sea.

The area now occupied by the San Juan

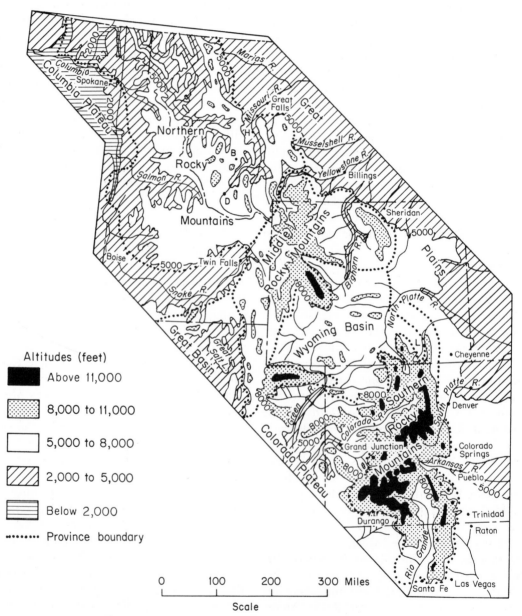

Figure 13.2 *Altitudes in the Rocky Mountain System.*

Mountains was once the site of a vast accumulation of volcanic materials—lavas, mud flows, and ash. One ash formation (San Juan Tuff) is estimated to include 1,000 cubic miles of ash. Volcanism was extensive in the Northern and Middle Rocky Mountains too, and volcanic activity continues today in the Yellowstone Park region.

Finally, in late Tertiary time, the entire region was uplifted, with the result that the early Tertiary lake beds and the bases of the mountains are now a full mile above sea level. The principal formations in the Southern Rocky Mountains are given in Table 13.1; Figure 13.3 is a geologic map with cross sections illustrating the structural geology of the mountains.

The Southern Rocky Mountains consist of a series of anticlinal uplifts in most of which Precambrian rocks are exposed in the cores, with Paleozoic and younger formations turned up steeply against the flanks, where the resistant beds form hogbacks. In places, as illustrated in the cross sections in Figure 13.3, the Precambrian rocks have been raised by faulting and have been thrust over the younger formations.

During the Tertiary Period a series of large, roughly cylindrical intrusions (stocks), probably related to the volcanic activity, were pushed upward in a belt that trends northeast across the central part of the Southern Rocky Mountains (Figure 13.3). Mineralization associated with these intrusions gave rise to the *Colorado mineral belt*. Much of Colorado's production of metals has come from the mineral deposits along this belt of stocks.

During Quaternary time snowfields formed on the summits of the Rocky Mountains, and glaciers developed. There was at least one major glaciation prior to Wisconsin time, and there were two during Wisconsin time. As a result of this phase of the area's geologic history, the summit ridges became scored with deep cirques, many with lakes. The alpine glaciers that headed in these cirques extended 5 to 10 miles down the valleys, a few even

farther. The glaciated valleys are U-shaped. Many or most of them are partly blocked with terminal moraines deposited at the ice front (Fig. 13.4).

During the glacial stages of late Pleistocene time, the tops of the Southern Rocky Mountains were capped with snow and ice. Even if this snow and ice covered only 10 percent of the Southern Rocky Mountains to an average depth of 100 feet, the volume of water held there must have amounted to between a quarter and a half billion acre feet—a quantity vastly larger than the total annual discharge of the present streams. During the waning of the glacial stage, and even during thaws when the ice was advancing, major floods must have been discharged onto the low country around the mountains. To these floods are attributed the gravel fills along the valleys crossing the Great Plains. The floodplains along these valleys were sources for the deposits of loess that blanket the Great Plains and Central Lowland.

Drainage System

Figure 13.5 illustrates differences in the gradients of the principal rivers draining the Southern Rocky Mountains. The parts of the courses below about 6,000 feet are outside the mountains; the parts higher than 6,000 feet are in the mountains.

Although two-thirds of the area of the Southern Rocky Mountains drains eastward and only one-third drains westward, the rivers draining to the west have cut their valleys more deeply than those draining east. The Arkansas and Colorado rivers in these mountains are comparable, both in drainage area and discharge, but the valley bottom of the Colorado River averages a thousand feet lower than that of the Arkansas. This seems anomalous, because the plateaus west of the Rocky Mountains average 1,500 to 2,000 feet higher than the Great Plains. The Colorado River is shorter, and therefore its average

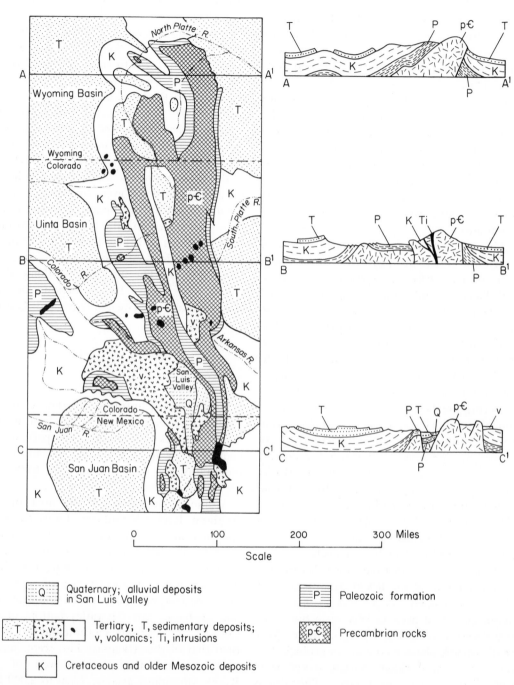

Figure 13.3 *Geologic map and cross sections of the Southern Rocky Mountains.*

TABLE 13.1 Geological formations in the Southern Rocky Mountains.

		Western slope	*Eastern slope*
Quaternary		Late Wisconsin moraines and related deposits, early Wisconsin moraines and related deposits, pre-Wisconsin deposits.	
Tertiary	Miocene	Browns Park Formation: sandstone, conglomerate, 1,200 feet thick.	Arikaree Formation: sandstone, shale, 500 feet thick.
	Oligocene	Duchesne River Formation: sandstone, 1,300 feet thick.	Castle Rock Conglomerate: 500 feet thick.
	Eocene	Uinta and Bridger Formations: fluviatile deposits, 2,000 feet thick. Green River Formation: lacustrine deposits 4,000 feet thick.	Missing.
	Paleocene	Wasatch Formation: fluviatile deposit 2,000 feet thick.	Denver Formation: fluviatile deposits 1,500 feet thick.
Cretaceous		Mesaverde Formation: coastal plain deposits, 3,000 feet thick. Mancos Shale: marine, 5,000 feet thick. Dakota Sandstone: beach deposit, 100 feet thick.	Arapahoe Formation: fluviatile conglomerate and sandstone, 400 feet thick; contains pebbles from Laramie and older formations. Laramie Formation: coastal plain deposits, 250 feet thick. Fox Hills standstone: beach deposit, 500 feet thick. Pierre Shale: marine, 3,000 feet thick. Niobrara Formation: marine shale and limestone, 300 feet thick. Benton Formation: marine shale and limestone, 300 feet thick. Dakota Sandstone: beach deposit, 100 feet thick.
Jurassic		Morrison Formation: fluviatile deposits, 500 feet thick.	
Triassic		Chinle Formation: generally red beds, 500 feet thick.	Lykins Formation: red beds, 500 feet thick.
Permian		Maroon Formation: red beds, 4,000 feet thick.	Lyons Formation: sandstone 250 feet thick.
Pennsylvanian		Hermosa Formation: shale and limestone, 1,800 feet thick.	Fountain Formation: red beds, 2,000 feet thick.
Early Paleozoic		Sandstone and limestone, 150 feet thick.	
Precambrian		Granite, schist, and gneiss.	

gradient is steeper than that of the Arkansas River, but the stretches along both rivers down to an altitude of about 500 feet are nearly equal in length.

Climate

The difference in mean annual temperature between the mountain tops in the Southern Rocky Mountains and the Great Plains, about 35°F, is as great as the difference between the mean annual temperature of the plains and that of much of Alaska. In parts of the mountains the growing season is no more than 40 days, about half that of Alaska's Yukon Valley. Average annual snowfall in parts of the San Juan Mountains exceeds 20 feet, and this amount of snow impedes travel on mountainside highways despite numerous and powerful snowplows. Figure 13.7 illustrates the close correlation between annual

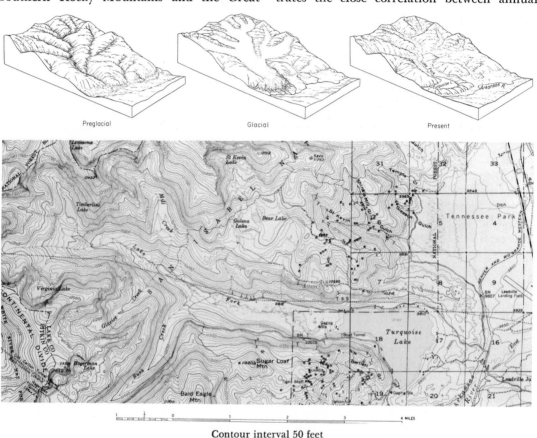

Contour interval 50 feet

Figure 13.4 *Map showing cirques, U-shaped valleys draining from them, and a terminal moraine along Lake Fork of the Arkansas River, on the east side of the Sawatch Range, Colorado. The diagrams illustrate the evolution of this topography. In preglacial time V-shaped stream valleys were cut into the mountain. In the glacial periods these valleys weer filled with ice, which formed a glacier that extended down Lake Fork to the valley of the Arkansas River. Gravel was deposited at the front of the glacier, forming a terminal moraine; when the ice melted, the depression behind the terminal moraine became a lake (Turquoise Lake), and the U-shaped valleys were exposed.*

precipitation and topography. The high-altitude areas have the greatest precipitation and the shortest frost-free period, less than 40 days. Conversely, the low-altitude areas have the least precipitation and the longest frost-free period, more than 120 days.

In the Southern Rocky Mountains, 50 percent of the runoff is due to thunderstorms, but this percentage decreases in the physiographic provinces to the west and northwest. Runoff attributable to thunderstorms in the Middle Rockies amounts to about 30 percent, in the Northern Rockies about 15 percent, and in the Sierra-Cascade less than 10 percent.

Along the eastern foot of the Rocky Mountains, the winter climate may suddenly turn mild because of certain westerly winds called *chinooks,* the equivalent of what in Europe is called foehns. A chinook originates when air moves up the western slope across the summit and down the eastern slope to the plains. As it ascends the western slope, the air cools as it expands (about 5.5°F for every thousand feet of rise). When sufficiently cooled, moisture is precipitated, heat is released, and the cooling process is slowed. During its descent, the air becomes more dense, and it would warm at the same rate at which it had cooled if it were not now dry. If during its descent the air absorbs little or no moisture—a cooling process that would slow the warming—then it reaches the plains much warmer than it was originally. An air mass starting at 50°F at the western foot of the Rocky Mountains may warm to 75°F by the time it reaches the edge of the Great Plains.

The effects of past climates in these and other mountain areas in the west are illustrated chiefly by the empty cirques on the mountain tops, the U-shaped valleys formerly occupied by ice, and the morainal deposits (Figs. 13.4, 13.13).

Forests in the Rocky Mountains region illustrate the climatic influence on the distribution of vegetation. Conversely, however, forests affect climate: they lower the temperature of the air inside and above them—in places,

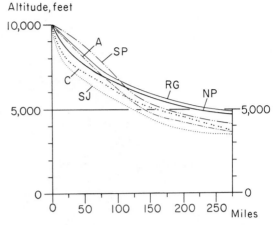

Figure 13.5 *Gradients of major streams draining the Southern Rocky Mountains. Broken lines represent streams draining east: A, Arkansas River; SP, South Platte River. Dotted Lines represent streams draining west: C, Colorado River; SJ, San Juan River. Solid lines represent streams draining south or north: RG, Rio Grande; NP, North Platte River.*

sufficiently so to increase local precipitation. Temperature ranges in forests are less extreme than on nonforested land; maximums are lower and minimums are higher. Consequently, frost penetration is less in forest soils—often only half as deep as in nearby, nonforested soils—and the snow melts more slowly under forest cover than in the open. Thus, the spring runoff is conserved, and groundwater, which helps maintain the flow of streams and springs through the summer, is replenished.

Vegetation

Vegetation on the Southern Rocky Mountains is altitudinally zoned in response to the altitudinal changes in climate (Figs. 13.6, 13.7). The animal life, including the fish, also is zoned altitudinally (p. 106).

Above timberline (about 11,500 feet), in the Alpine Zone, the only vegetation to be found

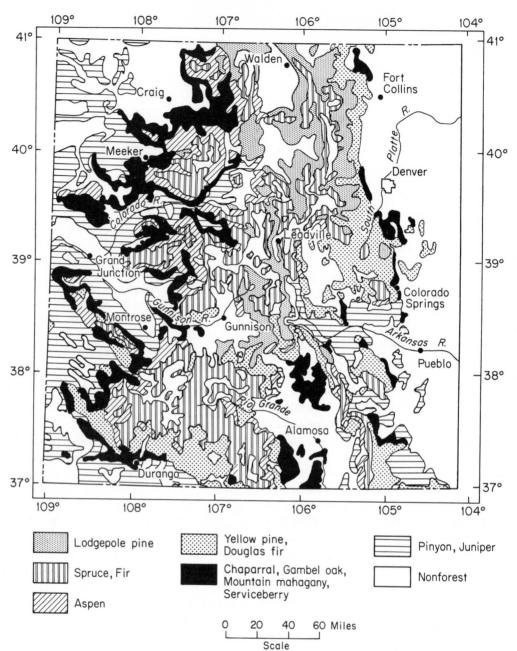

Figure 13.6 *Major forest types in Colorado. (From U.S.D.A.)*

Legend:
- Lodgepole pine
- Yellow pine, Douglas fir
- Pinyon, Juniper
- Spruce, Fir
- Chaparral, Gambel oak, Mountain mahagany, Serviceberry
- Nonforest
- Aspen

0 20 40 60 Miles
Scale

consists of small herbs and grasses. Much of this ground is bare rock. At timberline, in the Hudsonian Zone, trees are dwarfed and much deformed by wind. Below timberline, the Canadian Zone supports a dense forest of Englemann spruce and various firs, with considerable lodgepole pine, aspen, and some white pine. This forest extends down to about 9,500 feet on the eastern slope and to about 9,000 feet on the northern and western slopes.

Next lower is the Transition Zone, in which forests are open and are populated primarily by yellow pine but include considerable Douglas fir and, toward the upper limit of the zone, lodgepole pine and aspen. On the western slope, the lower limit of yellow pine is at about 7,500 feet, but on the eastern slope, the growth of yellow pine extends to the foot of

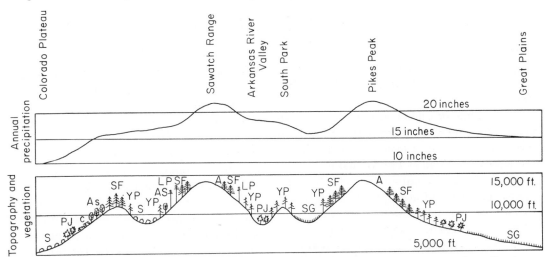

Figure 13.7 *Diagrammatic transect across the Southern Rocky Mountains, illustrating the altitudinal zoning of the vegetation. Alpine Zone (A); Canadian Zone with spruce-fir forest (SF); Transition Zone, mostly yellow pine forest (YP); Upper Sonoran Zone with pinyon-juniper woodland (PJ), short grass (SG), and sagebrush (S).*

the mountains and onto the Great Plains at altitudes as low as 6,500 feet.

Below the yellow pine forests is woodland of pinyon pine and juniper, representing the upper part of the Upper Sonoran Zone and extending around the southern base of the Southern Rocky Mountains. In the northern part of the zone and at the upper elevations in the southern part of the zone, the pinyon-juniper woodland is replaced by chaparral— a scrubby growth consisting principally of Gambel oak, mountain mahogany, and serviceberry. On the western slope the chaparral extends upward into the Transition Zone, and the pinyon-juniper extends downward to about 6,000 feet. Below that level, but still within the Upper Sonoran Zone, sagebrush grows on the west and mostly short grass on the east.

It should not be supposed that the boundaries between these vegetation zones follow contours, for in general the upper altitudinal zones extend far below their normal range along cool, moist valley bottoms; conversely, a particular zone may extend high above its normal range on a dry hillside with southern exposure.

The spruce-fir forests are the major timber resource. Engelmann spruce alone accounts for almost half the total sawtimber production in the Southern Rocky Mountains. Yel-

Figure 13.8 *Views of the Teton Range, Wyoming, from the east. In the foreground of both views is the broad valley of the Snake River, an outwash plain of glacial debris. In the lower view the foreground includes part of Jackson Lake, the second largest lake in Wyoming (altitude about 6,700 feet). The high peaks reach to about 12,000 feet.*

low pine was the principal source of saw-timber until recently, because of its lumber qualities and its accessibility. But heavy cutting of yellow pine and improved access to the higher forests have increased the production of spruce and fir.

The volume of timber in these forests, estimated at somewhat more than 50 billion board feet, is about a fifth the volume in all the Rocky Mountains. The annual cut in the Southern Rocky Mountains is about half the annual growth, and attempts are being made to increase the production. Even pulp mill plants are being encouraged, although in such environments these are notorious for polluting both atmosphere and streams. A pulp mill in any of the valleys on the windward side of the mountains could make considerable areas in those lovely mountains undesirable for man, other animals, or plants.

Poisonous Plants on the Western Range

Physiographic setting is a factor in the distribution of plants poisonous to livestock. Poisonous plants grow in all parts of the country; oak, bracken fern, chokecherry, milkweed, sneezeweed, water hemlock, and lupine are examples. Other poisonous plants that grow in semiarid regions include arrowgrass, death camas, greasewood, rubberweed, locoweed, and certain species of larkspur (the beautiful delphinium). Where feed is plentiful, livestock apparently either avoid most poisonous plants or do not consume enough to be poisoned. In the arid and semiarid regions poisonous plants are a serious menace to livestock because feed is frequently scarce, at least seasonally, and the poisonous plants may be consumed in toxic amounts.

Since most of the Rocky Mountains and intermontane plateaus and basins are used chiefly for grazing, the identification and control of poisonous plants are an important aspect of range management in those regions.

Surficial Deposits and Soils

Surficial deposits in the Southern Rocky Mountains include glacial moraines and gravelly alluvium in the valleys; colluvium, locally with boulder fields on the mountain sides; and some sand dunes. These deposits are largely late Pleistocene and Recent in age and the soils developed on them are correspondingly young.

The soils are zoned altitudinally to about the same degree as the vegetation, and in general, the sequence of soils encountered upward on the mountains parallels the sequence encountered eastward across the Interior Plains, for the climatic zoning is similar (Fig. 6.4). On the Great Plains, at the foot of the mountains, the soils are pedocals (Brown Soils) with a thick layer of lime in the subsoil. Upward on the mountains, in and near the Transition Zone, rainfall is greater and the lime zone is less well developed; the soils there are somewhat like the Chestnut Soils that occur in the Great Plains near the 100th meridian. In the upper part of the Transition Zone and higher, where the annual rainfall is 20 inches or more, the soils are pedalfers and resemble the Gray-Brown Podzols in the north-central United States.

These soils formed during very late Pleistocene and Recent time, and they are shallow. Here and there are remnants of deep, old soils that formed in pre-Wisconsin time, but these soils were largely eroded from the mountains during Wisconsin time, when the climate was rigorous. In general, soil erosion in the Rocky Mountains is severe only where remnants of the pre-Wisconsin soils are extensive. This relationship between soil age and susceptibility to erosion is similar to that in the Appalachian Highlands (p. 195).

The differences between the soils of pre-Wisconsin, Wisconsin, and Recent age on the Rocky Mountains are best shown by the differences in weathering of the moraines and other deposits of those ages. In Recent deposits, pebbles are fresh. In deposits of Wisconsin age, pebbles may have a weathered rind. In deposits of pre-Wisconsin age, pebbles may be altered to clay.

Middle Rocky Mountains and Wyoming Basin

The Middle Rocky Mountains and the Wyoming Basin (Fig. 13.1) include a miscellany of landforms bearing resemblances to all the neighboring provinces. The Bighorn Basin is nearly surrounded by mountains and is included in the Middle Rocky Mountains, but it connects with and is quite like the neighboring parts of the Great Plains. The eastern part of the Wyoming Basin connects with and resembles the Great Plains. To the south the Wyoming Basin connects with and resembles the adjoining part of the Colorado Plateau. The Bighorn, Wind River and Uinta mountains are like the ranges in the Southern Rocky Mountains; the Wasatch and other mountains on the west are like the ranges of the Basin and Range Province. The plateau at Yellowstone Park could as well be included in the Columbia Plateau as in the Middle Rocky Mountains. The Middle Rocky Mountains and Wyoming Basin differ from their neighbors chiefly because of their heterogeneity.

Cities and towns are located around the bases of the mountains and are dependent on them for their water, as in the Southern Rocky Mountains. Provo, Salt Lake City, and Ogden are situated along the western foot of the Wasatch Range. Sheridan, Wyoming, is located at the foot of the Bighorn Mountains. A number of towns—Laramie, Rawlins, Rock Springs, Green River, and Evanston—grew up along the Union Pacific Railroad and the highway across the southern part of the Wyoming Basin. Other towns have developed along the river valleys—Montpelier on the Bear River, Livingston and Big Timber on the Yellowstone, and Casper on the North Platte. The total population *within* the provinces is probably little more than a quarter of a million (1960 census).

The resources within these provinces are considerable and diverse. The region is rich in mineral fuels and other mineral deposits, especially in such nonmetals as phosphates and salts. It produces livestock, and there is some irrigation farming. It contains two of our best-known national parks, Yellowstone and Grand Teton, and forests that are popular for camping and for dude ranching. The Wyoming Basin, site of the Oregon and California trails of the last century, is still the major transcontinental route across the Rocky Mountains.

Structural Framework and Geologic History

Some of the ranges in the Middle Rocky Mountains, such as the Bighorn, Owl Creek, Wind River, and Uinta Mountains, are anticlinal uplifts, like the ranges in the Southern Rocky Mountains. Others, like the Wasatch Mountains and the ranges to the north, are block faulted and resemble mountains in the Basin and Range Province. Most of Yellowstone Park is an elevated lava plateau. Moreover, the trends of the ranges are so diverse that they nearly box the compass. The Middle Rocky Mountains include not only some of the most impressive mountains in the western United States—for example, the Teton Range (Fig. 13.8)—but some of the least impressive and least mountainous ranges in the western United States. Only small parts of the Middle Rocky Mountains are higher than 11,000 feet (Fig. 13.2).

The Wyoming Basin, an elevated depression separating the Middle and Southern Rocky Mountains, consists of a series of broad structural and topographic basins. These are partly filled with Tertiary deposits and are separated by low anticlinal uplifts of older rocks. Altitudes are mostly between 6,000 and 8,000 feet and average about 7,000 feet. The continental divide here is scarcely noticeable. In fact, a shallow depression almost 100 miles wide, the Washakie Basin, crosses it. The basins along the Green, North Platte, and Wind rivers are topographically and geologically, like the Powder River Basin on the Great Plains, the Bighorn Basin in the Middle Rocky Mountains, and the Uinta Basin, which is included in the Colorado Plateau (Fig. 14.9). Further, the climate, soils, and vegetation are not very different. The Wyoming Basin connects the Great Plains with the Colorado Plateau; one can go from one to the other without crossing a mountain range.

Each of the individual ranges in the Middle Rocky Mountains, and each of the several basins that make up the Wyoming Basin are structural as well as topographic units. The Southern Rocky Mountains divide northward into three anticlinal uplifts (represented by the Laramie, Medicine Bow, and Park Ranges) that plunge northwestward under the Wyoming Basin and divide it into small basins like the one at Laramie. Precambrian rocks form the cores of these anticlines. Paleozoic and Mesozoic formations form hogbacks along their flanks, and these formations dip under younger ones of Tertiary age that dip more gently into the basins and form cuestas. The structure of the Tertiary formations is like that of a saucer. If we could see through one of the basins it might look like the idealized cross section in Figure 13.9. The Mesozoic and Paleozoic formations are downfolded more deeply under the basins and have deeper, bowl-like structures. An unconformity between the Tertiary and older formations shows that part of the folding occurred before the Tertiary formations were deposited.

Unconformities separating some of the Tertiary formations show that the folding was resumed intermittently while the Tertiary formations were being deposited. The deposits, of course, began collecting in the basins as soon as the folding started, and the folding progressed intermittently from then on while

deposition continued. This explains why the older deposits are more folded than the younger ones. Unfortunately we see the contacts only around the rims of such basins, and this limited view minimizes the extent of unconformities, which record the structural movements.

The Uinta Mountains, which separate the Wyoming Basin from the Uinta Basin, are an anticlinal uplift of Precambrian rocks (Fig. 13.10). The Wind River Mountains are a similar anticline separating the Green River and Wind River Basins. The Owl Creek Mountains, another anticline, separate the Wind River and Bighorn basins, and the Bighorn Mountains similarly separate the Bighorn and Powder River basins.

The mountain ranges west of the Wyoming Basin consist of Paleozoic and Mesozoic formations. Along some of these ranges the Paleozoic formations are thrust eastward onto Cretaceous or older Mesozoic formations. The westernmost range, the Wasatch Range, consists of complexly folded and thrust-faulted

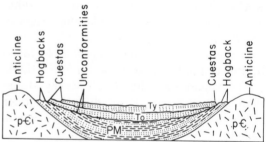

Figure 13.9 *Idealized cross section of a structural basin in Wyoming.* p Є, *Precambrian;* PM, *Paleozoic and Mesozoic formations;* To, *older Tertiary deposits;* Ty, *younger Tertiary deposits. The steeply upturned Paleozoic and Mesozoic formations form cuestas and hogbacks along the flanks of the basin. The older Tertiary formations were first deposited in the center of the basin; as accumulation proceeded, the deposits gradually extended outward onto its flanks. Continued folding during Tertiary deposits to unconformably overlap the older Tertiary deposits. (Compare Fig. 11.12.)*

Paleozoic formations intruded by granitic stocks and later elevated and rotated in a tremendous fault block, or series of fault blocks, overlooking Great Salt Lake (Fig. 13.11). In all of these structural features the Wasatch Mountains resemble the ranges in the Basin and Range Province. In addition, mineralization associated with the granitic stocks (silver and lead, with some zinc and copper) is like that around numerous stocks in the Basin and Range Province.

The Teton Mountains in Wyoming are a similar fault block but tilted west, and that fault block extends northward, and is buried by, the lavas and other volcanic rocks that cap the Yellowstone Plateau (Fig. 13.12). These volcanic rocks are younger than much of the structural deformation. They are more than 2,000 feet thick and they spread unconformably across folded and faulted early Tertiary formations.

Volcanism on the Yellowstone volcanic plateau has continued to Recent time. Yellowstone Park contains thousands of hot springs and geysers. Most of the water is supplied by seepage from the surface. The heat is supplied by shallow lavas and other rocks that are still hot. Gases escaping from the heated rocks become dissolved in the hot water, which then becomes a powerful solvent that can dissolve silica from the rocks and transport it to the surface, where the water issues from springs and geysers. These are of many kinds, differing in temperature, quantity and mode of discharge, and in composition of the waters. The springs presumably have open underground passages that permit steady discharge. The geysers are thought to have underground passages that are irregular or so constricted that discharge is interrupted until the accumulated pressure is sufficient to cause the water to erupt violently. Most geysers erupt intermittently; a few, like Old Faithful, erupt periodically. Some springs discharge clear water;

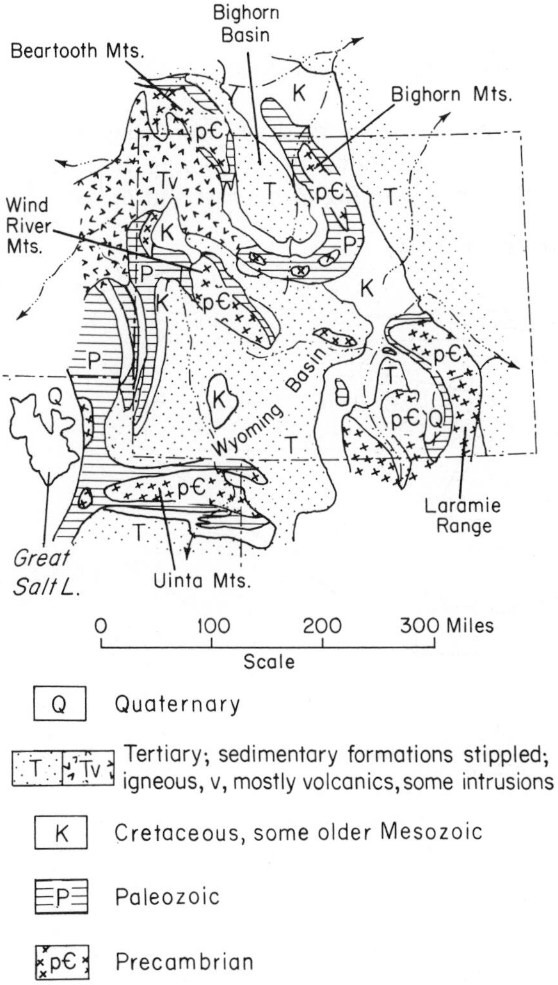

Beartooth Mts.

Bighorn Basin

Bighorn Mts.

Wind River Mts.

Wyoming Basin

Laramie Range

Great Salt L.

Uinta Mts.

0   100   200   300 Miles

Scale

Q   Quaternary

T / Tv   Tertiary; sedimentary formations stippled; igneous, v, mostly volcanics, some intrusions

K   Cretaceous, some older Mesozoic

P   Paleozoic

p€   Precambrian

Figure 13.10 *Geologic map showing the principal structural units in the Middle Rocky Mountains and the Wyoming Basin.*

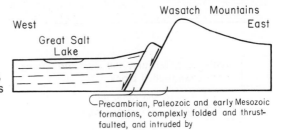

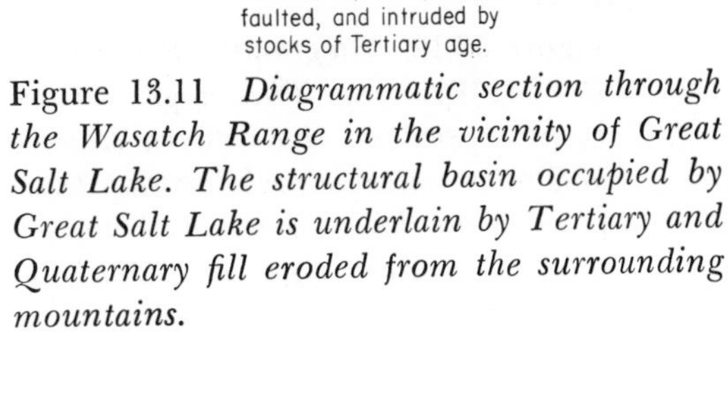

West — Wasatch Mountains — East

Great Salt Lake

Precambrian, Paleozoic and early Mesozoic formations, complexly folded and thrust-faulted, and intruded by stocks of Tertiary age.

Figure 13.11 *Diagrammatic section through the Wasatch Range in the vicinity of Great Salt Lake. The structural basin occupied by Great Salt Lake is underlain by Tertiary and Quaternary fill eroded from the surrounding mountains.*

others are highly colored. One group, known as the paint pots, discharges a pasty mud.

Glaciation during the Pleistocene period was the last geologic event that played a major part in shaping the Middle Rocky Mountains. All the major ranges were glaciated. Although they are not as high as the Southern Rocky Mountains, the snow and ice on these mountains extended to lower levels because they are farther north. The snow and ice must have covered most of the mountains above the 8,000-foot level. The alpine glaciers in the Teton Mountains descended to the level of Jackson Hole at 6,500 feet, where they deposited terminal moraines that still contain lakes (Fig. 13.13). On the west front of the Wasatch Mountains and northeast front of the Beartooth Mountains the glaciers extended to the foot of the mountains at an altitude of about 5,000 feet. The extent and

volume of the glacial ice and snow probably was as great as in the higher Southern Rocky Mountains.

Streams draining from the alpine glaciers in the mountains transported vast quantities of sediments, and most valleys became filled with sand and gravel. These fills are now exposed in gravel terraces formed along the valley sides by streams that have excavated new valleys in the fill. The valley of the Snake River, south of Jackson Lake, is an outwash plain; that valley is still buried by the glacial fill.

Rivers and Lakes

Six major rivers drain from the Middle Rocky Mountains and Wyoming Basin, and the areas draining to the east and to the west

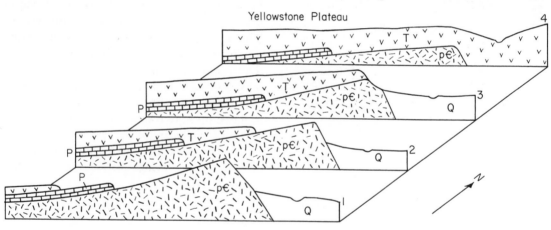

Q — Quaternary, Tertiary, and older formations in the down faulted block.

T — Lavas and other volcanic rocks of Tertiary age.

P — Paleozoic formations

p€ — Precambrian rocks

Figure 13.12 *Diagrammatic cross sections illustrating the structure of the Teton Range, Wyoming. The range is a fault block composed largely of Precambrian rocks capped on the western slope by Paleozoic formations (section 1). Lavas and other volcanic rocks overlap the western slope of the range. As the structure plunges northward (sections 2 and 3) the volcanics extend progressively farther onto the western slope and, finally, at the Yellowstone volcanic plateau (section 4), completely bury it.*

Figure 13.13 *A lake contained by a terminal moraine at the mouth of a glaciated canyon at the eastern foot of the Teton Range.*

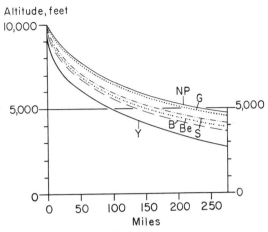

Figure 13.14 *Gradients of major streams draining the Wyoming Basin and the Middle Rocky Mountains. NP, North Platte River; B, Bighorn River and Wind River; Y, Yellowstone River; S, Snake River; Be, Bear River; G, Green River.*

are about equal. The North Platte River, which heads in the Southern Rocky Mountains, and its principal tributary, the Sweetwater River, drain eastward. The Green River, and its principal tributaries—the Yampa River, Blacks Fork River, and Sandy Creek, drain southward. The Bear River drains westward to Great Salt Lake. The Snake River heads in Jackson Lake and drains westward into the Columbia River. The Yellowstone and Bighorn rivers, together with their numerous tributaries, drain northeastward to the Missouri River. Of these streams, the Yellowstone River has cut most deeply into this region (Fig. 13.14). The North Platte and Green rivers are the least incised.

Lakes in the Middle Rocky Mountains and Wyoming Basin are numerous. Some, including the large Yellowstone Lake, occupy depressions in the Yellowstone lava plateau. They have been dammed partly by faulting or tilting, partly by volcanic deposits, and partly by glacial deposits. Yellowstone Lake, which covers 138 square miles and is above 7,500 feet, discharges into the Yellowstone River. This lake, which receives most of its water from the Absaroka Mountains to the east, occupies a glacial valley and was once 160 feet deeper and drained southward to the Snake River. That outlet became dammed, probably by faulting and tilting, and the lake began draining northward to the Yellowstone River. The overflow in that direction has eroded the Grand Canyon of the Yellowstone River and lowered the lake level. Small lakes

are abundant in glacial cirques on all the high mountains, especially on the Bighorn, Teton, Wind River, and Uinta mountains. Some of the cirques in the Tetons contain icefields.

Other lakes have been formed along the bases of the Teton and Wind River mountains, where the Pleistocene glaciers reached the low country and built terminal moraines across the mouths of canyons. These lakes are larger than the cirque lakes, and many exceed 100 feet in depth. The lake illustrated in Figure 13.13 is one of several along the east foot of the Teton Mountains. Such lakes are not found around the bases of the Uinta Mountains and Southern Rocky Mountains because the glaciers there did not extend to the foot of the mountains. In those mountains the terminal moraines are in the canyons, well in from the base of the mountains.

Bear Lake, which covers more than 100 square miles, is situated on the Utah-Idaho boundary at an altitude just under 6,000 feet. The lake is one of several that occupy structural depressions. Bear Lake fills the southern part of a structural valley that is crossed by the Bear River. The valley was tilted southward and flooded by streams from the surrounding high mountains. A lava flow across the lower, north end of the valley forms a natural spillway for the lake.

Still other lakes occupy small depressions in the southeastern part of the Wyoming Basin. Most of these depressions cover only a few acres, and most are dry, but a few contain small, shallow lakes or ponds. Others are marshy. They seem to have formed in at least four ways. Some of the largest of these small depressions are apparently due to structural downwarping. Some of the smallest ones may be sinkholes due to solution of buried gypsum or other salts. Still others are attributable to wind scour, and are referred to as *deflation hollows*. A few may be due to ponding of washes by sand dunes or by deposits brought in by flash floods from tributaries.

A number of water storage reservoirs have been built in the basins and in the mountains. Two major reservoirs along the North Platte River are the Seminoe and Pathfinder Reservoirs. Several small ones in the Wasatch Mountains store water for cities and farms along the west foot of the range. Irrigation developments along the headward part of the Snake River include the Palisades Reservoir, located where the river turns northwest to the Snake River Plain after rounding the south end of the Teton Range. In the Absaroka Mountains the Buffalo Bill Reservoir on the Shoshone River stores water for irrigation in the Bighorn Basin. Several reservoirs in the Wind River Basin store water for irrigation there and downstream in the Bighorn Basin. Of all the rivers in Wyoming, the Green River most nearly maintains its natural flow without artificial controls.

Climate, Vegetation, and Soils

Some climatic data for the Middle Rocky Mountains and Wyoming Basin are given in Figure 13.15. Both temperature and precip-

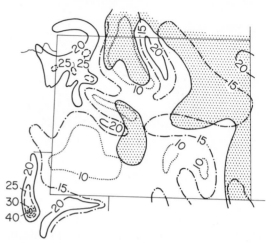

Figure 13.15 *Map showing average annual precipitation in the Middle Rocky Mountains and the Wyoming Basin. The average growing season is more than 120 days in the stippled areas; less than 120 days in the unstippled areas. (From U.S.D.A.)*

itation average slightly lower than in the Southern Rocky Mountains. The basins on the lee (east) side of mountains are favored by chinook winds during the winter, as are the Great Plains east of the Southern Rocky Mountains (p. 253). Other, more northerly winds that attain high velocities and give rise to ground blizzards are not regarded so favorably.

Vegetation on the Middle Rocky Mountains is altitudinally zoned, as it is on other high mountains. Timberline on the high summits rises southward from about 9,500 feet at the northwest end of the Beartooth Mountains, to 10,000 feet in the Bighorn Mountains, and to about 11,000 feet in the Uinta Mountains. Above timberline are grasses, sedges, and other low alpine plants. Their total area is only a little less than that of summits above timberline in the lofty Southern Rocky Mountains (Fig. 13.16), where timberline also rises southward, from about 11,000 to about 12,000 feet.

Although timberline rises generally southward, its position varies considerably with exposure. On the Beartooth Mountains, for example, timberline is at about 9,300 feet on northern and western slopes and at 9,800 feet on southern slopes.

The highest forest, populated by Englemann spruce with subalpine fir and whitebark pine (Fig. 13.17), extends 1,000 to 1,500 feet downward from timberline, but is much less extensive than its counterpart in the Southern Rocky Mountains. Below it is a forest of lodgepole pine, which extends downward into a lower forest having Douglas fir. The lodgepole pine forest forms one of the most important timber belts in the Middle Rocky Mountains. At still lower altitudes, and extending onto the Great Plains, far from the foot of the mountains, are scattered stands of yellow pine. On the plains, the yellow pine favors the sandstone ledges; the grasses favor the shale hills. Differences in kind of

ground limit the forests also along Jackson Hole, where the valley of the Snake River, mantled with glacial outwash, supports sagebrush and where the forests grow on the moraines and upward onto the mountains.

Pinyon-juniper woodland is hardly represented around either the Wyoming Basin or the Middle Rocky Mountains, although it forms major plant stands farther south. In the Wyoming Basin the chief vegetation is sagebrush.

Moist, alkaline locations, such as many of the alluvial flats, support alkali-tolerant greasewood. Along streams in and near the mountains, where the water is of good quality, valley bottoms are lined with willows and sedges, but farther from the mountains this vegetation gives way to greasewood and other alkali-tolerant plants.

Figure 13.16 *Extent of alpine grassland (black) above timberline on the Southern, Middle, and Northern Rocky Mountains. Altitudes are lower in the north than in the south, but so too is timberline.*

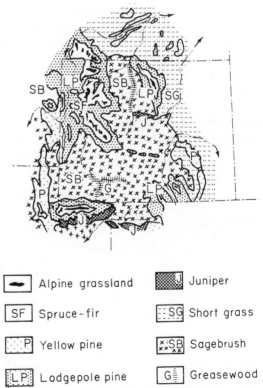

Alpine grassland Juniper

SF Spruce-fir SG Short grass

P Yellow pine SB Sagebrush

LP Lodgepole pine G Greasewood

Figure 13.17 *Principal vegetation zones in the Middle Rocky Mountains and the Wyoming Basin.*

Surficial deposits and soils in the Middle Rocky Mountains are like those in the Southern Rocky Mountains. The Wyoming Basin has, in addition, extensive alluvial deposits in floodplains of streams and in fans sloping from the foot of mountains. Dry lake beds are numerous, and there are extensive eolian deposits including both dune sand and loess.

Soils in the Wyoming Basin are pedocals and are classed with the desert soils. The surface layer typically contains but little organic matter and is calcareous, for leaching is slight. Subsoils are lighter in color and contain a layer enriched with lime and/or gypsum, which may develop into a caliche hardpan. Vegetation growing on these soils is mostly sagebrush or shadscale. Greasewood and other alkali-tolerant plants grow where there is an excess of alkalis or salts. Because the Wyoming Basin is semiarid and weathering correspondingly slight, the soil textures and compositions are dominated by the parent materials. The sandy formations produce sandy soils; the shale formations produce tight, impermeable, clayey soils. The land is used chiefly for grazing, but where irrigated, as along some floodplains, the land can be highly productive for farming.

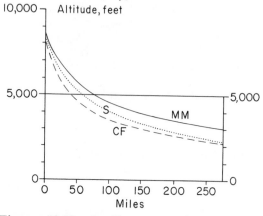

Figure 13.18 *Gradients of some major streams draining the Northern Rocky Mountains. MM, Madison and Missouri Rivers; S, Salmon River; CF, Clarks Fork. The valleys draining west average about 1,000 feet lower than those draining east.*

Northern Rocky Mountains

The Northern Rocky Mountains (Fig. 13.1) include a great many mountain ranges; many of them are not very high and not very different topographically from those in the Middle and Southern Rocky Mountains. About 90 percent of the Northern Rocky Mountains drains to the Pacific, and the continental divide is crowded against the easternmost part of the province. Not only have the streams draining west eroded farther into the province than those draining east, but they have incised themselves much more deeply (Fig. 13.18). The Kalispell Valley (labelled 2 in Fig. 13.19) is about 1,000 feet lower than the Great Plains 50 miles to the east.

Cities and towns are more numerous in these mountains than in the other provinces of the Rocky Mountain System. Population density in the mountainous western third of Montana is about the same as in the eastern two-thirds of the state in the Great Plains, roughly 4.5 persons per square mile. Most of the Idaho portion of the Northern Rocky Mountains is thinly populated (about one person per square mile) except in the northern panhandle and along the base of the mountains on the west and south sides, where there are several cities.

Structural Framework and Geologic History

Structurally the mountains are of five kinds, and the province can be divided into five sections with correspondingly different landforms.

At the northwest end, west of Spokane, are the Okanogan Highlands, which consist of broad, rounded hills, most of which are less than 5,000 feet in altitude and consist of granitic rocks intrusive into folded and metamorphosed Paleozoic rocks (Fig. 13.19). The structures trend northerly and drain southward to the Columbia River, where the highlands are cut off by overlap of the Columbia River basaltic lavas, which form the Columbia Plateau.

From the Okanogan Highlands eastward to the Great Plains and southward to the Clear-

water Mountains and the Garnet Range, the structure consists of horsts and grabens of Precambrian formations that are not strongly folded. The horsts form the mountain ranges and the grabens form the valleys. The structures trend east of north and the drainage has a trellis pattern. The structures and the trellis drainage pattern extend far northward into Canada. Most of the graben valleys are less than 3,000 feet in altitude; the mountain crests reach 9,000 to 10,000 feet. The Rocky Mountain Trench—the principal graben, or rift, valley—extends northward along the Kalispell Valley (2, in Fig. 13.19) and 900 miles into Canada. Only the southern tip of the Rocky Mountain Trench reaches into the United States. Another trench, referred to as the Purcell Trench, branches from the Rocky Mountain Trench about 175 miles north of the International Boundary and enters the United States along the lower course of the Kootenai River on the west side of the Purcell Mountains.

Most of central Idaho and the Clearwater and Salmon River mountains are formed by the granitic intrusions of Cretaceous age that collectively make up the Idaho batholith (Fig. 13.19), one of the largest batholiths on the continent. It is about 100 miles wide and 300 miles long. Altitudes range between 3,000 and 7,000 feet (Fig. 13.2). The Idaho batholith is a deeply dissected plateau (Fig. 13.20) that lies about 2,000 feet higher than the Colum-

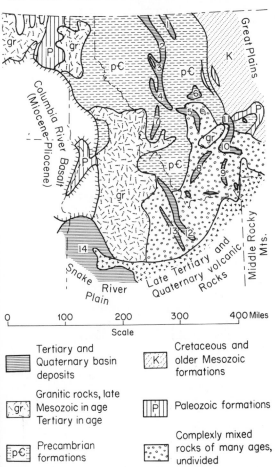

Tertiary and Quaternary basin deposits	Cretaceous and older Mesozoic formations
Granitic rocks, late Mesozoic in age Tertiary in age	Paleozoic formations
Precambrian formations	Complexly mixed rocks of many ages, undivided

Figure 13.19 *Major geologic units in the Northern Rocky Mountains. The Tertiary and Quarternary structural basins, identified by number, are: 1, Flathead Valley; 2, Kalispell Valley; 3, Mission Valley; 4, Missoula Valley; 5, Flint Creek and Deer Lodge Valleys; 6, Blackfoot Valley; 7, Bitterroot Valley; 8, Jefferson and Beaverhead Valleys; 9, Madison Valley; 10, Gallatin Valley; 11, Prickly Pear and Townsend Valleys; 12, Lemhi Valley; 13, Pahsimeroi Valley; 14, lower part of Snake River Valley. (From U.S.G.S.)*

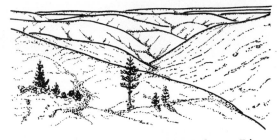

Figure 13.20 *View across the Salmon River Mountains, part of the dissected plateau formed by the Idaho Batholith. Ridge tops are accordant; valleys are deep, about 3,000 feet. (From U.S.G.S.)*

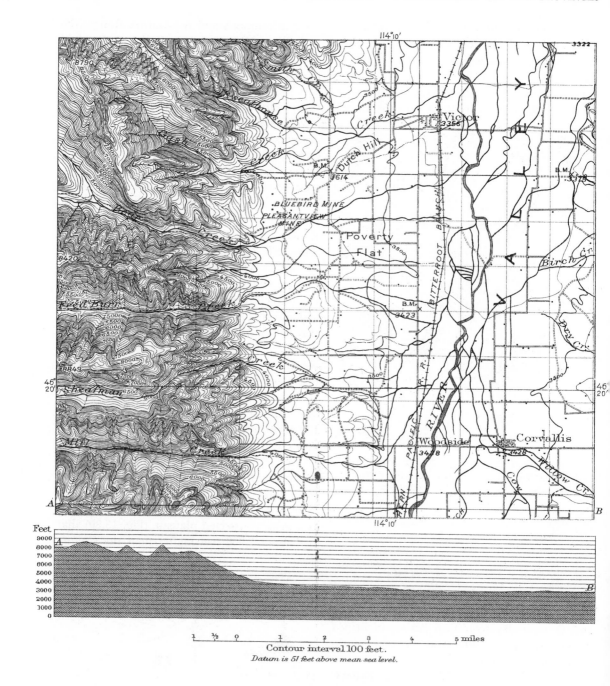

Figure 13.21 *Topographic map and profile across a range and a basin in the southeastern part of the Northern Rocky Mountains. This part of the Northern Rockies resembles parts of the Basin and Range Province and is characterized by three kinds of terrain—mountains, alluvial fans at their bases, and floodplains along the streams draining the valleys. (From U.S.G.S. Hamilton, Montana-Idaho, sheet, 1908.)*

bia Plateau to the west. It is bordered on the east by the Bitterroot Mountains, which rise 1,000 feet above summits on the dissected plateau. The central part of the batholith is homogeneous granite, but the ridges and drainage there tend to be parallel, as if the granite were broken into structures that trend north. Along the eastern and western edges of the batholith are linear ridges of metamorphosed Paleozoic and Precambrian sedimentary rocks that were intruded by the batholith and turned up along its flanks. In these areas, too, the ridges and valleys trend roughly north to south. Over large areas the granite of the batholith is deeply weathered.

The ranges from the Bitterroot Mountains eastward to the Great Plains and south of Clark Fork (Fig. 13.21) are very much like those in the Basin and Range Province, and many consist of complexly folded and faulted Paleozoic and Mesozoic formations in north-trending fault blocks. Between these fault-block mountains are structural basins partly filled with debris eroded from the mountains. Other mountains in this section consist of volcanic rocks or granitic intrusions that apparently are eastern satellites of the Idaho batholith. The largest of these granitic masses, known as the Boulder batholith, extends from Helena to south of Butte. Most of the mountain summits are under 10,500 feet, but a few reach to 12,000 feet; the altitudes of the basins and valleys average about 5,000 feet.

The Little Belt Mountains are dome mountains formed by the intrusion of laccoliths, like the isolated mountains farther east on the Great Plains in Montana (p. 222).

As in other northern provinces, or in those of high altitude, Pleistocene glaciation played an important part in developing the terrain of the Northern Rocky Mountains. Yet despite the northerly location and high altitude of the Province, the glaciers were curiously of only moderate extent (Fig. 13.22).

The ice extended from Canada into the United States, but only for about 100 miles. In the Middle West the ice extended from Canada southward half way to the Gulf of Mexico because the ice caps, which formed on each side of Hudson Bay, gravitated down the trough along the middle of the continent.

A complex of alpine glaciers formed in the Canadian Rockies, and ice was pushed southward along the trenches into the United States. The structural origin of the trenches is obscured because they have been gouged by glacial ice and mantled with glacial drift. South of the limit shown in Figure 13.22, only isolated glaciers existed on the highest mountains.

The alpine glaciers pushed down valley to altitudes of about 4,500 feet on the Great Plains and, in the western valleys, to about 3,500 feet, which is a thousand feet lower than the level reached by the ice in the Middle Rockies and 2,500 feet lower than the level reached in the Southern Rockies. This northward decrease in the level reached by the

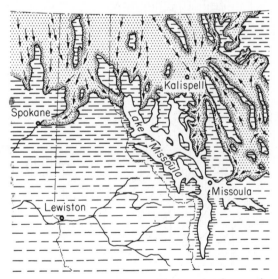

Figure 13.22 *Southern limit of the main mass of late Pleistocene ice in the Northern Rocky Mountains. The ice extended to Clarks Fork near the western border of Montana and dammed it, forming Lake Missoula, which was more than 200 miles long and about 1,000 feet deep; some estimates indicate a depth of 2,000 feet. (From U.S.G.S.)*

Pleistocene mountain glaciers roughly parallels the northward decrease in altitude of the climatic and vegetational zones.

Climate, Vegetation, and Soils

Despite the northerly latitudes and the high altitudes, the climates in the Northern Rocky Mountains are surprisingly mild. In the mountain valleys January temperatures average as much as 10 degrees warmer and summer temperatures average about 5 to 10 degrees cooler than on the Great Plains just east of the mountains. The average length of the growing season is about the same, roughly 120 days. Temperatures and snowfall, of course, vary greatly with altitude.

Winds are from the west, and much of the moisture is precipitated where the air masses cross the Bitterroot Mountains (Fig. 13.23).

Consequently, most of the Montana portion of the Northern Rocky Mountains is semiarid, with less than 20 inches of rainfall.

As a result of this aridity, the forests on mountains directly east of the Bitterroot Mountains commonly are restricted to the northern and eastern slopes. Although the south-facing and west-facing slopes receive comparable precipitation, they are hotter; they support few trees and are covered with shrubs and grasses.

One of the principal kinds of forests in the Northern Rocky Mountains (Fig. 13.24) consists of larch, a deciduous conifer (not an evergreen), and western white pine. Most of this forest lies in the northeastern part of the province, on the rift-faulted Precambrian blocks along the Purcell and Rocky Mountain trenches. In these forests, areas that have been burned or cut are invaded first by larch. This is followed by white pine, which may crowd

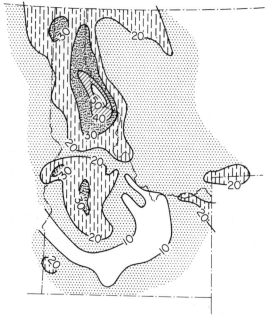

Figure 13.23 *Average annual precipitation (inches) in the Northern Rocky Mountains. In much of the low country the growing season lasts 120 days, about the same as on the Great Plains just east of the mountains. (From U.S.D.A.)*

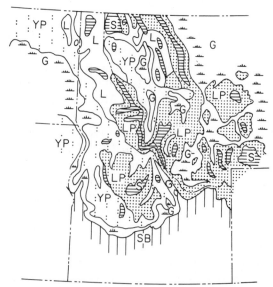

Figure 13.24 *Distribution of the major kinds of vegetation in the Northern Rocky Mountains. SB, sagebrush; G, grasses; YP, yellow pine and Douglas fir; LP, lodgepole pine; L, larch and western pine; S, spruce and fir. (From U.S.D.A.)*

out the larch but in turn may be crowded out by hemlock, red cedar, and lowland white fir. The larch is used for ship timber and boxes; white pine is used for cabinet work and boxes.

Yellow pine and Douglas fir form commercial stands in the Salmon River Mountains, Okanogan Highlands, and along Clarks Fork. Lodgepole pine grows principally in the basins and ranges in the southeastern part of the Northern Rocky Mountains, but it spreads northward and westward too. The high mountain forests of spruce and fir are accessible only with difficulty and are not yet as valuable commercially as the other types.

Forests in the Northern Rocky Mountains are estimated to contain more than 175 billion board feet of commercial timber. The annual cut is roughly equal to the annual growth, about 2 billion board feet, which is about 5 percent of the United States production.

The most recent estimates of timber reserves are practically double those made in the 1940's. This apparent increase in reserves has been attributed to earlier tendencies to underestimate, but may also result in part from the lowering of specifications for timber grades brought about by changes in the economic situation. The problem of estimating reserves is not peculiar to forestry; comparisons of early and recent estimates of mineral reserves show a similar apparent increase. The forest resources of the Northern Rocky Mountains are about three times those of the Southern Rockies. For the entire Rocky Mountain region, the relative extent of different kinds of timber are roughly as follows:

Yellow pine and Douglas fir, about 35 percent;

Lodgepole pine, about 25 percent;

Larch and Western White pine, slightly more than 20 percent;

Spruce and fir, slightly less than 20 percent.

Surficial deposits in the Northern Rocky Mountains are like those in the Middle and Southern Rocky Mountains except for their greater extent and better development of gravel fans. Soils on the fans and valley floors, most of which are below about 2,000 feet, are classed as Chestnut Soils. The upper layers are gravelly loam; at depths of 1½ to 3 feet is a layer of lime-cemented gravel underlain by a porous gravel layer. These soils support sagebrush and bunch grass. Above 2,000 feet, under coniferous forest, the soils are Gray-Brown Podzols.

Seismic Activity

A seismically active belt that extends northward along the western edge of the Middle Rocky Mountains and across the southeastern part of the Northern Rocky Mountains to the Great Plains. This belt has been the site of numerous small earthquakes and two of severe intensity, one in 1925 and another in 1959. Elsewhere in the Rocky Mountains earthquakes have been few and of only moderate intensity.

The epicenter of the 1925 earthquake was east of Helena, Montana. It had an intensity of 9 or 10 (p. 34) and was felt over an area of 300,000 square miles. Property damage was extensive in an area of 600 square miles. Both the Northern Pacific and the Chicago, Milwaukee, and St. Paul Railroads were blocked by rocks falling from cliffs and by debris from buildings. A rock slide closed one tunnel.

The epicenter of the 1959 earthquake was near the head of the Madison River at Hebgen Lake. Tilting of the lake bed displaced the lake northward (Fig. 13.25). Jetties, docks, and beaches along the north shore were submerged; those along the south shore were stranded high above water. Water in the lake surged back and forth violently, sweeping over the dam that forms the lake and threatening to destroy it. South of the lake a fault more than 10 miles long formed an escarpment 10 feet high facing the lake. Buildings were broken in two, and highways crossed by the fault were displaced 10 feet. In the gorge where the Madison River crosses the Madison Range, a tremendous rock slide—38 million cubic yards of rock—broke from the south wall of the gorge, swept across the river, buried about 25 persons camping in the canyon, moved 400 feet up the north wall, and dammed the river, producing what has been named Earthquake Lake.

Drainage Anomalies

Many of the rivers in the Rocky Mountains have developed anomalous courses "through the mountains, not around them." In the Appalachian Mountains, rivers cross the mountain ridges in water gaps; in the Rocky Mountains many of the mountains are crossed by long canyons.

The Arkansas River flows south in the structural trough separating the Sawatch Range and the Mosquito Range. Then the river turns east and flows through Royal Gorge—a steep-walled canyon 2,000 feet deep that cuts through the mountains (Fig. 13.1). Royal Gorge is one of the routes of the Denver and Rio Grande Railroad through the Rocky Mountains.

The course of the Laramie River also is anomalous, though less spectacularly so. The Laramie River begins in the Laramie Basin and has cut northeastward across the anticlinally raised ridge of Precambrian rocks

forming the Laramie Range. Its tributaries, Sybille Creek and Blue Grass Creek do likewise. All of these streams flow through gorges about 500 feet deep and descend 2,000 feet from the Laramie Basin to the Great Plains (Fig. 13.26).

The Laramie Basin, a structural basin underlain by downfolded sedimentary rocks, lies west of the anticline of Precambrian rocks forming the Laramie Range (Fig. 13.3, section A-A'). The Basin is partly filled with alluvium, brought from the high mountains to the south and west and deposited there by the Laramie River and its tributaries. This fill may have raised the river bed to where it could spill over the range to the east.

The general course of the North Platte River avoids the mountains and is around the northwest end of the Laramie Range, but it crosses uplifts also. The river flows northward from North Park and enters a broad structural valley, but instead of staying there the river turns into the side of the Medicine Bow Mountains and is incised into their flank (Fig. 13.27). Forty miles farther north, the river flows toward a distant isolated mountain, and then follows a gorge about 1,000 feet deep through it rather than going around it (Fig. 13.28). This situation is repeated 40 miles farther downstream where the river cuts across the northwest tip of the Laramie Range in a gorge with rims about 1,000 feet higher than the lowlands around the tip. The easy route follows the open valleys and lowlands.

Sweetwater River, a western tributary of the

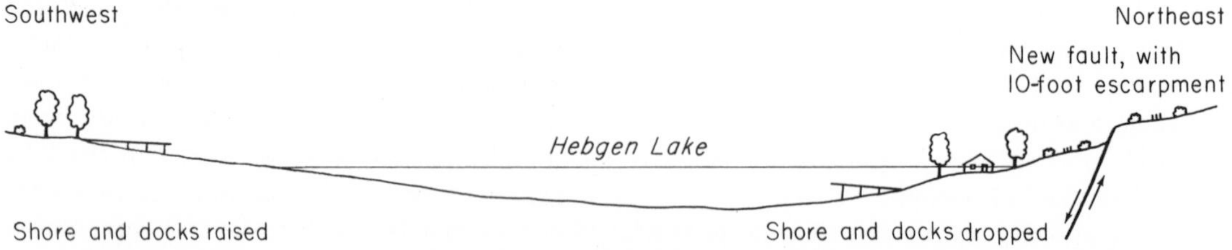

Southwest   Northeast

New fault, with
10-foot escarpment

Hebgen Lake

Shore and docks raised   Shore and docks dropped

Figure 13.25   *Cross section through Hebgen Lake, Montana, shows the tilting and faulting that accompanied the 1959 earthquake. The lake basin was tilted about 20 feet to the northeast along a new fault. A 10-foot escarpment parallels the northeast shore.*

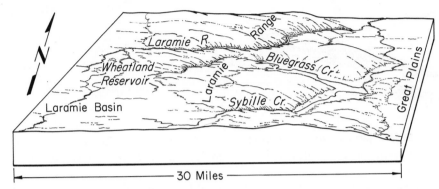

Figure 13.26   *Diagram illustrating the courses of the Laramie River and Sybille Creek across the Laramie Range, Wyoming.*

North Platte, follows an equally anomalous course and one that has considerable historic interest (Fig. 13.29). The river crosses a granite ridge in a narrow, V-shaped gorge more than 300 feet deep and only 30 feet wide at river level. The Oregon Trail passed by the foot of Independence Rock, crossed the river, and followed the open valley around the end of Devils Gate Ridge.

The Colorado River crosses several of the

ranges in the Southern Rocky Mountains. Its headwaters are in the Front Range, within 20 miles of the Great Plains. The river descends the west flank of the Front Range to a structural valley called Middle Park, which lies between the Front Range and the Park Range (Fig. 13.1). The river then leaves Middle Park and crosses the Park Range and the Gore Range through Gore Canyon, which is more than 2,000 feet deep. After being joined by the Eagle River, the Colorado River crosses a flank of the White River Plateau in a gorge (Glenwood Springs Canyon) 3,000 feet deep.

The Bighorn River, draining from the Wyoming Basin, takes seemingly difficult routes through mountains rather than across

Figure 13.27   *The North Platte River, instead of following the broad structural valley separating the Medicine Bow Mountains from the northwest end of the Park Range, turns into a gorge cut into hard rocks forming the flank of the Medicine Bow Mountains. The rim of the gorge is 700 feet higher than the valley at Spring Creek. Length of view, about 25 miles.*

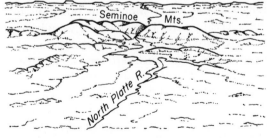

Figure 13.28   *View north (downstream) along the North Platte River to its gorge through the Seminoe Mountains, Wyoming. The lake (Seminoe Lake) is formed by a dam in the gorge.*

Figure 13.29 *Devils Gate, Wyoming, where the Sweetwater River is incised into a granite ridge. The rounded hill in the foreground is Independence Rock.*

the open, low country to the Powder River Basin and Great Plains. The river crosses two mountain ranges. It leaves the basin north of the Wind River Mountains and passes through a gorge in the Owl Creek Mountains. Then, instead of continuing on in the open Bighorn Basin and flowing to the Great Plains, it turns into a gorge through the Bighorn Mountains (Fig 13.1).

Other similarly anomalous stream courses are the Green River gorge (Lodore Canyon) across the Uinta Mountains and Black Canyon of the Gunnison River, which are National Monuments, and the canyons of several rivers crossing the Wasatch Range. The Northern Rocky Mountains provide still other examples.

These anomalies were originally attributed to antecedence (p. 54, Fig. 3.8,A). Later they were attributed to superposition (Fig. 3.8,B). However, the stream courses across the various ranges in the Rocky Mountains probably are not superimposed. Too much fill would have been required to bury the several mountain ranges, and too much erosion would have been required to remove that fill. The anomalous courses probably can be explained by a combination of antecedence and superposition, the process called anteconsequence, or anteposition (Fig. 3.8,C).

Range Lands

The Rocky Mountains and Wyoming Basin are farmed very little, but are extensively used for grazing livestock—in places, too much so. The mountains are used chiefly for summer range; the Wyoming Basin is used for winter range. Extensive areas in the Northern and Middle Rocky Mountains are not grazed. Farming is limited to irrigated lands along valley bottoms.

Most of the Rocky Mountains and Wyoming Basin are public lands belonging to the federal government, and the lands are leased to stockmen for grazing. In the past, serious overgrazing of much of the range resulted in damage by erosion and in elimination of plant species that provide good forage. Overgrazing is gradually being corrected by limiting the use of public lands, but such restrictions are politically painful. Ranchers who have become dependent upon the use of public range do not favor measures that might require a reduction in their livestock holdings.

Water

The Rocky Mountains collect and store the water carried by the rivers crossing the semiarid lands that lie east and west of the mountains. These semiarid lands, ten times the area of the mountains, comprise most of that half of the United States that is west of the 100th meridian. It would be difficult to overestimate the importance of the Rocky Mountains in the water economy of this vast region.

For example, three states wholly outside the Rocky Mountain System—Arizona, California, and Nevada—have been concerned with apportionment of Colorado River water. A decision by the Supreme Court of the United States in 1963 assumed the Colorado River flow to be 15 million acre feet per year and reserved half of this to Colorado, Wyoming, Utah, and New Mexico. The other half was divided 4.4 million acre feet to California, 2.8 million acre feet to Arizona, 0.3 million acre feet to Nevada, and legal provisions were added for dividing surpluses and deficits. Clearly, a major problem in the Rocky Mountains concerns methods for estimating annual and seasonal runoff of surface water and recharge of ground water aquifers.

The runoff chiefly is the water stored as snow and ice in the mountains during the winter. Additional runoff is provided by groundwater, which in turn is partly recharged by the melting of snow and ice. Still other runoff comes from rain storms.

Runoff from melting snow and ice is estimated by measuring the snow pack at selected places in the mountains. To a considerable degree this also measures the duration and discharge of springs where groundwater feeds streams. By anticipating the runoff from the snow melt it has been possible to predict when maximum flood heights would occur, and some disasters have thus been averted. In 1954 the anticipation by 6 weeks of a flood along the Kootenai River served to hold flood damage to a minimum. Similarly, a deficiency of runoff can be anticipated and steps taken to minimize the effect of drought, such as transferring livestock to other range, maturing crops early, and developing emergency water sources, as was done in Utah in 1934.

An extensive system of reservoirs has been constructed along the rivers in and near the foot of the Rocky Mountains, and the stored water is used for municipal supplies, irrigation, hydroelectric power, flood control, and recreation. Municipal supplies require no more than about 2 percent of all the stored water; most of the rest is lost by evaporation or consumed for irrigation, and much irrigation water is wasted on surplus crops.

The quality of water obtained from the mountains is generally excellent. The total dissolved solids in surface water commonly measures about 100 ppm; the groundwater commonly contains about twice that. Most of the water is bicarbonate water with a carbonate : sulfate ratio of 10 : 1 or more; the hardness of the water is high, considering the low content of dissolved solids. In a few valleys the quality of the surface water has been affected by industrial developments, which have introduced pollutants; further pollution can be expected unless rigorous controls are adopted.

Most water in the Wyoming and Bighorn basins contains about 500 ppm of dissolved solids, but the carbonate : sulfate ratio is nearly 1 : 1. The hardness of these waters is due more to the presence of calcium and magnesium than to the carbonate (Tables 5.1, 5.2).

Minerals

The Rocky Mountains contain important deposits of metallic minerals, principally copper, gold, silver, lead, zinc, molybdenum, antimony, and tungsten. Mining began there in the 1850's as a backwash from the California gold rushes. The first deposits to attract attention were the placer gold deposits discovered at the foot of some of the mountains. Tracing these deposits, by gold pan, to their sources led to the discovery of the lode deposits. The history of mineral exploration and mining in the Rocky Mountains forms a major part of the history of the settlement and development of the West. Some of the discoveries involved trespass on lands reserved for the Indians, but when mineral deposits were found it was convenient to draft new treaties that took the mineral lands out of the reservation, as happened in the Black Hills (p. 242). The same thing happened in Idaho in 1861, when gold was discovered on lands that had been reserved for the Nez Percé in 1855, and in the San Juan Mountains, which had been granted to the Ute Indians by treaty in 1868.

Most deposits of the metallic minerals are in the Middle, Southern, and Northern Rocky Mountain Provinces; the Wyoming Basin is important for its petroleum, natural gas, oil-shale, coal, and salines. Of the more than 300 mining districts that have been productive in the mountain provinces, some of the best known are (see also Fig. 13.30):

SOUTHERN ROCKY MOUNTAINS

Cripple Creek, Colorado. Gold telluride (calaverite) occurs in veins with quartz, fluorite, barite, and calcite in Tertiary volcanic rocks and intrusive Precambrian rocks. Some mines reach to depths of 3,000 feet.

Colorado mineral belt. This belt includes the mining districts at Breckenridge, Montezuma,

Silver Plume, Georgetown, Idaho Springs, Central city, Caribou, Nederland, Ward, Gold Hill, and Jamestown. One of the first mineral-producing areas in the Rocky Mountains, the belt was discovered after placer gold was found in the Denver area; the gold-bearing gravels were traced upstream to their sources in the mountains. Ores of lead, silver, gold, and tungsten occur in veins that fill faults and fissures.

Leadville, Colorado. Most ores are mined from flat veins (*blanket veins*) along or near the contacts between sills and dikes of igneous rocks that intrude Paleozoic formations. The principal minerals are sulfides of lead (galena), zinc (sphalerite), and iron (pyrite). Near-surface veins are weathered and oxidized, and the ore minerals in these veins include carbonates of lead (cerrusite) and zinc (smithsonite).

San Juan region, Colorado. The deposits are in vertical or near-vertical veins (*fissure veins*) and blanket veins in Paleozoic and Mesozoic formations intruded by Tertiary granite rocks, and fissure veins in younger Tertiary volcanic rocks. Since the 1870's major production has been gold, silver, copper, lead, and zinc. Ore minerals are copper- and gold-bearing iron oxide (magnetite), iron sulfide (pyrite), gold telluride (calaverite), silver telluride (sylvanite), zinc sulfide (sphalerite), lead sulfide (galena), and copper-iron sulfide (chalcopyrite).

Climax, Colorado. Molybdenite occurs in criss-crossing veinlets in a mass of Precambrian rocks cut by intrusions. The veinlets are so closely spaced that the entire mass is mined. Since the middle 1920's, this district has supplied a major part of the world's molybdenum production.

MIDDLE ROCKY MOUNTAINS

Park City and Alta districts, Utah. Ores in these districts yield mainly silver and lead with some copper, zinc, and gold. The ores are in late Paleozoic and early Mesozoic formations that have been fractured and altered by Tertiary granitic intrusions. The principal ore minerals are galena, sphalerite, tetrahedrite (copper, antimony, and sulfur), and chalcopyrite.

Utah-Idaho phosphate region. Extensive phosphate deposits occur in southeastern Idaho, northeastern Utah, and western Wyoming. This region has become one of the major phosphate-producing

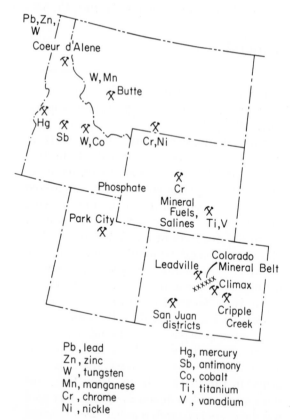

Pb, lead
Zn, zinc
W, tungsten
Mn, manganese
Cr, chrome
Ni, nickle

Hg, mercury
Sb, antimony
Co, cobalt
Ti, titanium
V, vanadium

Figure 13.30 *Some of the principal mining districts in the Rocky Mountains.*

areas, and there remain vast reserves of phosphatic shale in a late Paleozoic formation.

NORTHERN ROCKY MOUNTAINS

Butte, Montana. One of the world's most productive, this district contains some mines that are a mile deep. The mines produce mostly copper, silver, gold, zinc, and some lead. The ores occur in closely spaced veins cutting a granitic rock and consist mostly of sulfide minerals except within about 400 feet of the surface, where the minerals have been oxidized and leached. Gold and silver remain in the leached zone, but copper has been transported downward and has enriched the deposits with secondary minerals derived from the leaching. The district began as a gold placer camp about 1864.

Coeur d'Alene district, Idaho. Lead, silver, and zinc are produced from altered Precambrian sedimentary formations near the northern edge of the Idaho batholith.

Fur Trade and Early Trails West

Furs, skins, and hides were the first resources of the Rocky Mountains to be exploited, and trapping and trading began almost immediately after the return of the Lewis and Clark expedition in 1806. The trade that developed became a major business, and it involved Indians as well as whites. It was the fur traders who applied the name Rocky Mountains to the ranges along the continental divide.

Several companies engaged in the business, and their names are prominent in western United States history—the Missouri Fur Company, which had trappers in the Middle Rocky Mountains and Wyoming Basin by 1809; the Pacific Fur Company, which under the direction of John Jacob Astor explored the Columbia River and founded Astoria in 1811; the American Fur Company, another Astor enterprise, which had operated around the Great Lakes as early as 1808 and sent trappers west in the 1820's; and the Rocky

Mountain Fur Company and its predecessors, which were active as early as 1832. The northern areas were visited by the rival British companies, notably the Hudson Bay Company.

The magnitude of the business can perhaps be visualized from the size of the herds of buffalo that once roamed the plains. Clark, in 1806, estimated 80,000 head in one of the herds that he saw. Miles City, on the Great Plains in Montana, is said to have shipped as many as 250,000 buffalo hides in one season. By 1845, however, the fur-bearing animals had been greatly reduced in numbers, and the fur trade soon declined. The buffalo were nearly exterminated.

The routes for travel through the Rocky Mountains were found by the fur traders, and these routes became the trails to Utah, Oregon, California, and Santa Fe (Fig. 13.31). But the trip west was a long one, so much so that some easterners questioned the wisdom of acquiring land in the far west. A senator, arguing in 1825 against acquisition of the Oregon Territory, asked (U.S. Geol. Survey Bull. 612, p. 7):

> But is this Territory of Oregon ever to become a State, a member of the Union? Never. . . . The distance that a Member of Congress of this State of Oregon would be obliged to travel in coming to the seat of government and returning home would be 9,300 miles. . . . If he should travel at the rate of 30 miles per day, it would require 306 days. Allow for Sundays, 44, it would amount to 350 days. This would allow the Member a fortnight to rest himself at Washington before he should commence his journey home.

Some Resource Problems

The land, forest, water, and mineral resources of the Rocky Mountains have become major factors in the national economy, and there is great pressure to utilize them for developing local industries, as has been done elsewhere in the country. But the Rocky Mountains are physiographically different from the rest of the country, and their resources should be utilized in a different way.

For example, it probably is not possible to have factories with smoke-belching chimneys in a Rocky Mountain valley without developing smog and dumping industrial wastes into the streams. These problems are akin to some in the Appalachian Highlands, but with ma-

Figure 13.31 *Early trails across the western United States and their relationship to the physiographic provinces.*

jor differences. Industry is well established in the Appalachian Highlands, and the population now dependent on that industry is considerable. In the Rocky Mountains, industrial development has barely gotten started, the population is sparse, and most of that great area is still federal land, as much the property of those living elsewhere as of those living in it.

Assuming that our population continues to increase, there will be growing need for the water and the recreational facilities that the mountains provide. It would seem better for the nation that these mountains be industrialized as little as possible, limiting development to the production of raw materials and reserving the land primarily for recreational uses and watershed protection. We can have grazing *without* overgrazing. We can have mineral prospecting and mining *without* scarring the landscape or polluting the streams; lumbering *without* destroying the forests; highways *without* having the roadside marred by "No Trespass" signs, billboards, automobile morgues, and unkempt wayside stands. Those of us who share in the ownership of the vast, magnificent Rocky Mountains must insist that they not be spoiled by being placed in the hands of local interests, but that they be preserved and developed to served the greater national interest. The two interests need not conflict, but the national interest should be the more far-sighted.

14 Colorado Plateau

The Colorado Plateau (Fig. 14.1), covering about 130,000 square miles between the Rocky Mountain and Basin and Range provinces, is easily the most colorful part of the United States. It is not just desert; it is Painted Desert! Its spectacular geomorphic and geologic features may be seen in more than a dozen national parks and monuments created expressly for the purpose. It is an area of unusual archeological interest too, and another dozen national parks and monuments protect some of the better known examples of the cliff dwellings and other ruins of the prehistoric Anasazi, ancestors of the Pueblo Indians. Those of special geomorphic, geologic, or archeologic interest are indicated in Figure 14.1. In addition to these there are national recreational areas along the Colorado River at Lake Mead, which extends into the lower part of Grand Canyon, and at Powell Lake in Glen Canyon. Two national monuments of historical interest are El Moro (Inscription Rock) and Pipe Spring.

Outstanding physiographic features of the Colorado Plateau are:

1. Structural geology, which consists of
   A. extensive areas of nearly horizontal sedimentary formations;
   B. structural upwarps that form striking topographic features;
   C. igneous structures, including some large central-type volcanoes, numerous cinder cones and volcanic necks, high lava-capped plateaus and mesas, and dome mountains caused by intrusion of stocks and laccoliths.
2. Great altitude; the general plateau surface is higher than 5,000 feet; some plateaus and several peaks reach to 11,000 feet.
3. Drainage system, which is deeply incised and forming steep-walled canyons, most of which have brilliantly colored walls.
4. Aridity and shortage of water.
5. Extensive areas of bare rock.
6. Sparse vegetation and sparse population (about a half million, an average of about four persons per square mile).
7. Brightly colored and highly varied desert scenery.

Structural Framework

The Colorado Plateau has the general structure of a stack of saucers, tilted toward the northeast, where the plateau adjoins the Rocky Mountains. As a consequence of this structure, young rocks (Tertiary) crop out in basins on the north and east sides of the plateau and old rocks (Paleozoic and Pre-

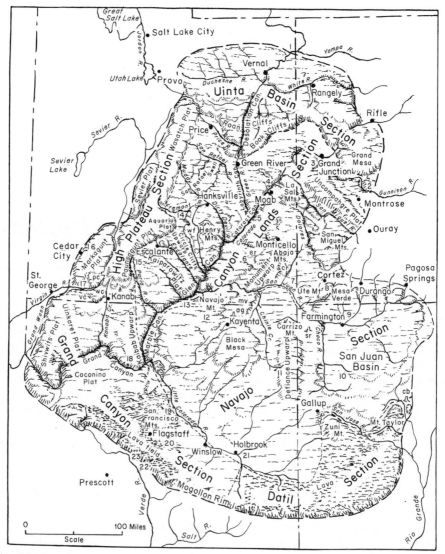

Figure 14.1   *Physiographic map of the Colorado Plateau.*

cambrian) crop out along the southwest rim, overlooking the much lower Basin and Range Province. Most of the plateau consists of Mesozoic formations.

The high southwest part of the Colorado Plateau is referred to as the Grand Canyon Section. The oldest rocks there are complexly deformed Precambrian formations. These are overlain by about 5,000 feet of Paleozoic formations that thicken northward to nearly 8,000 feet. The Precambrian and Paleozoic formations are exposed in the Grand Canyon (Fig. 14.2) and along the southwestern edge of the section. The topography of Grand Canyon is illustrated in Figure 14.3.

The western part of the Grand Canyon Section is divided into a series of blocks by the northerly trending Grand Wash, Hurricane, and Sevier faults (Fig. 14.4). Along each of these faults the blocks to the west have dropped downward relative to the blocks to the east. This structure is transitional between the Colorado Plateau, which in general is little faulted, and the much-faulted Basin and Range Province.

In general, the formations in these fault blocks and those farther east dip northeastward, but about 75 miles from the rim, the northeast dip is interrupted by the Kaibab Upwarp, one of several upwarps that characterize the Colorado Plateau. These upwarps are asymmetric anticlines with gently dipping west flanks and steeply dipping east flanks, exemplified by the Circle Cliffs Upwarp (Fig. 14.5). They represent a mile or more of vertical structural displacement. These folds may be the surface expression of faults deep in the crust.

About a third of the Grand Canyon Section is covered by lavas from the San Francisco Mountain volcanic field and from some isolated volcanoes north of Grand Canyon. These lavas unconformably overlie Paleozoic and later formations, which had been faulted, folded, tilted northeastward, and exposed by erosion long before the earliest lavas (Tertiary) were erupted. Enough time elapsed after the deformation and before the eruptions to permit the removal by erosion of thousands of feet of Mesozoic formations that once ex-

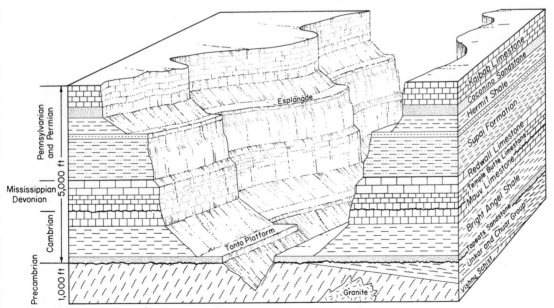

Figure 14.2 *Block diagram illustrating the formations in the Grand Canyon. Vertical scale exaggerated; the canyon rims are about 10 to 12 miles apart.*

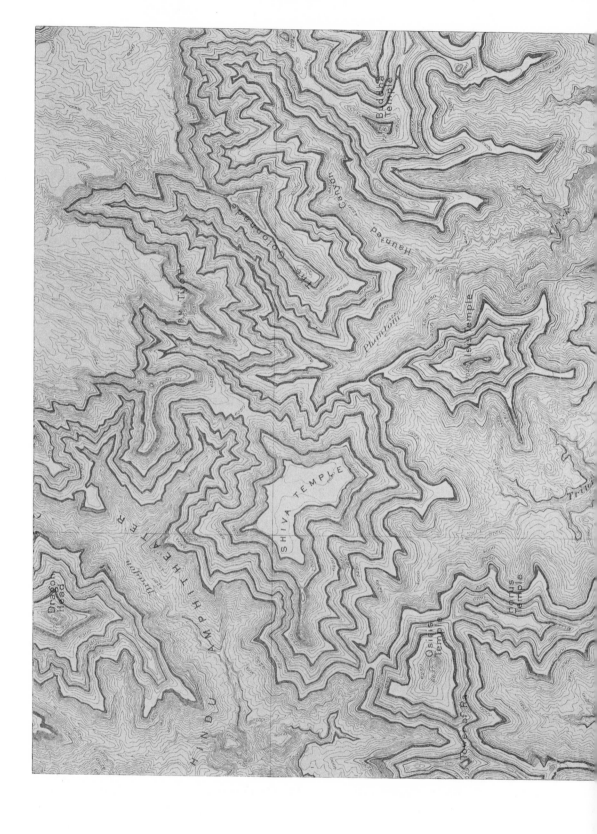

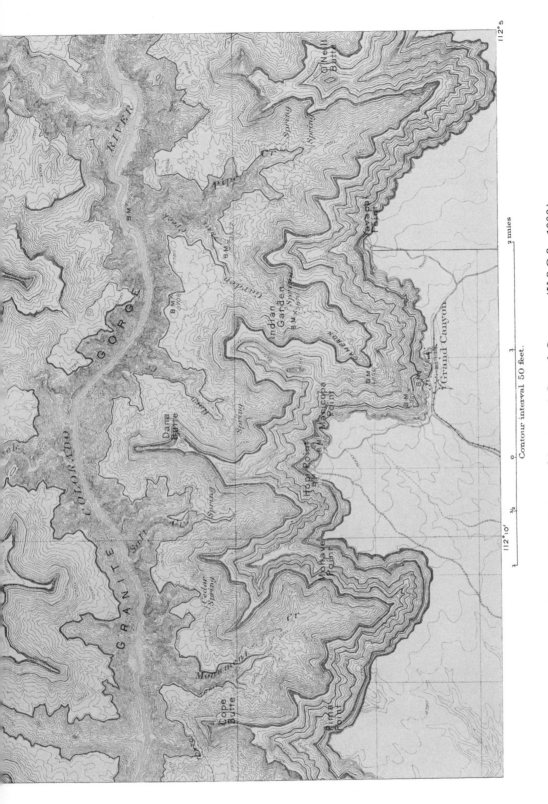

Figure 14.3   *Topographic map of Grand Canyon. (U.S.G.S., 1908.)*

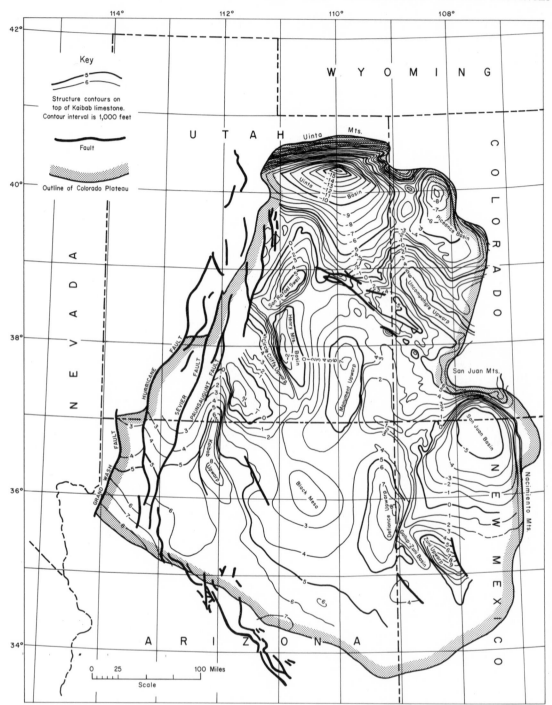

Figure 14.4 *Structure contour map of the Colorado Plateau. Contours drawn on a geologic formation reveal its changes in altitude and dip and bring out the locations, shapes, and dimensions of folds and faults. (From U.S.G.S.)*

tended across this part of the Colorado Plateau.

The Colorado River had already cut deeply into Grand Canyon by the time the first lavas were erupted, and some of the later lavas poured down the walls and into the bottom of Grand Canyon. One of the most recent eruptions took place in about the middle of the eleventh century A.D. at Sunset Crater, east of San Francisco Mountain. Volcanic cinders from the eruption buried a Pueblo Indian village very much in the way that Vesuvius buried Pompeii.

The south rim of the Colorado Plateau in New Mexico and eastern Arizona is known as the Datil Section (Fig. 14.1), an extensive area covered by thick lavas. The earliest lavas there probably are of middle Tertiary age, but the volcanism continued intermittently into Recent times. One Late Pleistocene or Recent lava flow in the San Jose Valley is so fresh that it still looks hot. Santa Fe Railroad conductors tell yarns about being on the last train through before the lava covered the tracks!

Principal structural features in this section are the upwarp at the Zuni Mountains, the large central-type volcano at Mount Taylor, the numerous smaller volcanic centers and volcanic necks (Fig. 14.6) around it, and the extensive lava-covered mesas and valleys to the south. The lavas at Mount Taylor, among the oldest in this section, unconformably overlap the tilted formations on the southern flank of the San Juan Basin. The folding, much older than the volcanism, is early Tertiary in age.

Erosion of the high mesas has, in some places, exposed natural cross sections of the lavas, the volcanic cones, and the feeder vents (Fig. 14.6,A). Elsewhere, continued erosion has completely exposed and isolated the plugs that filled the vents to form volcanic necks (Fig. 14.6,B). The surface onto which these lavas erupted was about 2,000 feet higher than the present surface; thus there has been that amount of downcutting by erosion since the earliest volcanism in that area.

These lavas extend southward into the Basin

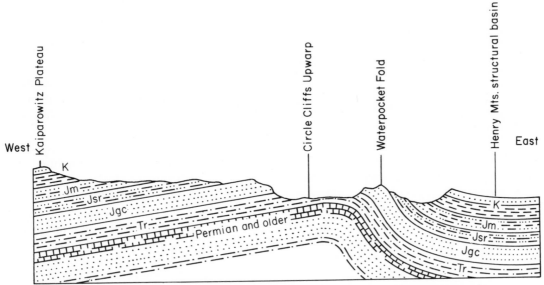

Figure 14.5 *Cross section of the Circle Cliffs Upwarp.* **Tr,** *Triassic formations;* **Jgc,** *Jurassic, Glen Canyon Group, cliff-forming sandstone formations;* **Jsr,** *San Rafael Group;* **Jm,** *Jurassic, Morrison formation;* **K,** *Cretaceous formations. The structural relief is about 6,500 feet; length of section approximately 40 miles.*

and Range Province, and consequently that boundary of the Colorado Plateau is arbitrary. Along the eastern edge of the Datil Section, the Basin and Range Province extends northward along the Rio Grande depression to the Southern Rocky Mountains, and the boundary between this depression and the uplifted Colorado Plateau is sharply defined by the westernmost faults of the depression.

North of the Grand Canyon and Datil Sections is a structural depression referred to as the Navajo Section, about half of which is in the Navajo Indian Reservation. The deepest part of the depression, the San Juan Basin, forms an embayment in the southwest corner of the Southern Rocky Mountains. Structurally, this basin is more than two miles lower than the rim of the Plateau at the southern edge of the Grand Canyon and Datil Sections (Fig. 14.4). Paleozoic rocks form the rim of the Plateau, but under the San Juan Basin these same rocks are overlain by more than 5,000 feet of Mesozoic formations and about 5,000 feet of Tertiary formations. The Defiance Upwarp separates the San Juan Basin from a shallower basin that lies to the west under Black Mesa.

North of the Navajo Section is the Canyon Lands Section of the Colorado Plateau, where, as the name implies, canyons are the dominant feature. This section has four large upwarps: the Uncompaghre Upwarp, the Monument Upwarp, the Circle Cliffs Upwarp, and the San Rafael Swell (Fig. 14.4). Between the upwarps are structural basins; there is a big one under the Henry Mountains and another big one between the Kaibab and Circle Clips upwarps. Very little faulting is associated with these structural upwarps and basins or with those in the Navajo Section, except in the northwest-trending basin south of and parallel to the Uncompaghre Upwarp. This basin differs from the others in that it contains thick deposits of salt. In the course of the deformation that produced the basin, the salt deposits, of late Paleozoic age, were squeezed around like taffy, and the overlying formations were folded in northwest-trending anticlines and synclines that became faulted.

Other distinctive structural features of the Canyon Lands Section are the laccolithic mountains, like the Henry Mountains (Fig. 14.7), the La Sal Mountains, and others. These mountains are structural domes that were produced by the forceful upward injection of molten igneous rock, which formed stocks. The injection of these plug-like masses domed the overlying rocks and those adjacent to them. As the stocks rose higher, they widened;

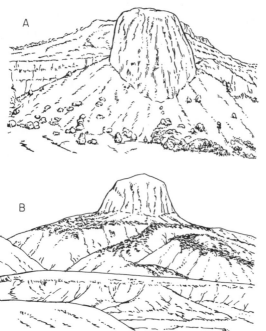

Figure 14.6 (A) Natural cross section of a volcano and of the vent feeding it near Mount Taylor, New Mexico. The half-exposed plug in the vent is 500 feet in diameter and about 1,000 feet high. A cone 400 feet high was built at the surface, and lava flows extend 7½ miles from it. (B) Volcanic neck (Cabezon Peak), also near Mount Taylor. This neck is 2,000 feet in diameter. The benches below are formed by Cretaceous sedimentary formations. The volcanic cone and lava flows have been completely removed by erosion from this volcanic center, and only the plug remains.

the wider the stock, the steeper and higher the dome (Fig. 14.8). Where the stocks encountered weak formations, such as thick shales, the magma was squeezed sideways into those formations to form laccoliths. The overlying beds were folded into anticlines, arranged around and radiating from the stocks. Some of the stocks may have reached the surface and erupted.

North of the Canyon Lands Section is the Uinta Basin Section, which forms an embayment between the Middle and Southern Rocky Mountains. This, the deepest part of the structural bowl, represented by the Plateau, contains the uppermost of the saucers and is structurally four miles lower than the southwest rim in the Grand Canyon Section (Fig. 14.4). Paleozoic formations under the basin are overlain by about two miles of Mesozoic formations and another two miles of Tertiary formations. Figure 14.9 shows the formations rising gently southward (to the Canyon Lands Section) and rising steeply northward onto the southern flank of the Uinta Mountains.

At the western edge of the Colorado Plateau is the High Plateaus Section, which consists of northerly trending fault blocks. Many of these are lava capped and form plateaus, all of which are higher than 9,000 feet and some as high as 11,000 feet. Mesozoic and Tertiary formations underlie the lavas.

This Section is a structurally high rim of the Colorado Plateau, but it differs from the high southwestern and southern rims in having been raised by faulting (Fig. 14.10). Deformation began in late Cretaceous time and continued intermittently throughout Tertiary and Quaternary time. The recency of some of the faulting, together with the fact that the western edge of the High Plateaus coincides with a more than average active seismic belt (Fig. 2.14), suggests that these fault blocks may still be moving.

It may be noted that the extrusive igneous rocks are scattered along the southern and western rims of the Colorado Plateau, whereas the intrusive bodies form the laccolithic mountains in the central part of the plateau (Fig. 14.11). The compositions of the igneous rocks at the big volcanoes and at the laccolithic mountains average about the same, but for reasons that are obscure the compositions

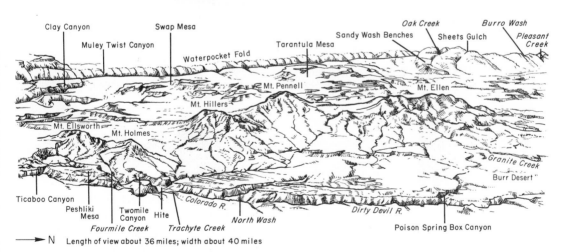

Figure 14.7 *Diagrammatic view of the Henry Mountains region, Utah. Mounts Ellen, Pennell, Hillers, Holmes, and Ellsworth are dome mountains produced by intrusion of stocks and laccoliths into the sedimentary formations. In the foreground are the canyons of the Colorado River and its tributary, the Dirty Devil. In the distance is the Waterpocket Fold. (After U.S.G.S.)*

changed in quite different ways as the igneous activity progressed. At the laccolithic mountains, the silica-poor dioritic rocks (Table 2.2) were first to form and the silica-rich rhyolitic rocks the last, whereas at the volcanoes, the silica-rich rocks were the first to form and the silica-poor rocks the last.

The structural relationship of the Colorado Plateau to the Rocky Mountains on the east and to the Great Basin, a Section of the Basin and Range Province, is illustrated in Figure 14.12 (see also Fig. 2.2). The Rocky Mountains are the high part of a tremendous arch, a geanticline, that extends from the central United States westward nearly to the Pacific Coast. The Great Basin, a block-faulted area, is the collapsed western flank of the arch. The Colorado Plateau is a mildly faulted segment of this flank that remains structurally attached to the Rocky Mountain geanticline.

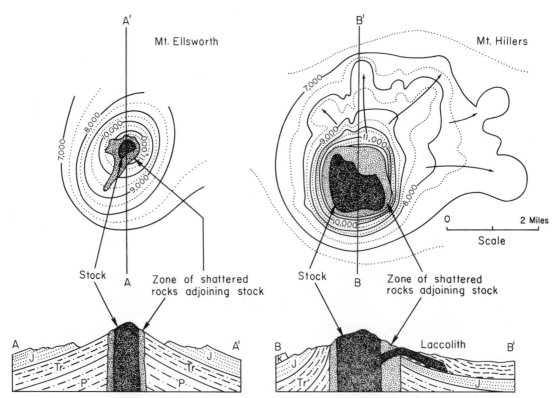

Figure 14.8 *Structure contour maps and diagrammatic cross sections of two laccolithic mountains on the Colorado Plateau. The sedimentary formations (P, Permian; Tr, Triassic; J, Jurassic, and K, Cretaceous) are turned up steeply around wide stocks like the one at Mt. Hillers (Fig. 14.7), and where these stocks reached the thick shale formations (K), tongue-like intrusions (laccoliths) were injected laterally between the sedimentary beds, forming anticlines whose axes (represented by arrows) radiate from the stock. Smaller stocks, like the one at Mt. Ellsworth (Fig. 14.7), caused less doming, less shattering of the wall rocks, and produced few, if any, laccoliths.*

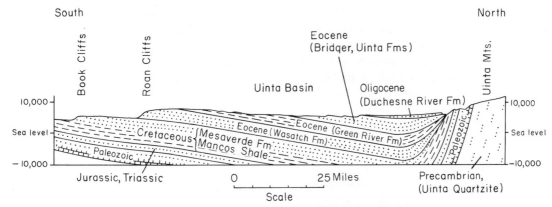

Figure 14.9 *Cross section of the Uinta Basin, showing thick Tertiary formations overlying the Cretaceous and older ones. Toward the south, the Tertiary formations are conformable with one another, but against the steep flank of the Uinta Mountain uplift, unconformities between these formations record a series of structural movements that began in latest Cretaceous time and did not end until sometime after the Oligocene—that is, in middle or late Tertiary time. General uplift of the Uinta Basin, along with the rest of the Colorado Plateau and Rocky Mountains, occurred in late Cenozoic time and may be continuing.*

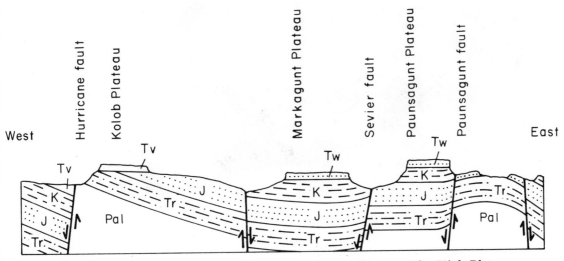

Figure 14.10 *The central part of the High Plateaus Section. The High Plateaus are between the Hurricane and Paunsagunt faults. To the east is the Canyon Lands Section (figure shows north end of the Kaibab Upwarp); to the west is the Basin and Range Province.* **Pal,** *Paleozoic;* **Tr,** *Triassic;* **J,** *Jurassic;* **K,** *Cretaceous;* **Tv,** *Tertiary volcanics;* **Tw,** *Tertiary sedimentary formations. Length of section, about 65 miles.*

Seismic Activity

The Colorado Plateau, a highly elevated block of the crust, may still be rising, as is suggested by the fact that its edges coincide with belts of more than average seismic activity. The epicenters of major earthquakes form lines along the western edge of the plateau, and along its southeastern edge in the Rio Grande Valley. In addition to these, epicenters of minor earthquakes form a line along the southwestern edge of the plateau and along its north and east sides where it joins the

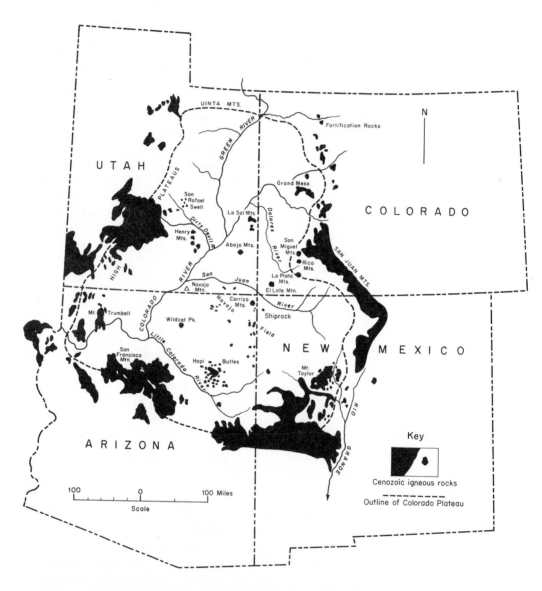

Figure 14.11 *Map illustrating distribution of Cenozoic igneous rocks on the Colorado Plateau. The laccolithic mountains are mostly in the interior of the plateau; the volcanic centers are mostly around the edges of the plateau.*

Rocky Mountains. Only a few minor earthquakes have had their focus under the Plateau.

This seismic record, together with the geology, suggests that not much differential earth movement is occurring within the Plateau, but that the province as a whole may be moving with respect to its neighbors, and is perhaps being tilted to the northeast. In accord with this interpretation is the fact that the area around Lake Mead, which lies southwest of the Plateau, is undergoing measurable southwestward tilt at the present time (p. 325).

Climate

The saucer-like form of the Colorado Plateau is expressed also in the climatic maps, because precipitation is greater and the evaporation rate lower along the rims than in the interior of the plateau (Fig. 14.13). In much of the interior, the average annual precipitation is less than 10 inches, whereas along the high

southwest rim it exceeds 20 inches. One reason for the aridity of the interior is the rain shadow caused by the High Plateaus.

Much of the province is arid because of the high evaporation rate. The effective moisture is even less than the average precipitation would suggest, and especially so during the

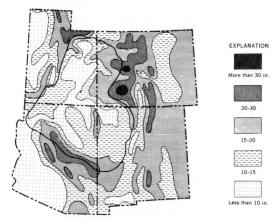

EXPLANATION

More than 30 in.

20–30

15–20

10–15

Less than 10 in.

Figure 14.13 *Average annual precipitation in Colorado, Utah, Arizona, and New Mexico (Colorado Plateau shown by heavy line). (From U.S.D.A.)*

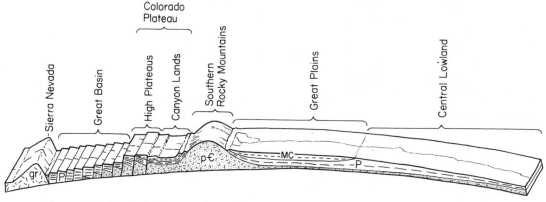

Figure 14.12 *Relation of the Colorado Plateau to the major structural blocks that make up the Rocky Mountain arch. The arch extends from the Central Lowland to the Sierra Nevada. The broad, east flank of the arch underlies the Great Plains and the western part of the Central Lowland. The structurally high central part is represented by the Rocky Mountains. The Colorado Plateau is an elevated segment of the west flank, which remains structurally attached to the Rocky Mountains. The Great Basin is a highly fractured part of the west flank. p Є, Precambrian; P, Paleozoic; MC, Mesozoic and Cenozoic; gr, granite of Sierra Nevada batholith.*

growing season. Probably 95 percent of the precipitation is lost by evaporation transpiration, and seepage into the ground.

Summers are hot and winters are cold. The frost-free period lasts about 200 days along the Colorado River, about 160 days in most of the uplands in the interior of the Plateau, and 100 days or less on the rims and mountains. Climatic maps more detailed than Figure 14.13 would show that each of the laccolithic mountains and large volcanoes receives more rainfall than the surrounding areas and that temperatures and rates of evaporation are lower than in the surrounding areas.

Late Quaternary climatic changes have left their mark on the Colorado Plateau by causing changes in the processes operating in that now-arid region. During dry periods erosion was dominant, as it is now; during wet periods alluvium was deposited on the floodplains, and colluvium accumulated on the hillsides.

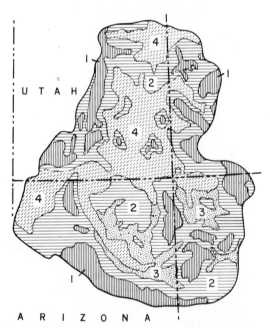

Figure 14.14 *Vegetation map of the Colorado Plateau. 1 = yellow pine and higher-zone forest; 2 = pinyon-juniper woodland; 3 = grassland; 4 = shrubland (sagebrush, blackbrush, saltbrush). (After U.S.D.A.)*

A geologically recent climatic change of special interest occurred at the end of the thirteenth century, which, according to tree-ring studies, was a dry period. During that time many Pueblo settlements were abandoned, and the Pueblo Indians moved to the Rio Grande Valley.

Vegetation

Vegetation on the Colorado Plateau, like the climate, also reflects the saucer-shaped form of the plateau surface. The rims of the plateau, and the isolated mountains, are forested; the interior supports desert shrub or grassland (Fig. 14.14).

The Lower Sonoran Zone, characterized by creosote bush and mesquite, extends into the Colorado Plateau along the bottom of Grand Canyon below about 2500 feet; most of the plateau is in the Upper Sonoran Zone, which extends to altitudes of about 7,500 feet.

The Upper Sonoran Zone is represented by several kinds of plant stands, most of which reflect differences in the availability of moisture. The effective moisture for a given rainfall within the zone is controlled chiefly by differences in the kind of ground, which in turn are caused by differences in the geology, but partly by altitude (evaporation is less at the higher and cooler elevations). Gravel-covered terraces at upper elevations generally support sagebrush and grama grass, whereas similar ground at lower altitudes is covered by shadscale and curly grass. Very sandy ground at upper elevations supports a variety of shrubs and even some scrub oak, whereas this kind of ground at lower elevations has mostly blackbrush. Impermeable ground on shaley formations supports a low-growing plant, mat saltbush (Fig. 8.10,C). Areas with loam tend to be grassy. Cracks and crevices on rocky benches or ledges have juniper, mountain ash, scrub oak, and bitterbrush—all xerophytes.

At the top of the Upper Sonoran Zone is a woodland of pinyon and juniper, the lower boundary of which is the so-called arid timber-line. Below this is treeless land with desert shrubs; above are the forested, higher-altitude zones.

Where groundwater is available in the Upper Sonoran Zone there are stands of phreatophytes, and the kinds depend on the quality of the water. Where the water is alkaline and fairly deep, as along many alluvial floodplains, the principal plant is greasewood. Where the groundwater is alkaline but shallow, the most common plant is saltgrass. Where the quality of groundwater is good, there is cottonwood, rabbitbrush, and sacaton grass.

Despite the vegetation maps, of which Figure 14.14 is an example, probably a quarter of the Canyon Lands Section is bare rock. This bare rock includes surfaces along the walls and rims of the canyons, and it includes badlands and flats in the shale formations.

Above the pinyon and juniper woodland of the Upper Sonoran Zone are forests of the higher zones: first, the Transition Zone, with yellow pine and Douglas fir from about 7,500 to about 9,500 feet; then the Canadian and Hudsonian zones, with spruce and fir to about 11,500 feet; and finally, above timberline, the Alpine Zone, with small herbs and grasses. The forests of these zones are like those in the Southern Rocky Mountains. In the Grand Canyon Section there is much lumbering.

The distribution of vegetation on gravel-covered benches (p. 296) around the foot of some of the mountains illustrates the close response of the vegetation to slight differences in availability of ground moisture (Fig. 14.15). For example, where a stream leaves the Henry Mountains and flows into the gravel, the water seeps into the ground. It then percolates along the base of the gravel; where it reappears in springs, there are stands of cottonwood, willow, rabbitbrush and other phreatophytes. Dry channels, which collect a little runoff, are marked by lines of pinyon and juniper extending down into the sagebrush zone and by lines of sagebrush and grama grass extending down into the zone of shadscale.

The Colorado Plateau is used mostly for grazing—winter grazing at the lower altitudes and summer grazing on the mountains and high plateaus. But the carrying capacity of the land is low. Even the forested areas of the Transition Zone and higher zones support only about 25 cows per square mile; the shrubland and grassland of the Upper Sonoran Zone will support only 5 or 6 cows per square mile, less than 5 percent of the productivity of an equal area in the central United States (Fig. 9.8). Is it in the national interest to expose such poor land to overgrazing?

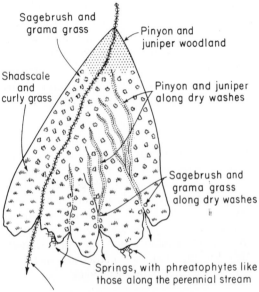

Figure 14.15 *Distribution of vegetation on gravel-covered benches at the foot of the Henry Mountains indicates altitudinal zoning within the Upper Sonoran Zone and the response of the vegetation to slight differences in moisture availability. The lower parts of the fans have shadscale and curly grass. Above this is a belt of sagebrush and grama grass. Pinyon and juniper grow at the apex of the fan. Perennial streams and springs are marked by phreatophytes. Dry washes, which collect a little runoff, are marked by xerophytes that extend from the upper zones downward into the lower zones.*

Surficial Deposits and Soils

Glacial deposits on the Colorado Plateau exist only on parts of the High Plateaus, the La Sal Mountains, and San Francisco Mountain— the only three areas known to have been glaciated. In each of these areas the moraines and other deposits attributable to the Wisconsin stage of glaciation are well developed, and there are deposits representing earlier glaciations. Although the Colorado Plateau had few glaciers, the effects of the several climatic changes were expressed there in several ways. Mountain tops that were not glaciated were subjected to intensive frost action that developed extensive boulder fields. Travel even on foot across these boulders can be difficult. Their origin was explained in graphic terms a hundred years ago by a British geologist (Jukes, 1853):

> Any one who ascends the mountains . . . will often be surprised at the multitude of angular fragments and fallen blocks he sees scattered over their summits. . . . Of these many, if not most, have been detached by the action of frost causing the water in the joints and crevices to expand and rend them asunder, just as in a cold winter's night the jugs and water-bottles are apt to be burst by the frost in our bed-rooms.

On northern exposures in parts of the plateau, notably along some escarpments west of the Abajo Mountains, so much snow collected at times during the Pleistocene that debris avalanches developed at time of thaw; some of these are about a mile long and scores of feet high. They are related to colluvial deposits that are widespread on shale slopes at the sides of mesas and canyons. Evidently, as a result of climatic changes, the stages during which colluvium accumulated alternated with stages during which erosion of the colluvium was accelerated. In many places colluvial deposits of two or more ages may be distinguished (Fig. 14.16).

Melt waters from the extensive Pleistocene glaciers in the Rocky Mountains, both to the east and to the north, swept down the Colorado River and deposited in it thick fills of gravel. Subsequently this gravel fill was partly re-excavated and the gravel left as terraces high above the river. These Pleistocene terraces are numerous up to about 500 feet above the river; the few terraces located at higher altitudes seem to be Tertiary in age.

Changes in climate have caused the streams alternately to aggrade their floodplains and then cut new arroyos in the alluvial fill. Figure 14.17, which illustrates some of the common stratigraphic relationships in the alluvial deposits on the Colorado Plateau, clearly shows that periods of alluviation have alternated with periods of arroyo cutting. This bears on the important question about the degree to which the present cycle of arroyo-cutting and other erosion should be attributed to overgrazing, climatic change, or both. Arroyo cutting is widespread on the Colorado

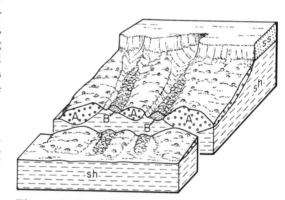

Figure 14.16 *Colluvium (A and B) on the Colorado Plateau forms apron-like deposits on shale (sh) slopes below rims of sandstone (ss). The older of the deposits (A), a thick accumulation containing boulders from the cliff, was eroded by gullies that cut into underlying shale. In these gullies a younger, thinner, and less bouldery colluvium (B) accumulated. Present gullies are cutting into the shale along the contacts between the deposits, and even the youngest colluvium is being eroded.*

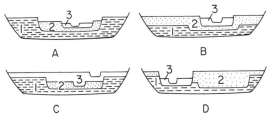

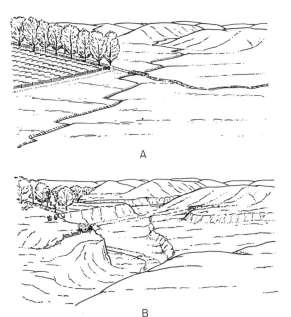

Figure 14.17 *Diagrammatic sections illustrating some common stratigraphic relationships in the alluvial deposits in the western states. 1, late Pleistocene alluvium; 2, pre-pottery, Recent alluvium; 3, historic alluvium. (A) From old to young, the alluvial deposits are progressively thinner, and the arroyos in which they were deposited are progressively smaller. (B) The second alluvium has overtopped the first. (C) The third alluvium has overtopped the older ones. (D) An example of a large number of complicated relationships that occur locally.*

Figure 14.18 *Pleasant Creek, Utah, in the western part of the Henry Mountains area before arroyo cutting (A) and in 1935 (B). The arroyo, about 20 feet deep, was eroded between 1900 and 1935. (After U.S.G.S.)*

Plateau; it is a historical fact that arroyo-cutting commenced in each valley a few years after the first settlers arrived, which indicates that the erosion was hastened by the grazing and other use. The geologic record, however, indicates that arroyo-cutting has occurred repeatedly in the past as a result of natural causes and that it would have occurred sooner or later in the valleys of the Colorado Plateau.

Present-day arroyo-cutting is severe and widespread in most of the interior of the Colorado Plateau. Figure 14.18 illustrates an arroyo near the Henry Mountains that was eroded in about 35 years. Figure 14.19 illustrates the extent of erosion along the Fremont River west of Hanksville, Utah, in the 40-year period 1897–1937. Such erosion not only destroys towns, homes, fields, and roads, but also lowers the water table under the alluvium, and this loss of water supply in the desert is perhaps the most damaging effect of arroyo-cutting. This lowering of the water table has occurred in the past, too, and forced the abandonment of some prehistoric settlements. Some of the washes on the Colorado Plateau

that are now dry once supplied water for irrigation systems that were abandoned in prehistoric time by Pueblo Indians.

The general extent of such erosion on the Colorado Plateau is shown in Figure 7.1. Erosion is slight on the western and southern rims of the plateau, chiefly because those areas have extensive flat benchlands, but also because they are well forested and have been protected by inclusion within national forests. The areas subject to severe erosion that are outside the Indian reservations have received some protection from the Bureau of Land Management, but that agency has never had adequate funds and staff to take proper care of so much public land.

Extensive upland areas on the Colorado Plateau are covered by sand dunes, which occur in crescentic forms and as linear ridges (Fig. 14.20). Most of the active sand dunes overlie older dune sand that is stabilized, and

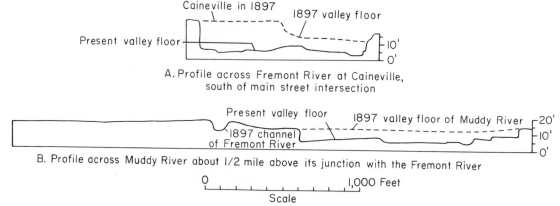

Figure 14.19 *Profiles across the Fremont River showing the amount of erosion since 1897. (After U.S.G.S.)*

the two generations of dune sand can be distinguished. Sand in the active dunes is loose; the underlying and older dune sand is iron stained and slightly consolidated. The older dune sand, which is of early Recent or perhaps late Pleistocene age, is the source of the sand in the active dunes. The dunes are developed where poorly consolidated sandy formations are exposed. As the dunes migrate from those formations into areas where shaley formations are exposed, they become smaller and finally disappear.

Soils on the Colorado Plateau have received very little study because of their slight agricultural use. Most are classed as lithosols—that is, soils derived from parent materials

that have been only slightly weathered. Nevertheless, as in other physiographic provinces, three very different kinds of soils representing three quite different geologic ages can be distinguished.

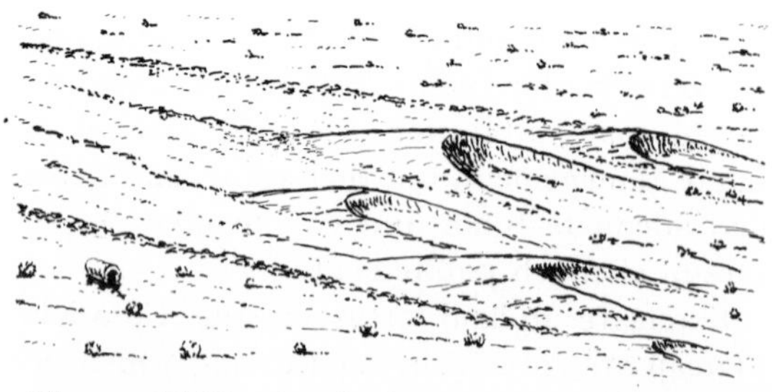

The oldest and most weathered of these soils developed in pre-Wisconsin time. In the upper layers of these soils, as in the Red and Yellow Podzols previously described, pebbles, even of granite, are weathered to clay. The upper clayey layer is a few feet thick where fully preserved. Below this is a layer in which the rocks retain their shape and structure but have been altered to clay and can be cut by a knife. In this layer, and in some lower layers, there is a thick accumulation of lime carbonate, called *caliche*. Below the caliche is fresh parent material. Agriculturally important pre-Wisconsin soil occurs along the Utah-Colorado boundary. This soil, shown as Chestnut Soil in Figure 6.2, developed on an ancient loess deposit, and both the loess and the soil are overlapped by gravel deposits of Wisconsin age.

The soils of Wisconsin age, exemplified by those developed on early Wisconsin glacial deposits and their gravel outwash, have a leached layer at the top that is a foot or two thick. Pebbles in this layer are fresh, but are likely to be deeply stained with iron oxide, as are the sand and silt. Recent soils show little or no

Figure 14.20 *Sand dunes on the Colorado Plateau. The wind direction is from the left. The arcuate dunes are called barchane dunes.*

signs of oxidation, and the leached layer is no more than a few inches thick. Wisconsin and Recent soils are farmed along some flood-plains.

Landforms

The several physiographic sections of the Colorado Plateau differ as greatly in their landforms as they do in their structures. The Tertiary formations in the Uinta Basin form broad hilly benches that slope north, and they form the south-facing escarpment known as the Roan Cliffs (Fig. 14.9). Cretaceous forma-tions, rising southward from under the Ter-tiary formations, form the south-facing Book Cliffs, an escarpment that is about 2,000 feet high and extends about 100 miles across the southern edge of the basin, overlooking the Canyon Lands Section.

The canyons in the Canyon Lands Section have been carved mostly in sandstones in the upper Paleozoic and lower Mesozoic forma-tions. The upper Jurassic and Cretaceous formations include thick shale units that form badlands arranged in belts between cuestas and benches formed by resistant beds of sand-stone.

Where the resistant, canyon-forming sand-stones are turned up steeply along the flanks of the asymmetric, anticlinal upwarps, they form great ridges generally known as hog-backs but referred to locally as "reefs." These form nearly impassable barriers, as do the canyons. The thick sandstones erode into characteristic dome-like forms; Capitol Reef (a national monument) was so-named be-cause its domes are suggestive of the dome on the capitol building in Washington, D.C. Back from the rims of canyons, nearly flat-ly-ing sandstone formations form bare, knobby rock surfaces deeply dissected by narrow, rock-walled gulches or small canyons. Friable and earthy sandstones that extend across broad areas form a sandy desert with dunes.

Other major geomorphic features in the Canyon Lands Section are the forested lacco-lithic mountains (Fig. 14.7). During the gla-cial stages the upper parts of these mountains lay within the zone of intensive frost action (p. 188) and are consequently rounded. The lower parts of the mountains faithfully re-flect the geologic structure. The contrast re-flects the difference in the processes of erosion. Still other erosion forms that are distinctive of the Canyon Lands Section are the pedi-ments, alcoves, arches, bridges, spires, and pedestal rocks. These are described later.

The High Plateaus include highly ele-vated, flat-topped benches separated by wide, flat-bottomed structural valleys trending north to south. Many of the benches are capped, and the floors of many of the valleys are covered with basaltic lava. The colorful Tertiary formations have been eroded into badlands at Bryce Canyon National Park and Cedar Breaks National Monument. Zion Can-yon, at the southern end of the High Plateaus, is similar to many of the canyons in the Can-yon Lands Section.

The High Plateaus end southward in three great escarpments that face southward and overlook the Grand Canyon Section. The northern escarpment, the Pink Cliffs, is formed by Tertiary formations (Fig. 14.1). The middle escarpment, the White Cliffs, is formed by upper Mesozoic sandstone. The southern escarpment, the Vermillion Cliffs, is formed by lower Mesozoic formations.

The Navajo Section is characterized by broad flats on the shaley formations separated by low cuestas where the more resistant sand-stones crop out. Colorful Triassic formations produce the Painted Desert, which extends far northwest of the national monument. In the San Juan Basin, the Tertiary and Cre-taceous formations resemble a series of stacked saucers that get progressively smaller toward the top and form cuestas that face outward.

Volcanic formations in the Navajo, Datil, and Grand Canyon sections, as already noted, form several distinctive kinds of landforms, including the large, central-type volcanoes (Mount Taylor and San Francisco Mountain), cinder cones in the lava fields, and the very young lava flows along some valleys. Erosion of the volcanic formations produced the lava-capped mesas and the volcanic necks.

Pediments

Around the foot of the mountains on the Colorado Plateau are extensive benches that have been planed by erosion of the bedrock. Most of these are partly covered by gravel. Such surfaces are particularly well developed, and their origin is clearly revealed along the foot of the Book Cliffs and around the foot of the Henry Mountains (Fig. 14.21). The processes that developed these surfaces have operated at numerous other places in the United States—for example, the Great Plains (p. 234).

Where streams that head in mountains dis

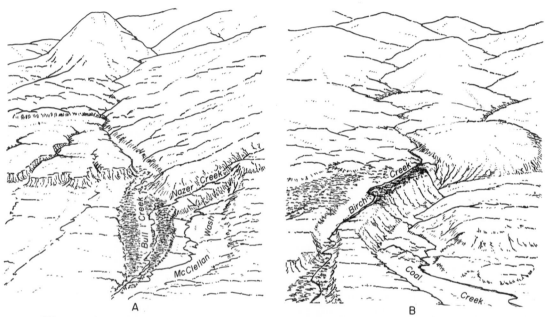

Figure 14.21 *Pediment development and stream diversions at the foot of the Henry Mountains, Utah. Streams draining from the mountains, like Bull Creek and Nazer Canyon (A) and Birch Creek (B), are aggrading their courses and depositing gravel where they emerge at the foot of the mountains. Streams rising in front of the mountains, like McClellan Wash (A) and Coal Creek (B), are free of gravel and have cut their courses much below the more watered streams from the mountains. McClellan Wash is 20 feet lower than Bull Creek and 55 feet lower than Nazer Creek. Coal Wash is 400 feet lower than Birch Creek. The divide holding Nazer Creek on its gravelly perch is only 5½ feet high, and any major flood may breach it. The divide holding Birch Creek at its height above Coal Creek is 10 feet high. When these divides are breached the streams from the mountains will deposit gravel on the pediments. The benches along each side of the streams are gravel-covered pediments that record a complex series of more ancient episodes of such pediment-cutting and burial beneath gravel because of stream diversion.*

charge into an area of lower rainfall, water
is lost by seepage and by evaporation. As the
volume of water in such a stream is reduced,
so is its power to transport its load; the gravel
being transported from the mountains becomes deposited, and the lower stretch of the
stream course becomes aggraded.

Streams rising within the desert carry water
infrequently, as when heavy rains cause local
floods. At such times these streams can erode
their beds, particularly if they are in easily
eroded formations, such as shale that is not
protected by gravel. The bed can be eroded
below that of a gravel-laddened stream draining from the mountains, in the same way that
Bear Creek has eroded its bed below that of
Rock River on the High Plains (Fig. 12.27).
In time, the stream draining from the mountains will be left perched, and sooner or later
be captured and turned into the lower stream
valley. When the stream originating in the
mountains is turned into the lower valley,
the new channel and associated pediment,
which have been free of gravel, become the
dumping ground for gravel being transported
by the captured stream. Gravel is deposited
at the point of capture, and a gravel fan begins to form and gradually spreads downstream from the point of capture and covers
the pediment. The gravel is younger than the
erosion surface on which it rests, and it was
not transported by the stream that eroded the
channel and planed the pediments. As erosion progresses and as more streams cut downward, the gravel-covered pediments are left
as gravel-capped benches high above the
drainage lines.

Around the foot of the Henry Mountains
are examples of every stage in the process—
incipient capture (Fig. 14.21), capture that occurred recently enough such that the gravel
fan only partly covers the pediment, and capture that occurred long enough ago such that
the pediment has been completely buried by
gravel and side streams have begun to cut
below the stream from the mountain.

Gravel resists erosion. The gravel-capped

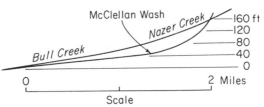

Figure 14.22 *Most master streams have
flatter gradients than their tributaries, but the
reverse is true along streams draining from
areas of high rainfall to areas of low rainfall.
Bull Creek and Nazer Creek are perennial
streams that rise in the Henry Mountains;
their courses are clogged with gravel and are
steeper than the course of the tributary, Mc-
Clellan Wash, which is usually dry but rises
in the desert and is free of gravel. Compare
with Figure 14.21, A. (After U.S.G.S.)*

pediments are remnants of benches reduced
by erosion that attacks the sides of the benches
and undermines the gravel cap. The streams
that cut downward almost invariably have
incised themselves along the edges of the
gravel fills, with the result that gravel benches
on one side of a valley are at different heights
from those on the opposite side.

Ordinarily a main stream has a flatter gradient than its tributaries, but the reverse is
true of streams draining from areas of high
rainfall to areas of low rainfall. The main
streams from the mountains have steeper gradients than their tributaries (Fig. 14.22).

Alcoves, Arches, Bridges, and Tanks

Overhanging cliffs in the sandstone formations are commonplace and almost a characteristic feature of the Colorado Plateau.
Some are so small that they can be used only
for nests by cliff swallows; others are large
enough to have afforded protection to the cliff
dwellings of the prehistoric Pueblo Indians

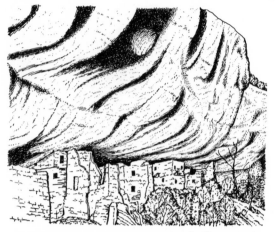

Figure 14.23 *Prehistoric Anasazi cliff dwelling under an overhanging cliff at Mesa Verde National Park. The Anasazi ruins at Mesa Verde and elsewhere on the Colorado Plateau were built during the period A.D. 500 to A.D. 1300. They were abandoned at the end of the thirteenth century after a period of drought. Streaks of desert varnish antedate the ruins.*

(Fig. 14.23). Some of the large alcoves beneath such cliffs in the Henry Mountains area are 600 feet long, 150 feet deep, and 200 feet high. They form in at least three ways, as illustrated in Figure 14.24.

An alcove arch that develops along the outside of a meander may evolve to a natural bridge as at Rainbow Bridge or the Natural Bridges National Monument. Where the meanders in a canyon are closely spaced, they may cut through an alcove and thereafter flow through it and under the arch that remains (Fig. 14.25).

Among other erosional features of the plateau are the depressions in sandstone surfaces, referred to locally as "tanks," for they fill with water after rains. The tanks are important in the water economy of the plateau; in some parts of the plateau desert travelers must depend on these natural cisterns for water. Some are as large as swimming pools.

The tanks are of at least three kinds. Some were formed as plunge pools below waterfalls

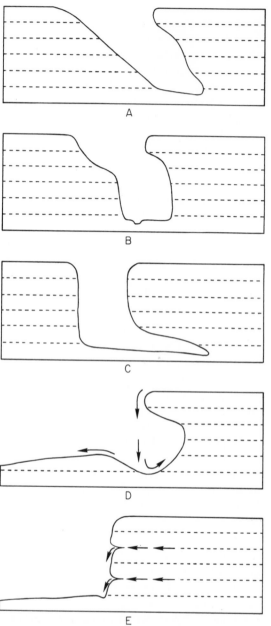

Figure 14.24 *Some alcove arches are formed by lateral cutting of streams (A, B, C). The forms depend on the relative progress of vertical and lateral cutting by the stream. Other arches are formed by the splash behind the plunge pool under waterfalls (D). Still others are due to groundwater softening the cement in the standstone, which permits loosened grains to be blown away (E).*

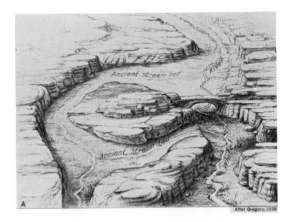

Ancient stream bed

River

Ancient stream bed

A

After Gregory, 1938

Figure 14.25 *How natural bridges are formed by a stream cutting off a meander in a canyon. (After U.S.G.S.)*

(Fig. 14.24,D); others, as potholes in the sandstone beds of rivers that are now dry. Still others are on upland surfaces and probably formed as standing water dissolved the cement in the sandstone and enabled the wind to blow away the loosened sand grains once the water had evaporated.

The alcoves, arches, bridges, tanks, and other unusual landforms on the Plateau commonly are attributed to wind erosion, but in general the wind merely removed the grains of sand that became loosened by water that dissolved the cement holding them together. Moreover, these erosion forms, obviously older than the cliff dwellings, probably date from the Pleistocene. During periods when the climate was less arid, the rate of erosion by streams and the rate of dissolution were greater than it is today, and the whole process took place at a correspondingly greater rate.

Paint on the Canyon Walls— Desert Varnish

Canyon-walls in the Colorado Plateau are decorated picturesquely with colorful patterns formed by a stain of iron and manganese oxides called desert varnish. Along the Colorado River in Glen Canyon the effects are like tapestry. The desert varnish is not limited to the canyons, but occurs widely on all kinds of rock surfaces, including gravels, boulder fields, and stones or boulders on hillsides. It is found at all altitudes from canyon bottoms to mountain tops.

How the stain was deposited is not entirely clear, but the iron and manganese must have been in solution in water. Some may have been leached from within the rock formations and deposited at the surface. At other places the iron and manganese must have been brought from farther away by surface water or by groundwater.

Iron and manganese oxides are being deposited today at seeps along the canyon walls, but these are minute areas compared to the dry areas of desert varnish. Furthermore, the desert varnish is being removed from these dry areas, and the fresh rock once again is being exposed. This desert varnish is older than the cliff dwellings and other prehistoric remains dating back at least to A.D. 500, for the dwellings are built against stained cliffs. Apparently, most desert varnish is an ancient deposit dating from a wetter time.

Hydrology

Drainage Patterns

Because of the aridity and because of the considerable differences in rainfall within short distances on and off the mountains, the drainage has developed nearly every type of pattern imaginable. The great variety of drainage patterns on the Colorado Plateau (Fig. 14.26) results primarily from the many differences in structure, although a few drainage patterns are due mainly to process and stage.

Differences in process and stage are represented by changes in drainage pattern as gravel fans are built onto the pediments at the

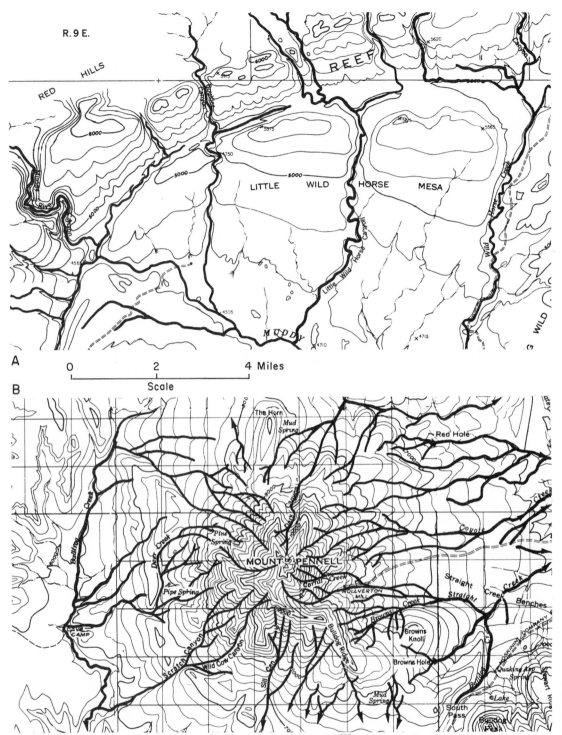

Figure 14.26 *Examples of differences in drainage patterns on the Colorado Plateau. The trellis pattern (A) is developed along a monoclinal fold (reef) at the southern end of the San Rafael Swell, Utah. The radial pattern (B) developed on Mount Pennell in the Henry Mountains.*

foot of the mountains. Drainage patterns on the gravel-free pediments are dendritic. When a stream draining from the mountains is captured and diverted onto such a pediment, a gravel fan is deposited and the drainage pattern on the gravel at that stage becomes braided. When the slope of the fan has been built to a grade sufficient for the stream to continue to transport the gravel, the drainage lines become nearly parallel (Fig. 14.27).

Drainage patterns attributable to structure are more common. On the steeply dipping, east flanks of the upwarps, the drainage has developed trellis patterns (Fig. 14.26,A). At the laccolithic mountains and volcanoes the drainage patterns are radial (Fig. 14.26,B). Trellis patterns have also developed in the block-faulted High Plateaus and in the faulted salt anticlines. On the badlands the drainage is dendritic. On gently dipping sandstone formations bare rock surfaces are extensive, and at such places minor joints in the sandstone cause the drainage to be parallel. On the sandy deserts, drainage courses become clogged with windblown sand, and the drainage there is disintegrated, with closed depressions between the sand dunes and up valley from them. On some lava-capped plateaus, especially in the High Plateaus and Datil Sections, the drainage is sluggish and meanders widely on the upland flats. On young lava flows the surfaces are exceedingly rough and are referred to by the Spanish term *malpais,* meaning bad country. In such areas much of the drainage is underground.

Some canyons, controlled by joints or faults and having small streams, are nearly straight, and deviate only a few hundred feet in several miles. Canyons of the larger streams meander widely and this meandering takes two forms. The main canyons of streams like the Dirty Devil River are straight, but within the main canyon is an inner gorge and this and the river in it meander widely almost wildly. The main canyons of other rivers meander as widely as the inner gorges and the streams within them. This is true along much of the Colorado, Green, Dolores, and San Juan rivers. As a general rule, the larger the stream the wider its meander belt (Fig. 14.28); this seems to be true of the canyons as well.

The origin of the meandering canyons on the Colorado Plateau has been a subject of wide interest and much discussion: but since present-day stream meanders in general are not well understood and since the meandering canyons must represent ancient features that have been modified as canyon cutting progressed, not much has come of the discussion. The varied shapes of alcoves show that some meanders have widened as down-cutting progressed (Fig. 14.24,A); other evidence shows that lateral widening of some meanders was interrupted by vertical down-cutting (Fig.

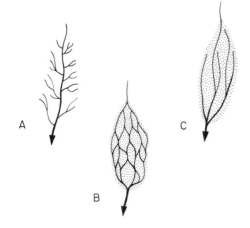

Figure 14.27 *Changes in drainage patterns on pediments and gravel fans attributable to differences in process and stage. On gravel-free pediments the drainage is dendritic (A). When a stream from a mountain is diverted onto a pediment, it builds a gravel fan there and the drainage pattern is braided (B) while the fan is being aggraded. When the fan has been built steeply enough so that new additions of gravel can be transported across its surface, the drainage pattern becomes parallel and consequent (C).*

14.24,B), and that others were produced only after a long period of vertical erosion (Fig. 14.24,C).

Drainage Anomalies

For an arid region the Colorado Plateau has more than its share of drainage anomalies. The two principal streams, the Colorado River and the Green River (Fig. 13.1), enter the plateau after crossing mountainous uplifts, the White River Plateaus and the Uinta Mountain Uplift, respectively (p. 271–272). Both uplifts are structural and topographic barriers.

The Gunnison River enters the plateau after crossing the uplift at the Black Canyon. Originally the Colorado and Gunnison rivers

entered the Colorado Plateau along a southwest course that crosses the Uncompahgre Upwarp in a wide, deep, but dry canyon, known as Unaweep Canyon, the floor of which is 2,000 feet higher than the present rivers. The Dolores River flows southwestward from the San Juan Mountains, but where it enters the Colorado Plateau, instead of continuing its southwestward course and joining the San Juan River, it turns northward 135 degrees, crosses the salt anticlines, and then turns around the north side of the La Sal Mountains to join the Colorado River. Price River heads in the High Plateaus and flows eastward to join the Green River, but instead of following an open shale valley around the south side of the Book Cliffs, this river continues eastward in a deep canyon across the southern rim of the Uinta Basin and joins the Green River in Desolation Canyon. The San Rafael

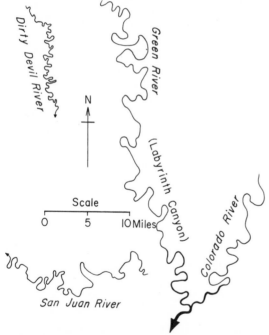

Figure 14.28 *River meanders in canyons. The canyon of the Dirty Devil River is as deep and as wide as Labyrinth Canyon, but the flow is small compared to that of the Green River. The flow of the San Juan River is greater than that of the Dirty Devil.*

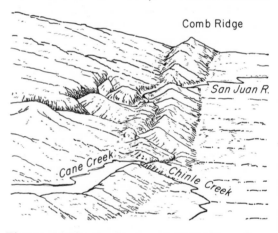

Figure 14.29 *Drainage relationships where the San Juan River crosses Comb Ridge to enter the Monument Upwarp. A tributary, Chinle Creek, flows north in a strike valley east (right) of Comb Ridge, but turns out of that lowland and into the Ridge to join the San Juan River in its canyon. Cane Creek follows a strike valley at the foot of Comb Ridge, but leaves that strike valley and joins Chinle Creek along Comb Ridge. This drainage must be superimposed, and probably from a surface that was only a few hundred feet higher than the present streams.*

and Muddy rivers, which head in the High Plateaus, cross the uplift at the San Rafael Swell. The San Juan River crosses the Monument Upwarp.

The Colorado River and the Green River, after they have entered the Colorado Plateau, are rather accordant with the principal structures. The southward course of the Green River follows a structural trough between the San Rafael Swell and Uncompaghre Upwarp (Fig. 14.4). The Colorado River swings in a wide arc around the northwest end of the Uncompaghre Upwarp, although it is incised in a canyon across the northwest tip of that structure. After being joined by Green River, the Colorado follows a course diagonally across the basin between the Monument and Circle Cliffs upwarps. In Arizona, the river swings far south as if partly diverted by the Kaibab Upwarp, and then turns westward to leave the Plateau in Grand Canyon, which crosses the highest part of the southwest rim of the Plateau.

Other drainage anomalies are found along certain intermittent tributaries. Hall Creek follows a structurally controlled valley along the Waterpocket Fold, but at two places the creek leaves the open valley and turns westward into canyons cut into the sandstones turned up in the fold. Chinle Creek flows northward in a broad valley, but joins the San Juan River by turning into a canyon on the flank of the Monument Upwarp (Fig. 14.29). The Chaco River, in New Mexico, follows a similar course.

Water Supply

More than nine-tenths of the Colorado Plateau drains to the Colorado River at Grand Canyon. The only parts draining other ways are narrow strips along the southern and western edges.

The average annual discharges (in acre feet) of streams on the Colorado Plateau are:

Colorado River, above mouth of Dolores River	6,000,000
Dolores River, near the mouth	870,000
Green River, at mouth	5,100,000
San Juan River, near mouth	2,100,000
Colorado River, above junction with Little Colorado	14,400,000
Little Colorado River, near the mouth	240,000
Colorado River, at Grand Canyon	13,000,000

These measurements of discharge cannot be compared closely because the records from which they were calculated are for different numbers of years and because the annual discharge fluctuates widely. For example, records from Lees Ferry—a station located on the Colorado River just above the junction with the Little Colorado—show that the discharge has ranged from a minimum of less than 4 million acre-feet to more than 23 million acre-feet.

What is important is the fact that the sum of the discharges of the rivers above Grand Canyon nearly equal, or may even slightly exceed, the discharge at Grand Canyon, which indicates that runoff from the central part of the Colorado Plateau is less than the water lost from the system by evaporation and seepage.

The amount of water lost by evaporation can be illustrated in another way. The annual discharge of the Colorado River at Grand Canyon has been as low as 4,000,000 acre feet, as high as 23,000,000 acre feet, and has averaged about 13,000,000 acre feet. Lake Powell in Glen Canyon has an area of about 250 square miles, which is 160,000 acres. The evaporation rate in Glen Canyon probably averages more than 6 feet per year, which means that more than 1,000,000 acre feet of water is lost annually by evaporation from that one reservoir—enough water to supply a metropolitan area as large as Denver. In addition, there are seepage losses. Many feel that this dam should not have been built. Certainly if more dams and reservoirs are built along the Colorado River, the evaporation and seepage losses will exceed the flow of the river, and it will become necessary to import water to maintain the river flow. Yet in the face of this, there have been proposals to build dams even in Grand Canyon.

Most of the streams that rise on the Colorado Plateau are intermittent, even those on the laccolithic mountains and the big volcanoes. A few streams on these mountains are perennial for short distances, but the annual discharge of even the largest of such streams is no more than a very few thousand acre feet. These streams, even when in flood, rarely extend far from the foot of the mountains. In crossing the deserts their water is lost by seepage and evaporation. The Dirty Devil River is an example of a stream classed as perennial, although in dry periods it fails to flow in some stretches. At the other extreme, floods in that stream may have peaks as high as 15,000 cfs.

Springs are important water sources on the Plateau and are of several kinds that differ in size, quality, and mode of occurrence. Springs in the mountains are most numerous. Many are perennial and may yield several gallons per minute; their water is uniformly good. Many such springs are at the toe of boulder fields. Snow that collects between the boulders melts slowly and feeds streams underneath that lose almost no water by evaporation. Springs in the foothill belt are fewer and average smaller in size than those in the mountains, and their water, although generally potable, commonly contains considerable dissolved solids. Most of these springs occur at the edge of gravel benches and are recharged by underflow from streams draining the mountains (Fig. 14.15). Springs in the desert are few and small. Their discharge rarely amounts to more than seepage, and many of them, perhaps a third, are too alkaline or saline for use.

Another important source for water is provided by natural tanks (p. 298). The Waterpocket Fold was so named by the Powell Survey because of its many water-bearing tanks. Additional water supplies on the Colorado

Plateau have been obtained locally by drilled wells. In some of the structural basins, aquifers have been found within a few hundred feet of the surface, but this groundwater is of limited supply and of uncertain quality. Much of it is too alkaline for use.

Municipal water supplies vary widely in quality, depending upon the source. Cities that obtain their supplies from the mountains have excellent water with little more than 100 ppm tds. Towns in the desert obtain their water from wells or streams, and water from these sources commonly contains 800 to 1,000 ppm tds and has a hardness of 250 to 300.

How Old Is Grand Canyon?

The history of the Colorado River is complex, the evidence for reconstructing it is incomplete, and different interpretations may be made about the age of Grand Canyon depending on the emphasis given to different kinds of evidence. Probably the general course of the Colorado River dates from an early stage in the structural history of the Colorado Plateau. The upwarps on the plateau date from late Cretaceous or earliest Tertiary time. General uplift of the plateau began in middle Tertiary time, and the river probably dates from then. River deposits thought to be late Miocene in age located 50 miles northeast of the upper end of Grand Canyon and 1,500 feet lower than the canyon rim contain gravels from the San Juan Mountains. The deposit shows that by late Miocene time the ancestral San Juan River had established its course westward across the Monument Upwarp and was, in all probability, established in Grand Canyon. This evidence, taken alone, suggests that Grand Canyon is old.

Conflicting with this evidence is that provided by other deposits at the foot of the Grand Wash Cliffs, which form the southwest edge of the Colorado Plateau. These deposits, thought to be of late Tertiary age, are locally derived gravels and not of a kind that would be deposited by the river. The deposits are crossed by the Colorado River where it emerges from Grand Canyon, and the river could not have discharged there while those gravels were being deposited. The present bed of the river at that location must be younger than the gravel. This evidence, alone, suggests that the Colorado River is young.

The conflict could be reconciled by assuming that the river was ponded by uplift at the southwest rim of the plateau at the time the gravels there were deposited. At some later time the river would have overflowed along its old canyon, cutting it deeper and establishing a course across the young deposits along the foot of Grand Wash Cliffs. Such ponding is reasonable to assume, because the ancestral Colorado River may have had substantially less flow than does the present river, which would facilitate the inferred ponding. The climate was arid in Tertiary time, and the Rocky Mountains, the source of the water, were not so high. Even if the mountains had as much relief then as now, their summits must have been 5,000 to 7,000 feet lower. The amount of available water may have been less, the river gradient must certainly have been flatter, and the losses by evaporation were probably no less than now. As brought out in the preceding pages, the present-day losses by evaporation are about as great as the flow of the river. The anomalous stretches of Hall Creek, Chinle Creek, and Chaco Canyon may have developed by superposition from fill that was deposited on the plateau during a stage of ponding caused by northeast tilting of the plateau.

Mineral Deposits

Most mineral resources on the Colorado Plateau (Fig. 14.30) come from the sedimentary formations, and uranium and mineral fuels account for most of the production.

Coal is extensive in Cretaceous formations in the Navajo Section, the High Plateaus, and the Uinta Basin; some less extensive deposits occur in the Canyon Lands Section. These were important coal fields when the railroads used steam locomotives, but production has waned. Lately coking coal has been produced to supply steel plants in the western states, and for steam-generated electricity.

Oil and gas have been produced in the San Juan Basin part of the Navajo Section and in the Uinta Basin; recent discoveries have been made in the central part of the Canyon Lands Section. Near Price, Utah, carbon dioxide gas has been produced for the manufacture of dry ice.

Vast deposits of oil-shale that underlie the Uinta Basin are an important resource for the future. These deposits are estimated to contain 50 times as much oil as the combined total of oil already produced and oil in reserve. At present, however, oil-shale cannot profitably compete with other sources of petroleum.

The plateau is an important source of uranium. For ten years it was the scene of mad scrambling for uranium prospects, a true uranium rush, and the effort led to the discovery of several major deposits. Now that these deposits have been brought into production, the rush is over.

Production of other minerals has been minor, but important deposits of potash and other salts underlie the salt anticlines southwest of the Uncompaghre Upwarp.

Land Use

Indian Reservations comprise a large part of the Colorado Plateau, roughly a third. Among them are:

1. Navajo, Hopi, Jicarilla Apache, and Ute Mountain Indian Reservations, which cover more than half the Navajo Section.
2. Zuni, Laguna, Acoma, Puerto Cito, and Mescalero Apache Reservations, which cover about a quarter of the Datil Section.

3. Kaibab and Hualpai Indian Reservations in the northwest part of the Grand Canyon Section.

4. Uinta and Ouray Indian Reservations along the northern and southern edges of the Uinta Basin.

Nearly half the plateau is public domain. This half is used chiefly for grazing, and much of it is severely overgrazed. The mountains are grazed in summer; the lower parts, which are desert, are used as winter range. Most of the rest of the Plateau is in national forests.

Private lands make up a small fraction of the Plateau. The two principal farming areas are the floodplain formed by the Colorado and Gunnison rivers in the Grand Junction area (peaches, melons, apples, and vegetables) and

the loessial belt in southwest Colorado and southeast Utah (pinto beans). Other valley areas also are farmed, notably in the vicinity of Farmington, New Mexico, and Moab, Green River, and Price, Utah.

Towns are few and widely separated. Farmington, the largest, has a population of less than 25,000. The total population on the plateau probably is less than 500,000.

Aridity—An Asset

The Colorado Plateau illustrates that aridity can be an asset, for given a humid climate the plateau would have lost most or all its spectacular features. Grand Canyon and the other

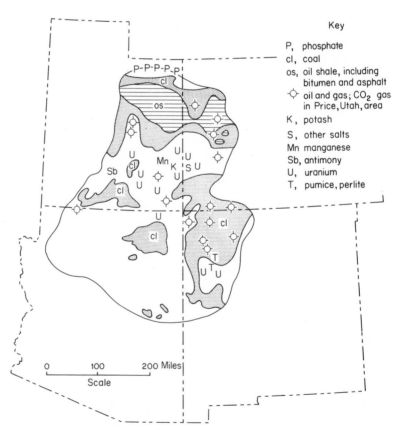

Key

P, phosphate
cl, coal
os, oil shale, including bitumen and asphalt
✧ oil and gas; CO_2 gas in Price, Utah, area
K, potash
S, other salts
Mn manganese
Sb, antimony
U, uranium
T, pumice, perlite

Figure 14.30 *Principal mineral deposits on the Colorado Plateau.*

canyons along the Colorado River would become as drab as Hells Canyon of the Snake River—still vast, but without the impressively distinctive sculpturing and without the color. The uplands would be grassed over and perhaps have trees and scenery not much different from that of the Appalachian Plateaus. The painted deserts would be gone, and Monument Valley would be a collection of rounded hillocks. There would be no Rainbow Bridge or other natural bridges, arches, or alcoves. There would be more agriculture, more industry, and the land would be as crowded with people as is the rest of the country and would be largely in private hands.

Instead, thanks to aridity, a spectacularly beautiful segment of our country remains public land available to 175,000,000 of us who annually or on weekends seek to escape from offices, industry, and urban crowds. To make best use of the Colorado Plateau requires further capitalizing on the aridity and the advantages it has brought.

This land, like the Rocky Mountains, is suitable for grazing in moderation. The new highways necessary to make maximum use of the incomparable scenery need not be like the Arizona segment of U. S. Highway 66—cluttered with billboards, stands selling imported "Indian" souvenirs, "zoos with real live animals," automobile morgues, and other roadside monstrosities wholly out of keeping with the rich Indian tradition of that beautiful painted desert. The plateau is large enough to provide wilderness areas for those who can afford the luxury of pack train and guide, but many, many more miles of that spectacular canyon country could be made accessible to the vastly more numerous families who want to take the kids camping too.

15 Basin and Range Province

The Basin and Range Province, covering about 300,000 square miles—about 8 percent of the United States—consists of desert basins and ranges that, on the average, are drier than the Colorado Plateau and that, in most places, have less vegetation. Altitudes of the basins range from below sea level (at Death Valley and Salton Sea) to about 5,000 feet above sea level. Many of them are closed and contain dry lake beds. The mountain ranges, numbering more than two hundred, tend to form parallel ridges, mostly less than 10,000 feet in altitude but reaching a maximum of more than 13,000 feet.

The population, totaling about 3,500,000, is distributed very unevenly. The few places having water are densely populated; most of the rest of the province is open and unfenced desert. The population is concentrated in a few areas: along the Rio Grande between Santa Fe and El Paso; in the Tucson-Phoenix area, Arizona; along the Humboldt River and in the Las Vegas and Reno areas, Nevada; in the area about Salt Lake City, Utah; and in the Yuma and Salton Sea areas.

The wide valleys are interconnected across low divides, a feature that has greatly favored transportation routes. The province is gridded with good highways in all directions, and five railroads cross the province. The Western Pacific and Southern Pacific Railroads, con-necting Salt Lake City and San Francisco, cross the northern part. The Union Pacific runs southwestward from Salt Lake City to Los Angeles. The Santa Fe and Southern Pacific railroads cross the southern part of the province and lead to Los Angeles.

National Parks and Monuments in the Basin and Range Province that illustrate its physiographic features include Death Valley and Joshua Tree National Monuments, California; Lake Mead Recreational Area, Nevada and Arizona; Saguaro Cactus, Organpipe Cactus, and Chiricahua National Monuments, Arizona; White Sands National Monument, New Mexico; Big Bend National Park, Texas; and Lehman Cave National Monument, Nevada. Others could well be added: Great Salt Lake and parts of the salt desert around it; Carson Sink and parts of the mountains bordering it; and some of the other lakes, basins, and ranges near the foot of the Sierra Nevada. Also, in my judgment, parks at some of the abandoned mining camps to illustrate early mining technology and the history of mining would be both educational and popular.

Other outstanding features of the Basin and Range Province include its

1. Complex geology and recency of faulting.
2. Structural rather than erosional valleys.
3. Warm desert climate.

4. Large numbers and large size of Pleistocene lakes.
5. Three quite different kinds of ground in every valley—gravel fans rising from valleys to the base of bordering mountains, dry lake beds or floodplains in the central parts of valleys, and rocky bordering mountains.
6. Deposits of various kinds of salts in the playas.
7. Metal resources, especially copper.
8. Picturesque vegetation, especially the cacti and yuccas.
9. Extensive use of adobe (mud brick) construction.

The Basin and Range Province, although distinct from the surrounding provinces, is gradational with each of them, and its boundaries are more arbitrary than most dealt with thus far. Similarly, the five sections into which the province has been divided (Fig. 15.1) are separated by arbitrary boundaries.

Structural Framework and Topography

Great Basin

The Great Basin makes up about half of the Basin and Range Province. This section centers in Nevada but extends into the adjoining states. The Great Basin consists typically of linear, north-south mountain ranges separated by valleys, many of which are closed basins. Only three small parts of the Great Basin drain to its exterior: a small part of the northeast corner of the section drains north to the Snake River; Pit River, a tributary of the Sacramento River, drains Goose Lake and part of the northwest corner of the section; part of the southeast corner drains to the Virgin River, which joins the Colorado at Lake Mead.

The relief between the valleys and adjoining mountains only locally exceeds 5,000 feet, although altitudes in the Great Basin range from below sea level, at Death Valley, to more than 13,000 feet. Five subdivisions of the Great Basin may be distinguished on the basis of their structure, topography, hydrography, and kind of ground (Fig. 15.2). These are:

1. The Central Area of elevated basins and ranges;
2. The Bonneville Basin east of the central area;
3. The Lahontan Basin west of the central area;
4. The Lava and Lake Area at the northwest corner of the Section;
5. The Southern Area.

The Central Area is characterized by valleys that are mostly near 5,000 feet in altitude. Some are closed, but none contain perennial lakes. Dry lake beds and alluvial flats make up about 10 percent of the Central Area. The remaining part is about equally divided between the mountains and the gravel fans sloping from them. A large part of the Central Area drains to the Lahontan Basin by way of the Humboldt River.

The mountain ranges in the eastern and northern parts of the Central Area are linear ridges (Fig. 15.3) of complexly deformed Paleozoic rocks consisting in large part of limestone. To the west the rocks are mostly sandstone, siltstone, and shale derived from volcanic rocks. Block faulting of these folded and faulted rocks produced the basins and ranges. At about the time this block faulting started there were extensive eruptions of lavas and tuffs in the southwest part of the Central Area, and these blockfaulted, volcanic rocks form the ranges there. The downfaulted blocks throughout the Central Area are buried under the debris washed into the valleys by erosion of the uplifted blocks. The block faulting has continued into historic time, and in many valleys the gravel fans and other valley fill are faulted along with the bedrock. This recent faulting and tilting of the block mountains has contributed to some of the drainage anomalies to be described later (p. 332ff).

Figure 15.1 *Physiographic map of the Basin and Range Province.*

(Key continued on next page.)

37. Pancake Range
38. Hot Creek Range
39. Wassuk Range
40. Gillis Range
41. Excelsior Mts.
42. Silver Peak Range
43. Cactus Range
44. Kawick Range
45. Reveille Range
46. Belted Range
47. Mormon Mts.
48. Virgin Mts.
49. Muddy Mts.
50. Sheep Range
51. Spring Mts.
52. McCollough Range

California

1. Warner Range
2. White Mts.
3. Inyo Mts.
4. Panamint Range
5. Funeral Mts.
6. Black Mts.
7. Avawatz Mts.
8. Ord Mts.
9. Bullion Mts.
10. Bristol Mts.
11. Providence Mts.
12. Chemehuevi Mts.
13. Whipple Mts.
14. Turtle Mts.
15. Chocolate Mts.

Arizona

1. Black Mts.
2. Cerbat Mts.
3. Hualpai Mts.
4. Chemehuevi Mts.
5. Harcuvar Mts.
6. Santa Maria Mts.
7. Bradshaw Mts.
8. Harquahala Mts.
9. White Tank Mts.
10. Gila Bend Mts.
11. SH Mts.
12. Kofa Mts.
13. Dome Rock Mts.
14. Trigo Mts.
15. Castle Dome Mts.
16. Gila Mts.
17. Cabeza Prieta Mts.
18. Mohawk Mts.
19. Grover Mts.
20. Sanceda Mts.
21. Sand Tank Mts.
22. Maricopa Mts.
23. Sierra Estrella
24. Salt River Mts.
25. Comobabi Mts.
26. Baboquivari Mts.
27. Sierrita Mts.
28. Tumacacori Mts.
29. Patagonia Mts.
30. Santa Rita Mts.
31. Huachuca Mts.
32. Whetstone Mts.
33. Rincon Mts.
34. Santa Catalina Mts.
35. Pinal Mts.
36. Superstition Mts.
37. Mazatal Mts.

38. Sierra Ancha
39. Gila Mts.
40. Santa Teresa Mts.
41. Galiuro Mts.
42. Pinaleno Mts.
43. Natanes Mts.
44. Peloncillo Mts.
45. Dos Cabezas Mts.
46. Chiricahua Mts.
47. Mule Mts.

New Mexico

1. Peloncillo Mts.
2. Animas Mts.
3. Big Hatchet Mts.
4. Big Burro Mts.
5. Summit Mts.
6. Pinos Altos Range
7. Mogollon Mts.
8. Black Range (Mimbres Mts.)
9. San Mateo Mts.
10. Sierra de las Uvas
11. Florida Mts.
12. Organ Mts.
13. San Andres Mts.
14. Caballo Mts.
15. Fra Cristobal Mts.
16. Magdalena Mts.
17. Sierra Ladron
18. Manzano Mts.
19. Sandia Mts.
20. Ortiz Mts.
21. Pedernal Hills
22. Gallinas Peak
23. Sierra Oscura
24. Capitan Mts.
25. Sacramento Mts.

Texas

1. Franklin Mts.
2. Hueco Mts.
3. Quitman Mts.
4. Sierra Diablo
5. Guadalupe Mts.
6. Delaware Mts.
7. Apache Mts.
8. Davis Mts.
9. Sierra Vieja
10. Glass Mts.

KEY TO LAKES AND PLAYAS

Utah

a. Utah L.
b. Sevier L.

Nevada

a. Franklin L.
b. Carson Sink
c. Black Rock Desert
d. Smoke Creek Desert
e. Pyramid L.
f. Winnemucca L.
g. Goshute Valley
h. Antelope Valley
i. Cave Valley
j. Railroad Valley
k. Gabbs Valley
l. Walker L.
m. Teels Marsh
n. Columbus Marsh

o. Clayton Valley
p. Penoyer Valley
q. Garden Valley
r. Coal Valley
s. Desert Valley
t. Dry Lake Valley
u. Indian Spring Valley
v. Pahrump Valley
w. Ivanpah Valley
x. Lake Mead

Oregon

a. Klamath Lakes
b. Summer L.
c. Abert L.
d. Goose L.

California

a. Deep Springs Valley
b. Eureka Valley
c. Saline Valley
d. Owens L.
e. Panamint Valley
f. China L.
g. Searles L.
h. Coyote L.
i. Soda L.
j. Bristol L.
k. Cadiz L.
l. Danby L.
m. Palen Dry L.
n. Salton Sea

Arizona

a. Lake Mohave
b. Red L.
c. Havasu L. (Parker Dam. Res.)
d. Theo. Roosevelt L.
e. San Carlos Res.
f. Wilcox Playa (Sulphur Springs Valley).

New Mexico

a. Alkali Flat
b. Plains of San Augustin
c. Elephant Butte Res.
d. Caballo Res.
e. Estancia Basin

Texas

a. Salt Basin

KEY TO NATIONAL PARKS
AND MONUMENTS

LC, Lehman Cave Nat. Mon., Nev.
  Death Valley Nat. Mon., Death Valley, Calif.
JT, Joshua Tree Nat. Mon., Calif.
LM, Lake Mead Recreational Area, Ariz.–Nev.
SC, Saguaro Cactus Nat. Mon., Ariz.
OP, Organpipe Cactus Nat. Mon., Ariz.
CH, Chiricahua Nat. Mon., Ariz.
WS, White Sands Nat. Mon., N. Mex.
  Big Bend Nat. Park, Big Bend, Texas

The Bonneville Basin, the eastern subdivision of the Great Basin, covers most of western Utah. It is structurally similar to the Central Area but lower. In most of this subsection the basins are below 5,000 feet in altitude. They are slightly higher in southwestern Utah.

Great Salt Lake, the lowest part of the subsection is at an altitude of 4,200 feet. In the Bonneville Basin, playas and alluvial flats are extensive and make up about 40 percent of the basin. The mountains cover about a quarter of the basin, and gravel fans cover the

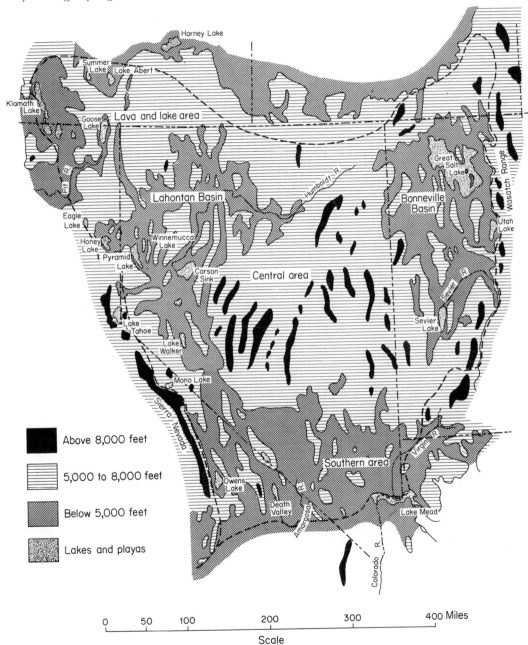

Figure 15.2 *Altitudes and subdivisions in the Great Basin.*

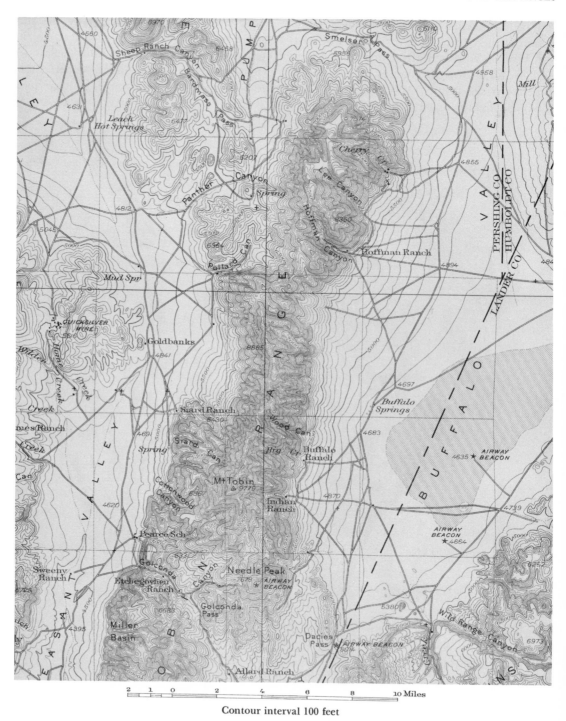

Contour interval 100 feet

Figure 15.3 *Topographic map of typical north-south basins and ranges in the Great Basin. There are three major kinds of ground in the Province: mountains, gravel fans sloping from them, and dry lake beds or alluvial flats in the middle of the basins. (From U.S.G.S. Sonoma Range, Nevada, Quadrangle.)*

rest—a proportion very different from that in the Central Area, probably because the Bonneville Basin is so much lower.

In structure and composition, most of the mountain ranges in the Bonneville Basin are like those in the northeastern part of the Central Area. The ranges are mostly complexly folded and faulted Paleozoic rocks that were later divided into structural blocks by late Tertiary and Quarternary block faulting. To the south, volcanic rocks form some of the mountain ranges; in the north, the volcanic rocks are young and occur mostly in the basins.

The Bonneville Basin lacks exterior drainage and has three major lakes within it— Great Salt Lake, Utah Lake, and Sevier Lake. Sevier Lake is dry much of the time now, but would be perennial if it received the water that is consumed for irrigation.

The Lahontan Basin, located between the Central Area and the Sierra Nevada, is structurally and topographically similar to the Bonneville Basin. The greater part of its area is alluvial flat and playa, and it too contains some large lakes—Pyramid Lake, Lake Winnemucca, and the playa at Carson Sink at the mouth of the Humboldt River. The mountain ranges are fault blocks of Triassic and Jurassic formations and Tertiary volcanic rocks. The Triassic and Jurassic formations are complexly folded and faulted in much the same way as are the Paleozoic formations in the Central Area and Bonneville Basin.

The Lava and Lake Area northwest of the Lahontan Basin is topographically higher than the Lahontan Basin. It is a block-faulted lava plateau with numerous high volcanic cones. The lavas probably bury complexly folded and faulted Jurassic and Triassic formations that are structurally lower than those in the Lahontan Basin. Several lakes— Honey Lake, Eagle Lake, and others in the Klamath area—are crowded against the foot of the mountains at the edge of the Great Basin. There is exterior drainage from Goose Lake via the Pit River and from Klamath Lakes via the Klamath River.

The topographic grain of the Lava and Lake Area has much less linearity than the other parts of the Great Basin because the thick, extensive lava flows and volcanic cones are young, in large part of Quarternary age, and they mask the effects of the block faulting, which in large part is of late Tertiary age.

The Southern Area bears some structural resemblances to the Central Area but is lower, both structurally and topographically. Toward the south, the mountain ranges trend northward, but they are separated from the ranges in the Central Area by a northwest-trending belt of mountains and hills, most of which are small and have very irregular outlines. This belt, which parallels the diagonal southwest border of Nevada, extends from the vicinity of Lake Mead to the vicinity of Walker Lake. It coincides with the Las Vegas shear zone, along which there seems to have been some miles of lateral movement; the blocks on the southwest side of the shear zone have moved northwestward relative to the blocks on the northeast side. The displacement seems to decrease northwestward.

The rocks forming the mountain ranges in the Southern Area include complexly folded and faulted Paleozoic and Precambrian rocks, some small masses of equally deformed Triassic and Jurassic rocks, granitic intrusions related to the Sierra Nevada batholith, and a thick series of Tertiary and Quaternary volcanic rocks. All these were block faulted during middle and late Tertiary and Quaternary time, as was the rest of the Great Basin.

Along the western boundary of the Southern Area, at the foot of the Sierra Nevada, are Mono Lake and Owens Lake. Death Valley, which covers more than 200 square miles and is more than 250 feet below sea level, collects the runoff from almost 9,000 square miles of surrounding area, but is rarely flooded. Most of the time it is a dry, salt-encrusted playa. The southeastern part of the Southern Area drains to the Colorado River.

Figure 15.4 illustrates the evolution of the structure and topography of the Great Basin.

In late Precambrian time there was a geosyncline in the Southern Area, where at least 30,000 feet of sediments accumulated. This geosyncline is not indicated in Figure 15.4 because its extent and trend are not known; the Precambrian rocks are buried in most other parts of the Great Basin.

In Paleozoic time a second geosyncline oc-

cupied much of what is now the Great Basin, and in it another 30,000 feet or more of sediments accumulated (Fig. 15.4, stage 1). In the Central Area and to the east there are formations of carbonate rocks (limestone and dolomite) and shale; toward the west there are formations derived in part from volcanic eruptives. Some folding and faulting took

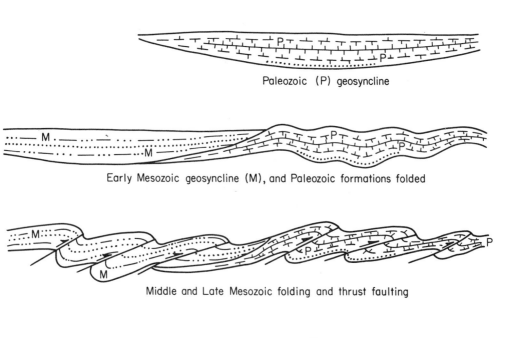

1

Paleozoic (P) geosyncline

2

Early Mesozoic geosyncline (M), and Paleozoic formations folded

3

Middle and Late Mesozoic folding and thrust faulting

4

Late Mesozoic and Early Tertiary (TM) stocks and laccoliths intruded

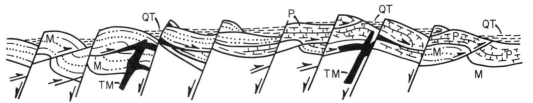

5

Middle and Late Cenozoic block faulting, with sediments (QT) deposited in the basins; Great Basin arched. Much volcanic action (not shown).

Figure 15.4 *Evolution of the structure and topography of the Great Basin.*

place at various times during the Paleozoic, but the resulting structures are not shown in Figure 15.4.

In Early Mesozoic time (stage 2) a third geosyncline developed and another 30,000 feet or so of sediments accumulated. These sediments, also derived in large part from volcanic eruptives, overlap the west flank of the Paleozoic geosyncline.

In middle and late Mesozoic time (stage 3) a batholith formed at the site of the Sierra Nevada (not shown), and the Mesozoic and Paleozoic formations in the Great Basin were folded, thrust faulted, and uplifted to form the mountains from which sediments were shed eastward into the Cretaceous geosyncline that had occupied the site of the Rocky Mountains and Great Plains. Later (stage 4), the igneous activity that had begun much earlier in the Sierra Nevada spread eastward, and stocks and laccoliths were intruded into the deformed Mesozoic and Paleozoic rocks.

In middle Tertiary time the Great Basin began to be block faulted, and this faulting has continued to the present time (stage 5). Volcanism (not shown), which was sporadic during the early Tertiary, became extensive during the stage of block faulting. Along the north side of the Great Basin, lavas and other eruptives completely buried the faulted and folded older rocks. As block-faulting progressed, sediments derived from the up-faulted blocks were deposited in the basins. In some, the fill is enormously thick. Death Valley, for example, is estimated to contain 8,000 feet of fill. Death Valley therefore has been down-faulted 2 miles below sea level, but has been kept nearly filled with sediments derived by erosion of the neighboring uplifted blocks.

Sonoran Desert

The Sonoran Desert Section, which includes the Mojave Desert in southeastern California and the deserts in southwestern Arizona, ex-tends far southward into Mexico along the east shore of the Gulf of California, and is named for the State of Sonora, in Mexico. Except where the province joins its higher neighbors, altitudes rarely exceed 3,000 feet and are mostly less than 2,000 feet (Fig. 15.5). Total relief and local relief are very much less than in the Great Basin, and much of the faulting may be older.

The Mojave Desert and southwest Arizona are structurally higher than the Great Basin. The rocks are mostly metamorphic. Some are of Precambrian age; some are younger. Presumably much of the metamorphism occurred in late Mesozoic and early Cenozoic time, when the Great Basin was intensely deformed and intruded by satellites of the Sierra Nevada batholith. Some of the granitic rocks in the Sonoran Desert Section are late Mesozoic and early Cenozoic in age, like those in the Great Basin, but some are of Precambrian age.

Possibly some of the granite is hybrid—that is, Precambrian granite that became partly recrystallized during the structural deformation and igneous activity that took place in late Mesozoic and early Cenozoic time. Some minerals in such hybrid granite are relict, and date from Precambrian time; others are new minerals dating from the metamorphism that formed the granite during late Mesozoic and early Cenozoic time.

Block faulting in the Sonoran Desert Section, as in the Great Basin, probably started in middle or early Tertiary time and continued until Pleistocene time, but the amount of Recent faulting has been less. The block mountains, however, are irregular in outline, perhaps indicating a greater frequency of transverse faults that divide the main blocks. The structure seems to consist of a series of horsts and grabens without dominant tilting in one direction. In the southern part of the section there is a northwest linearity in the grain of the topography. In the north-central part the linearity is northerly. In the Mojave Desert the outlines of the ranges are irregular, although the major block faults there trend northwest.

Mountains make up about 40 percent of the section; basins, about 60 percent. The mountain ranges, however, are short compared to those in the Great Basin. The Arizona part has through drainage to the Gila and Colorado Rivers (Fig. 15.6,A); there are few closed basins. The Mojave Desert part, however, lacks through drainage and consists of a series of closed basins (Fig. 15.6,B).

For more than 100 miles eastward from the Sierra Nevada, the boundary between the Mojave Desert and the Great Basin is along the Garlock fault—a major transverse fracture with many miles of displacement. The block on the Mojave Desert side of the fault has moved eastward relative to the block on the Great Basin side. The southern boundary of the Sonoran Desert Section is along the San Andreas and related faults at or near the foot of the San Gabriel and San Bernardino moun-

tains, and the Mojave block has moved eastward relative to them too. The Mojave Desert, therefore, is a pie-shaped structural block that has moved relatively eastward. It has also moved upward relative to the Great Basin.

Because of the scarcity of datable Mesozoic and older formations in the Sonoran Desert Section, the structural history is very poorly known. In Cretaceous time this area was probably part of the upland from which sediments were shed eastward and northeastward to the geosyncline that extended across the site of the Colorado Plateau and Rocky Mountains. This area is now structurally and topographically lower than the Colorado Plateau. The structural displacements that reversed the structural and topographic relationship by raising the Colorado Plateau high above the Basin and Range Province occurred during the Cenozoic.

Volcanism was widespread in the Sonoran Desert Section during Tertiary and Quater-

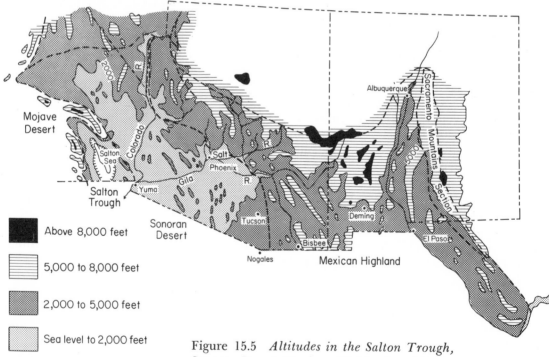

Figure 15.5 *Altitudes in the Salton Trough, Sonoran Desert, Mexican Highland, and Sacramento Mountains Sections of the Basin and Range Province.*

nary time, and some volcanic activity occurred during late Quaternary time. Structural movements in the Mojave Desert occurred recently enough for the drainage to be broken up into small closed basins (Fig. 15.6,B). Presumably the deformation there continued on a considerable scale for a longer time than it did farther east.

Salton Trough

The Salton Trough is the emerged part of the thousand-mile-long trough occupied by the Gulf of California. Three major faults extend northwestward into California from this structural and topographic depression—the San Andreas, San Jacinto, and Elsinore faults (Fig. 15.7).

The northeast side of the trough, along the San Andreas fault, is fairly straight and is marked topographically by the Gila Mountains, Chocolate Mountains, and the mountains near Joshua Tree National Monument. The southwest side has offsets along the San Jacinto and Elsinore faults. Horizontal move-

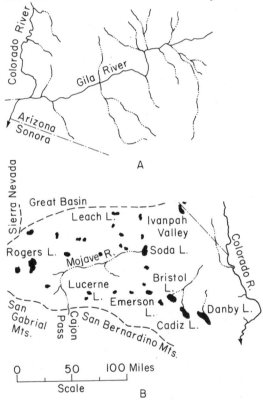

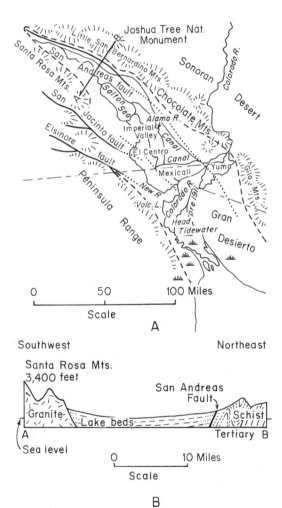

Figure 15.6 *Contrast in drainage systems in the Mojave Desert and in the parts of the Sonoran Desert Section that lie within Arizona. (A) Southwest Arizona has through drainage to the Colorado and Gila rivers and their tributaries. (B) Drainage in the Mojave Desert is broken up by a series of closed basins containing dry lakes.*

Figure 15.7 *(A) Salton Trough (boundary shown by broken line) and some of the principal faults outlining it. (B) Cross section north of Salton Sea.*

ment along these faults has been substantial, and along each one the block on the southwest side has moved northwestward relative to the block on the northeast side. This horizontal displacement amounts to many miles, probably scores of miles.

The Gulf of California and its northern extension, the Salton Trough, have been variously interpreted. One theory is that the gulf occupies a graben that has been faulted downward between the mainland and the Baja California. Another theory is that Baja California has been torn northwestward from the mainland and that the gulf and the trough are underlain shallowly by rocks belonging to the subcrust, an interpretation suggested by the fact that the underlying rocks are more dense than those that form the mountains on each side of the trough (Fig. 2.18).

The Colorado River is about 140 feet above sea level at Yuma, Arizona, which is situated near the apex of an alluvial fan that extends 50 miles southwestward across the trough. Where the fan joins the far side, the altitude is about 30 feet above sea level. From here the surface slopes southeastward about 15 miles to tidewater and northward about 50 miles to the Salton Sea, 235 feet below sea level.

Along the edges of the Salton Trough are marine deposits of late Tertiary age that contain pebbles derived from older formations in the adjoining mountains. The presence of these deposits indicates that the Trough was in existence in the late Tertiary and was inundated by the Gulf of California at that time. The marine beds are overlain by playa deposits, also of late Tertiary age, but apparently no marine deposits of Quaternary age have been found, which suggests that the gulf was excluded from the trough at about the beginning of Quaternary time, presumably by the formation of the Colorado River delta. Since then, during the Quaternary, the trough has been sinking, and the neighboring fault blocks, which include the Tertiary strata, have been rising. The mountains reach heights above 5,000 feet.

The trough and the delta have been downwarped during the Recent Epoch. The presence of fresh fault scarps north of Salton Sea and the frequent occurrence of earthquakes attest to continued structural movement. Associated Recent volcanic activity is indicated by deposits of volcanic ash (pumice) interbedded with lake beds and by the occurrence of mud volcanoes that emit sulfurous steam.

A prehistoric lake, called Lake Cahuilla, filled the trough to the level of the top of the delta. The beach line, which is marked by sand containing fresh-water shells and is distinct around much of the Salton Trough, varies in altitude from 30 to 57 feet above sea level, indicating at least 27 feet of warping since the lake features formed. Lake Cahuila may be only a few hundred years old.

An elaborate set of irrigation canals (Fig. 15.7) takes Colorado River water to the farmed land in the Imperial Valley, which is the area south of Salton Sea. In 1904 the River flooded and turned northward into the Salton Sea by way of old courses along the Alamo and New rivers. The steep slope northward favored those courses rather than the direction southward to the gulf. The depth of Salton Sea was doubled and a vast area inundated. The flooding was not checked until 1907, and in a few years after that evaporation had reduced the water to approximately its present level.

Mexican Highland Section

The Mexican Highland Section, which includes the Rio Grande Valley, is varied, both structurally and topographically. It grades westward into the Sonoran Desert Section, which is much lower, and it grades northward into the Colorado Plateau, which is much higher.

South of the Gila River and along the Rio Grande Valley, the section consists of well-defined mountain ranges separated by wide valleys. The mountains make up only a quarter or a third of the area; valleys occupy the rest. The mountain ranges consist of fault blocks. Along the Rio Grande Valley they trend north, but west of there they trend northwest. The direction of the tilting and faulting are variable. Many ranges tilt east and are down-faulted on the west side; others tilt west and are down-faulted on the east side (Fig. 15.8). The valleys are mostly between 4,000 and 5,000 feet in altitude, and the mountains are 3,000 to 5,000 feet higher.

The drainage system is moderately well developed. Most of the Arizona portion drains to the San Pedro and Gila rivers. Most of the New Mexico and Texas portions drain to the Rio Grande. A few basins, however, are closed and contain playas; in New Mexico, several valleys that are not topographically closed are long, and they are so broad and flat that they are not crossed by streams. The basins, like others in the province, are filled, or nearly so, with debris eroded from the mountains.

The structural history of the Mexican Highland Section is as complex as that of the Great Basin. Major deformation occurred in southern Arizona early in the Mesozoic, and at that time erosion stripped the Paleozoic formations from some areas of Precambrian rocks (Fig. 15.8,C). Some granitic intrusions were emplaced at this time and are overlapped by 15,000 feet of marine sedimentary formations of Early Cretaceous age. These formations include some volcanic debris, which suggests that the igneous activity may have continued into Early Cretaceous time and that some of the intrusions reached the surface and erupted.

In Early Cretaceous time this part of the Basin and Range Province must have been lower than the Colorado Plateau area, because the Lower Cretaceous formations thin toward the plateau. But in Late Cretaceous time the situation reversed. The southern part of the Mexican Highland Section was raised to become part of the upland that contributed sediments to the Upper Cretaceous sea that extended across the Colorado Plateau, the Rocky Mountains, and the Great Plains. Uplift of

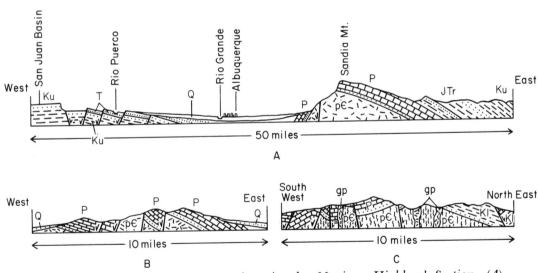

Figure 15.8 *Structural cross sections in the Mexican Highland Section. (A) Sandia Mountain and the Rio Grande Valley at Albuquerque, New Mexico. (B) Florida Mountains, New Mexico. (C) Mule Mountains at the Bisbee mining district, Arizona. p Є, Precambrian; P, Paleozoic; JTr, Jurassic and Triassic; Kl, Lower Cretaceous; Ku, Upper Cretaceous; T, Tertiary; Q, Quaternary; gp, granitic intrusions. (After U.S.G.S.)*

this part of the Mexican Highlands must have continued intermittently during Late Cretaceous time. The Lower Cretaceous formations are cut by granitic intrusions, some of which may be Late Cretaceous in age; others are of Tertiary age. In Tertiary time structural movements once again caused the Mexican Highland Section to drop below the Colorado Plateau.

The faulting that outlined the mountain ranges and basins apparently began in early or middle Tertiary time, as it did in the Great Basin. There was faulting prior to the deposition of late Tertiary formations along the Rio Grande, but these formations were involved in later movements along the faults (Fig. 15.8,A). Some volcanism occurred about this time also. The faulting here seems to have ceased earlier than it did in the Salton Trough, Mojave Desert, and Great Basin, as is suggested by the integration of the drainage and the scarcity of fresh fault scarps. However, the belt of earthquake epicenters that extends northward along the Rio Grande Valley suggests that earth movement is still going on.

Along its northern boundary, the Mexican Highland Section grades into the Colorado Plateau, both structurally and topographically. In New Mexico, the northern part of the Highland is a block-faulted lava plateau that grades northward into the lava-covered Datil Section of the Colorado Plateau. The relationship is very similar to that along the northern edge of the Great Basin, where block-faulted lavas grade northward into the lava-capped Columbia Plateau.

In Arizona, the northern boundary of the Highland is a dissected escarpment of Precambrian rocks capped by Paleozoic formations and Tertiary lavas. The escarpment is several thousand feet high, faces south, and extends 500 miles from the Colorado River to the Rio Grande Valley. The escarpment has acted as a structural hinge along which the country lying to the south has alternately been bent upward and downward relative to the country to the north. The country south of the escarpment was structurally lower than the country to the north during Paleozoic and Early Cretaceous time. It was higher during late Cretaceous times and again during late Tertiary time, when gravels were shed northward onto the Colorado Plateau. Today it is lower.

Sacramento Mountains Section

The Sacramento Mountains Section (Fig. 15.1), which forms the eastern border of the Basin and Range Province and adjoins the Great Plains, bears little resemblance to either province. It contains structural basins that are closed topographically; these basins seem to be due as much to downwarping as to faulting. Moreover, the structure of the fault blocks is not at all complex, for the formations in them have gentle dips suggestive of fault blocks on the Colorado Plateau. In addition, there are dome mountains with exposed cores of Precambrian rocks, and other dome mountains produced by the intrusion of stocks and laccoliths into the gently dipping sedimentary formations. The area of the section is small, but it comprises several distinctly different parts.

At the north is the Estancia Basin, which occupies a syncline between the Sandia-Manzano Mountains uplift on the west and an uplift of Precambrian rocks in the Pedernal Hills to the east. The basin is 50 miles long and 20 miles wide. A series of playas in the low part of the basin, near its southern end, are about 6,000 feet in altitude. The Sandia and Manzano mountains to the west exceed 10,000 feet; the Pedernal Hills to the east are about 7,500 feet in altitude. The basin is filled with Quaternary (and Tertiary?) deposits. The Paleozoic formations rise eastward and westward from under the fill. Beyond the Pedernal Hills the formations dip gently eastward under the head of the Pecos River Valley and under the Great Plains.

South of Estancia Valley is Chupadera Mesa, an east-sloping plateau formed by gently dipping Paleozoic formations that lie 1,500 to 2,000 feet above Estancia Valley. East and southeast of Chupadera Mesa are several mountains—the Gallinas, Jicarilla, and Capitan mountains, and Sierra Blanca (Fig. 15.9). Sierra Blanca Peak is about 12,000 feet in altitude; Capitan Peak, more than 10,000 feet. The mountains are formed of intrusive stocks and laccoliths, like the laccolithic mountains on the Colorado Plateau, but they also include volcanic rocks. Most of the igneous activity probably occurred during Tertiary time, but the volcanism continued into Quaternary time. A volcanic center near the southeast edge of Chupadera Mesa erupted a basaltic lava flow 40 miles long and 1 to 4 miles wide that descended 1,500 feet from the mesa into Tularosa Valley. The flow is young, like some in the northern part of the Datil Section.

South of these igneous centers is the Sacramento Range, which extends more than 80 miles to the Texas border. This range is a block of late Paleozoic formations that dip gently eastward under the broad valley of the Pecos River. The west side of the range is an escarpment 4,000 feet high, evidently formed by a fault that raised the mountain block above the Tularosa Basin. Southward, in Texas, the Sacramento Mountains become the Guadalupe (Fig. 15.10) and Delaware mountains; although structurally similar to the Sacramento Mountains, they are more faulted and they dip more steeply eastward.

The Tularosa Basin contains white sand that is composed of gypsum dissolved from Permian formations and redeposited in saline playas in the valley. At White Sands National Monument the sand covers an area of 250 square miles with dunes averaging about 20 feet high.

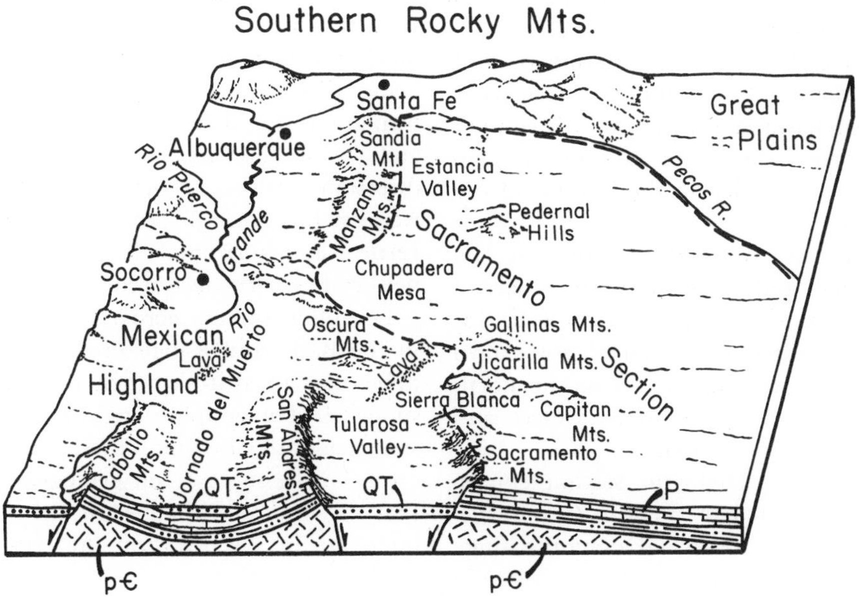

Figure 15.9 *Diagram of the Northern part of the Sacramento Section and of the structural basins along the Rio Grande in New Mexico.*

Seismic Activity and Present-day Earth Movements

At least three quite independent lines of evidence show that the Basin and Range Province is undergoing considerable earth movement (structural deformation) at the present time. These are:

1. The numerous earthquake epicenters in and around the province;
2. The numerous Recent fault scarps and warped or faulted shorelines; and
3. The measurable displacement of benchmarks and measurements by tiltmeters.

The distribution of earthquake epicenters in and around the Basin and Range Province (Fig. 2.14) suggests that the province as a whole may be moving relative to its neighbors, but that the interior of the province either is stable or is being arched without the kind of fracturing that produces earthquakes.

Earthquake data show a concentration of epicenters along the western and eastern parts of the Great Basin, and a few are distributed across its north and south borders. Few epicenters have been recorded in the interior of the Great Basin.

Epicenters are concentrated also in the Salton Trough and along the western part of the Sonoran Desert; a moderate number of epicenters of minor earthquakes, not shown on Figure 2.14, are aligned across the north and east sides of the Sonoran Desert and roughly outline that section.

In the Mexican Highland Section epicenters are concentrated in the Rio Grande depression, and there are several along the hinge line that joins this section with the Colorado Plateau. A few epicenters have been recorded in west Texas.

The southern third of the combined area of Arizona and New Mexico has few epicenters; apparently this is a stable area.

In general, the frequency of Recent fault scarps and of faulted or warped shorelines accords with the frequency of earthquake epicenters. These obviously Recent displacements are most common along the western part of the Basin and Range Province, which is the most active area seismically. Such features are common but less well developed along the eastern part of the Great Basin, and they are even less well developed elsewhere in the province.

Present-day earth movements also are indicated by three kinds of surveys. Precise level surveys made at Lake Mead show that the lake basin has sunk a few millimeters, presumably because of the weight of water on that part of the crust. At Las Vegas, Nevada, the same surveys show about 6 inches of sinking attributable to withdrawal of groundwater under that basin. The surveys also show that the entire area around Lake Mead has been regionally tilted a few millimeters southwestward since the surveys were begun in 1935.

In Death Valley, tiltmeters installed on various fault blocks show that tilting of the blocks is continuing. In general, the blocks are being tilted in the direction in which the formations dip. The rate of tilting is variable, and when there are earthquakes nearby the direction of tilting may reverse, as if the blocks were settling back. There may be considerable vertical and horizontal displacement too, but neither has been measured.

Level-line surveys across various structures in the Basin and Range Province also reveal differences in altitude when the lines are resurveyed. Topographic engineers and geodosists generally attribute these differences to errors in the surveys, but geologists point out that the indicated changes in altitude all too often are in the direction the crustal blocks have been moving.

Differences in the frequency of seismic activity and of Recent faulting and warping may be due to differences in the rate and severity of the displacements, to differences in the depth of the earth movements, or to differences in the kind of movement. If more were known about the measurable displacements now going on in the Basin and Range Province we would be far better equipped to understand the processes of crustal deformation. The matter is of more than academic interest, as any survivor of an earthquake disaster can testify, and the Basin and Range Province, which is known to be actively moving, is one of the outdoor laboratories where the necessary research should be undertaken.

The causes and cures of earthquakes have been the subject of accelerated studies undertaken since the 1964 disaster at Anchorage, Alaska; these studies have, understandably, been concentrated in the densely populated areas along the Pacific Coast, but much basic information applicable there could as well be obtained through more intensive studies of earth movement in the Basin and Range Province.

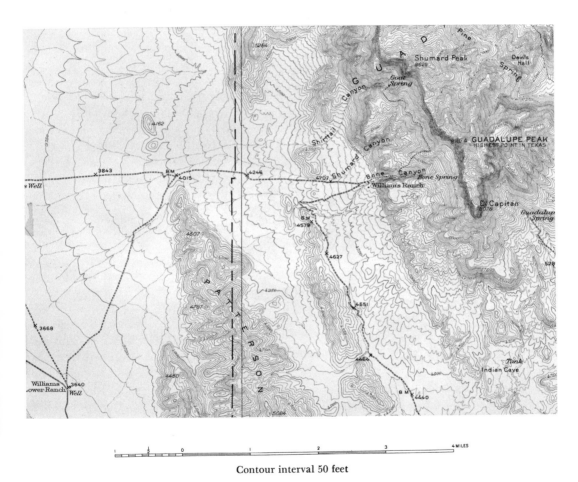

Contour interval 50 feet

Figure 15.10 *Guadalupe Mountains, Texas, southern part of the Sacramento Mountains Section. The mountains are a block of late Paleozoic limestone faulted upward on the west and tilted east. The ridges at the west are other fault blocks partly buried by the coalescing alluvial fans. (From U.S.G.S. Guadalupe Peak, Texas, quadrangle.)*

Climate

The present climate in the Basin and Range Province is arid. Except on a few mountain summits, annual precipitation averages less than 20 inches, and in about three-quarters of the province, less than 10 inches (Fig 15.11.) This extreme aridity accounts for the scarcity of perennial streams and the abundance of playas. It also explains why the large rivers flowing through the province all head elsewhere.

In the northern part of the Great Basin winters are cold, partly because of the northerly latitude and partly because of the high altitude. Summers are hot. The west side of the Great Basin is in the rain shadow of the Sierra Nevada and averages less than 5 inches of precipitation per year. Even in the eastern part, the average precipitation is barely twice that.

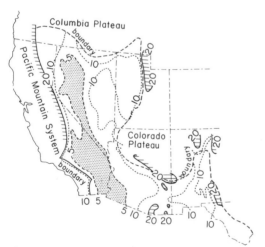

Figure 15.11 *Average annual precipitation (inches) in the Basin and Range Province. Not shown are the small areas of higher than average precipitation on some of the higher mountains. (After U.S.D.A.)*

The southern part of the Great Basin and the sections south of it have very mild winters that have favored these areas for winter visitors. But summers there are very hot. To reverse the old saying, "It's not the humidity, it's the heat!" It has been said that, in the summer, mules bray only at midnight, that birds flying across the valleys have died of desiccation, and that when the Devil visited this area he took off his coat, exclaiming "It's a dry heat."

Death Valley represents the extreme. July temperatures there *average* above 100°F, and a maximum of 134°F has been recorded. Ground-surface temperatures of 190°F have been recorded there in summer. Winters, though, are mild and at that time of year the valley is packed with people. Freezing temperatures are very uncommon. The average January temperature is above 50°F, which is about the same as the average *annual* temperature across the central United States! The average annual rainfall in Death Valley is only a little more than 1.5 inches; evaporation, if there were anything to evaporate, would take place at the rate of about 150 inches annually.

In most of the Sonoran Desert and Salton Trough, maximum summer temperatures are around 120°F. In the winter, freezing temperatures are uncommon, but low temperatures around 15 to 20°F have been recorded. Few places in those sections receive more than 5 inches of annual precipitation. The duration of snow cover in the Sonoran Desert and Salton Trough averages less than one day per year.

Temperatures in the Mexican Highland Section average considerably cooler than those in the Sonoran Desert and only slightly warmer than those in the northern part of the Great Basin. In much of this section the average annual precipitation is between 10 and 20 inches. The valleys along the Rio Grande, however, average less than 10 inches annually.

High parts of the Sacramento Mountains Section receive more than 20 inches of annual precipitation. Even the Estancia Basin, on the lee side of the Sandia and Manzano mountains, receives an average of 12 inches annually. On account of the altitude, the average temperature in the Sacramento Mountains Section is lower and the growing season shorter than in most of the Basin and Range Province.

The Basin and Range Province was not always a desert. In Pleistocene time the climate was wet enough to develop lakes hundreds of feet deep (p. 322). The shorelines of some of these are conspicuous topographic features (Fig. 15.19, 15.20). Other products of the past climates are some of the soils and caliche deposits (p. 330ff).

Vegetation

The Basin and Range Province is mostly shrub land and has few trees. Nevada is called the Sagebrush State, and Figure 15.12 shows why. The sagebrush extends over the Great Basin as a nearly continuous blanket covering thousands of square miles. Moreover, extensive areas contain no other shrubs. This land is highly aromatic, and pleasantly so, particularly after rains.

The sagebrush and the pinyon-juniper woodland together constitute the Upper Sonoran Zone. This zone embraces most of the Great Basin, whereas the Lower Sonoran Zone embraces most parts of the southern sections of the Basin and Range Province. High mountains support some yellow pine and Douglas fir, representing the Transition Zone, and a few of the highest mountain tops support spruce and fir, representing the Canadian Zone. The Upper Sonoran and higher zones are similar to those on the Colorado Plateau except at the salt flats and salt marshes, such as the extensive ones in Great Salt Lake Desert and the many smaller ones in the Great Basin and in the Mojave Desert. Only salt-tolerant plants grow in these places, the species depending on the kind and amount of salts.

The Lower Sonoran Zone is more extensive in the Basin and Range Province than in any other. It is characterized by the creosote bush (Fig. 15.12), although many other species with different water requirements are associated with it. Accordingly, the distribution of each species in large part reflects differences in ground conditions, which control the availability of water for plant growth. In most places, the plants must depend for water on the occasional and all too infrequent rain, and these places support stands of xerophytes.

At some places, such as near springs, or along certain washes where groundwater is shallow, there are distinctive stands of phreatophytes (Fig. 8.11). The different species of phreatophytes have different salt tolerances, and their distribution reflects the quality of the groundwater. In Death Valley, for example, where groundwater contains more than about 0.5 percent (5,000 ppm) of salts, honey mesquite cannot tolerate the salinity, but other phreatophytes can. Where the salinity increases toward the salt pan (Figs. 8.12,B, 15.13,B), arrowweed and salt grass form a stand panward from the mesquite and extend to where the groundwater contains about 3 percent of salts. Higher salinities exceed the tolerance of those species, and the arrowweed and salt grass give way to pickleweed, which can tolerate 6 percent of salts (twice the salinity of sea water) in the water around its roots. At the temperatures of Death Valley, no flowering plant can tolerate more than 6 percent of salts. Where groundwater contains more than 6 percent of salts, the ground is barren; a few hardy algae, fungi, and bacteria may grow in such ground, but these plants also have limits to the salinity they can tolerate and are zoned with respect to salinity in much the same way as are the flowering plants.

The xerophytes differ in drought resistance from one species to another; within the Lower Sonoran Zone their occurrence is controlled chiefly by the availability of moisture, which in turn is controlled by the kind of ground. Some ground is permeable; some impermeable. Some areas receive runoff from neighboring areas; others receive only the rainwater that falls on them. Some permeable ground is underlain at shallow depths by impermeable layers that catch and hold the moisture; some is permeable to great depth, and water seeping into it goes too deep for use by the plants. Such differences are reflected in the occurrence of the various species of xerophytes.

The importance of slight differences in the availability of moisture in an arid climate can be illustrated by the growth of xerophytes along highways. Highways commonly are lined by a luxuriant growth of species that are much less well developed away from the road, because the shoulders and edges, even where they are not ditched, collect some extra runoff from the pavement.

Creosote bush, which may be taken as the norm for the Lower Sonoran Zone, grows extensively on the sandy and gravelly parts of the basins, where slopes rise from playas or

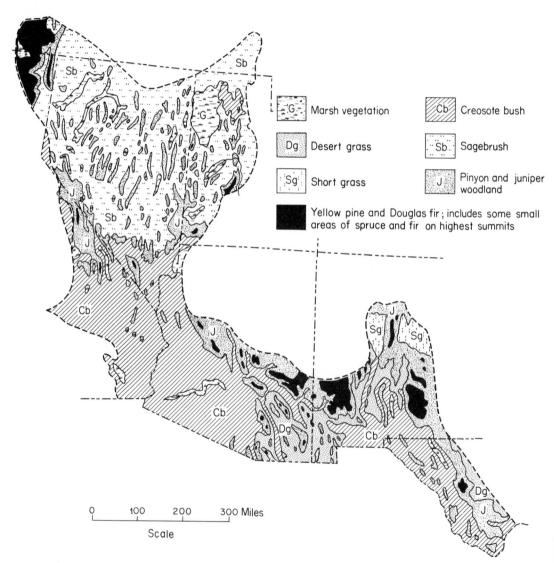

Figure 15.12 *Vegetation map of the Basin and Range Province. (After U.S.D.A.)*

alluvial floodplains to the mountains. The plant grows from 3 or 4 feet to 10 or 12 feet high. The density and height of stands vary widely, depending on size of catchment area and kind of ground.

Where somewhat more moisture is available than at the usual site for creosote bush, other species—such as burrowweed, encelia, yucca, and various cacti—may grow along with it. Where the moisture is less than is needed by the creosote bush, there may be stands of desert holly or, in some places, desert saltbush. If the available moisture is still less, there may be no vegetation at all, as on some gravel benches having small catchment areas and smooth surfaces covered by closely spaced pebbles (desert pavement), which facilitate runoff of the little rain that falls.

The higher parts of the Lower Sonoran Zone support some picturesque plants (Fig. 15.14), including the saguaro cactus, Joshua tree, and organ pipe cactus. The saguaro

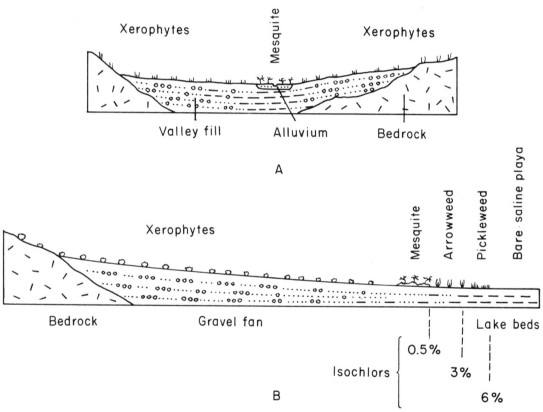

Figure 15.13 *Diagrams illustrating how groundwater conditions are indicated by stands of phreatophytes in the Lower Sonoran zone. (A) Mesquite growing where groundwater discharges in alluvium along a stream. The valley sides, which receive only the rainwater that falls on them and a small amount of run-off from uphill, support stands of xerophytes. (B) Saline playas are without vegetation even though groundwater may be near the surface. At the edges of the playas where the salinity is less, there are stands of phreatophytes zoned with respect to their salinity tolerances. The gravel fans and mountainsides, where groundwater is deep, support only xerophytes.*

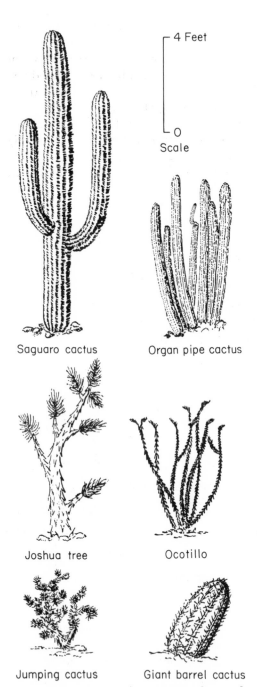

Saguaro cactus   Organ pipe cactus

Joshua tree   Ocotillo

Jumping cactus   Giant barrel cactus

Figure 15.14 *Some picturesque plants characteristic of the southern Basin and Range Province, especially the Arizona sections. The Joshua Tree and ocotillo are not cacti, although commonly included with them.*

cactus grows in Arizona; the Joshua tree grows mostly in southeastern California and southern Nevada, but extends into western Arizona. The organ pipe cactus grows in southern Arizona. Three national monuments have been created to preserve stands of these several plants. Other common and equally picturesque plants that grow in these areas are the palo verde, ocotillo, and huge barrel cacti, and the so-called jumping cholla, a branching cactus that seems to reach out and attach itself unpleasantly to anyone passing by. The ocotillo is grown very effectively for fences.

The Mexican Highland Section supports several distinctive oaks, some of them evergreen. These oaks range far southward into Mexico and northward to the foot of the escarpment under the south rim of the Colorado Plateau. Yuccas are characteristic of the Mexican Highland.

The spread of tamarisk (salt cedar), an attractive phreatotype of tree size that was introduced into the United States in the 1850's, poses a serious problem in the Southwest. It has spread along streams and irrigation ditches throughout the Southwest and even beyond. Its dense stands crowd out native plants and consume vast amounts of water that can ill be spared. Tamarisk is especially abundant along the Colorado River and the Rio Grande and their tributaries, and along streams to the east on the plains. It has spread into the Rocky Mountains and into Death Valley, growing wherever there is some water.

Surficial Deposits and Soils

Soils in the Basin and Range Province are classed as Gray Desert Soils in the Great Basin and as Red Desert Soils in the southern Sections. These soils are very limy beginning a few inches below the surface, and even the surface layers are only slightly leached. Although the subsoils are lighter in color than the surface soils, organic surface layers are thin or absent. The Gray and the Red Desert Soils occur mostly on the gravel fans and pediments. Alluvial soils are extensive in the Salton Trough and along the rivers. The alluvial soils along the Rio Grande and the Virgin River are subject to severe erosion. Most of the soils can be highly productive if irrigated, but generally this is possible only on the floodplains. Most of the land is used for grazing.

In the Mexican Highland Section, above 3,000 feet and up to about 6,000 feet, are some Red Brown Soils. Some of these, apparently the younger ones, are only slightly leached and have no layer of lime accumulation. The older soils have leached upper horizons and a thick zone of lime accumulation 3 to 6 feet below the surface. At still higher elevations in that area, the soils are reddish, clayey, and commonly leached of their lime carbonate. Some of these soils are evidently of pre-Wisconsin age.

The lime-cemented surficial layers, which may be a few inches or many feet thick, may be nearly as hard as concrete, or they may be friable. The lime may occur in layers or as nodules. Where well developed, the deposits are known as caliche, and they originate in at least four ways, only one of which is strictly a soil process.

Lime layers attributable to soil processes are the result of leaching by water filtering into the ground, dissolving lime carbonate in the upper layers, and transporting it downward (Fig. 15.15,A). But in deserts there is not enough water to wet more than the upper foot or so of the soil, and when that soil dries, the lime carbonate is deposited in the subsoil. This is the general process by which pedocals are formed.

A second kind of caliche deposit forms in the capillary fringe above a water table (Fig. 15.15,B). In general, these deposits are thicker and more strongly developed than those attributable to soil processes. Moreover, where the deposits are formed by downward filtration of water, the veinlets of calcium carbonate

branch downward; where they are formed by a rising capillary fringe, they branch upward. Unfortunately, the branching may be obscured by changes that have occurred since the deposit was formed, and in such cases the distinction may be based on whether the deposit conforms to a topographic surface, as do soil horizons, or to subsurface levels that are unrelated to topography, as are most water tables.

A third kind of caliche deposit in the Basin and Range Province occurs at springs that are charged with calcium carbonate. The springs deposit travertine on and below the surface (Fig. 15.15,C). Well-developed deposits of this kind are easily enough identified, but those that are weathered and eroded must be identified by relating them to existing or dried springs and to the surface and underground water courses draining from them.

A fourth kind of caliche in the Basin and Range Province was formed along the shorelines of the Pleistocene lakes (Fig. 15.15D). These deposits commonly occur at headlands or other exposed places along old shorelines, and are apparently due to aeration by wave action of the carbonate-charged waters.

Another kind of surficial deposit characteristic of the Basin and Range Province is known as desert pavement, which is a smooth surface built of pebbles on gravelly surfaces. These are often as smooth as a carefully laid pebble or cobble pavement, and they slope with the gravel fan or other surface. A cross section of desert pavement shows a layer of porous loam, a few inches thick, under a single layer of cobbles protecting the surface (Fig. 15.16). The origin of the surfaces and of the layering is not at all clear. Wind erosion could remove the silt and sand and allow the gravel to accumulate in a layer that protects the surface from further erosion, but some other processes must have operated where a layer of loam exists beneath the gravel layer. Perhaps volume changes due to wetting and drying, and heaving by salt crystals, cause the pebbles to work upward and the sandy silt to settle downward.

Rivers and Lakes, Wet Ones and Dry Ones

Despite their aridity the Great Basin and the Mojave Desert are curiously lands of lakes. They contain about two dozen fairly large perennial lakes and more than 100 dry ones.

In wetter times, during the Pleistocene, these lakes stored a lot of water. At the present time their water surface totals almost 5,000 square miles, and the water lost by evaporation from these surfaces equals the recharge by the streams draining into them—an amount roughly equal to the average annual discharge of the Colorado River.

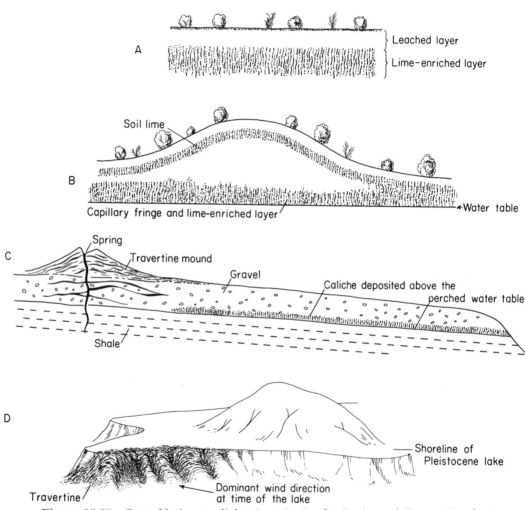

Figure 15.15 *Four kinds of caliche deposits in the Basin and Range Province. (A) Lime deposited by the soil process as a result of leaching of the surface layers and deposition of the lime in the subsoil. (B) Lime carbonate deposited in the capillary fringe above a water table. These deposits bear little or no relation to the topography. (C) Lime carbonate deposited as travertine at a spring and in the aerated zone above the perched water table. (D) Lime carbonate deposited at headlands along a Pleistocene shoreline.*

Lakes along the east side of the Great Basin (Fig. 15.17) are recharged by streams from the Rocky Mountains and High Plateaus in Utah. As already noted, Sevier Lake, fed by the Sevier River, would be a perennial lake but for the water taken from it for irrigation. Utah Lake, fed by the Provo River, is a fresh-water lake that overflows into Great Salt Lake by way of the Jordan River. Great Salt Lake, fed chiefly by the Jordan, Weber, and Bear rivers, covers about 2,000 square miles and has a maximum depth of about 30 feet.

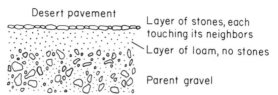

Figure 15.16 *Cross section of desert pavement. A layer of closely set stones overlies porous loam a few inches thick, which rests on the parent gravel deposit.*

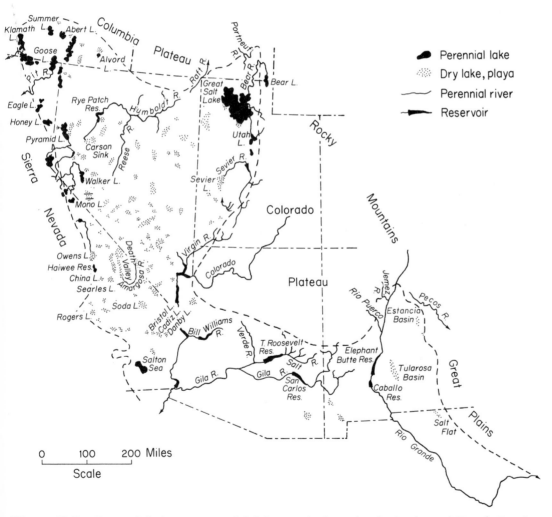

Figure 15.17 *Perennial rivers, perennial lakes, and playas in the Basin and Range Province.*

Having no outlet, and receiving the salts brought by the rivers, the lake water has become a brine containing more than 20 percent of salts, mostly sodium chloride and sodium sulfate. The lake has been estimated to contain 400 million tons of sodium chloride and 30 million tons of the sulfate. Some salt is produced from salt pans at the edge of the lake; potash is produced from the western salt flats.

Lakes along the west side of the Great Basin are numerous but mostly small. The waters of these lakes contain about 1,000 ppm of dissolved solids. Pyramid Lake and Walker Lake, which collect water from the Truckee, Carson, and Walker rivers, contain about 3,000 ppm of salts. The rivers contain 200 to 300 ppm of salts. Summer Lake and Abert Lake, Oregon, contain brines with 1 percent or more of dissolved solids.

The Humboldt River has an average annual discharge of perhaps 500,000 acre feet per year. Most of the water is consumed for irrigation, and the discharge in the lower stretch is barely 100,000 acre feet per year. Water in the river contains 300 to 600 ppm of salts; the water in Humboldt Lake contains at least 1,000 ppm.

The rivers in the Great Basin, especially those issuing from the Rocky Mountains and the Sierra Nevada, have excellent water, and the drainage map (Fig. 15.17) illustrates why the California Trail followed the course it did (Fig. 13.31). To avoid the desert west of Great Salt Lake, the trail followed Bear River, Snake River, and Raft River and then crossed low passes to the head of the Humboldt River. By this route perennial streams could be followed almost all the way from the Wyoming Basin to the Sierra Nevada. The importance of the Humboldt River to the 1849 California gold rush has been well summarized by the historian H. H. Bancroft (1890, *History of Nevada, Colorado, and Wyoming,* p. 15):

> In the progress of westward-marching empire few streams on the North American continent have played a more important part than the Humboldt River of Nevada. Among the watercourses of the world it can lay claim neither to great beauty nor to remarkable utility. Its great work was to open a way, first for the cattle train and then for the steam train, through a wilderness of mountains, through ranges which otherwise would run straight across its course. It is the largest river of this region, and the only one hereabout running from east to west. Most of the others are with the mountains, north and south.

The Humboldt is not a mighty stream, but it has been and still is a mighty important one.

The Humboldt River crosses one important structural barrier, about 30 miles below Elko, where the river flows through a gorge cut through a fault block of late Tertiary volcanic and sedimentary rocks. The rest of the course winds around the major uplifts rather than crossing them. The ancestral Humboldt River may have drained to the Pacific, perhaps by way of the Feather River (p. 379).

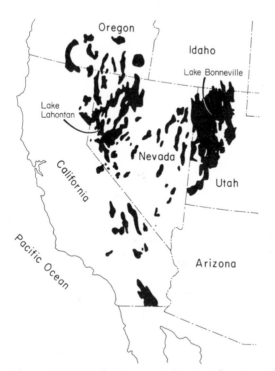

Figure 15.18 *Pleistocene lakes in the Great Basin and Mohave Desert. (From G.S.A.)*

One of the driest rivers in the Great Basin is the Amargosa. After following a southward course this river makes a U-turn northward into Death Valley. Most of the time the river bed is dry. The average annual discharge probably is no more than a few hundred acre feet. In the rare times when it flows throughout its 150-mile course, enough water is lost by evaporation to increase the salinity progressively as the river approaches the floor of Death Valley. At the mouth of the river the water is twice as salty as sea water.

During Pleistocene time the Great Basin and the Mojave Desert had numerous, large lakes (Fig. 15.18), with a total water surface of at least 50,000 square miles, which is ten times that of the present lakes. Assuming the evaporation rate then was half what it is now, roughly five times as much water must have drained into the basins. But it is doubtful if rainfall was five times greater. Probably the additional water came partly from greater rainfall and partly from water stored as ice in the glaciers. By this reasoning we might infer that the Pleistocene climate had half the present evaporation rate and twice the present precipitation; if so, it would still have been semiarid!

Largest of the Pleistocene lakes was Lake Bonneville, which covered 20,000 square miles in northwestern Utah and had a maximum depth of nearly 1,000 feet. The shorelines of this lake are unmistakably impressed on the sides of the bordering mountains (Figs. 15.19 and 15.20). The highest beach line is at an altitude ranging from about 5,100 to 5,200

Figure 15.19 *Beach deposits of Lake Bonneville at the south end of Salt Lake Valley. The highest beach (B), the Bonneville shoreline, is about 300 feet higher than the Provo shoreline (P) and nearly a thousand feet higher than Great Salt Lake.*

feet, the difference in height being due to later warping of the shoreline as a result of structural movements (Fig. 15.21).

At the level of the Bonneville shoreline, the lake overflowed to join the Snake River, and rapidly eroded alluvial fill at the divide. At a depth of 300 feet, bedrock was encountered and further downcutting checked. The lake stood for a long time at this lower level, the Provo level, and during this stage large deltas were built at the mouths of the rivers draining from the mountains. Most of the cities in this part of Utah, including Salt Lake City, are situated on deltas built at the Provo level.

Prehistoric men may have viewed this lake along with the Pleistocene elephants and camels, for paleo-Indians are known to have been in this country in late Pleistocene time. But the Pleistocene fauna became exterminated as the lake dropped to within 300 feet of the level of Great Salt Lake, and the first men known to have entered the basin arrived when the lake surface was less than 50 feet higher than the surface of Great Salt Lake. They lived in a cave (Danger Cave) on the west side of Great Salt Lake Desert. According to radiocarbon dating this cave was occupied 11,000 years ago, and since that time the lake has not risen high enough to flood the cave.

Structural movements since the time of Lake Bonneville have warped the shorelines a total of 300 feet. Part of this warp appears to be the result of doming centered in the lake basin (Fig. 15.21), as if the crust had risen when the load of water was removed— the opposite of what has happened recently at Lake Mead (p. 325). In addition to being warped, the shorelines have been faulted at a number of places (Figs. 15.21, 15.22).

As the Pleistocene drew to a close, evaporation began, and the level of the lake gradually lowered. There was another short still-stand at a level 300 feet below the Provo; this level, referred to as the Stansbury shoreline, marks the end of Lake Bonneville. Great Salt Lake is all that remains of the lake today.

The lake was contemporaneous with the

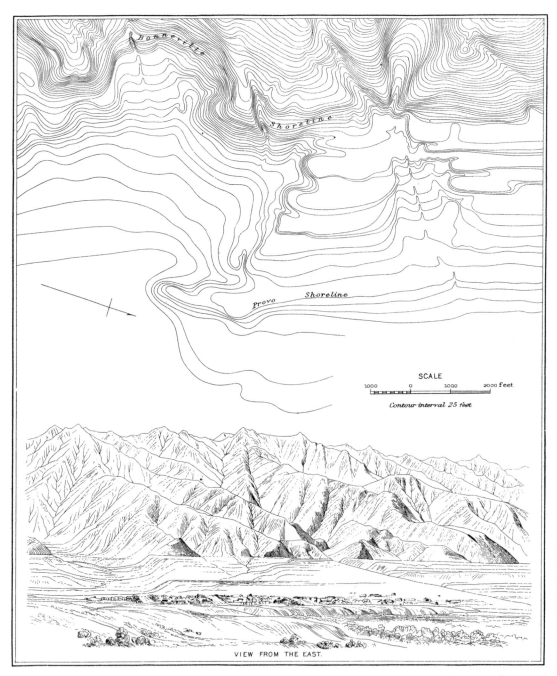

Figure 15.20 *Shore bars, terraces, and mountain front near Wellsville, Utah showing contrast between the littoral topography and the subaerial topography on the mountains above the old beach of Lake Bonneville. (By G. Thompson and W. H. Holmes.)*

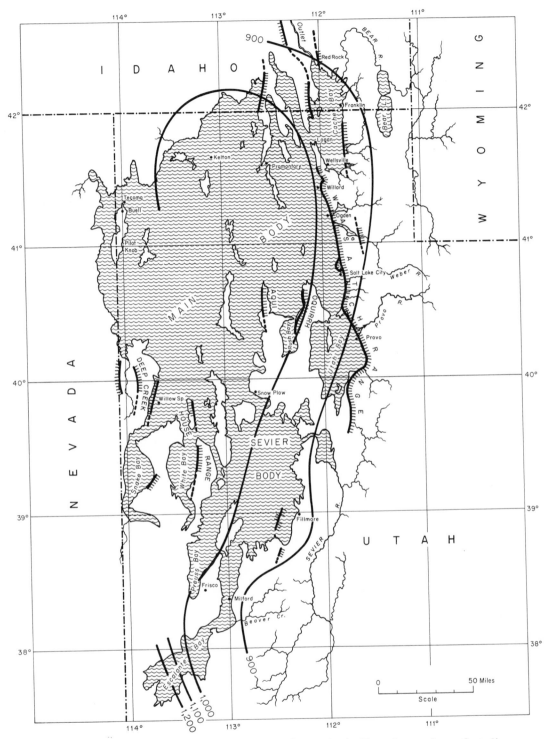

Figure 15.21 *Map of Lake Bonneville. The faults indicated are those that disrupted the shorelines; the contours show how the shorelines have been warped. (After U.S.G.S.)*

glaciers in the Wasatch Mountains, for the lake beds are interbedded with moraines and glacial outwash. Some basaltic volcanoes erupted during the time of the lake, but none have erupted since.

Another major lake in the Great Basin, with a history similar to that of Lake Bonneville, centered at Carson Sink and extended nearly to the foot of the Sierra Nevada. It is known as Lake Lahontan (Fig. 15.18).

Sometime during the Recent Epoch, apparently between 2,000 and 5,000 years ago, many of the dry lakes were flooded by shallow lakes or ponds. Death Valley, for example, contained a lake that was 30 feet deep, and it was in this lake that the salt pan was deposited. The deposits that formed in this shallow lake are overlain by sand dunes containing Indian artifacts—early pottery and arrow points. In the 2,000 or so years since this Recent lake was formed, the floor of the Valley has been tilted to the east; the eastern shoreline is 20 feet lower than the western one (Fig. 15.23). This tilting was accompanied by faulting, and the kind and amount of deformation closely duplicates that at Hebgen Lake, Montana, which resulted from the 1959 earthquake there (p. 269).

Some of the other playas have salt crusts similar to the one in Death Valley. Deposits at Searles Lake, about 40 miles southwest of Death Valley, and on the desert west of Great Salt Lake are commercially important sources for several kinds of salts. Most of the salts produced, however, come from brines under the surface rather than from the crusts. Still other playas are simply bare clay flats without salt crusts.

These different kinds of playas reflect differences in the hydrologic regimen. Playas consisting of clay flats without a salt crust are subject to frequent flooding by muddy streams draining into them. The salts in these basins are distributed throughout the muds and do not form a crust because there is very little standing water. Playas covered by a salt crust were either lakes or marshes.

In Pleistocene time, Death Valley contained a lake 600 feet deep, one of a chain of lakes that extended to the foot of the Sierra Nevada. At the foot of the Sierra was Owens Lake, fed by the Owens River (Fig. 15.17). This overflowed into China Lake, located between Owens and Searles lakes. China Lake, in turn, overflowed into Searles Lake, which overflowed into the Panamint Valley, a playa

Figure 15.22   *Fault scarps crossing a Lake Bonneville delta. (After U.S.G.S.)*

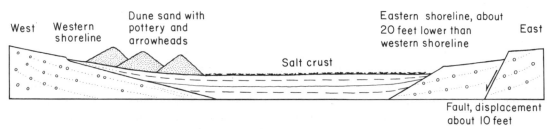

Figure 15.23 *Cross section of the floor of Death Valley. The salt pan, 5 to 6 miles wide, is represented by a crust of salts as much as 3 feet thick. These salts were deposited as a result of evaporation of a Recent lake.*

west of Death Valley. The Panamint Valley may have overflowed into Death Valley.

Water also spilled into Death Valley from the Mojave River, which empties into the playa at Soda Lake. In Pleistocene time this playa contained Lake Mojave, and it overflowed northward into the south bend of the Amargosa River and to Death Valley. The Mojave River at one time may have drained to the Colorado River, perhaps along the course marked by the playas at Emerson, Bristol, Cadiz, and Danby lakes. But there has not been sufficient flow in the stream to maintain its course across the structural blocks while they were being warped and faulted.

The Colorado River follows an anomalous course; after leaving Grand Canyon, the river crosses three structural uplifts and as many basins. Turning southward it crosses four more uplifts and basins before entering the Gulf. These structural features are late Tertiary and Quaternary in age. The basins contain deposits derived from the uplifts, and the deposits themselves are involved in the later structural movements. The river originally may have been superimposed across the uplifts during their early stages, while they were still low, but the canyons that have been cut into the uplifts must be the result of antecedence.

The Colorado River also is noteworthy for its load of silt, which averages about 20,000 ppm of suspended load, which amounts to more than 100,000 acre feet of mud annually.

A layer of silt quickly settles to the bottom of a cup of water dipped from the river. This water has body!

The Gila River and its tributaries cross structural barriers in the Mexican Highland Section, but in the Sonoran Desert Section the Gila winds around the uplifts rather than crossing them. If the flow of water had been less, this drainage very likely would have been disintegrated like that on the Mojave Desert. If the flow had been greater than it has been, the river might very well have maintained an antecedent course across one or another of the structural uplifts.

The Rio Grande, rather than crossing the basins and ranges, follows structural troughs for 600 miles to the Big Bend, Texas, where it turns northeast and crosses the southeast-trending structural barriers. The Big Bend and the canyons below are one of our national parks. The Rio Grande has no major tributaries in its long course across the Basin and Range Province. Between Albuquerque and El Paso the river loses about half its water, and its salinity increases (Fig. 15.30).

Alluvial Fans and Pediments

A typical basin in the Basin and Range Province consists of two kinds of ground. At the center is a playa or alluvial flat of clayey or silty ground, with or without a crust of salts, and surrounding this are gravel fans that rise from the flats to the foot of the bordering mountains. Many of the fans are several miles long and more than a thousand feet high (Figs. 15.3, 15.24, 15.25). They consist of coarse debris, mostly gravel and sand deposited at the mouths of canyons by streams flowing from the mountains.

The apexes of some alluvial fans are located at the mouths of canyons; the apexes of other fans have been extended up canyons into the mountains, as have those illustrated in Figure 15.24. Where a fan extends far into

a canyon it may engulf and largely bury the foothills, which then project above the surface of the fan as isolated rock hills (Fig. 15.25). These differences in form reflect differences in the histories of the fans.

Four major factors affect the composition and form of gravel fans: (1) structural movements taking place while the fan is building; (2) stream flow, present and past; (3) kind and size of debris transported to the fan; and (4) length of time the fan has been building —that is, stage. The problem of deciphering

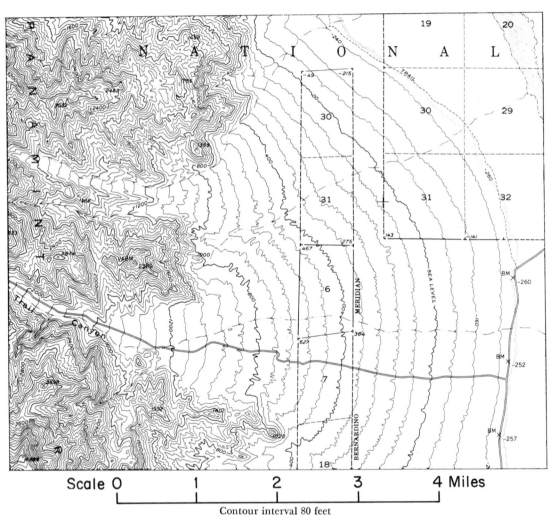

Figure 15.24   *Alluvial fan in the Great Basin Section. This fan, built of gravel, rises from the Death Valley salt pan (right) to the foot of the Panamint Range. (From U.S.G.S. Furnace Creek, California, quadrangle.)*

in detail the history of a particular fan is complicated by the fact that each of these factors is a variable, as may be illustrated by some examples.

A small fan at the base of a mountain (Fig. 15.26,A) may be a young fan, or it may be only the top of a much larger and older fan that has been subsiding structurally and is largely buried. Larger fans may extend into the canyons (Fig. 15.26,B), and some sufficiently so to isolate foothills (Fig. 15.27). Such fans may represent an advanced stage

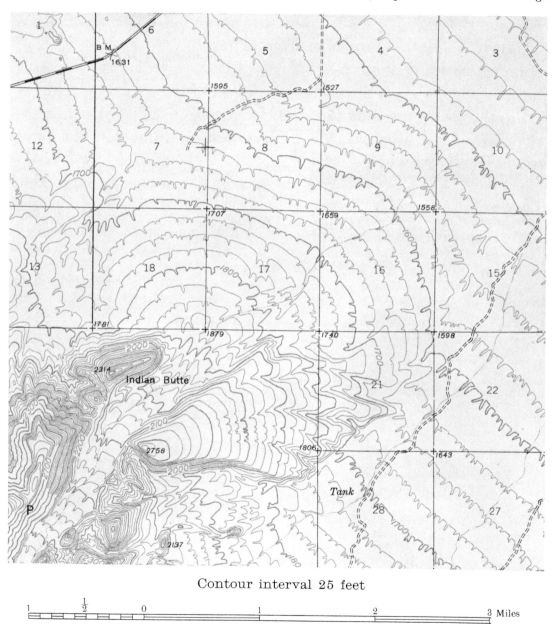

Contour interval 25 feet

Figure 15.25 *Alluvial fan and pediment in the Sonoran Desert Section. (From U.S.G.S. Antelope Peak, Arizona, quadrangle.)*

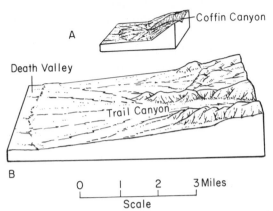

Figure 15.26 *Some different forms of gravel fans (see also Fig. 15.27). (A) A small fan at the straight front of a mountain range. (B) A fan that extends into the canyons. (After U.S.G.S.)*

of development where conditions have been stable or they may be the result of tilting while the fan was being built.

On most fans the slope is more than 100 feet per mile, and many have slopes of 500 feet per mile. In general, the coarser the gravel, the steeper the slope; but there are

exceptions, particularly where there has been recent tilting.

In general the gravel at the surface of fans in this province is well rounded, like typical stream gravel, but some fan surfaces are so old that the boulders and cobbles have disintegrated into a new crop of angular rock fragments. Younger gravel, not old enough to have been broken up by weathering, is darkly stained with desert varnish; some cobbles may have a weathered rind. The youngest gravel is well-rounded and without desert varnish.

In places there are orderly differences in drainage patterns on these different surfaces (Fig. 15.28), reminiscent of the differences in drainage patterns on fans built on pediments on the Colorado Plateau (Fig. 14.27). On the old and weathered surfaces, the drainage is parallel. Surfaces that are flooded infrequently have a dendritic and braided drainage pattern. On the youngest surfaces the drainage is braided.

Around the foot of the mountains in the Sonoran Desert and Mexican Highland Sec-

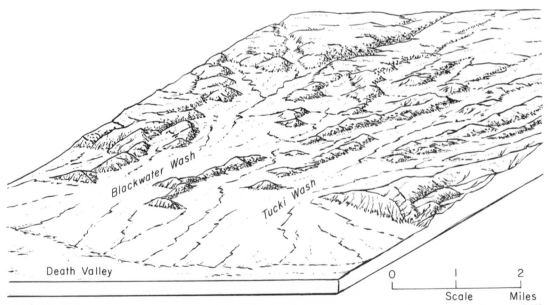

Figure 15.27 *Some fans deeply embay the mountain front and partly bury the foothills (compare with Fig. 15.26). (After U.S.G.S.)*

tions, pediments as well as gravel fans are extensive (Fig. 15.25). The pediments, which are surfaces of erosion as contrasted with the constructional or depositional surfaces on the alluvial fans, are in some ways similar to the pediments on the Colorado Plateau (p. 296) and in other ways different. One difference is that some of the extensive Sonoran Desert and Mexican Highland pediments have developed around the foot of low, small mountains where the rainfall is not much greater, if at all, than in the surrounding basin. These streams lack the change in regimen that characterizes the drainage on the pediments on the Colorado Plateau, but the kind of ground on which the pediments are eroded is the same—the easily eroded formations. Furthermore, the pediments in both areas have dendritic drainage patterns, and the gravel fans being built on them have braided patterns. They are also alike in that many streams rising on the pediments have lower gradients than the master streams transporting gravels from the mountains (Fig. 14.22). This relationship has been used in a practical way at the copper mine at Ajo, where a large arroyo draining from the mountain to the mine pit was turned through a tunnel to a neighboring and lower stream course that does not head in the mountain.

Water Supply

Supplies of surface water and groundwater in the Basin and Range Province are meager, for the rivers are few and small, and they become even smaller as they cross the province. In many of the basins both the surface water and the groundwater are saline. In most parts of the province the water table is deep and the water is of doubtful quality. Demand for water in the Basin and Range Province exceeds the supply.

The largest river, the Colorado, discharges between 10 and 15 million acre feet of water annually. Water from the river is used exten-

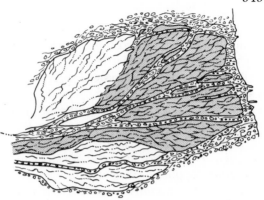

Figure 15.28 *Orderly differences in drainage pattern on different parts of a gravel fan. Old surfaces (white areas) that are high above the drainage and not subject to flooding have parallel drainage. Surfaces of intermediate age (stippled) and of intermediate height are flooded infrequently and have a mixed dendritic and braided drainage pattern. The youngest surfaces (circle pattern), which are subject to seasonal washing, have a braided drainage pattern. The example is Death Valley Canyon in Death Valley. (After U.S.G.S.)*

sively for irrigation and other supplies in the Imperial Valley, and some of it is taken to the Los Angeles metropolitan area. There is little irrigation along the river because most of the valley is narrow and lacks a broad floodplain. Water is pumped from the river to irrigate land south of Yuma.

There is irrigation along the Rio Grande, but this river has an average annual discharge of only about a million acre feet in the vicinity of Albuquerque, and the discharge has decreased by nearly a half by the time the river reaches El Paso. The Gila River, which has an annual flow of about 200,000 acre feet, and its tributary Salt River, which is three times as large, are used for irrigation along their valleys.

Irrigation is intensive and extensive along the eastern border of the Great Basin, where considerably more than a million acre feet is available annually in the several rivers (Bear, Weber, Provo, and Sevier) draining to the basin from the Rocky Mountains and High Plateaus. These water supplies already are highly developed and effectively so.

Rivers entering the western part of the Great Basin (Truckee, Carson, Walker, and Owens rivers) also deliver considerably more than a million acre feet annually. Owens River is diverted for municipal supplies at Los Angeles. The others are used for irrigation and other supplies in their drainage basins.

Another few hundred thousand acre-feet is available along the Humboldt and Reese rivers. Springs and groundwater are used to irrigate limited acreage in several of the basins in the central part of the Great Basin.

Groundwater supplies are being overdrawn in several basins. At Las Vegas, Nevada, the water level in the wells is declining and the land surface there has settled about 6 inches as a result of groundwater withdrawals. In the basins west of Las Vegas, at Pahrump Valley, and in the Amargosa Desert, groundwater is being pumped to irrigate cotton, and the groundwater levels there are falling. When tilled, those desert valleys are frightful dust bowls, yet they are being used to produce a crop that is already overproduced. Such misuse of the land and water resource is compelling argument why such lands should be held in the public domain.

Overdrafts of groundwater also are indicated in some of the basins near Phoenix and Tucson, Arizona, and along the Rio Grande Valley in Texas.

One of the chief needs for water in the Basin and Range Province is for livestock. Water is obtained largely from springs, but some is obtained from wells. Some common kinds of springs are diagrammed in Figure 15.29.

The limit of salinity for water to be used for irrigation or for livestock is about 4,000 ppm, and the water in the middle of many of the desert basins exceeds this limit. The decrease in stream flow across arid and semi-arid regions is accompanied by an increase in salinity. Irrigation contributes to the increase, but salinity increases even where there is no

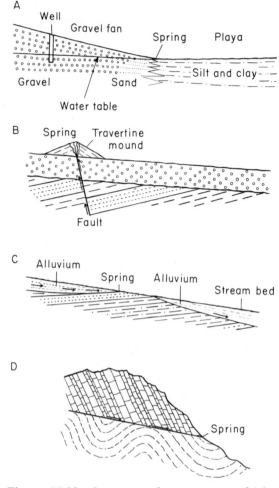

Figure 15.29 *Some of the ways in which groundwater occurs in the Basin and Range Province. (A) Water tables under gravel fans are deep, but may be reached by wells. The water table slopes gently toward the basin. Where the gravel and sand grade to silt and clay the water movement is checked and reaches the surface in a spring zone at the edge of the dry lake. (B) Water moving along high-angle faults may build mounds of travertine. These waters usually are warm. (C) Under-flow in alluvium along a stream bed is forced to the surface where a bedrock ridge is crossed. (D) In the mountains, perched water tables occur along faults and other structural discontinuities, and springs develop where these reach the surface.*

irrigation, as along the Amargosa River (Fig. 15.30). Along with the increase in total dissolved solids in the Amargosa River there is an increase in the proportion of chloride, from about 30 percent at station 1 to about 70 percent at station 5; most of the remaining salts are sulfates.

Mineral Resources

Mines and mining, a major activity in the Basin and Range Province, have centered on many kinds of deposits, but those of copper, gold, silver, lead, zinc, and salines are mined on a sufficient scale to be of national interest.

The Basin and Range Province have yielded about 70 percent of the copper produced in the United States. Most of the deposits, the so-called porphyry deposits, are mined by power shovel at vast open pits (Fig. 15.31). The ores are low grade, containing as little as 0.5 percent copper, but production is feasible because the deposits are huge, and the open-pit mining methods allow vast quantities to be handled. The principal deposits are at Bingham Canyon, Utah; Ely, Nevada; Ajo, Bagdad, Bisbee, Clifton-Morenci, Globe-Miami, Jerome, Ray, and Superior, Arizona; and Santa Rita, New Mexico (Fig. 15.32).

The deposits in these districts are much alike. They are associated with granitic stocks about a mile in diameter that have been thoroughly shattered. The stocks and the limestones intruded by them have been altered by hydrothermal solutions. The primary ore mineral, chalcopyrite (copper-iron sulfide), together with pyrite, occurs as isolated grains and as veins disseminated throughout the shattered and altered rocks.

The upper parts of the shattered intrusions have been weathered and the metallic minerals redeposited in zones, much like those of a soil profile, but scores of feet deep. In the ideal case, the copper and sulfur have been leached from the uppermost layer. Below this is an oxidized layer in which the leached copper was redeposited as carbonate (azurite and malachite), as oxides (cuprite, tenorite), and as silicate (chrysocolla). This layer is analagous to the limey B-horizon of the soils in

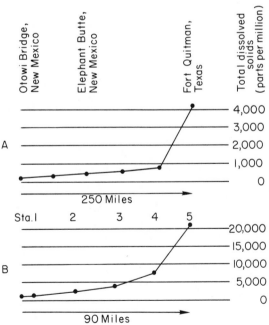

Figure 15.30 *Increase in salinity downstream along the Rio Grande River (A) and the Amargosa River (B).*

Figure 15.31 *Open-pit porphyry copper mine at Bingham Canyon, Utah. Some of the open-pit copper mines are a mile wide and hundreds of feet deep. Power shovels capable of handling many tons with each scoop operate on the terraces, which also serve as road beds for railroad trains into which the ore is loaded by the shovels.*

that region. Below the carbonate layer the downward-percolating solutions deposited both copper and sulfur as the sulfide, chalcocite. Below this is unweathered parent material—the shattered, hydrothermally altered rock containing primary chalcopyrite and pyrite.

Copper is not the only product of these porphyry ores. Other metals are present in minor amounts, but the quantity of ore mined and concentrated is tremendous, and some by-product metals—molybdenum and lead for example—are produced in large amounts.

In general, silver is obtained primarily from the mining of copper ores, but at Virginia City (the Comstock Lode) and at Tonopah, Nevada, silver was the principal metal sought. The Comstock Lode, discovered in 1859, produced enough silver to affect the nation's monetary system. The important deposits of silver at Tonopah were discovered in 1900. The gold camp at Goldfield, Nevada, was discovered in 1903.

These mines, and the porphyry copper ores, were for the most part discovered as a result of prospecting for placer gold. But placer gold production from the Basin and Range Province has not been large.

A complete map of the mining districts in the Basin and Range Province would show

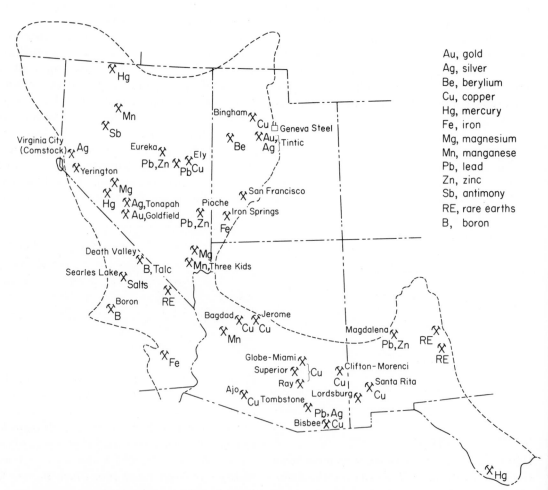

Au, gold
Ag, silver
Be, berylium
Cu, copper
Hg, mercury
Fe, iron
Mg, magnesium
Mn, manganese
Pb, lead
Zn, zinc
Sb, antimony
RE, rare earths
B, boron

Figure 15.32 *Some important mining districts in the Basin and Range Province.*

more than 500 locations; Figure 15.32 shows fewer than 50. Those indicated were selected to show the large porphyry copper mines (Cu) and some of the principal districts that have been productive or that contain considerable reserves of minerals other than copper. The province contains a great variety of mineral deposits, and the list given in the figure could be greatly expanded.

Although salts are omnipresent in the Basin and Range Province, there has been little production of common salt (sodium chloride) except from some salt pans adjacent to Great Salt Lake. Other salts have been important to the national economy, notably borax. This salt was first produced in quantity from Death Valley about 1882, and the deposits there were made famous by the well-advertised 20 mule teams that were used to haul borax from the valley to the railroad—a 10 day trip. The Death Valley borax mines are now closed, and production has shifted to more valuable deposits in the Mojave Desert.

Other salts produced from brines at Searles Lake, California, and Great Salt Lake Desert include potassium salts and such sodium salts as glauber salt (sodium sulfate) and soda ash (sodium carbonate).

The Death Valley area has also been a major source of talc, obtained from underground mines in Precambrian rocks. Important deposits of some of the rare earths occur in the Mojave Desert, although these have not yet been developed for production in large quantities.

More About the Resources

Aridity in the Basin and Range Province is not an asset, as it is on the Colorado Plateau, because few areas there have colorful rocks and picturesque landforms. Only confirmed denizens of the desert find it beautiful, and for them it does indeed have attractions, especially for those seeking solitude.

Mild winters in the Lower Sonoran zone of the southern part of the province has made that area a popular winter resort area. In addition to the pleasant climate, there is also the intangible asset of the colorful influence of Mexico and of the Indian cultures, ancient and modern. And the vegetation is exotic.

As a consequence of the many and varied mineral deposits in the Basin and Range Province, abandoned mining camps and ghost towns are legion. This is the land of the purple bottle, and the abandoned camps are increasing popular places for collecting not only glass that has turned purple, but mineral and rock specimens. Abandoned mines and mills have a special lure, including those that were more productive of stock issues than of ore. In a national park or national monument abandoned mines are of historic interest, for they have again become part of the wilderness, and visitors are guided to them. But a productive modern mine at the site would be deplored for marring the wilderness.

16 *Columbia Plateau*

The Columbia Plateau (Fig. 16.1), embracing a little more than 100,000 square miles (smaller than the Colorado Plateau), includes most of the Northwest's lava fields, the most distinctive feature of the province. In most of the plateau the lavas are nearly horizontal, but in some areas they are folded. The surface of the plateau, which averages only about half as high as that of the Colorado Plateau, is surmounted by ridges where the lavas have been folded or faulted, and by irregular mountains where older rocks protrude through the lavas. Southward the plateau grades into the Basin and Range Province, and this part of the plateau includes closed basins where drainage is ponded. The climate is semiarid, for the plateau is in the rain shadow of the high Cascade Range.

Altitudes in this province (Fig. 16.2) average much lower than those of the Colorado Plateau. The Walla Walla Section is below 2,000 feet and extends below 500 feet in altitude. The Harney and Payette sections and the Snake River Plain are all below 5,000 feet, except for a few small, isolated mountains not shown in the figure. Most of the Blue Mountains Section lies below 8,000 feet, but at least one peak reaches to 10,000 feet.

Unlike the Colorado Plateau, the Columbia Plateau has a considerable population, almost 1½ million. This population is not evenly distributed but is concentrated along the Snake River in Idaho and along the rivers draining to the plateau from the Northern Rocky Mountains and from the Cascades.

Outstanding features of the Columbia Plateau are the

1. Great extent of the lavas and their prevailing near-horizontality.
2. Semiarid climate.
3. Vegetation, which, except on the few mountains, consists chiefly of shrubs and grasses rather than trees.
4. Two great rivers, the Columbia and the Snake, and the reservoirs along them.
5. Extensive plain along the Snake River in Idaho.
6. Canyons in Washington and Oregon.
7. Great extent and thickness of ancient, weathered loess—known as Palouse soil.
8. Bare, stream-worn lava surfaces (scabland) in Washington, where the loess was eroded from the land between rivers by extraordinary floods during Pleistocene time.
9. Dry canyons (coulees) and dry falls that were eroded by the Pleistocene floods.

The land is used chiefly for farming and ranching. The principal crops are wheat, hay, and other forage, and Idaho's potatoes. Much of the farming is dry farming—that is, without irrigation. The chief livestock raised are beef cattle and sheep. Although the plateau is covered mainly by shrubs and grassland, sawmills are numerous around its edges, the logs being hauled from the bodering mountains. Except for some minor coal beds the plateau is without mineral fuels, and other mineral resources have not been important in its economy. Dams built across some of the rivers produce hydroelectric power.

The rivers once were an important source of salmon, especially for the Indians. But the dams have reduced the salmon runs despite attempts to devise ways for the salmon to pass the obstructions. Current studies show, how-

ever, that stocking more favorable streams with fertilized eggs might reverse this trend.

Structural Framework and Topography

The relation of the Columbia Plateau to the lava fields in the Pacific Northwest is illustrated in Figure 16.3. The northern boundary of the Province, from eastern Idaho to central Washington, is marked by the contact along which the plateau lavas overlap the older rocks

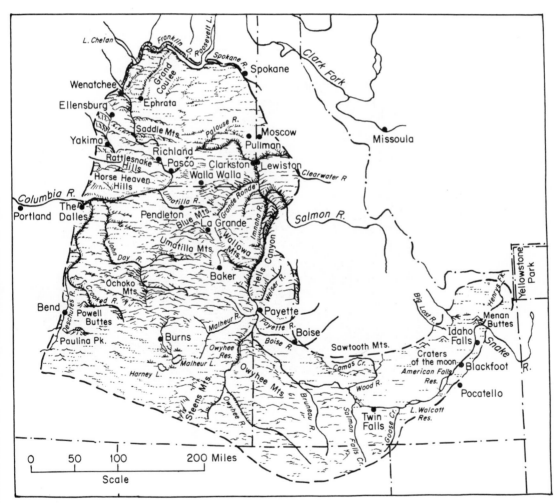

Figure 16.1 *Physiographic map of Columbia Plateau.*

forming the Northern Rocky Mountains and the northern end of the Cascade Range. The Cascade Range is composed of lavas and other volcanic rocks, but its structure is anticlinal, with towering volcanoes aligned along the crest of the anticline. Both structurally and topographically, this mountain range differs markedly from the plateau to the east, and the boundary between the two is marked by a sharp break in the topography.

On the east, the Yellowstone Plateau, included in the Middle Rocky Mountains, could as well be included in the Columbia Plateau, for it is continuous with the Columbia Plateau and resembles it as much as it does the Rockies. On the south, the lavas and other volcanic rocks extend from the Columbia Plateau into the northern part of the Basin and Range Province, where the lavas are disrupted by block faults and form north-trending ridges. Structurally and topographically, the Columbia Plateau grades into the Basin and Range Province, and the boundary between the two provinces is arbitrary.

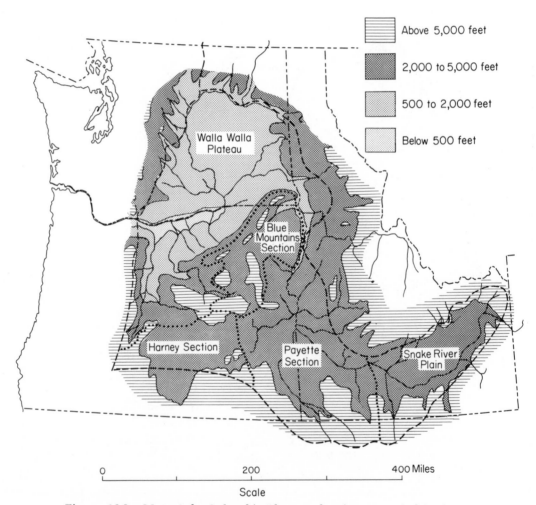

Figure 16.2   *Map of the Columbia Plateau, showing general altitudes.*

Walla Walla Section

The Walla Walla Section is a structural basin that was downwarped while the lavas were being erupted. The first eruptions, which occurred in early Tertiary time, ponded the drainage. Lavas filled the central part of the sinking basin, and lakes developed around its edges. Deposits of sandstone and shale accumulated in the lakes to a thickness of several thousand feet (Swauk and Roslyn Formations, Eocene). Away from the basin these deposits overlap the older crystalline rocks, and toward the basin they are interbedded with the lavas.

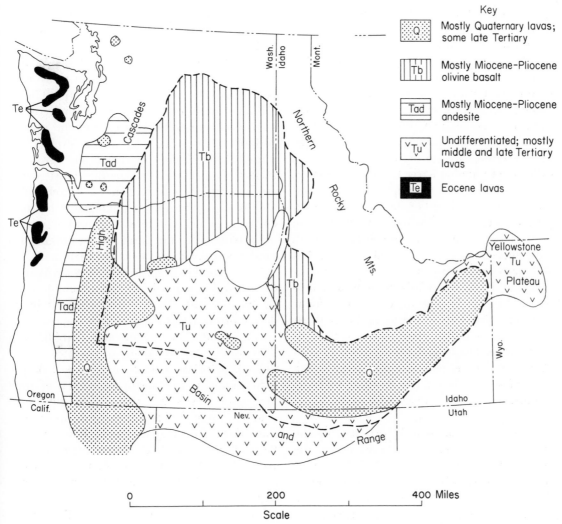

Figure 16.3 *Relation of the Columbia Plateau (boundary shown by broken line) to the lava fields (see key) in the Pacific Northwest. The white areas are nonvolcanic and mostly prevolcanic rocks. The lavas and other volcanic rocks forming the Cascade Range and extending into the Basin and Range Province are structurally and topographically different from those of the Columbia Plateau.*

To the west, in the Cascade Range, these deposits contain abundant plant remains, including some coal beds.

The downwarping and eruptions continued through Eocene time and into Oligocene time, and the deposits (Clarno Formation) contain a great deal of volcanic ash and other sediments of volcanic origin. The downwarping continued through the end of Oligocene time and into Miocene time, and a lake was formed along the south edge of the basin against the flank of the Blue Mountains uplift. Lake and stream deposits, which accumulated in the lake to a thickness of about 1 mile (John Day Formation) contain both animal and plant remains; basinward these sediments are interbedded with lavas. Similar deposits, formed later in Miocene time (Ellensburg and Mascall Formations), contain much volcanic debris, including a great accumulation of lavas called the Columbia River basalt. These lavas, about a mile thick, were spread farther and farther onto the flanks of the basin with each renewal of eruption. The total volume of these lavas may be as great as 100,000 cubic miles.

In Pliocene time (represented by the Dalles and Rattlesnake Formations) the volcanic activity in the Walla Walla Section began to wane, although it continued as vigorously as ever in the Snake River Plains, in the southern part of the Columbia Plateau, and in the Cascade Range. The Cascades became a high anticline at this time, and as uplift progressed a series of southeast- and east-trending folds developed along the northwest edge of the Walla Walla Section (Fig. 16.4).

As the structural basin represented by the Walla Walla Section was downwarped, the lavas and lake beds were folded. The anticlines are curiously persistent folds, longer than most in the Valley and Ridge Province of the Appalachian Highlands. Moreover, they are sharp folds that form ridges with smooth crests, 1,500 to 3,000 feet higher than the broad basins that separate them. The smooth crests of the ridges coincide with the axes of the anticlines, unlike the ridges in the Valley and Ridge Province most of which formed by erosion of the flanks of folds.

These folds, as a group, diverted the Columbia River a hundred miles eastward into the center of the section. Were it not for these folds, the river presumably would have continued its course along the edge of the lava field. Yet the Columbia River and the Yakima River, a tributary, have cut gorges across the folds (Fig. 16.5) and are antecedent. Repeated uplift at these anticlines is recorded by the overlap of some of the lavas against the flanks of the folds.

The structurally lowest part of the Walla Walla Section is the Pasco Basin, in which the Columbia River is joined by the Snake. There the lavas are buried under many hundreds of feet of silt, sand, and gravel, and the upper surface of the lavas is below sea level. This buried lava surface represents the ground surface that existed when the lavas were erupted, and its position below sea level probably is due to basinward sinking that has occurred since the eruptions. This area may still be sinking, but the kind of measurements needed to confirm this have not been made.

The Columbia River enters the Walla Walla Section from the north, and after being joined by the Spokane River, flows westward in a deep canyon along the northern edge of the lavas. Grand Coulee Dam and Franklin D. Roosevelt Lake are along this stretch. The canyon, in places more than 2,000 feet deep, turns south at the northwest corner of the lava basin, crosses an anticlinal fold and ridge (Saddle Mountains) and then turns southeastward to be joined by the Snake River in the Pasco Basin (Fig. 16.4). From there to the gorge through the Cascade Range the river is only a few hundred feet below the plateau surface.

The Snake River enters the Walla Walla Section in a canyon about 2,000 feet deep, but the plateau surface slopes westward and the canyon becomes less and less deep in that direction. In the Pasco Basin the lavas are buried under lake beds, and both the Snake and Co-

lumbia rivers flow through open valleys, one
of the few open stretches west of the Snake
River Plain.

Between the two rivers much of the plateau
surface is scabland. Enormous floods during
Pleistocene time (p. 367) overtopped the canyon walls of the Columbia and Spokane rivers
and discharged southwestward across the pla-

teau. The surface was stripped of its soil along
a network of channels (Fig. 16.6). Some valleys
cut in the lavas are tremendous; Grand Coulee is one of them (Fig. 16.20).

The Pasco Basin ends downstream at an
anticline that is breached by the Columbia
River. After crossing this uplift the river enters Umatilla Basin (Fig. 16.4), and skirts its

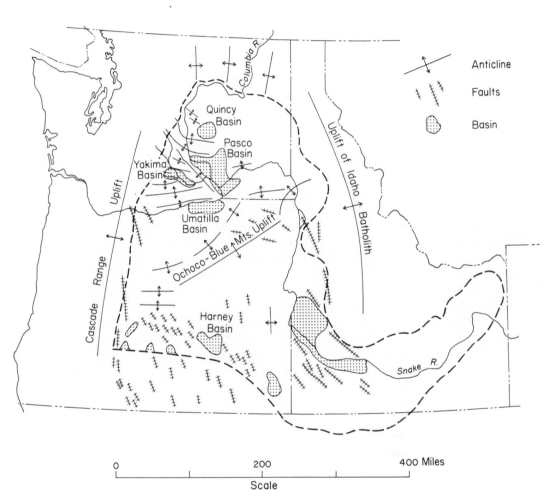

Figure 16.4 *Structural framework of the Columbia Plateau. The plateau is a
structural basin located between the Idaho Batholith and the Cascade Range.
The lavas north of the Ochoco-Blue Mountains Uplift are folded, especially at
the northwest edge of the basin. Southward the lavas are faulted, and the structure grades into that of the Basin and Range Province.*

northern edge. From here the lavas rise westward onto the uplift of the Cascade Range, and the Columbia River enters its gorge through that Range.

The lavas also rise southward toward the Ochoco-Blue Mountains uplift. Three tributaries of the Columbia River in this part of

the section are the Umatilla, John Day, and Deschutes rivers. The Umatilla River crosses the Umatilla Basin in an open valley to join the Columbia. The John Day River, which heads in the Ochoco-Blue Mountains, has eroded a canyon about 1,000 feet deep through lake beds in the shallow western end of the

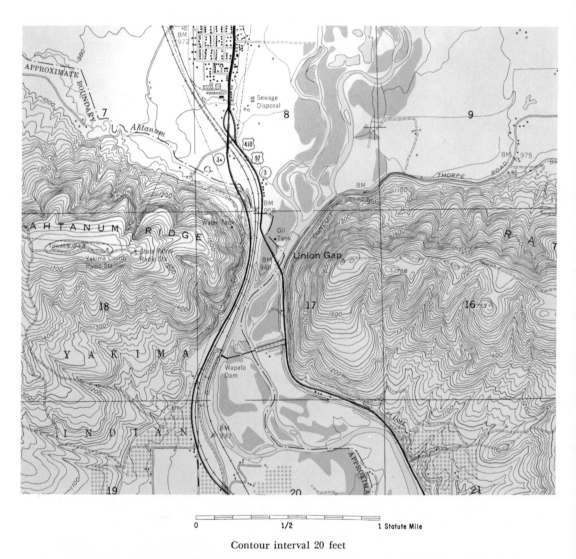

Contour interval 20 feet

Figure 16.5   *Topographic map of the Yakima River gorge through an anticlinal ridge of basaltic lavas. The axis of the anticline is along the crest of the ridge. The river, antecedent across the fold, was repeatedly ponded as the fold rose, but each pond overflowed through the gap and maintained the channel through it. (From U.S.G.S. Yakima East, Washington, quadrangle.)*

Umatilla Basin and exposed the underlying lavas where they begin their rise westward to the Cascades. Throughout its course this river flows through a canyon in which Tertiary lake beds, interbedded with the Columbia River basalt and other basalts are extensively exposed. The Deschutes River flows through a canyon more than 1,000 feet deep. The Deschutes, however, drains north along the east base of the Cascade Range and joins the Columbia at the western end of the Umatilla Basin. The drainage basin includes much Quaternary lava and many volcanic cones. Long stretches of the canyon are incised into the young lavas. The uplands are extensively mantled with volcanic ash from the nearby volcanic centers and from the larger ones on the Cascades.

Blue Mountains Section

The Blue Mountains Section is formed by an uplift of a complex of Paleozoic and Mesozoic sedimentary rocks and intrusive Cenozoic rocks. The structure and topography of this uplift have more in common with the Northern Rockies than with the Columbia Plateau, and this section could be considered a part of the Northern Rocky Mountains projecting westward into the Columbia Plateau. The mountains, which antedate the eruptions on the Columbia Plateau, once stood as islands in the sea of lavas, but they were further uplifted while the lavas were being erupted. Extensive areas, especially in the Umatilla and Blue mountains (Fig. 16.7), are elevated plateaus of basalt. These lavas are more than a mile higher than the lavas in the central part of the Walla Walla Section, and most or all of this difference in altitude represents uplift since the eruptions.

The Snake River crosses the uplift in Hells Canyon, which is deeper than Grand Canyon (Fig. 16.8). The river enters this canyon from the Payette Section at an altitude of about 2,100 feet (Fig. 16.9), and here the lavas of the Columbia Plateau are at river level. Fifty miles downstream the lava surface is above 6,500 feet and the altitude of the river is 1,300 feet. On the west wall of the canyon the base of the lavas is between 3,000 and 4,000 feet; on the east wall, a mountain of older rocks, known as the Seven Devils, projects above the lavas and reaches a peak of 9,410 feet. He Devil Mountain (Fig. 16.10), only six miles from the river, reaches an altitude of 8,000 feet.

A short distance north of the mouth of the Grande Ronde River, the Snake River leaves the uplifted area and enters the Walla Walla Basin. The base of the lavas dips downstream and passes below the bed of the river at an altitude of about 800 feet. The surface of the lavas and the rim of the canyon here are about 2,000 feet higher.

The Seven Devils and Wallowa mountains have peaks higher than 9,000 feet. Most of the rest of the section, although mountainous, is below 6,000 feet. The Wallowa Mountains were glaciated.

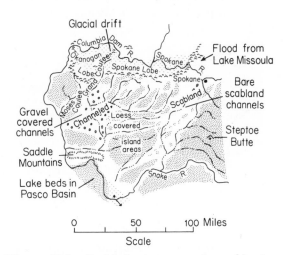

Figure 16.6 *Braided pattern of scabland channels on the Columbia Plateau between the Columbia and Snake rivers. (After Amer. Assoc. Geog.)*

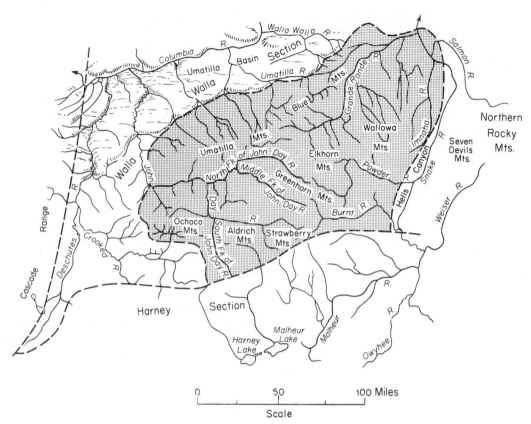

Figure 16.7 *Drainage pattern in and around the Blue Mountains Section (shaded area). The John Day River and its tributaries form a trellis drainage pattern; other streams are dendritic.*

Figure 16.8 *Hells Canyon of the Snake River, at the east edge of the Columbia Plateau, is deeper than Grand Canyon, but its walls are not as colorful or as steep as those in Grand Canyon.*

Figure 16.9 *View downstream at Farewell Bend, where the Snake River leaves the Payette Section (foreground) and enters Hells Canyon to cross the Ochoco-Blue Mountains Uplift.*

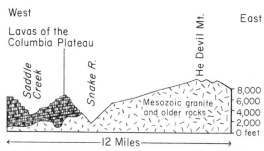

West   East

Lavas of the
Columbia Plateau

Saddle Creek

Snake R.

He Devil Mt.

Mesozoic granite
and older rocks

8,000
6,000
4,000
2,000
0 feet

←——————— 12 Miles ———————→

Figure 16.10 *Snake River at Hells Canyon. Here the westward-dipping lavas have been stripped from the east side of the canyon, and older rocks form the mountains there. The lavas rest on a rough, mountainous surface.*

Harney Lake Section

The Harney Lake Section, a volcanic plain at the southwest corner of the Columbia Plateau, has the least distinct boundaries of any section of the plateau. It grades northward into the Ochoco and Umatilla mountains and into the Walla Walla Section, and it grades southward into the Great Basin and eastward into the Payette Section.

The Harney Lake Section, located along a swarm of northwest-trending faults, is a plain with little local relief except at the volcanic centers. Variously referred to as the Great Sand Desert and as the Great Sage Plain, this plain is composed of nearly horizontal lava flows, most of which are Quaternary in age. The flows are largely covered with loose volcanic ash and are surmounted by hundreds of volcanic cones. Many of the lavas and cones are composed of fresh rock and cinders, for the volcanism is very young. Between the cones and the lava benches are short dry washes, which end in dry lakes. There is no exterior drainage except at the very edges of the section.

Volcanic cones are most numerous and highest in the northwest part of the section (Fig. 16.11). Southeastward the cones are lower, the lava flows more extensive, and the playas more numerous and larger. At the southeast end of the section, the basins culminate in a large marshy tract containing two lakes, Harney Lake and Malheur Lake. These lakes formerly overflowed to the Snake River by way of the Malheur River, but a lava flow has dammed the outlet.

These lakes, the lowest part of the section, lie at altitudes slightly above 4,000 feet. The highest peak, Paulina Peak, a little higher than 8,000 feet in altitude, is located at the west end of the section. Only a few of the volcanic mountains are more than 2,000 feet high, and most are only a few hundred feet higher than the plain around them. The topography has a striking northwest-southeast grain, reflecting the faulting and dominant direction of flow of the lavas.

Payette Section

The Payette Section (Fig. 16.12) consists of northwest-trending structural and topographic units. At the north a structural basin occupied by the Snake River lies between two uplifts, the Idaho Batholith on the northeast and the Owyhee Mountains on the southwest. There is a second basin south of the Owyhee Mountains.

The structural trough of the Snake River in the Payette Section is deeply buried under lake, playa, and stream deposits that were deposited upstream from Hells Canyon, where the Snake River enters the Ochoco-Blue Mountains Uplift. The deep fill of sediments in the trough evidently resulted from repeated ponding of the Snake River as the uplift was raised during Cenozoic time. The river maintained its course across the uplift by overflowing along its old channel each time it was raised by the folding. Moreover, the lake beds are dissected and form benches a few hundred feet higher than the rivers.

The Snake River enters the Payette Section

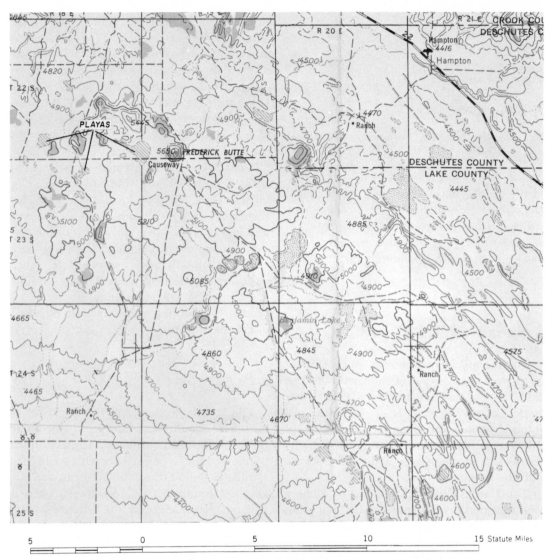

CONTOUR INTERVAL 200 FEET
WITH SUPPLEMENTARY CONTOURS AT 100 FOOT INTERVALS

Figure 16.11   *Topographic map of the western part of the Harney Lake Section, showing the abundant volcanic cones and playas. (From A.M.S. Crescent, Oregon, quadrangle.)*

below Twin Falls (Fig. 16.13) at an altitude of about 2,800 feet and follows the boundary between lake beds of the Payette Section and lava fields of the Snake River Plain. For more than 50 miles the river flows through a gorge 500 feet deep. Below the main gorge, where the Snake is joined by the Bruneau River, the altitude of the river drops to about 2,450 feet. Here the surface of the lavas lies a few hundred feet higher than the lake beds.

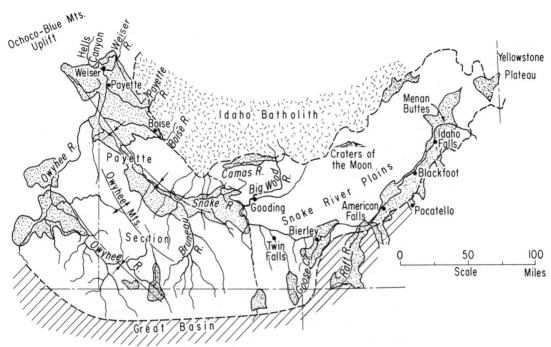

Figure 16.12 *Index map of the Payette Section and Snake River Plains. The stippled areas represent lake, playa, and stream deposits of Cenozoic age. The white areas in the sections are almost entirely lavas and related volcanic rocks.*

Southward the river valley gradually becomes more open. The Snake River crosses the lavas (Fig. 16.12) in a gorge 500 feet deep and then follows an open, flat-bottomed valley several miles wide between benches of lake beds that form the divides between the Snake, Boise, Payette, and Weiser rivers. By the time the Snake River reaches the entrance to Hells Canyon it has dropped to an altitude of about 2,100 feet. The gradient here is only half as steep as it is where the river enters the Payette Section.

The northern edge of the Payette Section, marked by the overlap of the lake beds and lavas onto the Idaho Batholith, is topographically and structurally distinct. At Boise, the mountains of the batholith rise above the plain nearly 5,000 feet in about 8 miles. Much of the uplift of the batholith occurred after

Figure 16.13 *Twin Falls of the Snake River, Idaho. The falls, almost 200 feet high, now are greatly reduced in volume because the water is used to produce hydroelectric power.*

the Columbia River basalts of Miocene-Pliocene age were erupted, for those lavas are turned up along the west flank of the batholith (Fig. 16.10). But the lavas of the Snake River Plain and those of the Payette

Section, are younger than the Columbia River basalts and are involved only in the latest structural movements.

The northern boundary of the Payette Section appears to be a major crustal break trending northwest and having at least $2\frac{1}{2}$ miles of displacement and probably very much more. Gravity data indicate that the basaltic rocks under the Payette Section are at least $2\frac{1}{2}$ miles thick, and may be as much as 7 miles thick. These dense rocks have been displaced downward against the light rocks of the Idaho Batholith. Late Tertiary and Quaternary formations that extend across the boundary are displaced downward toward the Snake River, and the amount of displacement is progressively less in the younger deposits. About 2,000 feet of the displacement occurred during the Quaternary, another 2,000 feet in late Pliocene time, and about 5,000 feet earlier in the Pliocene; an unknown amount of deformation took place at a still earlier time. Southward from the Snake River Plain the lava surface rises onto the uplift at the Owyhee Mountains.

Where the Owyhee River turns north it cuts across the Owyhee Mountains in a gorge 50 miles long and, for much of its length, is about 1,500 feet deep. The river, incised in the uplifted Tertiary and Quaternary lavas and lake beds, is at an elevation of about 3,000 feet where it enters the gorge, and is at about 2,300 feet where it emerges on the Snake River Plain. Owyhee Dam, near the lower end of the gorge, forms a reservoir that extends most of the way across the uplift. This reservoir provides a good datum for determining whether uplift across the gorge is continuing at the present time.

The southern boundary of the Payette Section is south of the Owyhee River trough, where the flank of that northwest-trending syncline is interrupted by the northerly trending block mountains of the Great Basin. The boundary is an arbitrary line through a zone almost 50 miles wide, where the two structures, although very different, grade into one

another. In general, the Payette Section is a northwest-trending structural basin separating the structurally higher Great Basin from the still higher Idaho batholith. Downwarping of the Payette Section in late Cenozoic time apparently was contemporaneous with the block faulting in the Great Basin.

Snake River Plain

The Snake River Plain (Fig. 16.12) represents a vast field of late Cenozoic (mostly Quaternary) lavas. The plain is a continuation of the structural trough represented by the Payette Section, but under the plain the trough is narrower and lacks the subsidiary anticlines and synclines that characterize the Payette Section. The boundary is drawn where the lake beds of the Payette Section abut against the lavas of the Snake River Plain. The plain is about 3,000 feet in altitude at the west, and it rises to about 5,000 feet at the east. The north side, formed by the mountainous uplift of the Idaho batholith, is about 5,000 feet high. The Snake River flows along the southern edge of the plain, which is about 500 feet lower than the northern edge. For most of its course along the plain, the Snake River flows on top of the lavas, but for 30 miles below American Falls it is incised in the lavas and flows through a shallow gorge that is impressive because of the size of the river (Fig. 16.14).

The plain is interrupted by many volcanic cones—among them Craters of the Moon, a national monument. Two unusually striking volcanic cones, named Menan Buttes, are located above Idaho Falls. Figure 16.15 illustrates one of them.

The structural transition between the synclinal trough of the Snake River Plain and the north-trending fault-block mountains of the Great Basin is concealed under the lavas forming the plain. The lavas at the surface are mostly Quaternary in age and are younger than most of the block faulting, but downwarping of the syncline may have progressed contemporaneously with the block faulting.

East of the Snake River Plain is the Yellowstone Plateau, where the volcanic deposits are even younger than those on the plain. Volcanism still continues in the form of hot springs and other fumarolic activity.

Figure 16.14 *Gorge of the Snake River in the plain below American Falls, Idaho.*

Present-day Earth Movements

The Columbia Plateau has not been subject to frequent or to severe earthquakes, but, like the Colorado Plateau, is partly ringed by a belt of earthquake epicenters (Fig. 2.14). Gravity relationships, however, are quite different in the two plateaus, for the Columbia Plateau is underlain by a thick sequence of dense rocks that greatly contrast with the light rocks in the adjoining provinces to the

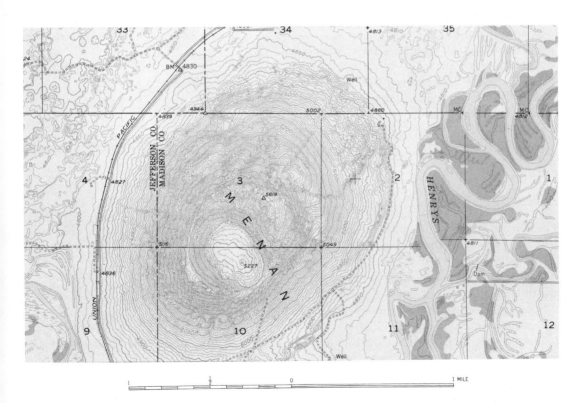

Figure 16.15 *Topographic map of the north Menan Butte, a volcanic cinder cone near the head of the Snake River Plain, Idaho. East of the butte is the floodplain of the Henrys River. Note the cutoff meanders. To the west is lava plain. (From U.S.G.S. Menan Buttes, Idaho, quadrangle.)*

north and to the south. The boundaries between the dense rocks and light rocks are marked by earthquake epicenters and correspond to the northern boundary of the Columbia Plateau and to most of its southern boundary.

The distribution of these epicenters, together with evidence of tremendous displacement along at least part of the boundaries in late Tertiary and Quaternary time (p. 360), suggests that the plateau as a whole is still moving downward relative to the neighboring provinces. During the last 10 million or so years the Snake River Plain has been sinking, relative to the Idaho Batholith, and the displacement amounts to an average rate of a few inches every hundred years. There is no reason to suppose that movement has ceased. It probably is continuing, perhaps as rapidly as ever, and measurements are much needed to determine this displacement.

A few earthquake epicenters have been recorded along the Snake River trough; along the Ochoco-Blue Mountains Uplift, where it is crossed by the Snake River; and north of the uplift, in the southeastern part of the Walla Walla Section.

Climate

The climate on the Columbia Plateau is semi-arid and cool. Both the average annual rainfall and the average annual temperature are about the same as on the more southerly but higher Colorado Plateau.

Except on the mountains, the average annual temperature is about 50°F. The average January temperature is about 32°F; the average July temperature is about 70°F. The average annual minimum temperature is −10°F, and the average annual maximum is more than 100°F. Despite the altitude and latitude the temperatures in the Walla Walla Section are moderate, and the growing season is long (Fig. 16.16) because the surrounding

mountains shelter the section against cold winter winds.

The bordering mountains also reduce the rainfall in this section. Average annual precipitation is only about 10 inches, although it increases to more than 20 inches on the mountains (Fig. 16.16). The precipitation is fairly evenly distributed throughout the year, except during the summer months, when there is little rain. During many summers the rainfall may amount to only a half inch. Average annual snowfall on the mountains is as high as 100 inches, but on most of the plateau the average is about 2 feet. Snow cover usually exceeds 1 inch for about 60 days each year.

Thunderstorms and hail storms are infrequent in the western part of the plateau, but they are not uncommon in the eastern part.

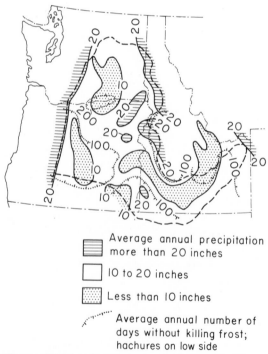

Average annual precipitation more than 20 inches

10 to 20 inches

Less than 10 inches

Average annual number of days without killing frost; hachures on low side

Figure 16.16 *Average annual precipitation and average annual number of days without killing frost on the Columbia Plateau. (From U.S.D.A.)*

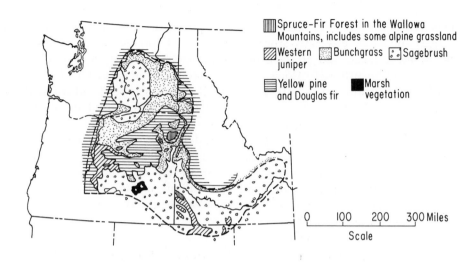

Spruce-Fir Forest in the Wallowa Mountains, includes some alpine grassland

Western juniper   Bunchgrass   Sagebrush

Yellow pine and Douglas fir   Marsh vegetation

0   100   200   300 Miles
Scale

Figure 16.17   *Map of natural vegetation on the Columbia Plateau. (After U.S.D.A.)*

There is considerable cloudiness and fog in the semiarid Walla Walla and Payette sections.

The semiarid climate is new to the Columbia Plateau. Here as elsewhere during Pleistocene time the climate was very different, but it was also different during most of Tertiary time, before the Cascades had been raised to their present height. Until Miocene time the climate was like that along the Pacific Coast. Not until Pliocene time did it become semiarid as it is today. In Pleistocene time the climate was alternately warm-dry and cold-wet. Two important effects of these Pleistocene climates are the scablands (p. 365) and the Palouse Soils (p. 364).

Vegetation

In about half the Columbia Plateau, the natural vegetation is sagebrush. About a quarter of the plateau is grassland and another quar-

ter woodland and forest (Fig. 16.17). West and north of the plateau are forested mountains; to the south is the sagebrush land of the Great Basin.

Two species of sagebrush grow on the Columbia Plateau. The predominant species is the common one that grows in abundance in the Great Basin. The land on which this species grows is suitable for farming, especially if it can be irrigated. The other species, low-growing and gnarled, grows in the scablands, which are not suited for agriculture. In most of the sagebrush lands the average annual precipitation is less than 10 inches—they are the driest parts of the plateau.

Areas that receive more than about 10 inches of rain per year have an open cover of bunch grass, which reflects not only the amount of rainfall but also its seasonal distribution. If more water were available during the growing season, the bunch grass would be replaced by grasses that form denser stands. If the available moisture were any less than it is, the bunch grass would be replaced by sagebrush.

Associated with the grasses is a great profusion of flowering plants. These lands are excellent for raising wheat.

Marsh grasses and shrubs grow along the edges of sloughs and lakes, especially around Harney and Malheur lakes, and at some of the playas that are frequently wet. Along the valleys are willows and cottonwoods. Alkaline ground supports greasewood.

A woodland of western juniper grows in the area of low rainfall in central Oregon (Fig. 16.17). Juniper grows widely in the sagebrush and grassland country, but only locally in stands that can be called woodland, and most of these cover very small areas where runoff is collected or evaporation reduced so that more moisture is available than on the surrounding shrubland and grassland.

Forests of western yellow pine and Douglas fir grow mostly in the areas that receive more than 15 inches of annual precipitation. These forests are important sources of lumber, and are favored by vacationists because the summer climate is highly agreeable and because the forest stands are open and have an understory of grasses like a park. Other trees in these forests are the western white pine, aspen, Rocky Mountain juniper, and white fir.

The Wallowa Mountains are high enough to extend into the Canadian Zone of Engelmann spruce and alpine fir and the highest peaks reach to alpine grassland. Timberline here is a little over 7,000 feet.

The vegetation, as well as the climate, is new to the Columbia Plateau. In early Tertiary (Eocene) time, before the Cascades had been raised, the vegetation was uniform all the way to the coast, and the common trees were tropical or subtropical types, including palms. There were few conifers. In middle Tertiary (Oligocene and Miocene) time, still before the Cascades had become high mountains, the climate cooled and the tropical flora was pushed southward by a highly diversified temperate-climate flora. These forests included hardwood trees like those now growing in the eastern United States and some trees known

only in eastern Asia: the ginkgo and a relative of the redwood. In late Tertiary (Pliocene) time the Columbia Plateau became semiarid. From then on, the flora became reduced in numbers of species, and the forests lost their resemblance to those along the coast and to the forests of the eastern United States. During Quaternary time the altitudinal positions of the life zones must have shifted upward and downward as the climate alternately chilled and warmed during the glacial and interglacial stages, but this record is complicated by the structural movements and by the building of high volcanoes that imposed topographic effects on the climate.

Surficial Deposits and Soils

In the Walla Walla Section there are loess deposits as much as 150 feet thick. Soils developed on these deposits are called Palouse Soils; they are zoned like the soils in the central United States (Fig. 16.18). In the lowest, driest, and hottest part of the section, the weathering of the loess is slight, as in Desert Soils, and the soil horizons are only weakly developed. Bordering this part of the section is a belt of Brown Soils, also loessial, which is in turn bordered by belts of loess on which Chestnut, Chernozem, and Prairie soils have developed. The loess deposits and soils are missing in the channeled scablands but are preserved on the divides where they overlie the basalt. Where they are 2 feet or more deep, these soils may be cultivated.

The weathering of these loesses represents the superimposed effects of several different climatic conditions, for most of the loess deposits are ancient. They antedate the last glaciation, and much or most of the weathering does also. The dark, organic-rich, surface layers are Recent, but the limey zones may be ancient. These soils probably represent a complex of loessial deposits of different ages, and part of the alteration and layering is attributable to soil processes that occurred under climatic conditions and vegetative cover that differed considerably from those of the present time.

The loessial soils in the Walla Walla Section and along the Snake River are subject to severe erosion, both by gullying and by wind. The farmed lands produce clouds of dust.

Soils on the hilly and mountainous parts of the Columbia Plateau are shallow and are not shown in Figure 16.18. They are derived in part from weathering of the underlying bedrock, but mostly they are wind-deposited volcanic ash from the Cascades and other volcanic centers, and loessial dust from the desert basins. Presumably there are podzolic soils under the yellow pine and higher-altitude forests.

Soils in the Harney Basin Section are Desert

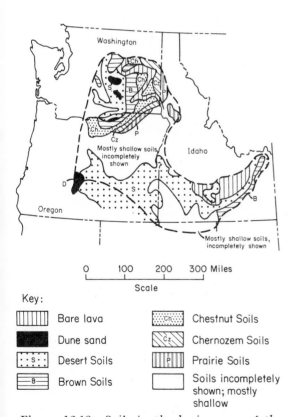

Key:

▦	Bare lava	⠂Ch⠂	Chestnut Soils
■	Dune sand	⌇Cz⌇	Chernozem Soils
⠂s⠂	Desert Soils	▥P▥	Prairie Soils
▤B▤	Brown Soils	☐	Soils incompletely shown; mostly shallow

Figure 16.18 *Soils in the basin areas of the Columbia Plateau. (After U.S.D.A.)*

Soils largely developed on loamy or sandy volcanic ash 25 to 50 feet deep. The soils are thin and weakly developed, for the ash is young and not deeply weathered. The organic layer is thin or lacking. At many playas the soils are alkaline or saline.

The Payette Section and the Snake River Plain are mantled with loess 2 to 10 feet deep, and these soils also have weakly developed profiles and are classed as Desert Soils. In places, however, there are Brown Soils with distinct soil horizons. On the north side of the Snake River Plain extensive areas are bare lava.

Grand Coulee and the Scablands

The scablands (Fig. 16.6), which extend across the Walla Walla Section from the Spokane and Columbia rivers southward to the Snake River, are the result of several major floods that evidently occurred during Pleistocene time, when ice dammed the Columbia River (Fig. 16.19). One ice lobe, the Okanogan lobe, dammed the Columbia River at the big bend below Grand Coulee Dam. Earlier, the Spokane lobe had dammed the Spokane River. The meltwaters overflowed across the plateau, producing a number of anomalous features.

The most impressive feature is the Grand Coulee (Fig. 16.20). This canyon cut into the lavas is about 50 miles long, almost 1,000 feet deep, and about 1 mile wide. It contains cataracts higher than the falls at Niagara, plunge pools more than 100 feet deep, and river bars about 150 feet high. Until water from above Grand Coulee Dam was turned into it, the canyon was without water except for intermittent streams and small alkaline lakes. The canyon was cut by the Columbia, when it was dammed by ice and swollen with meltwaters; when the glaciers receded, the floods subsided and the river returned to its canyon.

The Grand Coulee crosses a monocline in a set of dry cataracts more than 3 miles wide and about 400 feet high that divide the canyon into two parts. The upper canyon is cut in the elevated beds west of the monocline, and the lower canyon follows the fold, with the result that its west wall is higher than the east wall. At the mouth, in the Quincy Basin, are huge gravel fans.

The Grand Coulee heads in a wind gap in the south rim of the canyon of the Columbia River, just above Grand Coulee Dam. The rims on each side of the gap are about 800 feet higher than the floor of the coulee, which is about that much higher than the Columbia River.

Eastward from Grand Coulee to the Palouse River is a network of braided scabland channels. These broad channels are about 50 to 100 feet deep and are separated by uplands mantled with loess. Some have bars, others have cataracts, many have potholes. In many places the floods that developed these channels had to overflow high divides to get from one channel to another, and some of these divides

are hundreds of feet high. The Palouse River crosses a divide hundreds of feet high to join the Snake River. Where canyons were not incised across divides, the floodwaters eroded scabland surfaces on the lavas.

Valleys draining westward to the scabland area—even the valley of the Snake River—contain remnants of deltaic deposits having foreset beds that dip upstream—that is, to the east. A delta built eastward into the Palouse River where it enters the scabland is more than 75 feet thick. Another built eastward up the Snake River from the mouth of the Pa-

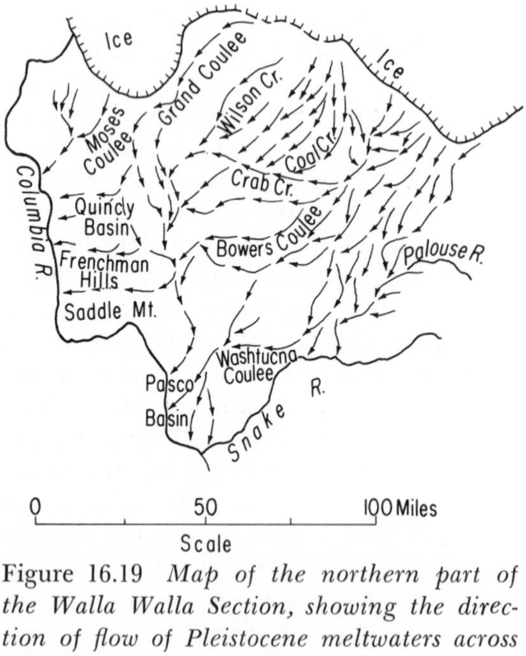

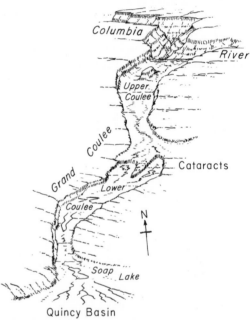

Figure 16.20 *The Grand Coulee, Washington. The coulee heads at the rim of the canyon of the Columbia River. Grand Coulee Dam, not shown, is at the bend in the canyon just west of the head of the coulee. The walls of the Upper Coulee, which is about 25 miles long, reach heights of about 800 feet. They decrease in height southward, and the Upper Coulee ends in a set of cataracts 400 feet high that mark the head of Lower Coulee. The Lower Coulee, also about 25 miles long, crosses a monocline in the lavas. The west wall is higher than the east wall.*

Figure 16.19 *Map of the northern part of the Walla Walla Section, showing the direction of flow of Pleistocene meltwaters across the plateau surface during the period in which the rivers at the north were dammed by glacial ice.*

louse is 260 feet thick and extends about 5 miles up valley. These deltaic deposits indicate a reversal of the direction of flow of the streams and are attributed to floods that backed up the valleys from the scabland area.

A vast quantity of water was required to erode the scablands and to deposit the deltas and huge bars. Some geologists have doubted that the melting glaciers alone could have provided the necessary floods, and have postulated a catastrophic release of water from glacial Lake Missoula (Fig. 13.22), along Clarks Fork, in Montana. The ice front extended from the vicinity of Spokane northeastward across the Spokane River and Clarks Fork. If water stored in Lake Missoula had been released suddenly by failure of the ice dam, the resulting flood would have discharged into the scabland part of the Columbia Plateau. There may have been a succession of such floods. Lake Missoula may have alternately filled and overflowed, thereby cutting an escape channel in the ice, which could have been sealed again by the ice when the flood had subsided.

Landslides

Several hundred landslides have developed along the Columbia River around the north and west sides of the Walla Walla Section (Fig. 16.21); landslides have developed also along the river gorge through the Cascade Range. The Bonneville Dam abuts against a landslide that covers several square miles; a major earthquake in that area could cause a disaster.

Most of the slides have occurred in Pleistocene and Recent stream and lake deposits of silt, sand, and gravel, like the deposits upstream from Grand Coulee Dam that were laid down in the lake upstream from the Okanogan lobe of glacial ice. The sliding dates back to the time of these Pleistocene lakes, but the number of landslides has greatly increased as a result of the newly built reservoirs. The

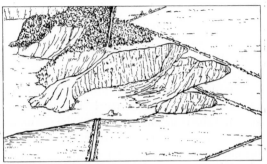

Figure 16.21 *Landslide along the shore of Franklin D. Roosevelt Lake on the Columbia River. In three days a multicove slide here severed the highway (foreground), which was located 2,000 feet back from the original lakeshore. The sliding created large waves on the lake; the largest reached a height of 65 feet on the opposite shore.*

slides, which are due partly to the lubricating effect of the water, partly to the weight of water, and partly to the water undercutting unstable formations, are of four major kinds.

Most commonly a block or series of blocks have slid on a surface that is concave toward the slid block, and the blocks have rotated backward along that surface (Fig. 16.22,A). The top of the block is a slumped mass; the lower end may be an earthflow. In the next most common kind of slide, the block or blocks rotate forward (Fig. 16.22,B). A third kind of slide develops where the slip surface is a series of scoops that develop alcoves along the rim above the slid blocks (Fig. 16.21). The alcoves originate as parts of one slide, but they grow by slump. A fourth kind of landslide consists of mudflows in which the material moves as a pasty fluid (Fig. 16.22,C). Considerable property damage has resulted from the landslides.

Some Valley Characteristics

Although the Columbia and Snake rivers make some large bends in crossing the Columbia Plateau, the general positions of the rivers and of the bends are structurally controlled. Hells Canyon is the outstanding exception, and an anomaly, but the rest of the course of the Snake River accords with the structure. The Columbia River crosses some folds at Frenchman Hills and Saddle Mountain, but except for these its course also accords with the structure. Between the big bends the river courses are straight. The only stretches that suggest meandering are the stretch of the Columbia River upstream from its gorge through the Cascade Range and the stretches of the Snake River upstream from its junction with the Columbia and upstream from Hell's Canyon. The straightness of these rivers contrasts with the meandering courses of the Colorado and Green rivers on the Colorado Plateau and

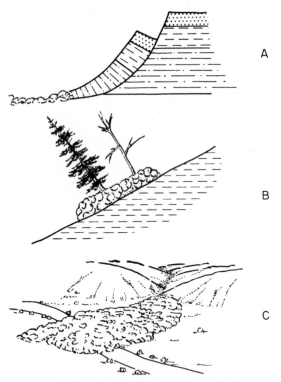

Figure 16.22 *In some landslides (A) the surface of sliding is concave toward the slid block, which rotates backward. In others (B) the slide surface is not concave, and the slid block rotates forward. Other slides (C) consist of mudflows.*

implies that the two plateaus have undergone different erosional histories.

Perhaps the most evident difference between the plateaus is that for most of its meandering course the Colorado River flows against the dip of the saucer-like structure of the Colorado Plateau, whereas the Columbia River first winds around the rim of the Columbia Plateau and then down into the center. The Columbia does not flow against the regional dip until it approaches the east flank of the Cascade uplift. The Colorado Plateau was tilted against its drainage, whereas much of the Columbia Plateau drained in the direction of the tilting.

Tributaries of the Columbia and Snake rivers have a curious mixture of straight and meandering courses (Fig. 16.23). The John Day River has perhaps the most sinuous course of any on the Columbia Plateau (Fig. 16.23,A). In the lower 50 miles, its canyon, which is about 1,500 feet deep, makes about 25 U-turns. The Deschutes River, 25 miles to the west, is more than twice the size of the John Day River but also has a meandering course. One of its tributaries is appropriately named Crooked River. Both the Deschutes and John Day rivers join the Columbia where the lavas begin their rise onto the Cascade Mountains.

In contrast to these rivers, other tributaries joining the Columbia River in the Umatilla and Pasco basins have nearly straight courses. Willow Creek, 25 miles east of the John Day, and Umatilla River, 35 miles farther east, meander very little either near their headwaters or in their lower courses where they join the Columbia (Fig. 16.23,A). These comparatively straight streams and their straight tributaries drain northward to the central part of the structural basin of the Columbia Plateau.

The Yakima River has closely spaced meanders where it crosses the anticlines north of Yakima and downstream where it emerges onto the broad plain of fill in the structural trough. The Columbia River has rapids (Priest Rapids) where it crosses the same set of anticlines, but its course is straight (Fig. 16.23,B). This difference probably reflects the difference in the volume and eroding power of the two streams.

Tributaries of the Snake River flow in straight courses down the north flank of the Blue Mountains. The Grande Ronde (Great Roundabout) River, however, which flows east to join the Snake River in a canyon about 2,000 feet deep, makes a U-turn every mile in the last 20 miles of its course (Fig. 16.23,C).

Hells Canyon is straight, but immediately upstream is one of the few stretches along which the Snake River has developed meanders. The relationship of meanders to struc-

ture is similar to that along the Yakima River and suggests that the uplift across Hells Canyon was sufficiently rapid to impede this river. Burnt River and Weiser River, the principal tributaries of the Snake River in this area, drain southward off the uplift to join the Snake at the head of Hells Canyon. Their general courses are straight, although they have developed small meanders within their valleys. The Payette, Boise, and Owyhee rivers meander on the floodplain in this area, as does the Snake.

Between this area and the eastern part of

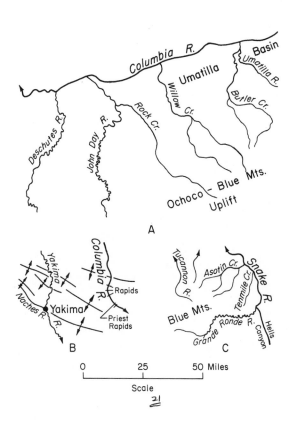

Figure 16.23 *Sketch maps illustrating some meander patterns on the Columbia Plateau. (A) Columbia River and its principal tributaries at the western edge of the plateau. (B) Yakima River and Columbia River where they cross anticlinally folded lavas. (C) Snake River and tributaries at the lower end of Hells Canyon and north flank of the Blue Mountains.*

the Snake River Plain, the Snake River does little meandering. Above American Falls, however, the river has developed a moderately meandering course, and the meanders have short radii and are closely spaced; meanders at the head of Hells Canyon have long radii and are correspondingly widely spaced. The difference may reflect the westward increase in size of the Snake River.

The straightness or degree of meandering of streams on the Columbia Plateau seems to correlate with the geologic structure. Streams draining down structure—that is, down the dip—tend to have straight courses; those along or crossing the structures tend to meander. But whether a stream develops meanders across an obstruction, such as a rising anticline, also seems to depend on the capacity of the stream

to erode its channel. This, in turn, is controlled by such factors as gradient, volume of water, roughness of the channel, and load. An additional complication is the likelihood that some drainage patterns are relicts of conditions that no longer exist, such as the floods that carved Grand Coulee.

Water Resources

Despite being semiarid the Columbia Plateau has abundant water supplies, both as surface water and as groundwater. The Columbia River enters the province with an average annual discharge greater than the Missouri River. Where it leaves the province and enters

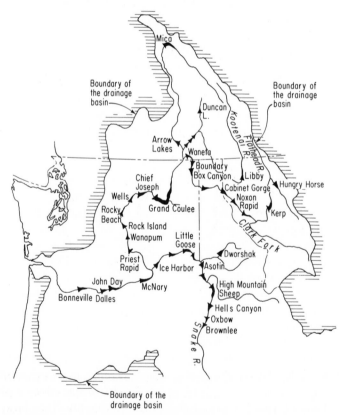

Figure 16.24   *Network of dams and reservoirs (some under construction, 1966)* *along the Columbia River and its principal tributaries.*

the Cascade Range the discharge is nearly half that of the Mississippi River at Memphis. Its principal tributary, the Snake River, has a discharge 3 or 4 times that of the Colorado River.

A network of dams and reservoirs has been constructed along the Columbia River (Fig. 16.24). The largest of these dams is the Grand Coulee Dam, which partly takes the place of the Pleistocene ice dam of the Okanogan glacial lobe. The dam is 550 feet high and more than 4,000 feet long. The Franklin D. Roosevelt Lake above it stores nearly 20,000,000 acre-feet of water, some of which is pumped to a storage reservoir in Grand Coulee, where it is distributed for irrigation in Quincy Basin (Fig. 16.20).

Where the Columbia River enters the United States its average annual discharge is about 71 million acre feet. By the time it leaves the Columbia Plateau and enters the Cascade Range, its discharge has doubled (Fig. 5.1). The total water-power potential in the Columbia Plateau is very much greater than that of the Tennessee Valley and Colorado River combined.

The Snake River enters the Snake River Plain above Idaho Falls, and from there to the mouth of the Boise River (Fig. 16.12), a distance of more than 300 miles, it has few tributaries. The Wood (Malad) River is the only stream from the mountains north of the plain that reaches the Snake River. Water from these streams is lost by seepage into the lavas and by evaporation. The tributaries from the south rise on the north rim of the Great Basin and are small. Despite the lack of large tributaries the volume of water in the Snake River increases greatly as it flows westward to the Payette Section, for it is supplied by groundwater. The annual discharge from one group of springs along a 40-mile stretch near Twin Falls is about 4,000,000 acre feet (Fig. 16.25).

The basaltic lavas through which the groundwater moves vary greatly in permeability. Some are dense and nearly impermeable; others have open lava tubes through which groundwater moves freely. Some permeable lavas overlie impermeable sedimentary beds, and the groundwater is perched. Figure 16.25 illustrates the setting of some of the springs that discharge to the Snake River in this area.

Groundwater supplies in the Snake River Plain and in the Payette Section are large, but heavy drafts are being made on that resource, and the surface waters are largely already allotted.

As the Snake River leaves the Payette Section and crosses the Ochoco-Blue Mountains Uplift, it is joined by several tributaries. On the west are the Owyhee River, Malheur River, Willow Creek, Burnt River, and Pine Creek. On the east are the Boise, Payette, Weiser, and Wildhorse rivers. More large tributaries join the Snake where it leaves the uplift and enters the Walla Walla Section. On the west are the Imnaha and Grande Ronde rivers; on the east the Salmon and Clearwater rivers. These tributaries more than triple the volume of the river along a 200-mile stretch.

The importance of groundwater to the flow of Snake River, as contrasted to the Columbia, is illustrated also by the difference in the quality of their water. Snake River at Twin Falls, Idaho, contains nearly 300 ppm of dissolved solids. It is an alkaline, calcium-magnesium bicarbonate water with a hardness of nearly 200. The Columbia River, above the mouth of Snake River, contains only 100 ppm of dissolved solids. It is slightly alkaline, and the hardness is well under 100.

Most towns on the Snake River Plain obtain their water from wells rather than from the river, because the river flows in a gorge that is in many places rather deep. Most of the wells are 100 to 500 feet deep, but one well at Idaho Falls is 1,600 feet deep. The total dissolved solids in this groundwater is commonly around 300 ppm, but locally exceeds 500 ppm. This is an alkaline, bicarbonate water that contains a moderate amount of sulfate. Where the content of alkalis (Na and K) equals that of alkali earths (Ca and Mg), the water is only moderately hard, but where there is much calcium and magnesium the hardness may be as high as 350.

Towns in the Payette Section also use groundwater rather than river water for their municipal supplies. The wells are 100 to 600 feet deep, and the water is of better quality than that farther east in the Snake River Plain. Groundwater in the Payette Section generally contains less than 200 ppm dissolved solids. The water is mostly bicarbonate water

but contains enough sulfate and alkalis to class most of it as a soft water with a hardness of less than 100.

The quality of water is excellent in those tributaries of the Columbia and Snake rivers that rise in the Cascades, in the Northern Rocky Mountains, and in the Ochoco-Blue Mountains Uplift. These waters have less than 75 ppm of dissolved solids, and commonly less than 50. By contrast, the southern tributaries of the Snake, which head in the rim of the Great Basin, have hard, alkaline waters con-

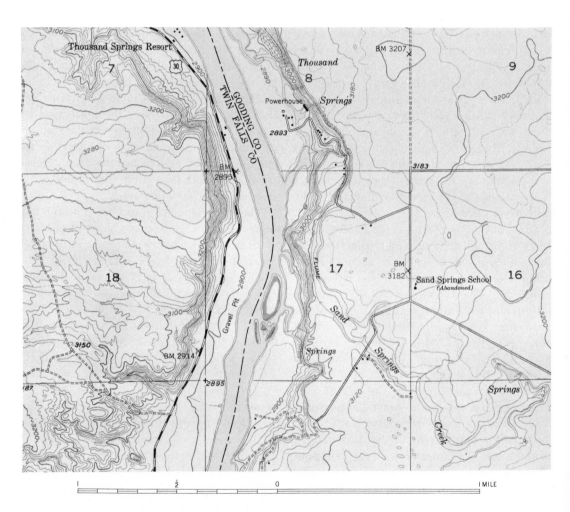

Figure 16.25 *Map of the Thousand Springs area along the Snake River, below Twin Falls, Idaho. These springs are large enough and high enough to supply a power plant. (From U.S.G.S. Thousand Springs, Idaho, quadrangle.)*

taining more than 250 ppm of dissolved solids.

In brief, water problems in the parts of the Columbia Plateau drained by the Columbia and Snake rivers relate to water distribution and floods, and both of these problems are gradually being eliminated by the dams and reservoirs that have been and will be constructed. Quantity, quality, and seasonal variability pose no problems. Nor has pollution been a problem, although it could become one if wastes escape from the atomic plant near Pasco.

Water supplies in the Harney Lake Section, are like those of the Great Basin. The playas are saline or alkaline, and the streams draining to them are intermittent. Harney Lake is generally too saline to be used by humans or livestock. Malheur Lake, which occasionally overflows to Harney Lake, is fresher, but even it is little used. Groundwater from bedrock formations, though not abundant, generally contains less than 700 ppm of dissolved solids and is satisfactory for irrigation, but some of this groundwater contains more than 2,000 ppm of dissolved solids and is not suitable.

Other Resources

The principal produce from the Columbia Plateau is agricultural. About 20 percent of the Columbia Plateau is arable land (Fig. 16.26) and the remainder is chiefly grazing land. About half the arable land is irrigated; the rest is dry-farmed.

The value of the agricultural produce exceeds a half billion dollars yearly. Almost half the produce consists of wheat and small grains; fruits account for about a quarter, and the remainder is about equally divided between livestock (including some dairying) and other crops, especially potatoes and sugar beets.

The grazing lands on the plateau are somewhat better than in the Great Basin, yet the three southern sections—Harney Basin, Payette, and Snake River Plain—on the average

cannot support even a dozen cows per square mile (about 50 acres per cow). Grazing lands are much better in the mountain sections.

Salmon fishing, formerly considerable, has declined because the dams and reservoirs have obstructed the salmon runs.

Sawmills are numerous, especially in the Spokane area. There is little manufacturing, although this is changing because of the availability of ample hydroelectric power. At Richland, in southeastern Washington, is the government's huge Hanford plant and reservation for separating plutonium from uranium. The plant stands on the site of the former village of Hanford.

The mineral production and resources of the Columbia Plateau have not been nationally significant. Considerable chromite has been found in the Ochoco and Blue mountains, and undeveloped deposits of clay with a high alumina content are extensive in a belt

Key:

▓▓▓	Wheat
⋯⋯	Peas, wheat
≡≡≡	Irrigated; special crops; hay, fruit, dairy
∴∴∴	Irrigated; potatoes, sugar beets, grain
☐	Grazing

Figure 16.26 *Land utilization in the Columbia Plateau.*

of Palouse Soil extending 75 miles southeast from Spokane. Some of these clays are residual deposits (ancient soils) resulting from the weathering of the Columbia River basalts. Others, similar to those on the basalts, developed on the granitic rocks of the Idaho batholith. Still others are transported deposits derived by erosion of the residual ones. The deposits could become an important source of aluminum ore when methods are found for economically extracting the metal from the clay.

Other mineral deposits on the Columbia Plateau are minor. Some antimony, mercury, gold, and silver have been found in the Ochoco and Blue mountains. Small zinc deposits are known in the Owyhee Mountains, but the future of the mineral industry in the Columbia Plateau depends on someone finding a use for that black rock known as basalt.

Pacific Mountain System

17

The Pacific Mountain System (Fig. 17.1) comprises about 200,000 square miles along the coast and extending east to the deserts in the Basin and Range Province and the Columbia Plateau. The mountains, which are among the highest in the United States, account for those deserts, for they wring the moisture from air moving inland from the ocean.

Structurally and topographically the mountains are of five kinds:

1. Granitic mountains, represented by the Sierra Nevada, Klamath Mountains, some ranges in the northern part of the Cascades, and the Lower California Province.
2. Volcanic mountains, represented by the Cascade Range.
3. Mountains composed of complexly folded and faulted formations that are mostly pre-Tertiary in age; represented by the Transverse Ranges, California Coast Ranges north of San Francisco Bay, Olympic Mountains, and some of the ranges at the north end of the Cascades.
4. Mountains composed of moderately folded but much faulted formations that are mostly Tertiary in age and easily eroded; represented by the Oregon Coast Range and by the California Coast Ranges south of San Francisco Bay.
5. Dome mountains, represented by the Marysville Buttes in the Central Valley of California near Sacramento.

The mountains in this system are arranged like three links of a chain. The northern link —formed by the Cascade Range, the Oregon Coast Range, and the Olympic Mountains— is joined at the south by the Klamath Mountains. The Puget Trough, which includes the Willamette Valley in Oregon, forms the hole in the northern link.

South of the Klamath Mountains the Central Valley of California forms the hole in the middle link, which is made up of the Sierra Nevada and the California Coast Ranges. These mountains are joined at the south where the Sierra curves westward. The southern link is formed by the Transverse Ranges, the Lower California Province, and the Salton Trough.

Perhaps the two most distinctive features of the Pacific Mountain System are its variety and the number of its extremes, for it is a land of superlatives. It has mountains that are among the highest, roughest, and most scenic in the United States, but the troughs between the mountains are superlatively low, flat, and monotonous. Part of the land is as densely populated as any part of the United States, yet other parts are wilderness. Average annual rainfall ranges from less than 10 inches to more than 140 inches. Some parts are hot; others are the site of glaciers. Desert shrubs grow in some areas, whereas other areas sup-

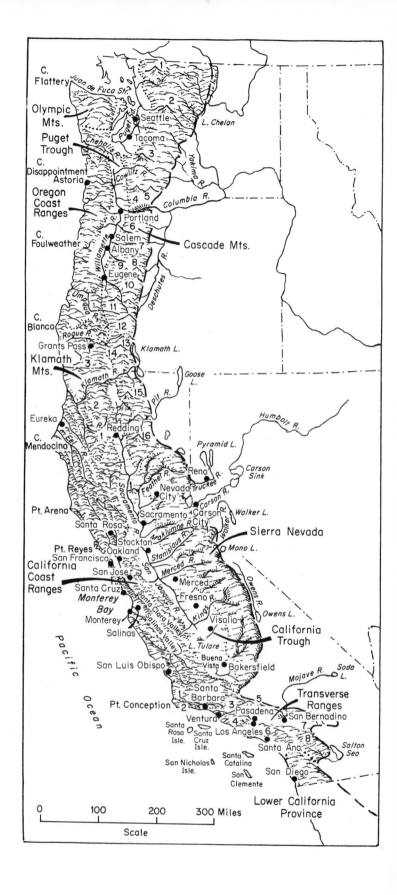

Volcanic Peaks Along
the Cascade Range

1. Mt. Baker
2. Glacier Peak
3. Mt. Rainier
4. Mt. St. Helens
5. Mt. Adams
6. Mt. Hood
7. Mt. Jefferson
8. Black Butte
9. Belknap Crater
10. Three Sisters
11. Diamond Peak
12. Mt. Thielsen
13. Crater Lake
14. Mt. Loughlin
15. Mt. Shasta
16. Lassen Peak

Mountains in the Klamath
Mountains Province

1. Trinity Mts.
2. Salmon Mts.
3. Siskiyou Mts.

Mountains in the
California Trough

1. Marysville Buttes

Mountains in the
Transverse Ranges

1. San Rafael Mts.
2. Santa Ynez Mts.
3. Topatopa Mts.
4. Santa Monica Mts.
5. San Gabriel Mts.
6. Santa Ana Mts.
7. San Bernardino Mts.
8. San Jacinto Mts.

Figure 17.1 *Physio-
graphic map of the Pa-
cific Mountain System.*

port dense forests of giant redwoods. And it includes some of the sunniest and some of the foggiest and smoggiest parts of the United States.

The mountainous coast, which contrasts sharply with the broad coastal plain along the Atlantic seaboard, is part of the circum-Pacific volcanic belt and has been the site of volcanic eruptions in historic time, at Mount Lassen. It also is part of the seismically active belt bordering the Pacific and is subject to frequent, severe earthquakes.

The resources are richly productive and varied. Energy resources include hydroelectric power, a little coal, and tremendous quantities of petroleum. Of the metals there is iron and mercury, and gold was once important in California's economy. Among the nonmetals there is substantial salt production. Agricultural products include fruits of all kinds, vegetables, and grains. Lumbering is a major industry; so too are fishing and wine-growing (in California). San Francisco has one of the world's finest harbors, and it is most favorably located midway along the Pacific Coast and beside the great circle route from the Panama Canal to the Asiatic ports (Fig. 17.2). This, combined with the abundant and varied natural resources, has led to extensive industrial de-

velopment. There was a time when goods manufactured in the east were advertised as, "prices slightly higher west of the Rocky Mountains," but that day has almost gone. Prices that are "slightly higher" cannot compete for long in a market so big with an economy so nearly self-sufficient.

The population, about 20 million, averages close to 100 per square mile but is concentrated toward the coast; the Cascades and Sierra Nevada are thinly populated.

Structural Framework and Topography

Cascade-Sierra Mountains

The Sierra Nevada and Cascade Mountains are combined as a physiographic province 1,000 miles long and 50 to 100 miles wide. These are the highest mountains discussed thus far, and they form a barrier that can be crossed at only a few places.

Structurally the mountains are an uplift, in places surmounted by volcanoes and lavas.

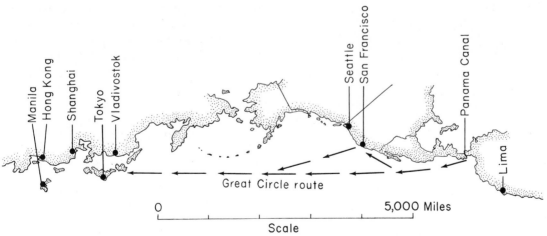

Figure 17.2 *Location of San Francisco relative to the Great Circle route between the Panama Canal and Asiatic ports.*

The highest parts of the uplift are at the ends —at the south end of the Sierra Nevada and at the north end of the Cascades. At these ends of the province granitic rocks and older metamorphosed sedimentary formations are exposed. A sag in the uplift is represented by the Southern Cascades Section, and the old rocks there are buried under young volcanoes and lavas. This sag is the site of two streams that cross the uplift, Klamath River and Pit River. Besides the mighty Columbia, they are the only rivers that do. The Feather River, at the north end of the Sierra Nevada, extends very nearly across the barrier.

This elongate uplift marks a sharp western boundary of the Great Basin and Columbia Plateau. The west side of the uplift is marked by narrow structural and topographic troughs, except at the Klamath Mountains, which adjoin the sag at the Southern Cascades Section.

SIERRA NEVADA

The Sierra Nevada is a huge block mountain, about 350 miles long and roughly 60 miles wide, raised by faulting on the east and tilted west (Figs. 17.3, 17.4). The fault-block structure is similar to that in the Great Basin (Fig. 14.12), but the Sierra stands apart because it is so very large and is composed chiefly of granite. It is a block-faulted granitic batholith.

The Sierra Nevada reaches its maximum height along the eastern fault scarp, only 5 to 10 miles from the eastern foot of the mountains (Fig. 17.5). The eastern foot is at altitudes between 4,500 and 5,000 feet; the summit is 9,000 feet higher. From the summit, the mountains slope westward for more than 50 miles and pass under the fill in the California Trough at an altitude of about 1,000 feet (Fig. 17.4).

As a consequence of this structure, the mountains drain mostly to the west, and the dozen or so major rivers have cut deep valleys, some nearly a mile deep, into the granite. Yosemite Valley is the best known of these. The sediments derived by erosion of these valleys have been deposited as huge alluvial fans at the edge of the California Trough, and as older fill within it.

Carboniferous, Triassic, and Jurassic formations are extensive along the western foot of the Sierra, especially toward the north, and they form a belt 25 miles wide extending diagonally across the Sierra just north of the latitude of Sacramento (Fig. 2.1). These formations, all folded and faulted and consider-

Figure 17.3 *Diagram of the Sierra Nevada, the California Trough, and the California Coast Ranges.*

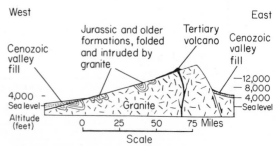

Figure 17.4 *Cross section illustrating the general structure of the Sierra Nevada.*

ably metamorphosed, were intruded by, and form the roof of, the granite of the batholith.

The roof of the granite batholith dips northward as well as westward, and the recency of this northward structural tilt is shown by the progressive northward decrease in the altitudes of passes across the mountains. The lowest pass, at the head of the Feather River, is at an altitude of 5,218 feet. This pass is used by the Western Pacific Railroad and Alternate U. S. Highway 40. Altitudes of the passes and the routes that utilize them are, in order from north to south (Fig. 17.3):

> Donner Pass, northwest of Lake Tahoe; U. S. 40 and Southern Pacific Railroad; 7,089 feet.
>
> Emerald Pass, south of Lake Tahoe; U. S. 50; about 7,100 feet.
>
> Carson Pass, north of the North Fork of the Mokelumne River; Route 88; 8,573 feet.
>
> Ebbets Pass, into the North Fork of the Stanislaus River; Route 4; 8,730 feet.
>
> Sonora Pass, into South Fork of the Stanislaus River; Route 108; 9,626 feet.
>
> Tioga Pass, north of Yosemite Valley; Route 120; 9,941 feet.

For a distance of 150 miles south of Tioga Pass no road crosses the Sierra Nevada. Toward the south end the range slopes southward. Walker Pass, used by Route 178, between the Kern River and Owens River, is at an altitude of 5,250 feet. Tehachapi Pass, used by U. S. Highway 466 and the railroads between the Central Valley and Mojave Desert, is at an altitude of 3,988 feet.

The Sierra Nevada, a truly formidable barrier (Fig. 17.6), is unique among the mountain ranges of the United States in that its great length is not crossed by any river. The Feather River, which extends almost across it, heads in an open, lava-filled valley at about 5,000 feet in altitude. A wind gap at the head of that valley is only 200 feet higher than the Great Basin drainage a mile to the east. Almost certainly the Humboldt River and other streams draining the Great Basin once discharged westward through this wind gap and

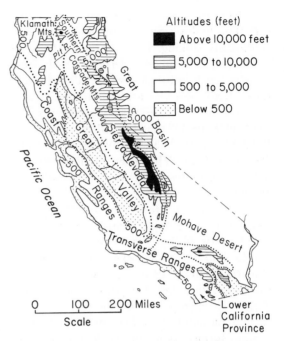

Figure 17.5 *Altitudes in the southern provinces of the Pacific Mountain System.*

across the Sierra Nevada by way of the Feather River. This drainage probably was disrupted in late Quaternary time as a result of a few scores of feet of displacement of the Sierra block, coupled perhaps with lava flows that may have contributed to damming the drainage courses.

The granitic batholith began forming in late Jurassic time, and the Jurassic and older sedimentary formations that formed the roof were folded, faulted, and metamorphosed, and granitic masses were intruded into them in late Jurassic and in Cretaceous time. Veins of gold-bearing quartz were deposited in the fractured rocks in a belt almost parallel to the range and near its western base. This belt of veins later became known as the Mother Lode; these are the deposits that led to the great gold rush of 1849.

During Cretaceous time, the Sierra was high enough to have been the source of thick sediments (Chico Formation) deposited in basins parallel to the coast and just west of the batholith. The basins were shallow, but they were continually sinking, and a total thickness of 25,000 feet of sediments, derived largely from granitic rock, was deposited. The present Great Basin also was a mountainous area at this time (p. 317), for it shed sediments into the Cretaceous sea that flooded the sites of the Colorado Plateau, the Rocky Mountains, and the Great Plains. The ancestral Sierra Nevada formed the western edge of that mountainous area.

In early Eocene time, the ancestral Sierra continued to be high enough to shed sediments westward, but the western edges of the granite and the roof rocks were submerged. The sedimentary deposits, about 7,500 feet thick (Martinez and Tejon formations), were derived in large part from the erosion of the granitic batholith. Coal beds developed where swamps formed along the ancient shore, now the western foot of the Sierra.

During the Oligocene Epoch the Sierran granite and other rocks were deeply weathered. Sediments eroded from the weathered zones were deposited in troughs farther west than those that existed during Eocene.

In Miocene time the Sierra Nevada was largely buried under volcanic ash and lava flows. The erosion of this volcanic cover and of the underlying rocks resulted in the deposition of 12,000 feet of sediments in marine basins to the west (Vaqueros, Temblor, Monterey, and Santa Margarita Formations). By this time, though, the Great Basin, which had begun to break up as a result of faulting in Oligocene time, was sufficiently broken to disrupt much of the drainage from that area across the ancestral Sierra, and the physiographic provinces in that part of the country began to take the forms we know today.

The Sierra Nevada appears to have become defined as a distinct structural unit during Pliocene time. The summit, now 11,000 to 14,000 feet high, is thought to have reached a height of about 7,000 feet during the Pliocene, and canyons about 1,000 feet deep had been cut into the western slope. These structural movements were accompanied by volcanism, and lava flows poured down the canyons. The Pliocene deposits west of the Sierra Nevada (Jacalitos, Etchegoin, and Tulare Formations) are 10,000 feet thick, but only parts of these sediments were derived by erosion of the Sierra; some of these sediments were derived from highlands that lay farther to the west and now are submerged under the Pacific Ocean.

It was in Pleistocene time that the Sierra became raised and tilted to its present height and

Figure 17.6 *Eastern front of the Sierra Nevada, overlooking the Great Basin in the vicinity of the Owens River. The summit, 11,000 to 14,000 feet in altitude, is 6,000 to 8,000 feet higher than the Owens Valley. This is the faulted, east side of the Sierra; the displacement is at least as great as the topographic relief and may be two or three times that amount.*

position. The mountain tops were glaciated at least three times, and the canyons were eroded to their present depths. In places the topography has become inverted, for some of the Tertiary lavas that had flowed down canyons now form ridges, because erosion has reduced the surrounding granitic terrain to lower levels than the lava.

The glaciers deepened some valleys to such an extent that tributaries were left as hanging valleys, like the many examples in Yosemite Valley (Fig. 17.7). The glaciers extended down the faulted east side of the Sierra to the desert basin below, depositing huge terminal moraines at the mouths of canyons at altitudes of about 6,000 feet. On the wetter west side the glaciers extended down to about 3,000 feet. The summit is scored with cirques. Many of them contain lakes, and some sheltered ones contain ice fields.

As a result of this structural history, there are two quite different ages and kinds of topography in the Sierra Nevada. The older topography, represented by the uplands between the canyons, was and still is a surface without great local relief and without steep slopes. Subsequent uplift and westward tilting of that surface enabled the glaciers and rivers to cut deeply into it and to develop a younger and very rugged topography between the remnants of the older surface. Such differences in kind and age of landforms are referred to as *topographic unconformities.* They are characteristic of recently elevated mountains, and are a distinctive feature of the Klamath and Northern Cascade mountains as well as of the Sierra Nevada.

CASCADE MOUNTAINS

The Cascade Range is divided into three sections (Fig. 17.8). The Southern Cascades mark the lava-covered structural sag in the Sierra-Cascade uplift, and they end southward where the granitic and older rocks of the Sierra Nevada rise southward from beneath the lavas. The structure rises northward too, and the Middle Cascades consist of an uplift of middle

Tertiary lavas surmounted by huge volcanic cones of Pleistocene age. The Northern Cascades, structurally the highest part of these mountains, are like the Sierra Nevada in that they are composed of granitic rocks and older metamorphosed sedimentary formations.

Much of the lava field of the Southern Cascades is less than 5,000 feet in altitude. It extends eastward far into the Great Basin and westward to the west side of the California Trough. Its surface is studded with volcanic cones (Fig. 17.9), many of them a few thousand feet high. Two of the high ones are Mount Shasta, which exceeds 14,000 feet (Fig. 17.10), and Mount Lassen, which reaches to about 10,500 feet. Mount Lassen, which erupted in 1914 and 1915, has been made a national park. Although the Southern Cascades are crossed by the Klamath and Pit rivers, much of the drainage has been disrupted by the flows. Lakes are numerous, but many are dry because the lavas are porous.

In the Middle Cascades Section early and middle Tertiary lavas rise northward from under the late Tertiary and Quaternary ones. As the uplifted lavas rise northward, the Quaternary lavas decrease in extent but form an imposing row of huge Quaternary volcanoes (Fig. 17.11).

The high part of the mountains is near the east side, overlooking the Columbia Plateau. This crest, which is marked by a row of Quaternary volcanoes, is referred to as the High Cascades; the mountainous west slope, composed almost wholly of dissected early and middle Tertiary lavas, is referred to as the Western Cascades. The Western Cascades are so eroded that no trace remains of their original volcanic landscape.

Uplift had begun by Miocene time, and by the end of that epoch the mountains were high enough to cut off moisture from the Columbia Plateau, which became increasingly arid. The uplift was accomplished partly by arching of the Miocene lavas and partly by faulting along the east side (Fig. 17.12,B). The Miocene lavas were highly fluid basalt and formed

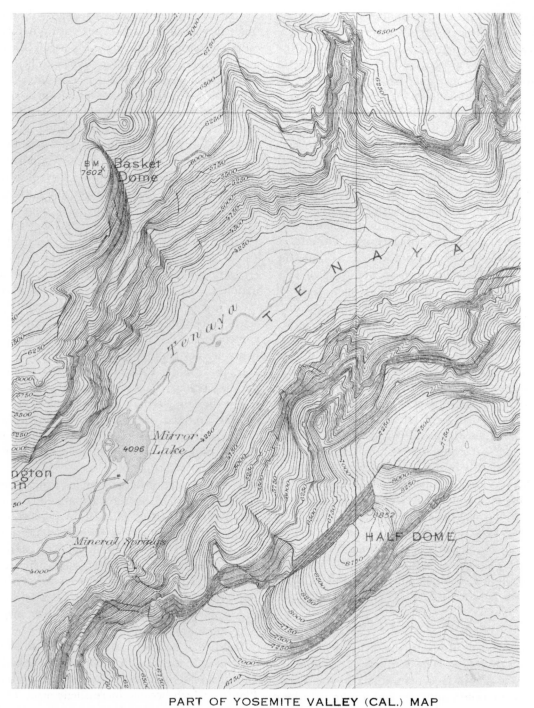

PART OF YOSEMITE VALLEY (CAL.) MAP

Contour interval 50 feet.

Figure 17.7 *U-shaped, glaciated valley at Half Dome, in Yosemite National Park. (From U.S.G.S. Yosemite Valley map, 1908.)*

broad, low, shield volcanoes; the later eruptives were more viscous andesite, which built high, steep-sided cones of interlayered volcanic ash and lavas on the broad shield volcanoes (Figs. 17.12,C; 17.13).

Crater Lake, another national park, once was a high volcanic cone, referred to as Mount Mazama. It was not unlike Mount Rainier and was once probably as high, but an eruption in late Pleistocene time fractured the cone, ejected great quantities of ash, and caused the remaining part to collapse into the throat of the volcano. This kind of structure is called a *caldera* (Fig. 17.12,D). The lake partly filling it is about 2,000 feet deep.

During Pleistocene time glaciers formed on all the peaks of the High Cascades above 9,000 feet, and glaciers still remain on the high peaks. These have greatly modified the volcanoes, but the conical forms are still clearly preserved. On Mount Mazama glaciers truncated by the collapse of the caldera provide evidence of the former great height of the original volcano.

Only one river, the Columbia, crosses the Middle Cascades (Figs. 17.11, 17.14). Since the present course of the river is almost the same as it was in Miocene time, the river is essentially antecedent across the Miocene and later uplifts. Lake beds on the Columbia Plateau side of the gorge indicate that the river was ponded at times, probably by a combination of lava flows and uplift of the channel. But the tremendous discharge of the river caused it to overflow each time along its former elevated course.

North of Mount Rainier the Cascades were greatly uplifted. The mountains there are composed of granitic rocks intrusive into older metamorphosed sedimentary rocks, and resemble the Northern Rocky Mountains to the east, except that the Cascades are several thousands of feet higher. The rocks and structures of the Northern Cascades are like those in the Sierra Nevada, and the landforms are of two ages and of two kinds, as are those in the Sierra. The upland is an old surface without

much relief, and incised into it are steep-sided, deep valleys that developed as a result of the uplift. In addition, the Northern Cascades are surmounted by Quaternary volcanic cones like those in the south. One of these is Mount Baker (altitude 10,750 feet).

Pacific Border Province

CALIFORNIA TROUGH

The California Trough, which forms the Great Valley between the Sierra Nevada and the Coast Ranges, is a structural trough—part of a Tertiary and Quaternary geosyncline. In the southern part of the trough, where the structural depth is greatest, Tertiary and younger formations bury the granitic batholith and its roof rocks to a depth of at least 3 miles. The axis of the trough is near the western edge of the Great Valley, and there the base of the geosynclinal sediments

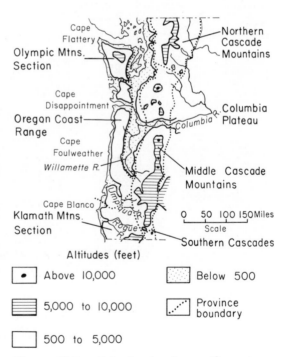

Altitudes (feet)

•	Above 10,000	▦	Below 500
☰	5,000 to 10,000	⬚	Province boundary
☐	500 to 5,000		

Figure 17.8 *Altitudes in the northern provinces of the Pacific Mountain System.*

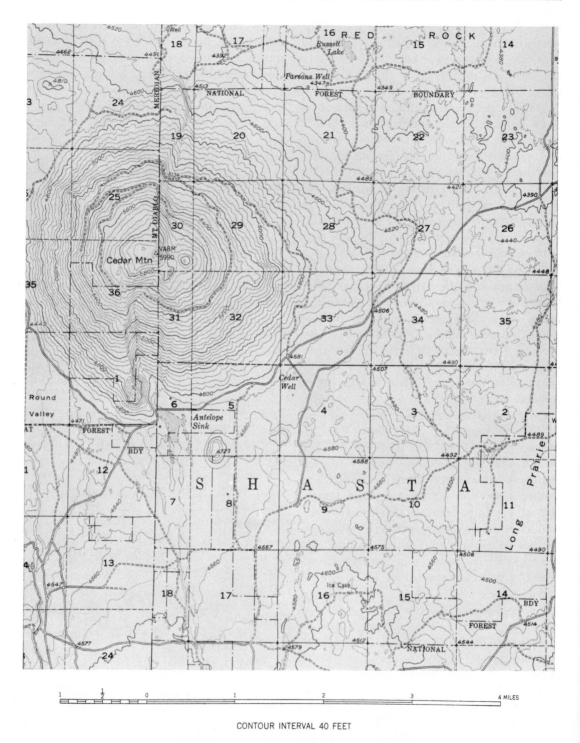

CONTOUR INTERVAL 40 FEET

Figure 17.9 *Map of volcanic cone and lava field in the Southern Cascade Mountains. (From U.S.G.S. Bray, California, quadrangle.)*

has not been reached by even the deepest drill holes. Most of the sedimentary deposits were derived by erosion of the Sierra Nevada; the youngest deposits form long, low alluvial fans that slope westward from the foot of the Sierra. The sedimentary formations deposited in the trough, especially toward the south, are richly petroliferous, and some of California's principal oil fields are producing from them.

Most of the California Trough is below 500 feet in altitude, and about a third of it is less than 100 feet in altitude. The northern part is drained by the Sacramento River. Most of the southern part drains to the San Joaquin River, but the southernmost quarter is a closed basin containing two playas, Tulare Lake and Buena Vista Lake. This basin probably is due chiefly to structural sinking of the south end of the Great Valley, but may be due in part to deposition of an alluvial fan at the mouth of Kings River.

The Marysville Buttes, located between the Sacramento and Feather rivers, about 50 miles north of Sacramento, are about 10 miles in diameter and about 2,000 feet higher than the surrounding plain. They are dome mountains caused by the intrusion of stocks and laccoliths. As the igneous activity continued, the intrusions broke through to the surface and erupted as a volcano.

Figure 17.10 *Mount Shasta, California, a volcano in the Southern Cascades. The volcanic cone is about 2 miles high. The altitude of the base is about 3,500 feet; the peak is above 14,000 feet. The upper limit of plant growth is about 13,000 feet; timberline is at about 9,000 to 9,500 feet. The base of the mountain is in the Transition Zone, here characterized by sugar pine.*

CALIFORNIA COAST RANGES

The California Coast Ranges (Fig. 17.3) consist of a series of ridges and valleys trending about northwest and about parallel to the coast. The summits of most ridges are below 5,000 feet, and a good many are below 3,000 feet (Fig. 17.5). Along most of the coast there are four ranges separated by three valleys; most of the ranges and valleys are short and interrupted by offsets.

North of San Francisco Bay the rocks that make up the Coast Ranges are complexly

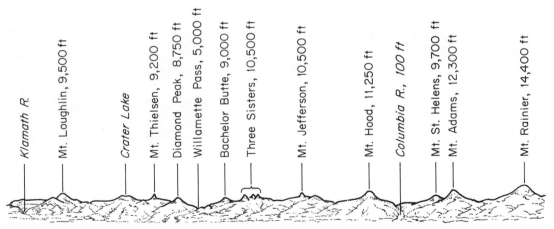

Figure 17.11 *Diagram of the middle Cascade Mountains as seen from the east. The mountains are an anticlinal uplift of early and middle Tertiary lavas surmounted by volcanic cones of late Tertiary and Quarternary age.*

folded and faulted Mesozoic formations, mostly Cretaceous and older. These formations continue in the ranges south of the bay, but along with them are younger formations that are also folded and faulted, although less so than the older rocks (Fig. 17.15).

One of the principal faults controlling the Coast Ranges is the San Andreas fault (Figs. 2.11, 17.16). Displacement along this fault is mostly lateral; the block on the west is moving northward relative to the one on the east.

Since Cretaceous time this displacement may have been more than 100 miles; this could have been accomplished at a rate of only 15 to 20 feet in every thousand years. The displacement at the time of the 1906 earthquake was as much as 20 feet. Some effects of geologic structure on topography are strikingly illustrated by the San Andreas fault near Point

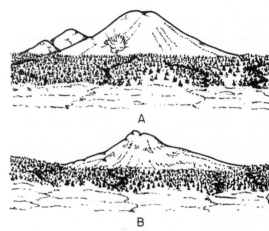

Figure 17.13   *Mt. Rainier (A) and Mt. Hood (B) viewed from the west. The base of the cone of Mt. Rainier is about 5,000 feet in altitude and about 15 miles in diameter; the peak is at 14,408 feet. The base of the cone of Mt. Hood is about 4,500 feet in altitude and 10 miles in diameter; its peak is at 11,245 feet.*

A. Early Tertiary shield volcanoes.

B. Middle Tertiary. Shield volcanoes continue to grow, and the lavas become arched and faulted upward.

C. Late Tertiary and Quaternary. Shield volcanoes continue to be arched and faulted upward; steep sided cones of andesitic lavas and ash are built on the arch.

D. Late Quaternary at Crater Lake. An eruption destroys the top of the ancient volcano, Mt. Mazama, and deposits a layer of ash over the Pacific Northwest; collapse of the cone into the throat of the volcano develops a caldera, which contains Crater Lake.

Figure 17.12   *Cross sections of the Middle Cascades, illustrating the arching of the early and middle Tertiary lavas, faulting along the east side of the mountains, and the late Tertiary and Quarternary volcanic cones built on top of the earlier structures.*

Figure 17.14   *Gorge of the Columbia River across the Cascade Mountains (view up river). The mountains are formed by Miocene and Pliocene lavas that were raised anticlinally across the River's course. The altitude of the upper surface of these lavas is 4,500 to 5,000 feet, and at least that amount of uplift has occurred.*

Reyes, 20 miles northwest of San Francisco Bay (Fig. 17.16).

Because of the geologic structure, drainage in the Coast Ranges has developed a trellis pattern. Many streams, after following a strike valley, turn and cut across one or more structural ridges. Russian River (Fig. 17.3) is an example. Drainage from the California Trough crosses the Coast Ranges only at San Francisco Bay.

There is some question about how long the Sacramento and San Joaquin rivers have discharged into the Pacific Ocean through the Golden Gate. The absence of a submarine canyon off San Francisco Bay, and the existence of a sizable one off Monterey Bay (Fig. 17.15), suggests that drainage into San Francisco Bay may once have discharged by way of the Santa Clara Valley, which now drains northward, and then across the divide separating the Santa Clara and Salinas valleys (Fig. 17.3) and into the ocean at Monterey Bay.

TRANSVERSE RANGES

The Transverse Ranges (Fig. 17.17), classed as a section of the Pacific Border Province, consist of ranges and basins trending nearly east and transverse to the southeasterly trends of the adjoining areas, as in the Sierra Nevada, California Trough, and Coast Ranges at the north, and in the Lower California, or Peninsular, Province at the south. The transverse structures also control the easterly trending coast between Point Conception and Santa Monica, the Santa Barbara Channel, and Channel Islands. The ranges are mostly

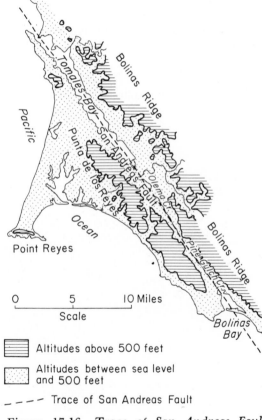

Figure 17.16 *Trace of San Andreas Fault in the vicinity of Point Reyes. The northwest-trending ridges and valleys in the California Coast Ranges are structurally controlled, like the valley between Bolinas Ridge and Point Reyes. (From U.S.G.S. Point Reyes, California, quadrangle.)*

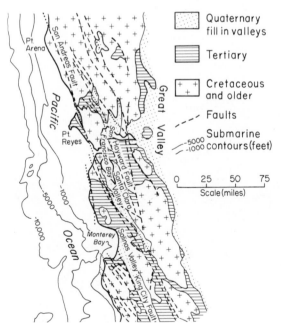

Figure 17.15 *Geologic map of part of the California Coast Ranges, illustrating the fault system. (Generalized from U.S.G.S. and A.A.P.G.)*

faulted anticlines, structurally rather like the Coast Ranges to the north, and the basins are faulted synclines. The Channel Islands are peaks on the otherwise submerged parts of the uplift at the Santa Monica Mountains, and the Santa Barbara Channel is the still-submerged western extension of the Ventura Basin (Fig. 17.18).

Toward the west the mountains consist mostly of marine formations of Tertiary age; those to the east are higher and consist mostly of older rocks, including much granite. The basins contain thick deposits of Tertiary age that are buried under Quaternary fill, much of it marine.

The highest ranges in this section—the San Gabriel and San Bernardino mountains—are located along the San Andreas fault. Both ranges reach altitudes of more than 10,000 feet. They consist of Mesozoic granite and older, highly metamorphosed sedimentary and volcanic rocks. Both ranges are bounded by faults.

The Los Angeles Basin, a coastal lowland covering about a thousand square miles, is the only part of the Pacific Border Province that might be referred to as a coastal plain. Its structure, though, is quite unlike that of the Atlantic or Gulf Coastal Plains, for the structural floor of the basin is buried under 30,000 feet of folded and faulted Cretaceous, Tertiary, and Quaternary deposits. In Miocene time the basin extended beyond its present limits, but it became smaller as it filled. Today, only the western part remains submerged. The faults in the Los Angeles Basin are marked by rows of hills. Most of these are uplifts and are the site of oil fields.

KLAMATH MOUNTAINS

The Klamath Mountains Section of the Pacific Border Province (Fig. 17.19) is a mountainous

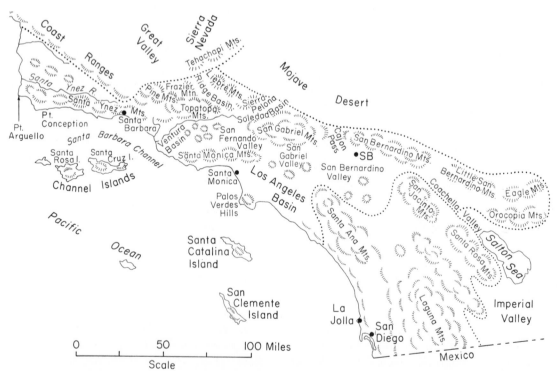

Figure 17.17 *Principal ranges and basins in the Transverse Ranges.*

coastal area between the Coast Ranges of California and Oregon. The rocks in this section, and their structures, are like those of the Sierra Nevada. Paleozoic and early Mesozoic formations, much deformed and metamorphosed, were intruded by Cretaceous(?) granite, and the older rocks and structures were further modified during Tertiary and Quaternary time by uplift and other deformation that has elevated the mountains to their present position.

The uplifted formations plunge gradually southward and extend under the California Coast Ranges, the northern parts of which are composed of Mesozoic formations. The general southward plunge continues to the southern part of the California Coast Ranges, which are composed of Tertiary formations. To the north, the Klamath Mountains uplift plunges sharply under the Oregon Coast Range, which is composed of Tertiary formations, and east-

ward the uplift extends beneath the Quaternary lavas that form the Cascade Mountains.

Klamath River and Rogue River, antecedent across the uplift, follow meandering gorges incised to depths of 1,500 to 2,500 feet into an old erosion surface that is preserved across the uplands. The high peaks, most of which are between 5,000 and 7,500 feet in altitude, are monadnocks that rise above the upland marking the old erosion surface.

The geologic structures in the granitic and older rocks of the Klamath Mountains Section are arcuate in plan. At the south, where the folds and faults emerge from beneath the California Trough and the lavas of the Southern Cascades, the trends are northwest. Viewed from south to north, these structures curve first to the north, and then, in the northern part of the section, to the northeast where they extend under the Middle Cascades. If projected southward, the trends would con-

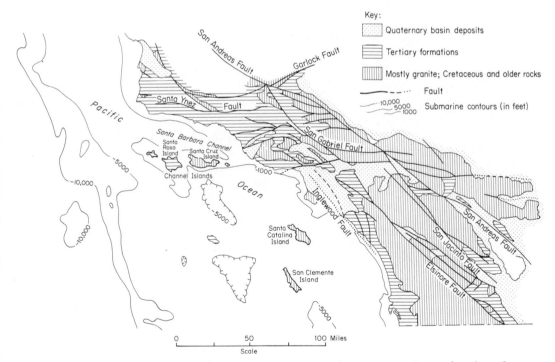

Figure 17.18 *Transverse Ranges and Lower California Province, showing the fault pattern that controls those ranges and basins. (Generalized from U.S.G.S. and A.A.P.G.)*

nect with the structures in the Sierra Nevada; if projected northeastward, they would connect with the Ochoco-Blue Mountains uplift on the Columbia Plateau (p. 355). The uplifts at the Sierra Nevada, Klamath Mountains, and Ochoco-Blue Mountains may be one continuous, sinuous structure.

OREGON COAST RANGE

The Oregon Coast Range consists of irregular hills and low mountains along the coast of

Figure 17.19 *Orientation map of the Klamath Mountains Section in the Pacific Border Province.*

Oregon and southwestern Washington. The highest summits are a little more than 3,000 feet in altitude; the relief is generally less than 2,000 feet (Fig. 17.8). Hillsides are rounded and the valleys are open. The topography resembles that of some parts of the Appalachian Plateaus.

Some valleys head within 15 miles of the coast and flow eastward to the Willamette Valley; others head within 5 miles of the edge of that valley and flow westward to the coast. The mouths of the valleys are drowned, and increasingly so northward, which suggests that the most recent structural movement has involved northward tilting.

The rocks are Tertiary in age and form a plateau structure interrupted by open, short folds and without much faulting. The east base of the range is at the Willamette Valley, which is the south end of the Puget Trough, a structural as well as topographic trough. In Eocene time the entire area was a structural depression, and the ocean shore was along the site of the Cascade Mountains, about 100 miles inland from its present position (Fig. 17.20,A). The Klamath Mountains were an upland of pre-Tertiary rocks. The site of the Cascades was an area of extensive volcanism and lay near sea level. Later, in Oligocene time (Fig. 17.20,B), the influx of volcanic debris and other sediments exceeded the rate of subsidence of the basin, and the shore was pushed seaward. By Miocene time the shore had almost reached its present position, and the Cascades began to be elevated. Uplift and warping continued during the Pliocene while the Cascade Mountains were being built higher. Uplift that continued into Quaternary time is recorded by wave-cut bluffs along the coast and by a series of marine terraces as high as 1,500 feet above sea level.

OLYMPIC MOUNTAINS

The Olympic Mountains, the northernmost section of the Pacific Border Province (Fig. 17.8), are formed by a domal structural uplift much higher than the uplift at the Oregon

Coast Range, and the mountains are very much higher topographically, reaching to altitudes of about 8,000 feet. The core of the uplift consists of resistant pre-Tertiary rocks around which Tertiary formations, including thick Eocene pillow lavas, are turned up to form the flanks. During early Eocene time the site of the Olympic Mountains was below sea level, but uplift had produced a low peninsula by late Eocene time. Uplift continued throughout the rest of the Tertiary Period,

and the mountains reached their present height during Quaternary time. During Pleistocene time the Olympic Mountains were glaciated, and many cirques still contain glaciers. Glacial deposits at the foot of the mountains are folded and tilted, indicating the recency of uplift, which is probably still continuing.

PUGET TROUGH

The Puget Trough, a partly submerged lowland that is less than 500 feet in altitude in the

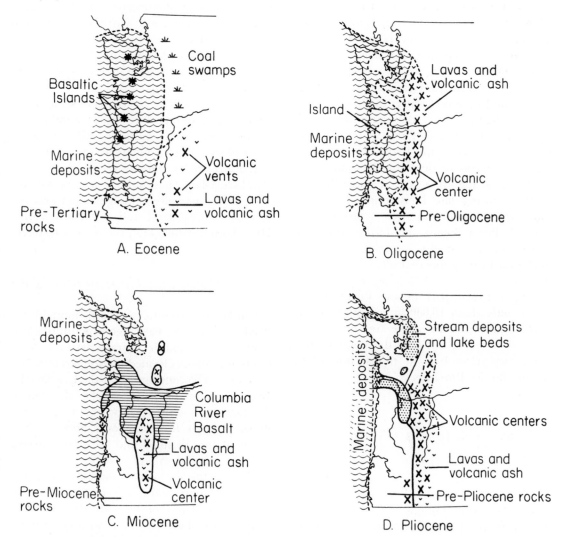

Figure 17.20 *Paleogeographic maps illustrating four stages in the development of the landscape in the northern part of the Pacific Mountain System. (Generalized from Washington Div. Mines and Geol.)*

emerged part, is the southern end of a structural and topographic depression that extends from the Willamette Valley in Oregon northward for about 1,500 miles into Washington, British Columbia, and Alaska. At the south the trough forms a lowland 200 miles long and barely 25 miles wide between the Oregon Coast Range and the Cascade Mountains. Northward, the trough is partly filled with glacial outwash. It slopes under Puget Sound, and where it is incompletely submerged, it forms hundreds of islands. Farther north, along the coast of British Columbia and Alaska, the trough is deeply submerged and bordered by steep mountainsides.

In Pleistocene time even the lowland at the south was submerged. Glaciers dammed Puget Sound, and their meltwaters discharged to the Pacific Ocean around the south side of the Olympic Mountains. The Columbia River was a strait across the Coast Range, and it built an extensive delta in the quiet water that flooded the lower part of the Willamette Valley. During late Pleistocene and Recent time, this lowland has risen a few hundred feet; at Puget Sound and farther north the trough has remained submerged, resulting in northward tilting like that of the ranges along the coast.

The emerged part of the Puget Trough covers only about 10,000 square miles, a little more than 5 percent of the area of Washington and Oregon, but half the population of those two states lives in this section of the Pacific Border Province.

Lower California (Peninsular Range) Province

The Lower California Province, situated between the Salton Trough and the coast, is the northern end of Baja California. The province is a batholith of granite that, in part at least, is of Cretaceous age, intrusive into Lower Cretaceous formations and overlain by younger, Upper Cretaceous ones. The granite forms a westward-tilted plateau, the east front of which is a tremendous east-facing escarpment, like the east front of the Sierra Nevada. San Jacinto Peak at the north end is more than 11,000 feet in altitude and overlooks Salton Trough, which extends below sea level. Northwest-trending faults extend obliquely across the escarpment and divide it into a series of northwest-trending mountains.

Along the coast is a series of wave-cut marine terraces of Pleistocene age (Fig. 17.21). These terraces, some of which are as much as 1,300 feet above sea level, record a series of uplifts that took place during the Pleistocene. The terraces are not level, but are warped, for the uplift was irregular.

Similar terraces on the coasts of some of the offshore islands are further evidence of different amounts of uplift on different structural blocks. San Clemente Island is terraced practically to its summit (1,480 feet). Santa Catalina Island has only a few poorly developed terraces, even though it lies between San Clemente Island and the Palos Verdes Hills, both of which are prominently terraced.

The Coast and Continental Shelf

Unlike the Atlantic seaboard, most of the Pacific Coast has been recently uplifted, is mountainous, and is characterized by steep bluffs and highly elevated marine terraces. Uplift seems to be continuing. At the Los Angeles Basin a coastal plain slopes from the foot of the mountains to the sea, but from there to the Puget Trough there are only about a half dozen plains, all small and all located at the mouths of broad valleys.

Most of the geologic formations along the coast are nonresistant and readily erode to form bluffs. The shorelines are straight, fully exposed to the surf, and without barrier beaches and lagoons. North of Puget Sound the coast has been downwarped, like the north end of the Atlantic seaboard, and the coastal

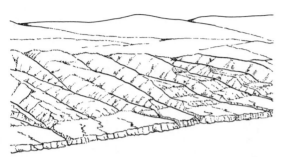

Figure 17.21 *Wave-cut marine terraces along the coast of the Peninsular Range about 50 miles north of San Diego. A conspicuous low terrace and remnants of several higher ones, cut into Tertiary formations and veneered with marine deposits of Pleistocene age, record a series of uplifts of this part of the coast during Pleistocene time.*

features are like those along the Maine coast, except that the mountains are much higher.

Southward as far as Point Conception the continental shelf off the Pacific Coast is barely 50 miles wide, and it is ruggedly mountainous. South of Point Conception the width of the shelf increases to about 150 miles. The offshore islands there are the peaks of mountains that have as much relief as those on the land.

Two major structurally controlled mountain ridges, each with relief about equal to that of the Sierra Nevada, extend about 1,500 miles westward from the coast into the Pacific Ocean (Fig. 19.2). The more northerly of these joins the coast at Cape Mendocino, where the San Andreas fault extends into the ocean. This submerged ridge, called the Mendocino Mountains, is seismically active and may be a westward continuation, or branch, of the San Andreas fault. These submerged mountains form a southward-facing escarpment. To the south the ocean averages about a half mile deeper than to the north.

The more southerly ridge, known as the Murray Mountains, extends westward from the Transverse Ranges. These submerged mountains form a north-facing escarpment. The ocean bottom north of the Murray Mountains is deeper than it is to the south.

Seismic Activity

The mountains of the Pacific Mountain System are young and are still being uplifted. Earthquakes are frequent. This seismically active area is part of the circum-Pacific belt of volcanic activity and earthquake centers that extends 15,000 miles along the Pacific coasts of South America, North America, and Asia (Fig. 3.6). On maps this belt appears strongly arcuate, but on the globe it is much less arcuate and for long distances is nearly straight, like the great circle route shown in Figure 17.2. The California segment is one of the least active parts, yet in 100 years has experienced about 200 earthquakes classed as destructive or near destructive. There have been, of course, countless other minor tremors detected only by seismographs.

The following list gives the dates and origins of the three strongest California earthquakes.

1. 1857; origin along or near the San Andreas fault, in the vicinity of the junction of the Sierra Nevada and the Transverse Range.
2. 1872; origin in Owens Valley at the east foot of the Sierra Nevada.
3. 1906; referred to as the San Francisco earthquake, but affected long stretches of the Coast Ranges; due to movement along the San Andreas fault.

The destructiveness of an earthquake is not necessarily related to the magnitude of the shocks. The Long Beach earthquake in 1933, for example, is not regarded as of major magnitude seismically, but it ranks as one of the most destructive earthquakes in United States history because it centered in a densely populated area. Conversely, the earthquake of 1872, in Owens Valley at the east foot of the Sierra Nevada, like the New Madrid Earthquake in the Mississippi Valley in 1811 (p. 150), was of major magnitude but damage was slight because the affected area was sparsely populated.

The rise of sea level along the Pacific Coast, between 2 and $2\frac{1}{2}$ inches in the last half century, is only one-half to one-quarter as great as that along the Atlantic seaboard and the Gulf of Mexico (p. 160). This difference is very possibly due to uplift of the Pacific Coast at a rate only slightly less than the rate of rise of sea level. If we assume sea level has risen 5 to 6 inches in 50 years, which is roughly the average for the Atlantic seaboard, we might infer that the Pacific Coast has been uplifted 3 to 4 inches in that time. This

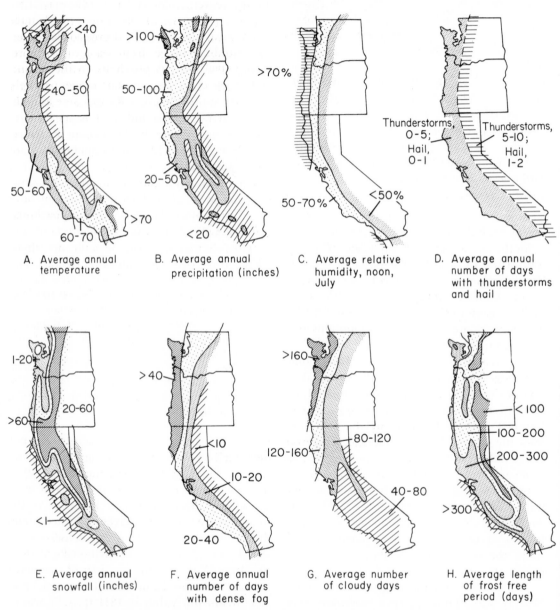

Figure 17.22 *Climatic maps of the Pacific Mountain System. (Generalized from U.S.D.A.)*

would amount to 5 or 6 feet of uplift per thousand years—a rate quite commensurate with the record of mountain building along the Pacific Coast during late Tertiary and Quaternary time.

When will crustal strains along the Pacific Coast again be relieved by sudden movement and cause the next earthquake? Nobody knows, and, unfortunately, we have not been making sufficient observations and measurements that might serve as the basis for such forecasting. The problem has practical as well as theoretical interest, because parts of the Pacific Coast, especially California, are crowded and becoming more so. The land must be used, but care could be taken in selecting building sites. It is questionable, for example, whether buildings should be constructed on very low land subject to submergence, such as the land adjoining San Francisco Bay. Bluffs along the southern coast of California are notorious for landsliding. Such lands could be better used for parks rather than for residences.

At least four kinds of observations and measurements could be made to locate ground that is actively moving and to determine the directions and rates of the movement:

1. Install tiltmeters at critical locations (p. 325).
2. Make precise level surveys of selected areas, of the kind made at Lake Mead (p. 325).
3. Determine precise azimuth and precise relative heights across selected geologic structures to detect local differential movement.
4. In seismically active areas reappraise previous leveling surveys on the assumption that corrections that have been applied are due to earth movement rather than to engineering error (p. 325).

We cannot hope to stop the mountain-making forces, but we can live with them more safely if we understand them and adapt ourselves to their ways.

Climate

Almost every type of climate is represented in the Pacific Mountain System: warm-dry, temperate-wet, cold-dry, and cold-wet. The differences (Fig. 17.22) reflect the great length of the area, more than 16 degrees of latitude; its altitudinal range, from sea level to more than 14,000 feet; its proximity to the ocean; and the effects of the mountain ranges paralleling the coast. If the Coast Ranges were as high as the Sierra Nevada and the Cascade Mountains, most of the Pacific Border Province would be semiarid like the Columbia Plateau and Great Basin.

The maps in Figure 17.22 illustrate how the climate is affected by differences in latitude (A, H), altitude (B, E, H), and proximity to the ocean (C, D, F, G). Some effects of differences in exposure and altitude are illustrated in Figures 17.23 and 8.8. Average annual precipitation in the Sierra Nevada increases about a half inch with every 100-foot increase in altitude.

Not brought out by the maps is the highly seasonal distribution of the rainfall, which, in contrast to the Middle West and eastern seaboard (Fig. 4.3), takes place mostly during the fall, winter, and spring months. Summers are dry. During the winter, southwesterly winds bring warm ocean air over the cold land; during the summer, winds from the northwest bring cold ocean air over warm land (Fig. 4.7,D). As a result, there are two seasons: one wet, the other dry. Forests that are soaked and dripping in the wet season become dry as tinder and highly susceptible to forest fires in the dry season. Forest fires are a major hazard in the region (Fig. 8.15). In summer, California's grasslands become golden brown, and in allusion to this, the state is sometimes referred to as the "Golden Bare." Fortunately, thunderstorms, which could cause forest fires, are far less frequent

0   200   400 Miles

Scale

●	Bare ground, summits	⌐○⌐	Oak and grass
≡S≡	Spruce-Fir Forest on Cascades, fir and hemlock on Sierra Nevada	⌐C⌐	Chapparal
YP	Yellow pine; lodgepole pine	⌐BG⌐	Bunch grass
♯DF	Douglas fir forest	⌐SG⌐	Short grass
SP	Sugar pine forest	G	Greasewood
R	Redwood forest	D	Desert shrub

Figure 17.23 *Natural vegetation in the Pacific Mountain System.*

than in the other physiographic provinces (Fig. 4.4).

Vegetation, Agriculture, Lumbering

As a consequence of the great variety in climate, all the vegetation zones from Lower Sonoran to Alpine are represented in the Pacific Mountain System. Moreover, each of the zones has a humid and semiarid facies.

The Lower Sonoran Zone is represented by grasslands in the California Trough (Great Valley) and in some of the inland valleys south of the Transverse Ranges. In these areas, shown as bunch grass and greasewood in Figure 17.23, the rainfall is greater and the temperature ranges less extreme than in the Mojave Desert and other Lower Sonoran Zone deserts farther inland and leeward of the mountains, and the composition of the floras are correspondingly different. In the Great Valley and other areas near the coast, the Lower Sonoran Zone is characterized by annual plants. The lower parts of the Great Valley along the rivers are alkaline flats with greasewood, pickleweed, salt grass, and shadscale.

The Upper Sonoran Zone supports two kinds of plant stands—chaparral, and oak and grass (Fig. 17.23). Chaparral is a mixture of stout woody shrubs and small trees that grow in almost impenetrable thickets. It has peculiarities that are attributed to repeated burning, including fires in prehistoric time. Some of the shrubs develop horizontal roots that can sprout again after the tops are burned; other shrubs in the chaparral are kinds that can reseed freely after fire and reestablish themselves in the burned area. Along the coast of southern California the chaparral extends upward to about 5,000 feet in altitude; northward, where there is more rainfall and fog, the chaparral gives way to forests of redwood.

The Transition Zone descends to sea level along the northern coast. Inland, along the Sierra Nevada, it begins at about 3,000 feet in altitude. This zone is the great forest region of the Pacific Mountains and comprises four main kinds of forests, each with numerous subtypes.

In the north is the forest of Douglas fir, the most important lumber tree in the Pacific states and perhaps the most important in the whole country. This forest, which extends from sea level to about 5,000 feet along the western slope of the Cascade Mountains, includes (in addition to Douglas fir) western hemlock, white fir, grand fir, western red cedar, maples, and oaks. Sitka spruce grows along the coast.

Southward along the coast is redwood forest, which extends from sea level to about 2,500 feet in altitude. Associated with the redwood are Douglas fir, western hemlock, grand fir, and tideland spruce. Redwood and Douglas fir are the tallest American trees; some specimens are about 400 feet high and would not be dwarfed by the Washington Monument.

Inland from the redwood forest is a forest of sugar pine, a 5-needle pine with tremendous cones 12 to 24 inches long. This forest, which includes white fir, lies mostly between 2,000 and 5,000 feet in altitude. The more arid parts support yellow pine, incense cedar, and sagebrush. In the south, on the west slope of the Sierra Nevada, this forest includes the giant redwood, or sequoia, including the stand at Sequoia National Park.

The fourth forest of the Transition Zone, composed chiefly of western yellow pine, grows along the dry, eastern slope of the Sierra Nevada and Cascade mountains. Its lower limit along the foot of the Sierra is at about 5,500 feet, but it descends to 500 feet along the east foot of the Cascades at the Columbia River.

The Canadian and Hudsonian zones in the Pacific Mountain System extend from the Transition Zone to timberline, which slopes

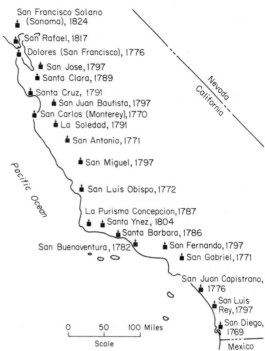

Figure 17.24 *The Franciscan Missions, established along the coast of California from 1769 to 1824, were the first western ranches.*

northward from about 10,500 feet in the southern part of the Sierra Nevada to about 6,000 feet in the northern part of the Cascade Mountains. In the north the forests consist of Engelmann spruce, western white pine, whitebark pine, lodgepole pine, white fir, and subalpine fir. In the south the forests consist mostly of Shasta red fir, Jeffrey pine, western white pine, and lodgepole pine. Upward from timberline is the Alpine Zone, which supports various shrubs and herbs.

The southern provinces in the Pacific Mountain System include major agricultural producing areas. The acreage in harvested produce is only about 2 percent of the United States total, and most of it is irrigated, but the value of the produce, more than $10 billion annually, is 10 percent of the United

States total. The per-acre value of the farmland is higher than in any other part of the country except around New York City. Important crops include barley, cotton, dry beans, potatoes, rice, sugar beets, wine grapes, citrus fruits, figs, avocados, walnuts, and olives. Honey is another important product; a bee ranch may produce 150,000 pounds of honey in a year. That takes a lot of busy bees!

Agriculture in California began with the establishment of the Franciscan Missions, the first western ranches. Beginning in 1769 the Franciscan friars established 21 missions, located about one day's travel apart, along the coast from San Diego to San Francisco Bay (Fig. 17.24). They produced fruits, cereals, vegetables, and herds of sheep, cattle, and horses. Each was a self-sufficient economy utilizing Indians as serf labor while Christianizing them. After Mexico obtained independence from Spain in 1821, the Indians were given their independence, and the Missions declined.

The first orange grove was started at San Gabriel Mission in 1804, and by 1841 groves of oranges were being raised commercially. Since 1900 citrus growing has passed cereals in importance. Irrigation projects were undertaken along the San Joaquin and Kings rivers as early as 1872.

Today fruit farming is big business. A large-scale fruit farm covers thousands of acres, has its own packing house, may employ thousands of pickers and packers at peak season, manufactures its own crates, owns tractors and trucks by the dozen, and ships fruit by the carload. At the other extreme are small orchards operated part time by retired families.

Lumber and timber production from the Pacific Mountain System totals about 15 billion board feet annually, and is valued at around $600,000,000. This is about half the United States production, and three quarters of it is from the Douglas fir forests in Oregon and Washington; the remainder is from the Transition Zone forests in California. The forests in California, except the redwood forests, are also used for stock grazing, but the Douglas fir forests in Oregon and Washington are used very little for grazing.

Surficial Deposits and Soils

Residual deposits due to deep weathering of various kinds of sedimentary, volcanic, granitic, and metamorphic rocks are extensive in the mountains along the coast north of San Francisco Bay and on the wet west slopes of the Cascades and Sierra Nevada. They occur also in the Puget Trough, where they are overlapped by outwash from glacial deposits of Wisconsin age. The residuum is deep-red clay and is older than the Wisconsin glaciation; some of it dates from the Tertiary. Soils developed on this residuum are classed with the Red and Yellow Podzols.

This residuum is mostly below 4,000 feet in altitude. At higher altitudes the surficial deposits and soils are mostly late Pleistocene and Recent in age and are classed with the Gray-Brown Podzols. These soils are developed on moraines, colluvium, and other deposits of Wisconsin and Recent age.

The Puget Trough contains lake beds, alluvium, and glacial deposits; along the coast are beach deposits and dunes. The deposits that are pre-Wisconsin in age are deeply weathered and are parent material for Red and Yellow Podzols. The Wisconsin and younger deposits are parent material for Gray-Brown Podzols.

The California Trough contains broad floodplains of alluvium along the rivers, and alluvial fans with gravel rise from the floodplains to the base of the bordering mountains. Soils developed on these deposits, especially in the warm, dry southern part, are varied. Figure 17.25 illustrates some of the principal soil differences along a transect from the coast to the Sierra Nevada.

Along the ocean side of the Coast Ranges of

California the soils are mostly Prairie Soils. These slightly acid soils have well-developed, organic-rich, brown to black surface layers about 10 inches thick. The subsoils, which are 18 to 30 inches thick, are light-brown, blocky, and slightly alkaline. The Prairie Soils are not well dated, but seem to be no older than late Pleistocene. In some places there are older, residual deposits that developed from hard rocks and consist of deep-red clays like the pre-Wisconsin residuum.

Along the inland and dry side of the Coast Ranges, Rendzina Soils have developed on the limy formations. These soils have a surface layer similar to that on the Prairie Soils except that it is less acid even though it is lime-free. The subsoil is brown, clayey, and very limy. Eastward, near the edge of the Great Valley, the subsoils are more calcareous and the surface soils are slightly calcareous and not so dark.

The Rendzina Soils end at the edge of the Great Valley at about 500 feet in altitude, where the Coast Range formations are overlapped by the gravel fans and the alluvium deposited by streams discharging eastward to

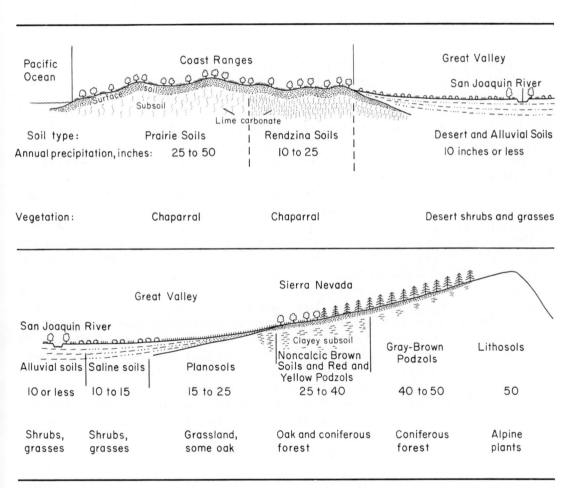

Figure 17.25 *Cross sections illustrating differences in soils from the coast of California to the Sierra Nevada.*

the San Joaquin River. Desert Soils have developed in this part of the valley, which receives only 10 inches or less of annual rainfall. The deposits are young, the soil processes are weak, and the profiles consequently are weakly developed and very limy throughout. These Desert Soils grade eastward into the equally young alluvial soils along the San Joaquin River.

East of the River is a belt of saline soils subject to flooding by streams from the Sierra Nevada. As a consequence of frequent wetting and drying the soils have accumulated soluble salts. In places there are salt crusts.

Eastward the land is better drained, and it rises to roughly 600 feet in altitude at the foot of the Sierra Nevada. The land consists of low ridges and broad valleys draining west; the surficial deposits are fan gravels and alluvium deposited by streams discharging from the Sierra Nevada. The soils in this belt, other than those in the valley bottoms, are planosols, which are related to the Prairie Soils (Table 6.1) but have well-defined clayey hardpans. These are acid soils. The surface layers, about 5 inches thick, are brown and contain little organic matter. The subsoil is lighter in color and is compact and clayey. One to $3\frac{1}{2}$ feet below the surface there is brownish-red hardpan cemented with iron and silica. Some of these soils must be as old as late Pleistocene.

On the western slope of the Sierra Nevada, as on the western slope of the Cascades, there is a lower belt of ancient soils and an upper belt of young soils. The younger soils, Gray-Brown Podzols, occur on the higher parts of the Sierra that were subjected to glacial erosion or intensive frost action during late Pleistocene time. They are only a foot or two thick, with an ashy-gray leached layer over a compact and gray-brown subsoil. The ancient soils, Red and Yellow Podzols and noncalcic Brown Soils, occur in a belt along the foot of the mountains. These soils are red-brown clay and may be many feet deep. The parent materials are the granitic or volcanic rocks. All these soils have thin surface layers of forest litter.

Glaciers, Rivers, and Lakes

Glaciers—relics from the Pleistocene ice ages—and perennial snow and ice cover about 500 square miles of the high parts of the Sierra Nevada, the Cascades, and the Olympic Mountains. Ice is most extensive on Mount Rainier, in the Northern Cascades, and on the Olympic Mountains. Both areas are preserved as national parks. The lower limit of perennial snow and ice, controlled both by temperature and precipitation, is determined by the relative rates of accumulation and removal, the chief modes of removal being melting and evaporation. In the Sierra Nevada the lower limit is around 12,000 feet but varies with the exposure; in the Northern Cascades the limit is perhaps 8,000 feet, although at Mount Rainier glacial tongues extend down the valleys to about 4,500 feet. During the glacial periods the lower limit of perennial snow and ice was about 5,000 feet lower than it is today, and the glaciers extended correspondingly farther down the valleys. Pleistocene glaciers also developed on some of the southern ranges, such as the San Bernardino Mountains. In Pleistocene time, the area covered by snow and ice in the Pacific Mountain System was probably a hundred times greater than it is today.

Along with the southward decrease in snow and ice in the mountains, there is a corresponding southward decrease in the size of the streams discharging from the mountains. No large rivers drain from the southern 250 miles of the Pacific Mountains. North of the latitude of San Francisco, however, large streams are the rule; such rivers as the Sacramento, Klamath, and Willamette are larger than the Colorado River, although they are short and drain small areas.

Lakes are numerous in the Cascades and in the Sierra Nevada. Many of the glacial cirques contain lakes, and other lakes are formed by morainal dams. One of the largest is Lake Chelan in Washington, which is contained by a morainal dam. The dam is east of the mountain front, and the lake, which is 65 miles long, extends far back into the glaciated valley in the mountains. The altitude of the lake surface is almost 1,100 feet, but the lake is 1,400 feet deep, and its bottom is below sea level. Most of the great depth is due to glacial gouging, but it may have been lowered too by the northward tilting that drowned the northern part of the Puget Trough (p. 391).

Among the high-altitude lakes in the Cascade Range is Crater Lake (altitude 6,239 feet), which has had a complex history involving both volcanism and glaciation (Fig. 17.12,D). Lake Tahoe, in the Sierra Nevada, is at about the same altitude as Crater Lake. The lake was formed when the valley that it occupies was dammed by a lava flow, but its history is complicated by the glacial processes too. Yosemite Lake, in the bottom of Yosemite Valley, is a moraine-dammed lake in the bottom of a glaciated valley.

Water-power resources of the Pacific Mountains are considerable, and, combined with the tremendous hydroelectric power resources along the Columbia, Snake, and Colorado rivers, amount to more than half the total water-power resources of the United States.

Water Supplies

The Pacific Mountain System in Washington, Oregon, and northern California has plentiful supplies of water. Water problems there are due to pollution and floods, not to adequacy of the supply. The quality of the water ranks it as some of the best in the United States, with total dissolved solids generally less than 100 ppm. The hardness is less than 10.

Because California receives most of its rainfall in winter rather than during the growing season, crops have to be irrigated. The southern provinces are short of water, for the annual precipitation there is deficient and the seasonal distribution is unfavorable. Total annual requirements exceed 2 million acre feet, and about half of this water must be brought long distances. The imported supplies are obtained from the Colorado River (about 600,000 acre feet in 1960) and Owens River (about 300,000 acre feet in 1960). There are plans to construct canals to transport water from the northern rivers to the southern provinces. Since these settled areas are not high above sea level they appear to be promising places in which to employ desalinization of sea water.

Not only is water scarce in the southern provinces, but the local supplies are not of good quality. Well water with 650 ppm of dissolved solids and a hardness of almost 400 is used by some cities in the Los Angeles Basin. Figure 17.26 shows the differences in the quality of water from various sources in the basin.

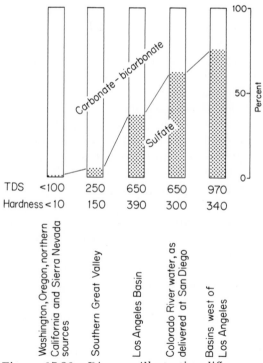

Figure 17.26 *Diagram illustrating differences in quality of water used for municipal supplies in various parts of the Pacific Mountain System. The chloride content is generally less than 10 percent and is not included.*

Fish and Wildlife

Fish and wildlife were the first resources to be exploited in the Pacific Northwest. Astoria, Oregon, was founded in 1811 by the Pacific Fur Company. The large game that was sought included elk, deer, and bear. Smaller game included beaver, badger, mink, weasel, raccoon, and various rabbits. Among the predatory animals were timber wolf, mountain lion, wild cat, red fox, and coyote. Fur trading declined after 1840, and about 50 years later fishing became a major industry.

Best known of the Pacific Coast fish is the amazing salmon, which leaves the sea in breeding season and ascends the rivers for hundreds of miles. The favorite variety is the sockeye (red) salmon, which commonly weighs 5 pounds. It is most abundant in the north. Another favorite is the chinook (king) salmon, which commonly weighs 25 pounds and may reach 100 pounds. It was common along the Columbia River and its tributaries, but has been decreasing since the construction of the many dams that obstruct its migration upstream. Other varieties are the chum, pink, and silver salmon, all mostly around 5 pounds. The Indians who lived on salmon preserved their fish by drying them. During the 1830's the white settlers began preserving fish by salting them in kegs; canning was started during the 1860's.

Marine environments along the Pacific Coast are zoned like those along the Atlantic Coast (p. 164), latitudinally and at right angles to the shore. The boundary between the northern and southern faunas, the analogue of Cape Cod, is at about the middle of the California Coast, in the vicinity of San Francisco and Monterey.

Off the northern Pacific Coast the most important fisheries are for salmon, flounder, halibut, albacore (tuna), crab, and rockfish. Other northern fishes are two trout (close relatives of the salmon) that also live in the ocean and ascend the rivers to spawn. These are the steelhead, an ocean-dwelling rainbow trout, and the dolly varden. Other fish are the mackerel, smelt, and candlefish, so named because it was used by Indians as a source for fuel oil. Shad, a herring, was introduced to the Pacific Coast in about 1870 and has become a major commercial fish. Marine mammals of the northern fauna include the northern sea lion, Alaska fur seal, and sea otter.

Along the southern Pacific Coast the principal commercial fish are pilchard (sardines), tuna, and mackerel. Other fishes characteristic of the southern coast are the striped marlin (300 to 400 pounds), giant sea bass, skipjacks, anchovies, and the shell fish abalone. With these live the California sea lion, Guadalupe fur seal, and elephant seal—all mammals.

Of the total quantity of Pacific Coast fish produced annually, about 1½ billion pounds, more than half are sardines. The gross value is more than $60 million.

Mineral Resources

One of the significant events in United States history, and certainly one of the most colorful, was the discovery of gold in California in 1848. Until that time, settlement and development of the Pacific mountains and valleys had been slow; when gold was discovered the westward trickle of emigration became a flood.

Only minor deposits of gold had been worked in California while it was part of Mexico. In January 1848, less than two weeks before the signing of the Treaty of Guadalupe Hidalgo, James W. Marshall discovered gold in a sawmill flume near Sacramento. Within a year the rush was on. The discovery of gold in California and the subsequent discovery of silver in Nevada greatly increased interest in all minerals. Prior to those discoveries iron and lead were the only industrial metals of importance in United States commerce. The importance of the precious metals, gold and silver, in the national economy of that period is illustrated perhaps by the fact that our first mineral resources inventory was sponsored by the Treasury Department.

The principal California lode gold deposits occur in the Mother Lode belt near the western foot of the Sierra Nevada. This belt is about a mile wide and about 100 miles long. The productive ground consists of quartz veins in steeply dipping black slates and altered volcanic rocks of late Paleozoic and Jurassic age. The ore consists of native gold and of gold-bearing pyrite accompanied by minor quantities of various other sulfides. A total of about $2 billion in gold has been produced. About three-quarters of this has come from placers and the reminder from lode mines, some of which are about a mile deep.

The discovery of gold contributed to the development of quicksilver deposits in the Pacific Mountains, because quicksilver was used for recovering gold by amalgamation. The highest production came from the New Almaden mine, located south of San Francisco Bay. The mine, named after Almaden, Spain, where there are rich deposits of quicksilver, was first opened in 1845. The New Almaden mine has produced a third of the total production of the United States. The mercury occurs as cinnabar (mercury sulfide) accompanied by metallic mercury and various sulfides of iron, copper, lead, and antimony.

California, our second largest oil-producing state, has numerous productive fields in the San Joaquin Valley, Los Angeles Basin, and Coast Ranges. Most of the production has come from Miocene and Pliocene formations, but the Eocene and Cretaceous deposits also contain petroleum. The state's first oil well, drilled by hand in 1875 to a depth of 30 feet at a tar pool near Los Angeles, produced for more than half a century!

The oil fields in the Los Angeles Basin are aligned along the northwest-trending faults (Fig. 17.27). In the San Joaquin Valley the principal fields produce from anticlines and other structures along the western edge of the valley, near the foot of the Coast Ranges. Other fields are located along the coast northwest of Los Angeles.

Other mineral production in the Pacific Mountains has been comparatively minor. Gold accompanied by silver, copper, and lead has been produced in the Klamath Mountains and Northern Cascades. From the Tertiary formations, in California, there has been production of diatomite, glass sand, and clay. Coal has been produced chiefly in Washington.

Some Resource Problems

During the 1850's, the decade following the discovery of gold in California, that state's population grew at the rate of 50,000 per year. A hundred years later, during the 1950's, the increase in population averaged 10 times the earlier rate. The 1950 population of California was about 10 million; in 1960 it was about 15 million. The present California growth rate

Figure 17.27 *Oil fields in the Los Angeles Basin are aligned along the northwest-trending faults.*

is about twice the growth rate of China or India.

Water needs can be met in two ways. North of the Great Valley water is plentiful and can be canalled southward to the more heavily populated areas. Furthermore, the populous areas are only a little higher than sea level, and desalinization of sea water, already technically feasible, will become economically feasible when there is a great enough demand for the additional water.

With increased population there is certain to be increased atmospheric pollution, except as drastic means are taken to minimize the causes. The man-made smog problem still awaits solution.

The farms, forests, fisheries, and hydroelectric plants can continue or even increase their present high rate of productivity. Oil and gas production will continue at a high level for a long time to come, but petroleum is an expendable resource and its supply sooner or later will be depleted. Offshore fields may become the chief sources of the future.

18 Alaska

Alaska, by far our largest state, covers 586,000 square miles, which is almost one-fifth the combined area of all the other 49 states (Fig. 18.1). The population, though, is scanty, estimated (1962) to be 239,000. This is an average of only one person for every two square miles. According to the 1960 census, only five towns had populations greater than 5,000.

This highly varied and vast terrain can be divided into seven physiographic provinces (Fig. 18.1):

1. Southeastern Coast Mountains, including the southeastern panhandle, a mountainous coastal area with numerous islands and fjords.
2. Glaciered Coast, another mountainous coastal area, largely covered by a vast system of glaciers.
3. South-central Alaska, a coastal and inland belt consisting of mountains and lowlands that in ground plan are arcuate and curve around the Gulf of Alaska.
4. Alaska Peninsula and Aleutian Islands, the southwestern panhandle formed by a volcanic arc and bordered on the south by the Aleutian Trench, an active, present-day geosyncline.
5. Interior Alaska, including: Yukon Valley lowlands and uplands, Kilbuck-Kuskokwim mountains and uplands, and the Brooks Range. Extensive areas in this province have permanently frozen ground.
6. Seward Peninsula and Bering Coast Uplands, a roughly dissected plateau with low mountains, forming a projection westward to Bering Strait; most of the ground in this province is permanently frozen.
7. Arctic Slope, the coastal plain bordering the Arctic Ocean; all this ground is permanently frozen.

Looking at Alaska as a whole, its many outstanding features include its

1. Great relief; Mount McKinley (altitude 20,300 feet) is the highest point in North America; the Aleutian Trench (Fig. 18.2), 25,000 feet below sea level, is the lowest point around North America.
2. Hundreds of volcanoes.
3. Thousands of glaciers; 4 percent of Alaska is covered by glacial ice; one glacier, the Malaspina, is larger than the state of Rhode Island.
4. Vast extent of permanently frozen ground, perhaps as much as 250,000 square miles.
5. Extreme range of climate. The southern coast, warmed by the Japan Current, rarely has temperatures below 0°F, but winter lows in the interior may reach 78°F below zero and summer highs may reach 100°F above. The southeast coast of Alaska, one

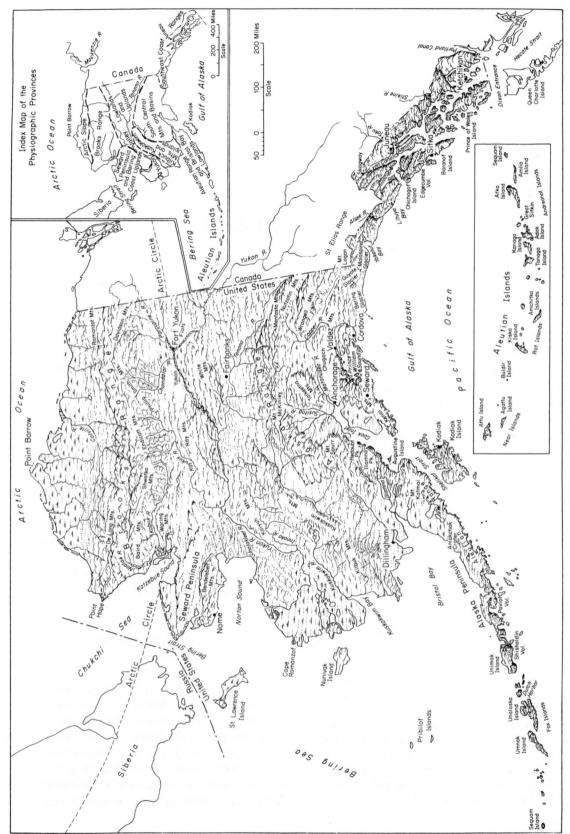

Figure 18.1 *Physiographic map of Alaska.*

of the rainiest parts of the United States, receives more than 150 inches annually; the Arctic slope, one of the driest, receives less than 5 inches.

6. Frequent and severe earthquakes along the south coast; these are sometimes accompanied by giant waves.

Other outstanding features of Alaska are its mosquitoes and bear stories.

About 15 percent of Alaska's population and much of its industry—all highly developed—are in Southeast Alaska. The principal industry is fishing, especially for salmon, halibut, and herring. Mining, particularly of gold, has been important, but activity now is slight. Southeast Alaska contains the state's principal forest resources (Fig. 18.20.) Lumber production has been slight, but there are large pulp mills near Ketchikan and Sitka. Shipping to and from Seattle is favored by the inside passage.

South-central Alaska holds about half of Alaska's population. The economy includes farming as well as fishing, oil production, and mining. Production of oil on the Kenai Peninsula is the most important effort in the minerals field. Coal is mined, and there has been mining for gold, silver, copper, chromite, fluorspar, and zinc. Rivers draining from the Alaska Range are large, but the rivers are swift and turbulent and only the lower courses are navigable. At the heads of the rivers, passes across the Alaska Range provide access to the Yukon River Basin.

The Alaska Peninsula and Aleutian Islands are thinly populated. They have a rich fauna of fish, sea fowl, and fur-bearing animals, especially seal, sea otter, and blue fox. Report of these by the explorer Bering caused the Siberian fur hunters and fishermen to move eastward into Alaska, bringing it under Russian control. Hunting, fishing, and domestic raising of fox, have been major economic ac-

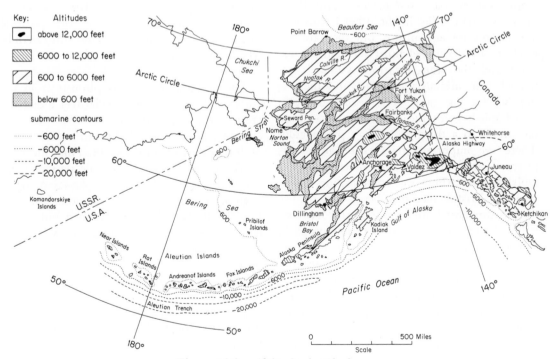

Figure 18.2 *Altitudes in Alaska.*

tivities. Agriculture and mining have not been of importance.

Despite the lack of population, this area poses knotty international problems. Is the Bering Sea beyond the 12-mile limit a part of the United States, or is it part of the Pacific and, therefore, international water? The United States owns the islands, which are the home of the fur seals, but does it own the seals when they go to sea? The questions still are not resolved, but conservation of the resources is greatly improved as a result of international agreements beginning with the Bering Sea Arbitration in 1893. Still to be settled is the question of national ownership and regulation of activities over the continental shelf areas, not only off the coast of Alaska but off all coasts. The shelf area in the Bering Sea is more than half the size of all Alaska (Fig. 18.2).

Interior Alaska holds about a quarter of the state's population, mostly in a single basin along the Tanana River near Fairbanks. In that area there is some agriculture, mostly root crops, cabbage, oats, and barley. Many thousands of square miles in the other basins also are suitable for agriculture, but they are not likely to be developed until the markets expand and the transportation system is extended. Fur animals are raised, and there is hunting for big game. The region has produced much gold; the Fairbanks area alone has produced a third of Alaska's placer gold. There are important reserves of antimony, mercury, and tungsten, and some silver and molybdenum. Along the coast fishing is important; Bristol Bay has been one of the world's foremost fishing centers, and has contributed a major part of Alaska's salmon pack.

The Seward Peninsula and Bering Coast Uplands are thinly populated. Nome, the principal town, had a population of 2,300 in 1960. For eight months of the year Nome and the surrounding area are frozen in and inaccessible to shipping.

The Arctic Slope is even more thinly populated. It is ice-free and open to shipping only about one month each year, but it is of economic interest because of its oil and gas reserves and because it is the breeding ground for wild fowl. This area is a long way from the Gulf of Mexico, but many of the fowl that breed along the Arctic Slope of Alaska, winter along the shores of the Gulf of Mexico.

Structural Framework and Topography

Southeastern Coast Mountains

The panhandle of southeastern Alaska, including the islands, is a mountainous uplift of late Mesozoic and early Cenozoic granitic rocks flanked on the west by Paleozoic and Mesozoic sedimentary rocks. The axis of the uplift is in the Coast Range along the boundary between the panhandle and British Columbia (Fig. 18.3). Paleozoic and Mesozoic formations and some outliers of the granitic intrusions form the coast and the islands, which are referred to as the Alexander Archipelago.

The mountains rise precipitously from the sea to altitudes of about 9,000 feet along the crest of the Coast Mountains. The coast and archipelago are marked by intricate network of deep, narrow fjords (Fig. 18.4) that form the north end of the famous inside passage from Seattle to Alaska. This inside passage occupies a structural trough that was probably once like the Rocky Mountain Trench but which is now submerged. The connecting waterways are variously referred to as canals, passages, sounds, and straits. Many are long and straight like Lynn Canal and Chatham Strait, and evidently mark fault lines.

The Alexander Archipelago, representing the partly submerged western foothills of the Coast Range, consists of hundreds of islands. The large ones are 3,000 to 5,000 feet high

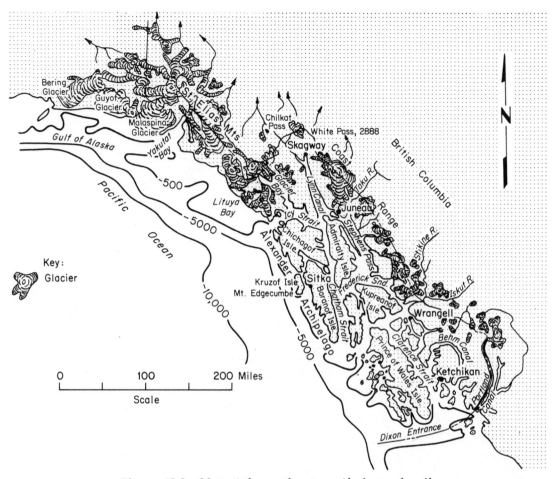

Figure 18.3 *Map of the southeastern Alaska panhandle.*

with steep sides, and where the slopes are not too steep, they are covered with dense forests. Northward, at Glacier Bay, are the lofty St. Elias Mountains, where several peaks reach to more than 15,000 feet in altitude. Offshore from the archipelago the submarine surface slopes steeply to a depth of about 7,500 feet and then slopes gradually to a depth of about 10,000 feet (Fig. 18.2).

Uplift began in Jurassic time, and during the Cretaceous Period this was part of a mountainous area west of the geosynclinal sea that connected the Gulf of Mexico and the Arctic Ocean (Fig. 2.7,C; p. 42). Structural deforma-

Figure 18.4 *Alaskan fjord. Heavily forested mountains rise directly from sea level.*

tion and igneous activity have continued to the present time. One volcano, Mount Edgecumbe on Kruzof Island, west of Sitka (Fig. 18.3), has been active during Recent time. Frequent and severe earthquakes indicate that structural movements are continuing (Fig. 18.13). In 1899 the Yakutat Bay area experienced a major earthquake during which the shore was greatly elevated; at one fault there was vertical displacement of 49 feet. In 1958

another earthquake in that area caused a slide that created huge waves (p. 419). This area, like much of the Pacific Mountain System, could serve as laboratory for studying directions and rates of present-day earth movement.

Two rivers, the Stikine and Taku, cross

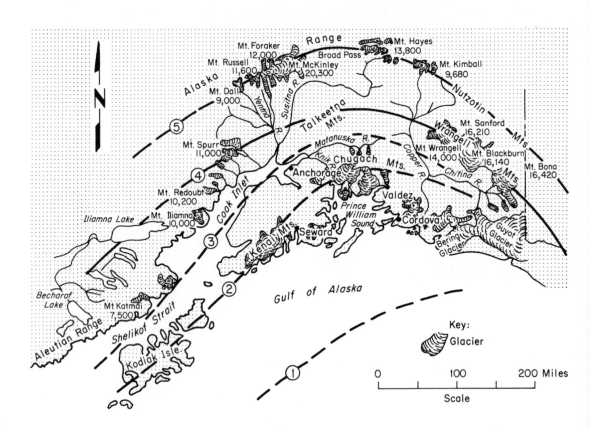

1. Aleutian Trench—a Quaternary geosyncline.

2. Kodiak-Kenai-Chugach Mountains arc—a geosyncline during Cretaceous time; uplifted to form mountains during Tertiary and Quaternary time.

3. Matanuska-Cook Inlet-Shelikof Strait arc—a geosyncline during Mesozoic and early Tertiary time; partly filled with Tertiary and Quaternary sediments; now a structural trough between uplifts 2 and 4.

4. Talkeetna-Aleutian Range arc—an uplifted belt of Paleozoic and older rocks intruded by granitic batholiths; probably a geanticline during most of the Mesozoic and Cenozoic.

5. Alaska Range arc—a geosyncline during most of Mesozoic time; intruded by granitic batholiths in Mesozoic and Tertiary time; uplifted in late Tertiary and Quaternary time.

Figure 18.5 *Map of South-central Alaska, showing five major structural elements that control the topographic grain of the area, and the principal active glaciers. (Generalized from U.S.G.S.)*

the Coast Mountains and discharge into the Alexander Archipelago. The Stikine River heads on the west slope of the Canadian Rockies and, after crossing the Coast Mountains, discharges to an inlet about 15 miles north of Wrangell. The Taku River also heads east of the Coast Mountains, crosses them, and discharges into an inlet south of Juneau and at the head of Stephens Passage. At Taku Inlet there is a glacier a mile wide and 100 to 300 feet high at its terminus. Here, as along other ice fronts, tidal changes break icebergs from the front of the glacier.

Glaciered Coast

North of Glacier Bay the structural uplift increases at the St. Elias Mountains, where several peaks are higher than 15,000 feet, and one, Mount Logan, nearly 20,000 feet. One river, the Alsek, crosses the mountain range. Indeed, rivers are few; most of the precipitation is snow and is discharged as glacial ice. This system of glaciers is extensive, and because of the ice cover not much is known about the geologic structure. Along the coast there are Tertiary formations, and toward the west these have yielded some petroleum.

South-central Alaska

South-central Alaska (Figs. 18.5, 18.6) includes the coast from the Copper River west to Shelikof Strait. Along the eastern segment of this coast are the Chugach Mountains, and farther inland the Wrangell and Talkeetna Mountains and the Alaska Range. To the west is the Aleutian Range.

The structural and topographic grain consists of a series of huge arcs around the Gulf of Alaska (Fig. 18.5), reflecting a series of nearly parallel arcuate geosynclines of different ages. Two arcs, one represented by the Alaska Range and another by the Matanuska-Cook Inlet-Shelikof Strait, were geosynclines

during most of Mesozoic time and were separated by the Talkeetna geanticline. In late Mesozoic time another geosyncline formed along the Kodiak-Kenai-Chugach Mountains arc. In Tertiary time the Alaska Range and the Kodiak-Kenai-Chugach arc were uplifted, but the Matanuska-Cook Inlet-Shelikof Strait arc remained low and was partly filled with Tertiary sediments. In late Tertiary time the Aleutian Trench developed, and during Quaternary time its eastern part, extending into the Gulf of Alaska, was largely filled with sediments.

Throughout its geologic history this section has been the center of much igneous activity, and the formations in the geosynclines include considerable sediments of volcanic origin. In the uplifted areas there are large granitic intrusions; uplift probably accompanied their emplacement. Igneous activity today is represented by active volcanoes at Mount Wrangell and at a half dozen active volcanic centers in the Aleutian Range north of Mount Katmai (Fig. 18.7).

The Aleutian Range, bordering Shelikof Strait and Cook Inlet, is transitional between this section and the volcanic arc that forms the Alaska Peninsula and the Aleutian Islands. The Aleutian Range is a structural uplift of Mesozoic formations and granitic intrusions and is topographically continuous with the Alaska Range. The volcanoes in the range mark the eastern end of the volcanic arc, which extends about 2,000 miles to the west.

The Tertiary formations in the structural troughs are many thousands of feet thick and intensely folded and faulted. The formations are in part coal-bearing, and where the deformation is slight, as along parts of Cook Inlet, the coals are lignite, but where the formations are strongly folded, as along Matanuska Valley, volatile matter has been driven from the coal and it is bituminous. This relationship between structural geology and rank of coal is similar to the relationships previously noted in the Appalachians (Fig. 11.29).

Deformation of the structural trough at Shelikof Strait, Cook Inlet, and Susitna River is continuing, as is indicated by the frequency of severe earthquakes originating in that area (Figs. 18.12, 18.13).

Alaska Peninsula and Aleutian Islands

The Alaska Peninsula and Aleutian Islands form an arc consisting of more than 75 volcanoes, about half of which are known to have erupted during the last 200 years (Fig.

18.7). The volcanic belt extends 1,500 miles from Mount Spurr, opposite Cook Inlet, to Buldir Volcano between the Rat Islands and Near Islands.

The volcanoes are aligned along a structural uplift that plunges southwestward from the Alaska Range. The highest volcanoes are at the high, northern end of the uplift. Altitudes of the peaks decrease southwestward from 11,000 feet at Mount Spurr to 10,200 feet at Mount Redoubt, 10,000 feet at Mount Iliamna, and 7,500 feet at Mount Katmai. Most of the other volcanoes on the Peninsula are below 6,000 feet except Pavlof Volcano, which is almost 9,000 feet high. Mt. Shis-

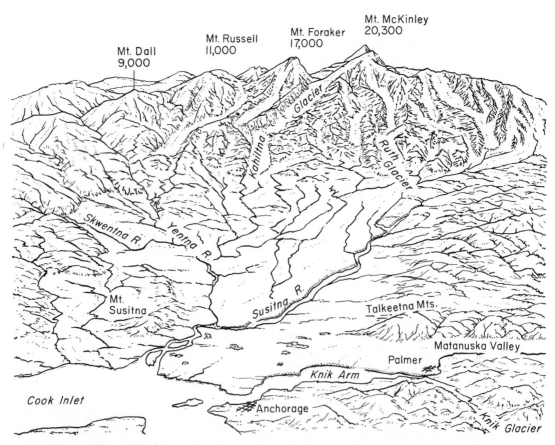

Figure 18.6 *Diagrammatic view of South-central Alaska looking from above Cook Inlet to Mount McKinley. The glaciers are small remnants of the Pleistocene ice sheet, which covered these mountains and filled the valleys, including Cook Inlet.*

haldin on Unimak Island is more than 9,000 feet in altitude, but farther west the volcanoes are lower (below 4,000 feet). In addition to the volcanoes that form islands, others are submerged.

Four kinds of volcanic structures are represented along the arc. The first kind, and the earliest to form, is the shield volcano—composed of thin lava flows that spread widely and built broad, low cones. The second kind, younger than the first, is the steep-sided cone, composed both of lavas and of fragmental material. Some of these are still active. This superposition of steep-sided volcanoes on broad, low ones resembles the structure of the Cascade Mountains. The third kind is the caldera—a volcano from which the upper parts of the cone have collapsed, as at Crater Lake, Oregon. The fourth kind is the volcanic dome, formed where steep-sided bulbous masses of viscous lava were partly extruded at a vent (Fig. 18.8).

The older rocks in the uplift under the volcanoes are poorly exposed along the Aleu-

tian Islands. But the narrowness of the long volcanic belt, the frequency of earthquakes along the arc, and the fact that earthquakes along the south side of the arc originate at shallower depths than those along the north side all suggest that the arc may represent the upper plate of a north-dipping fault whose trace is along the Aleutian Trench (Fig. 18.9).

Not much of the land on the islands or on the peninsula is level. Steep slopes prevail all the way to the water's edge. Shores are rocky and craggy (Fig. 18.10). A continental shelf borders the Alaska Peninsula and Unimak Island (Fig. 18.2), but the rest of the islands are the emerged peaks of a narrow ridge, most of which is submerged. South of the islands the submarine topography to a depth of about 150 feet consists of valleys and ridges, whereas from 150 down to 325 feet the slope is smooth. This contrast in submarine topography suggests that sea level once stood about 150 feet lower than it does now. Beyond a depth of 325 feet the slope

1. Mt. Spurr
2. Mt. Redoubt
3. Mt. Iliamna
4. Augustine Volcano
5. Mt. Douglas
6. Mt. Katmai
7. Aniakchak Crater
8. Pavlof Volcano
9. Mt. Shishaldin
10. Bogoslof Volcano
11. Great Sitkin Volcano
12. Little Sitkin Volcano

Figure 18.7 *Volcanoes on the Alaska Peninsula and Aleutian Islands. Almost all these volcanoes have been active during Recent time; about 36 have erupted since 1760.*

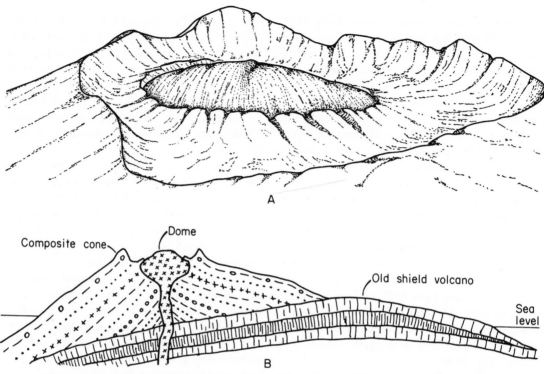

Figure 18.8   *Great Sitkin Volcano. (A) View of the crater and the basalt dome within it. The crater is about 0.75 mile in diameter and about 4,000 feet in altitude. The basaltic dome formed in 1945. (B) Cross section illustrating the structure of the Great Sitkin Volcano. Composed of lavas and volcanic ash, the volcano is built on the flank of a broad, low shield volcano of basaltic lavas. (Generalized after U.S.G.S.)*

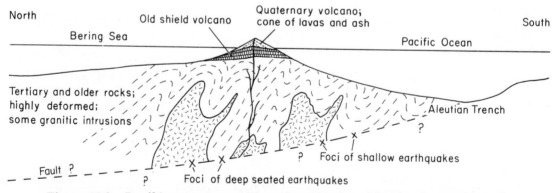

Figure 18.9   *Possible structure under the Aleutian Islands. Composite volcanoes of lavas and volcanic ash have built high, steep-sided cones on broad, low shield volcanoes that overlie complexly deformed Tertiary and older rocks. Earthquakes south of the islands are shallow compared to those north of the islands. Perhaps a deep-seated fault dips north under an upper plate of deformed rocks capped by the volcanoes.*

steepens and the submarine topography suggests faulting.

The Aleutian Trench, a geosyncline undergoing present-day deformation, is a deep, narrow, submarine trough south of the Aleutian Islands and Alaska Peninsula (Fig. 18.2), but becomes shallower in the Gulf of Alaska and finally disappears. This shallowing is thought to be due to filling of the geosyncline by Quaternary sediments. The deep western part receives little sediment because the land area draining to it is small. Gravity measurements indicate that the trench is underlain by light rock between masses of heavier rock that form the higher ground on each side of the trench, as if the structural trough were formed between convection cells in the mantle (Fig. 2.13).

The Pribilof Islands and other islands in the Bering Sea are like the Aleutian Islands in that they are composed largely of Quaternary eruptives, but unlike the Aleutians these islands are isolated mountains rising from a plain—the continental shelf under the Bering Sea. The Pribilof Islands are important as the breeding ground of the Alaska fur seal.

Blue and white foxes, native to these islands, are also sought for their furs.

Interior Alaska

Interior Alaska consists of the tremendous area lying between the Alaska Range on the south and the Arctic Slope on the north, roughly half the State. It consists mostly of the drainage basin of the Yukon River, one of the world's longest rivers, which is about 2,000 miles long and is navigable by river steamer most of the way to its headwaters in Canada. Its general trend is northwest, and its principal tributaries are the Koyukuk, Tanana, and Porcupine rivers. In Canada it is joined by the Klondike River at Dawson, where the discovery of large quantities of placer gold in 1896 led to a rush of prospectors into Alaska as well as into Canada. The Kuskokwim, the other major river in this area, rises in the Alaska Range, flows southwest, and is navigable by steamer for about 600 miles.

The lower Yukon and lower Kuskokwim rivers, for about 150 miles, cross an extensive,

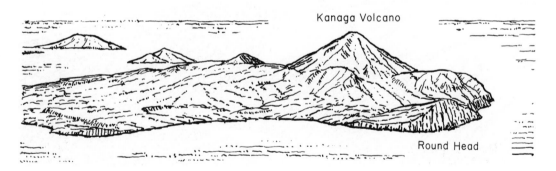

Figure 18.10 *View west to Kanaga Island, one of the Andreanof group, a typical view of the Aleutian Islands except for absence of fog. Width of foreground about 12 miles. Kanaga Volcano is a steep-sided cone, 4300 feet high, composed of lavas and volcanic ash. Round Head, at the northeast corner of the island, is an older volcano composed of basaltic lava. Its vent is submerged and lies northeast of the island; the Kanaga Volcano is built on the southwest flank of the older volcano.*

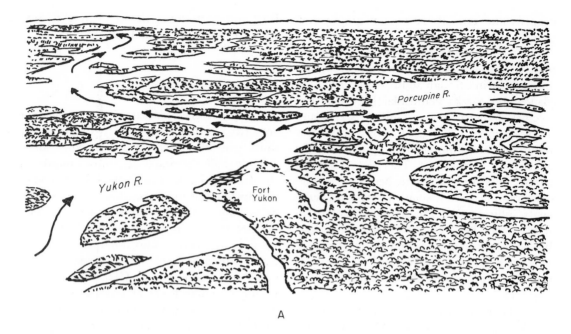

A

B

Figure 18.11 *Topography along the Yukon River. (A) Yukon Flats. For 150 miles in the vicinity of Fort Yukon the River meanders with a braided pattern across a vast alluvial flat, built partly of alluvium deposited by the Yukon and partly of alluvial fans deposited by its tributaries. (B) For much of its course the river flows between bluffs a few hundred feet high. The bluffs shown in this view are at the head of the gorge below the Yukon Flats.*

low, deltaic flat containing numerous large swamps. Tidewater extends about 100 miles up the rivers. Topographically this area is like the Mississippi Delta, but is twice as large.

Upstream from the deltaic lowland the river gradients remain low; at Fort Yukon (Fig. 18.2) the river is little more than 400 feet above sea level; Fairbanks, on the Tanana, is 450 feet above sea level. Beyond the deltaic lowland the Yukon and its tributaries have cut into a dissected plateau 1,000 to 2,000 feet higher than the rivers, which are in wide valleys bordered by bluffs a few hundred feet high (Fig. 18.11,B). Northward and southward from the Yukon River the plateau slopes upward and joins the bordering mountain ranges at altitudes around 3,000 or 4,000 feet. The plateau, however, is not a structural surface; it is an erosion surface that truncates complex structures in resistant Paleozoic and Mesozoic rocks and granitic rocks intrusive into them: numerous monadnocks rise above its surface.

Most of the valleys are narrow and deeply incised into the plateau surface, but this terrain is interrupted by about a dozen structural basins, in which the rivers meander across vast flats. One of these forms the Yukon Flats (Fig. 18.11,A), which extend 150 miles along the river in the vicinity of Fort Yukon and cover 10,000 square miles. Downwarping of the basins began in the Tertiary and apparently continued into the Quaternary, for the basins are filled to unknown depths with glacial outwash. The basins in almost half of this region are floored with Tertiary and Quaternary fill.

During the geologic past much of this area was geanticlinal and shed sediments northward and southward to bordering geosynclines. The southwest courses of the Kuskokwim, Koyukuk, and lower part of the Yukon rivers are controlled by southwest-trending structures inherited from two geosynclines and an intervening geanticline.

At the north, along the Brooks Range, altitudes are more than 8,000 feet in the east, but decrease to less than 5,000 feet toward the west (Fig. 18.2). This range, which trends east-west, marks the boundary between a Mesozoic geosyncline located along the north flank and a geanticline located along the south flank of the range. The Mesozoic formations thicken greatly northward from the mountains to the coast. The uplift of these old rocks to form the Brooks Range occurred during Tertiary and Quaternary time. This uplift is separated from that at the Seward Peninsula by the Quaternary Selawik Basin.

Seward Peninsula and Bering Coast Uplands

The Seward Peninsula and the Bering Coast Uplands are part of an uplift that extends westward into Siberia and is breached at the Bering Strait. Uplift has been progressing for a long time; Quaternary uplift is recorded by marine terraces of Quaternary age along the narrow coastal plain. The surface on the Peninsula truncates complex structures in resistant Paleozoic formations and granite bodies intruding them. It is a rough plateau with monadnocks rising 1,500 to 2,000 feet above the general surface; steep-walled canyons have been incised into the plateau. Most of this ground is permanently frozen.

Arctic Slope

The Arctic Slope is a nearly featureless coastal plain as much as 100 miles wide. It is not much higher than sea level. The ground is permanently frozen to great depths. During the brief summer the surface is dotted with lakes and ponds. Point Barrow is the northernmost point in the United States.

Earthquakes and Tsunami

Earthquakes are frequent in two belts in Alaska. One forms an arc along the Aleutian Islands, Alaska Peninsula, and across the

Alaska Range to the vicinity of Fairbanks. The other begins in the St. Elias Mountains and extends southeastward along the southeastern panhandle and the coast of British Columbia to the Puget Trough. According to Figure 18.12, the area between these two belts is at least comparatively quiescent. However, the structural grain indicated by the seismic epicenters differs from that indicated by the structural geology shown in Figure 18.5, and probably the earthquake belts parallel the structural geology more than is indicated in Figure 18.12.

In Anchorage, a household may feel a half dozen earthquakes annually. The 1964 earthquake originated in Prince William Sound. It was accompanied by earth movements that in places amounted to 50 feet of vertical uplift. Unsatisfactory foundation conditions, however, were the principal factors contributing to the tremendous property damage. The city is situated on a plain of glacial outwash and related glacial deposits resting on an impermeable clay formation. The shaking by the earthquake caused sliding on the wet clay. Many residences along the bluffs overlooking Cook Inlet were carried to destruction by landslides set in motion by the earthquake (Fig. 18.13).

Earthquakes that center near the coast of Alaska are commonly accompanied by huge waves, erroneously called "tidal waves." One kind, tsunami, can cross the Pacific in a matter of hours and cause destruction on distant shores. In 1946 an earthquake with an epicenter near Unimak Island in the Aleutian Island arc destroyed a lighthouse high on a cliff and generated a tsunami that reached the Hawaiian Islands, about 2,500 miles away, in 5 hours and caused $25 million damage there. In 1957 an earthquake in the Andreanof Islands generated a tsunami that caused $3 million damage on the Hawaiian Islands. The 1964 earthquake that so heavily damaged Anchorage created a tsunami that caused loss of life and property damage along the coast of California.

The tsunami are apparently caused when the ocean bottom is suddenly raised or dropped. A network of specially equipped seismological stations provides warnings when the kind of earthquake occurs that may generate a tsunami. The stations are operated around the Pacific in a cooperative venture by several countries.

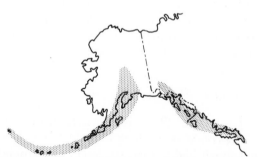

Figure 18.12 *Earthquake belts (stippled areas) in Alaska. One belt extends from the Alaska Range southwestward along the Alaska Peninsula, and westward along the Aleutian Islands and Trench. The western end of the belt connects with one extending from Kamchatka to Japan. The other belt of earthquakes in Alaska extends southeastward along the St. Elias Mountains and along the Panhandle and coast of British Columbia to Puget Trough. (From U.S.C. and G.S.)*

Figure 18.13 *Unsatisfactory foundation conditions were responsible for much of the property damage at Anchorage in the 1964 earthquake. Homes on the bluffs overlooking Cook Inlet (back of the observer) were tumbled down in landslides resulting from the shaking. The landslid blocks in this view have the structure illustrated in Figure 16.22, A.*

Another kind of destructive sea wave is caused by submarine slides. These may be generated in the fjords, where the combination of shaking and avalanches, whether of rock or glacial ice, creates waves not unlike those that children create by sliding in a bathtub. In Lituya Bay, about 100 miles southeast of Yakutat Bay, an avalanche accompanying an earthquake in 1958 created a wave 100 to 200 feet high that surged onto the shore with sufficient force to strip all the forest from a promontory 1,720 feet high (Fig. 18.14).

Climate

Climatic data for Alaska are woefully inadequate. Few stations have records that date back more than 25 years, and inasmuch as these stations necessarily are located in the principal towns the data are not evenly distributed areally or altitudinally. The climatic map (Fig. 18.15) leaves much to be desired.

In the Southeast Coast Ranges, despite the presence of many glaciers, the climate near the coast is surprisingly mild, with average winter temperatures at about 32°F and with minimum winter temperatures about 0°F. The waterways remain open during the winter. Summer temperatures average in the 50's (°F) and maximum temperatures are in the 90's. The growing season lasts 4 months or more.

The precipitation is heavy, generally averaging more than 80 inches annually and in places more than 150 inches. Inland from the coast the climate becomes increasingly severe, partly because of increased distance from the ocean but chiefly because of the increase in altitude. It is the topography, together with the high precipitation, that maintains such a huge volume of ice in the mountains that the glaciers extend down to sea level despite the mild temperatures there. Above 3,000 feet

there is perennial ice. Above 8,000 feet most storms, even during summer, are accompanied by snow.

Temperatures along the coast of South-central Alaska during the winter average about 5°F lower than in southeastern Alaska; summer temperatures average little if any lower. The growing season is 2 to 3 weeks shorter, except on islands like Kodiak, where the growing season is about as long as in southeastern Alaska. Inland from the coast the range in temperature greatly increases with summer maxima around 90°F and winter minima around −40°F. The growing season lasts about 3 months. Average annual precipitation along the coast is in the range of 50 to 70 inches and increases southeastward. Inland the average annual precipitation greatly decreases, being in the range of 15 to 30 inches depending on location relative to nearby mountains.

Temperatures in the Aleutian Islands are about the same as in the islands along the southeast coast of Alaska. Winters are slightly warmer and summers slightly cooler. Annual precipitation is less, averaging about 50 inches on Unalaska, but the islands are almost constantly shrouded by fog. Records are not at hand, but the islands are fog-covered probably 90 percent or more of the year. Islands in the Bering Sea are very much colder than the Aleutian Islands, and their annual precipitation is much less.

Lowlands and uplands in the Yukon Valley have a continental climate, with long, cold winters and short, hot summers. Fort Yukon has recorded a minimum of 78°F below zero and a maximum of 100°F. The growing season is less than 3 months long. The region is semi-arid, with average annual precipitation less than 20 inches, and in much of the region less than 15 inches. At Fort Yukon the average is 7 inches. Despite the low temperatures and long winters, the valleys of the Yukon and Kuskokwim were not glaciated during the Pleistocene (Fig. 18.16), probably because of insufficient precipitation.

On the Seward Peninsula, Nome has re-

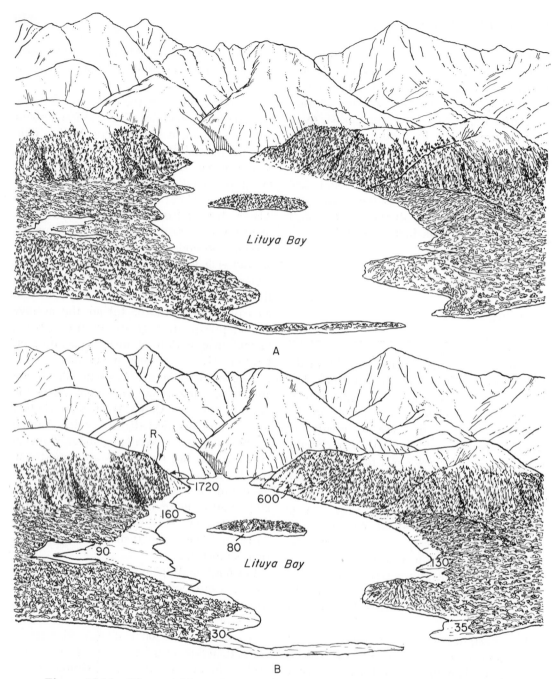

Figure 18.14 *Views of Lituya Bay, southeastern Alaska, before (A) and after (B) the destructive great wave of 1958. The lower slopes of the mountains, from sea level to about 2,500 feet, are heavily forested. Higher up, the mountains are bare. Glaciers descend each of the valleys in the mountains (Fairweather Range) at the head of the bay. A rock slide at R, triggered by the 1958 earthquake, created a wave that completely destroyed the forest up to the altitudes shown (feet). At the promontory across from the slide the wave swept away forest to a height of 1,720 feet. Three boats were in the bay at the time of the wave. One, behind the island, rode out the wave. Another was washed into the ocean across the top of the sand spit at the mouth of the bay. A third was destroyed. (Data from U.S.G.S.)*

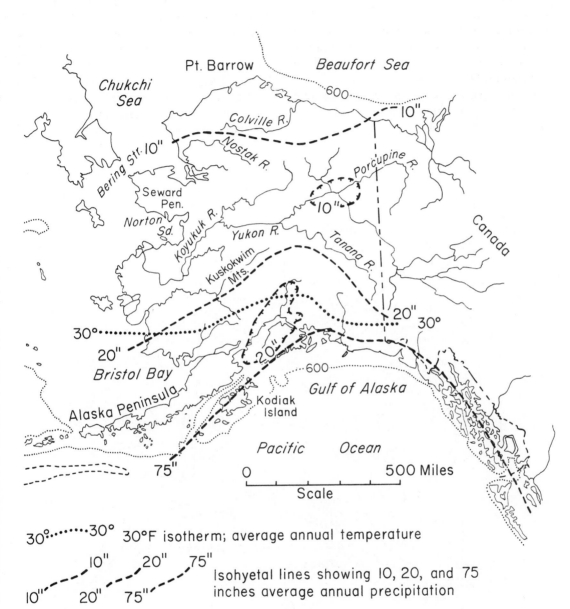

Figure 18.15 *Climatic map of Alaska. South of the 30° isotherm the average annual temperature is above 30°F; to the north the average is below 30°F. Along the coast precipitation is at a maximum during the fall; in the interior and in northern Alaska, there is precipitation throughout the year. In winter a low pressure area forms over the Gulf of Alaska, bringing southwesterly winds to the Panhandle; in summer a high-pressure area forms over the gulf, bringing westerly winds to the southern and southeastern coasts.*

corded a minimum temperature of −47°F and a maximum of 84°F. The average January temperature is about 3°F and the average July temperature is less than 50°F. The growing season is less than 2 months long. Average annual precipitation is about 18 inches. Much of the ground is permanently frozen.

North of the Brooks Range winters are long and cold. January temperatures at Point Barrow *average* 17°F below zero; July tempera-

tures average about 40°F. The growing season lasts about 2 weeks. Average annual precipitation is less than 5 inches. During the Pleistocene the summit of the Brooks Range was glaciated, but the glaciers did not extend far down the north slope (Fig. 18.16). Because of the low precipitation, the mountains have only small glaciers, but the ground is permanently frozen throughout this region, both in the mountains and on the coastal plain.

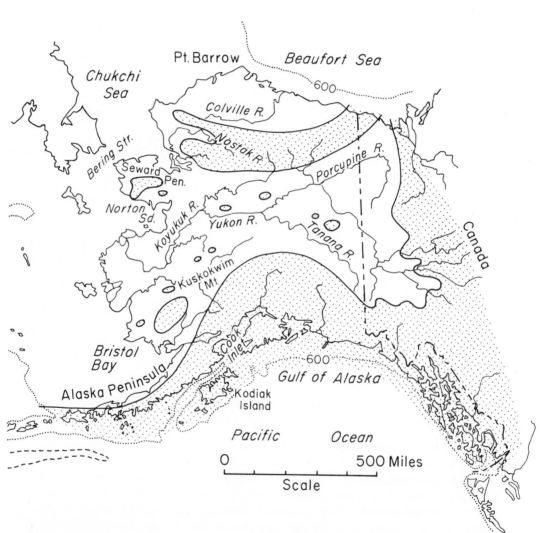

Figure 18.16 *Extent of Pleistocene glaciers (stippled area) in Alaska. (After U.S.G.S.)*

Glaciers, Glacial Deposits, and the Glacial Process

With its glaciers and permanently frozen ground, Alaska seems less removed from the Pleistocene than most of the rest of the United States, and the effects of the past climates are less noticeable there. In the Coast Mountains of southeast Alaska, glaciers are numerous (Fig. 18.3), especially along the Gulf of Alaska. From Yakutat Bay west to Copper River the mountains are largely covered by glacial ice.

Many hundreds of alpine glaciers fill the valleys of the Coast Mountains, and many extend down valley to the sea. One of the best known, Muir glacier, is only about 20 miles long but is fed by numerous tributaries and covers 350 square miles. The front of the glacier—about a mile wide and 100 to 200 feet high—has receded despite the fact that the ice advances at the rate of a few feet per day. Melting and the breaking off of icebergs where the glacier enters the sea exceed the rate of ice advance. Many Alaska glaciers are receding.

Along the flanks of the mountains from Glacier Bay to Copper River, a distance of more than 250 miles, there is almost continuous glacier several thousands of feet thick. The large glaciers, including the Malaspina, Guyot, and Bering glaciers, are piedmont glaciers that extend onto flat country beyond the foot of the mountains and form ice plateaus up to 1,500 feet high, but sloping to sea level. They are fed by valley glaciers that head in the mountains above the line of perpetual snow, which is at an altitude of about 2,500 feet. The snowline is 5,000 feet higher on the dry, northeast side of the coastal mountains.

This system of glaciers is the largest in the world outside Greenland and the polar ice caps. In Alaska and Canada the ice-covered area probably exceeds 5,000 square miles, which is about one-third the area of Switzerland.

The edges of the ice plateaus are covered with moraines that support forests. The edge of the huge Malaspina glacier is so heavily forested that it was not identified as a glacier until 1880. The interior of the plateau, however, is clear ice with a gently undulating but crevassed surface. Streams flow on this ice until they discharge into a crevasse and join the subglacial drainage.

In South-central Alaska valley floors are covered by Pleistocene glacial drift, including till, glacial outwash, and lake and estuarine deposits, all mantled by loess. Much of Matanuska Valley is covered by loess, and this ground is well suited for agriculture. At least three ages of Pleistocene glacial deposits have been recognized, and they record that all of this part of Alaska was covered by ice during the Pleistocene (Fig. 18.16).

The valleys, filled with the glacial deposits, have level or gently rolling floors flanked by steep mountains (Fig. 18.6). The valley sides were steepened as a result of downfaulting or downwarping of the troughs, and they have been further steepened by glacial erosion.

At Mount McKinley, the upper 18,000 feet of the mountain is in the zone of perennial ice (Fig. 8.5). At altitudes higher than 12,000 feet, it is doubtful if precipitation ever takes the form of rain. But despite this, glaciers in the Alaska Range are small compared to those in southeast Alaska because of the difference in precipitation, which is only 30 inches at valley stations on the Susitna River below Mount McKinley, and less than 20 inches in the valleys north of the Range.

The lowlands and uplands in the Yukon River valley were not glaciated during Pleistocene time, but glacial effects are considerable because the rivers received the meltwaters discharging from the glaciers in the mountains to the north, east, and south. The sediments deposited by these meltwaters built the alluvial flats in the structural basins, like Yukon Flats, and the floods must also have contributed greatly to enlarging the delta, which has probably had a history similar to that of the Mississippi River delta, where the river course has continually shifted across the growing front of the delta.

The alluvial flats were the source of loess deposited across the uplands, quite like the loesses bordering the lee sides of rivers in the central United States (p. 230). The loess blanket on the uplands north of the Tanana River in the Fairbanks area is more than 100 feet thick in places, but it thins northward away from the river. Interbedded with this loess are layers of volcanic ash as much as 6 inches thick.

Extensive as Alaska's glaciers are, they are only small remnants of those that formed during the Pleistocene (Fig. 18.16). Two glacial advances in Alaska are thought to be of Wisconsin age, and there were at least two earlier, pre-Wisconsin glacial advances. Alaska's existing glaciers illustrate three quite different ways in which glaciers occur. Where the ice is thick enough to bury the mountains as well as the valleys, the glaciers occur as *ice sheets.* The world's most extensive ice sheets are in Greenland and in the Antarctic, but small ones bury some Alaska mountaintops, especially east of Copper River. *Valley glaciers,* the most common kind in Alaska, are those that are confined within valleys and descend them without overtopping the ridges. *Piedmont glaciers,* like the mighty Malaspina, form where glaciers emerge at the foot of a mountain and spread like viscous dough on the piedmont flat.

In the collecting area above the snowline, the snow compacts into granules, known as *firn,* and the granules in turn compact into massive ice. This compaction is due to alternate melting and freezing of the particles. Solid ice will flow on a flat surface under its own weight if the thickness exceeds about 250 feet. On sloping surfaces, however, much lesser thicknesses move easily under their own weight. Many Alaskan glaciers are more than 1,000 feet thick, and their rates of advance may be several feet per day, although generally less. This movement of the ice takes place partly by shearing, partly by recrystallization, and partly by granulation.

Below the snowline is a zone of seasonal melting, the *ablation zone,* where the ice is reduced by meltwater runoff. If the melting exceeds the recharge by flow of ice from above the snowline, the glacier front retreats. If recharge exceeds the melting, the glacier front advances. Most Alaskan glaciers have retreated during the last few decades. Between 1936 and 1950 the rate of retreat of the Muir glacier averaged 1,500 feet per year.

In advancing down a valley the ice erodes its base and sides, partly by plucking and partly by abrasion. Debris that moves down the valley walls as a result of washing and slow creep collects along the sides on the ice surface and forms lateral moraines. Where two valley glaciers join, two of the lateral moraines come together to form a *medial* moraine. At the front of the ice, a terminal moraine is deposited. The morainal material and debris within the ice are carried from the front by meltwaters and deposited as glacial outwash.

Erosion is active at the very head of a glacier, too, and produces the cirques that are so characteristic of glaciated mountains. This erosion involves several processes. In the warm season the ice moving down valley pulls away from the country rock, forming an arcuate crevasse (*bergschrund*) along which the exposed rock wall becomes subject to accelerated frost action because it is alternately soaked by meltwaters, and frozen, and then thawed. In the next cold season the crevasse fills with snow which compacts to firn and then to solid ice. In the next warm period the rocks loosened by frost heaving are pulled from the wall as the bergschrund opens. Retreat of the head wall, combined with lowering of the floor, produces the highly characteristic, steep-walled cirque.

Permanently Frozen Ground

North of the 30°F isotherm in Alaska (Fig. 18.14) much of the ground remains permanently frozen (Fig. 18.17), a condition referred to as *permafrost*. The thickness of the permafrost ranges from a few feet at the south to about 1,000 feet at the north. In the north the permafrost layer is practically continuous, but as it thins southward it becomes discontinuous (Fig. 18.18). The interior forests correspond approximately to the zone of discontinuous permafrost; tundra corresponds approximately to the zone of continuous permafrost.

Permafrost is defined on the basis of temperature. The ground may be soil, other surficial deposit, or bedrock, and may contain no ice, but if its temperature is permanently below freezing it is referred to as *dry permafrost*. More commonly the ground is cemented with ice.

The permafrost layer does not extend to the surface because the surface layers thaw

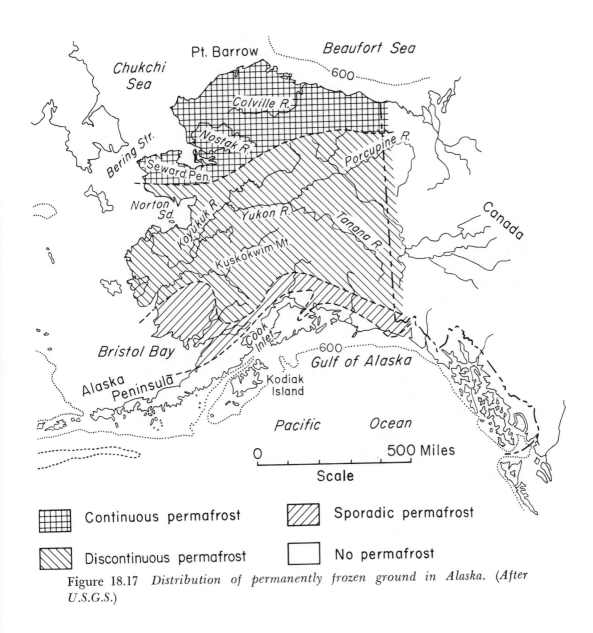

Figure 18.17 *Distribution of permanently frozen ground in Alaska. (After U.S.G.S.)*

during the warm season. The surface layers freeze again during the next cold season, but this frozen ground is not part of the permafrost. The layer that freezes and thaws seasonally, the *active layer,* may be 20 feet deep in gravel but only 3 feet or less in silt or under peat. In many places the top of the permafrost layer is deeper than the base of the active layer, and the two are separated by a layer of unfrozen ground.

These relations help explain some of the extraordinary frost and ice features of the north country. For example, groundwater commonly becomes trapped between the layer of permafrost and the base of the active layer. When the active layer freezes, the confined water may be squeezed upward to form an ice core that domes the overlying ground, to form steep-sided hillocks as much as 50 feet high, known as *pingos.* They are common in the zone of continuous permafrost, rare elsewhere. If the process continues, the water may be ejected, forming a spring that freezes into a surface mound of ice. This phenomena may do no harm in a wilderness location, but in settled areas buildings may be tilted or become engulfed by ice, or the trapped groundwater may convert the unfrozen layer to mud and cause landsliding on slopes. Where the

permafrost is shallow, only such shallow-rooted species as black spruce can grow.

In permafrost areas special engineering designing is required to avoid foundation failures under buildings, highways, bridge pilings, pipelines, and other structures. The engineer must consider frost heaving of the surface layer, the depth of this active layer, the depth of the permafrost, and their effects on the ground drainage system.

Abundant fossil remains of animals and plants have been recovered from permafrost in Interior Alaska, chiefly as a result of the gold-mining operations. Many of the animal remains are of extinct Pleistocene forms, but complete animals, like the frozen mammoths recovered in Siberia, have not been found. Plant remains found in the permafrost are the same species that are common today.

Patterned Ground

In the frozen north, where frost action is intensive, the ground may develop characteristic patterns due to regularly spaced hummocks, depressions, or ridges (Fig. 18.19). The hummocks and depressions may be circular or po-

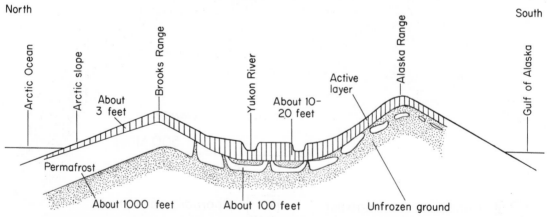

Figure 18.18 *Diagrammatic section illustrating permanently frozen ground in Alaska. In the north the permafrost is about 1,000 feet thick; the active layer is about 3 feet thick. Southward the permafrost thins and becomes discontinuous; the active layer thickens. Unfrozen ground underlies the permafrost, and unfrozen layers may lie between the permafrost and the active layer.*

lygonal. They may be a few feet or many feet wide and may be distributed over many square miles. The hummocks range from a few inches to a few feet high. The ground may be uniformly silty or gravelly. Where the ground contains stones, these are likely to be concentrated around the edges of the mound or hummocks, or if the pattern is linear the stones are generally concentrated in ridges. The features become greatly accentuated by the vegetation, which reflects the considerable differences in microclimate, ground texture, and topographic position between the interiors and edges of the mounds, depressions, or ridges.

Similar patterned ground has developed on mountains in the Rocky Mountain and Pacific Coast states, especially those subjected to glaciation and intensive frost action during Pleistocene time. In those mountains the features seem to be in large part relics from the Pleistocene. Curiously, very similar ground patterns develop in hot, saline deserts. For example, ground patterns in Death Valley, California are not very different from those on the Arctic Slope of Alaska.

The conditions necessary for development of patterned ground are freezing and thawing or, in the deserts, solution and recrystallization of salts. Apparently the ground must alternately become soaking wet and then solidify by freezing or by crystallization of salts. In any ground, freezing and thawing work stones to the surface, but in truly patterned ground the stones are sorted from the silt and arranged in orderly patterns, like the depressions around mounds or the ridges around depressions, or in linear ridges. The regularity in the spacing of the features, however, is not well understood. The polygonal patterns commonly are due to a shallow substrate that has cracked polygonally. In the cold country this shallow substrate is a subsurface layer of ice; in the deserts, a subsurface layer of salt.

Soils and Vegetation

Soils most suitable for farming are those developed on glacial outwash in the valleys and basins, and those developed on loessial de-

Figure 18.19 *A net of depressions 50 to 100 feet in diameter, containing ponds and separated by low ridges with crudely polygonal outlines form one kind of ground pattern on the Arctic Coast of Alaska.*

posits on rolling uplands. The upper layers of these soils contain considerable volcanic ash. The farmed soils are podzolic, and most are Recent in age.

More than half of Alaska is treeless (Fig. 18.20). In southeastern and South-central Alaska the treeless ground is bare rock, glacial ice, and snowfields. The southern slopes of the Alaska Range, the Alaska Peninsula, and the Aleutian Islands are grassland with some sedge and dwarf willows. The east coast of the Bering Sea, the north flank of the Brooks Range, and the coastal plain along the north coast have short, cool summers; the ground

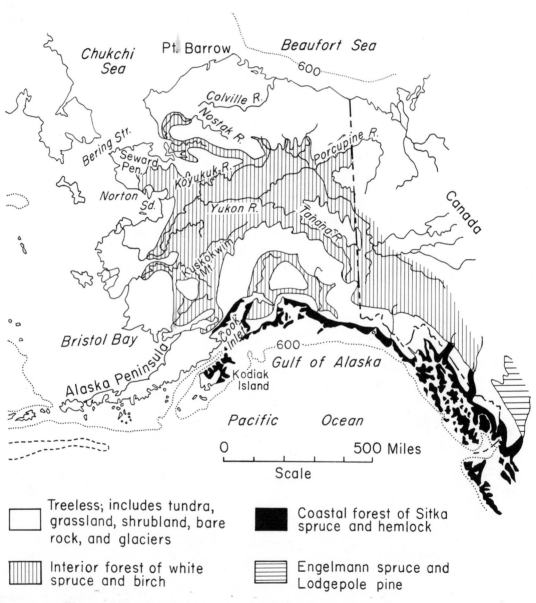

Figure 18.20   *Forests in Alaska.* (*Generalized from U.S.G.S. and U.S.D.A.*)

supports tundra vegetation, which includes several kinds of growths. Some is shrubby with willow, alder, and dwarf birch. Some is herbaceous, with sedge and grass. In the north some of the well-drained ground is rock desert, with various shrubs and herbs growing amid the rock rubble. Tundra-like vegetation in swampy areas is referred to as muskeg. Vegetation on the Alaskan tundra probably consists of about equal proportions of lichens, sedges, shrubs, and mixed grasses, weeds, and mosses. This is the summer feed for the reindeer; in winter their diet consists almost entirely of a branching lichen a few inches high, known as reindeer moss and regarded as the most characteristic plant of the tundra.

Alaska has two principal kinds of forests. Along the coast, where winters are mild, the forest is Sitka spruce and hemlock. About 70 percent of the growth is hemlock, 25 percent is spruce, and the remaining 5 percent is mostly Alaska cedar, western red cedar, white birch, alder, and lodgepole pine. In the interior, where winters are severe, forests consist chiefly of white spruce and birch. White spruce occupies the better-drained ground; black spruce occupies swampy ground. Cottonwood, aspen, alder, and willows grow along the streams. Other trees in the interior forest include the balsam poplar, larch, and tamarack. The interior forests are dense along the valley bottoms and in the several basins, but the growth is more open on the uplands.

Forests of Engelmann spruce and lodgepole pine that grow in the Northern Cascades and Rocky Mountains extend northward in British Columbia to about the latitude of Juneau (Fig. 18.20).

Volcanic Ash

The parts of Alaska that are subject to ash falls are of special ecological interest because a major volcanic eruption may deposit a widespread thick blanket of ash, like the one that buried Pompeii in A.D. 79. The eruption of Mt. Katmai in 1912 deposited a few feet of ash near the volcano and a foot of ash on Kodiak Island a hundred miles to the east. An eruption at Mount Spurr in 1953 deposited ash at Valdez, 200 miles away. The effects of such ash falls on the vegetation may be zoned as follows:

Zone 1, near the volcanic center: vegetation incinerated by incandescent ash;

Zone 2, heavy ash fall: trees killed, herbage killed by burial;

Zone 3, moderate ash fall: trees killed but grasses recover;

Zone 4, lighter ash fall: trees and shrubs little affected; small plants damaged;

Zone 5, farthest from the center: plants locally affected by acid rains but not otherwise damaged.

The rates of weathering, revegetation, and other recovery of these zones involves a complex of factors. The ash, composed of minerals and glass shards, changes texture and composition rapidly because of compaction, washing by rains, and high susceptibility to erosion. The soil acidity and content of soluble elements change as weathering progresses; moisture retention is changed by compaction and by erosion. Moreover, plants differ in their resistance to damage by ash falls. Conifers may yield under ash without damage, as they do under snow. Plants differ in their resistance to damage by sandblasting, which is an important process on fresh volcanic ash. Plants also differ in their moisture requirements and in their need for or tolerance of the available soluble elements. In general, liverworts have been the first to grow on fresh surfaces of volcanic ash in Alaska; lichens generally are first on lava surfaces, but no simple succession of plants follows these pioneers.

An equally complex array of factors controls the rates and order of weathering and revegetation of deposits laid bare by retreating glaciers. Figure 18.21 illustrates one kind of succession in such environments.

Bering Land Bridge

The land bridge across the Bering Strait and the Bering Sea has long been supposed to be the route by which man reached North America from Asia. The concept, which is doctrine in archeology, may be right, but it could be wrong and merely a durable fallacious assumption.

Alaska was connected with Siberia through much of Cenozoic time. Fossil marine molluscs found in late Tertiary deposits on the north coast of Alaska are North Atlantic species. In that area the oldest fossils of Pacific species are found in deposits of early Pleistocene age, when the Bering Strait was apparently opened. During the Pleistocene, as a result of crustal movements and eustatic changes in sea level, the land bridge apparently underwent alternate emergence and submergence. There is no question about the existence of the land bridge, but it is questionable whether it was used by man.

The land bridge evidently was not a satisfactory route between the continents, because during most of Tertiary time the vertebrate fauna of North America did not mix with the fauna of the eastern hemisphere. Paleontologists tell us that faunal interchanges between the two hemispheres took place during early Eocene, late Eocene, early Oligocene, late Miocene, and middle to late Pliocene time. At other times during the Tertiary the faunas were separated and speciated differently. The marine molluscs indicate that the bridge was there during much if not all of Tertiary time, but the vertebrate animals seem to have used it very little if at all. The earliest known remains of man in North America are dated as late Pleistocene; therefore, man did not use the bridge before late Pleistocene time, if then.

The inhospitable, cold, and mountainous north country, especially in Siberia, more than likely served as a barrier to intercontinental migration rather than as a bridge. No other intercontinental route is evident, but perhaps another should be sought in view of the lack of paleontological or archeological evidence indicating use of the Bering Bridge either by man or the other mammals.

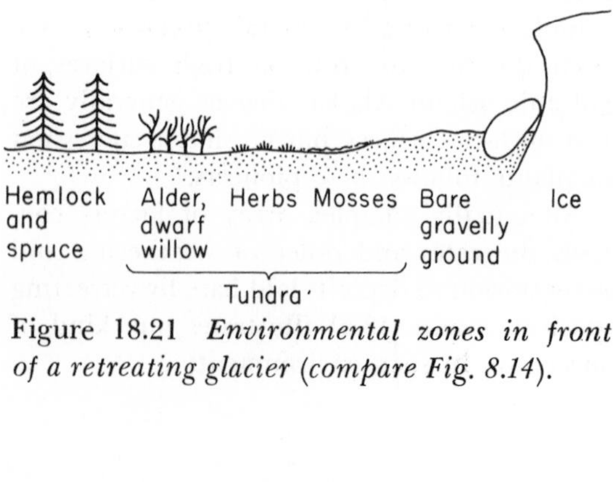

Resources for the Future

Alaska's resources are mostly for the future, because they have been little developed. Fisheries, the principal basis of the present economy, produce mostly salmon but include considerable herring, halibut, shrimp, and crab. The fishing is mostly in the Gulf of Alaska and Bristol Bay. Major canneries are located along the coast.

Besides gold deposits Alaska has important deposits of copper and some lead and zinc, especially in the coastal mountains bordering the Gulf of Alaska. Coal is available in many parts of the country, and supplies local needs. Petroleum, the principal mineral product, occurs on the Kenai Peninsula, along the Cook Inlet, and on the Arctic Slope.

Fur animals, another major resource, were overexploited until control measures were adopted to preserve the herds of seal, sea otter, and other fur-bearing animals. Besides the sea animals there are fox, marten, mink, bear, beaver, weasel (ermine), muskrat, and caribou. Some of these animals are bred and raised for their furs.

Farmlands in Alaska probably total less than 100 square miles in area, but at least

Figure 18.21 *Environmental zones in front of a retreating glacier (compare Fig. 8.14).*

fifty times that area is available and suitable for farming. Agriculture will probably increase at least to the extent of supplying many local needs as the population increases and the transportation system becomes extended.

Timber resources are huge. It has been estimated that the annual forest crop could supply the pulpwood for a million tons of newsprint annually, and the estimate is probably conservative.

Unique scenery and unique natural phenomena such as the volcanoes and glaciers are other Alaska resources that should attract increasing thousands of visitors annually. The fjords are equal to those of Norway. The glaciers of Switzerland are minor compared to those of Alaska; Mount McKinley is a mile higher than the Alps and closer to New York. And why go to Africa for big game?

Alaska could become a major world competitor in attracting vacationers from the other states. Trans-Atlantic airfares continue high. If Alaska were to advertise what it can offer, and if our airlines were to reduce rates in that direction, there could be diversion of travel there. It might also be in the national interest to give less subsidy to the trans-Atlantic luxury liners and more to the Alaska coastal lines.

On the debit side are the fogs, mosquitoes, and charges for tourist facilities that are hardly commensurate with the services rendered. The last could be corrected by drawing more capital to Alaska by advertising its attractions. The fogs will remain, but fog has not been a handicap to some California Chambers of Commerce. Ingenuity will be taxed, however, to make the mosquitoes into an asset.

19 Hawaii

The physiography of the United States described up to this point has been developed on continental structures; not so the Hawaiian Islands. They are located near the middle of the Pacific Ocean along a northwest-trending ridge that divides two oceanic deeps, each of which descends more than 18,000 feet below sea level. The islands are merely peaks along the ridge. The highest peaks are more than 13,000 feet above sea level, resulting in a total relief of more than 6 miles.

Other outstanding features of the islands include their

1. Composition and structure; they are all basaltic volcanoes.
2. Climate, which is oceanic; despite the tropical latitude, temperatures are moderate. Windward sides of the islands are wet, but the leeward sides are semiarid.
3. Tropical-zone fauna, which, for the United States, is unique; coral reefs flank parts of the islands; there are no snakes and few other reptiles; the bat, whale, and dolphin are the only indigenous mammals.
4. Tropical-zone flora, which is equally unique; before man's arrival upset nature's balance, it consisted of 85 percent endemic species.
5. Soils, which in large part are lateritic.

6. Economy, which is based almost wholly on sugar, pineapple, tourism, and military establishments.
7. Lack of variety of resources but high standard of living.
8. Racial integration, which is probably more advanced than at any other place in the world.

The area of the islands is about 6,400 square miles, approximately equal to the combined areas of Connecticut and Rhode Island. The population is about 675,000 (1962 estimate), or about one-fifth the population of Connecticut and Rhode Island.

Structural Framework and Topography

The mountains in the Pacific Ocean seem to be mostly of volcanic origin, but they are of three principal types. The first type, represented by the Hawaiian Islands, includes the conical, active or extinct volcanoes that have been topographically reduced by erosion (Fig. 19.1,A,B). Many are bordered by coral reefs, and the submerged parts of the mountain sides are steep. The second type (Fig. 19.1,C,D) includes the submerged mountains with irregular summits (*seamounts*) and those with tops that are smooth and flat, as if planed by erosion (*guyots*). Seamounts and guyots may be flanked by coral reefs (Fig. 19.1, F). The third type, referred to as banks, includes the broad, submerged plateau-like mountains (Fig. 19.1,E).

Seamounts, guyots, and the submerged parts of the Hawaiian Islands have steep sides, steeper than the sides of subaerial volcanoes and attributed to rapid cooling of submarine lavas. Guyots may be seamounts that have been planed by wave erosion when their tops were at sea level. If so, their submergence may be due to downwarping of the ocean floor. Supporting this view is the fact that where guyots are grouped together their depths are about the same. Some guyots, however, may be due to explosive submarine eruptions, which can produce steep-sided but flat-topped, plateau-like volcanic piles. The process seems

to depend upon violent blasting of highly porous, vesiculated debris into the water, and this slowly settling debris may be spread widely by the turbulence caused by the eruption.

Rocks dredged from these submerged mountains are almost entirely basalt. Some coral has been found at depths greater than 150 feet, which is about the lower limit of coral growth. Deeply submerged reefs seem to indicate considerable downwarping or rise of sea level. Shallow, live reefs may form atolls or fringe reefs.

The Hawaiian Islands are at the junction of two submarine ridges (Fig. 19.2). One of these extends 2,000 miles northwest and includes the Midway Islands; the other extends 3,000 miles west to the Marcus Islands. Eastward from the Hawaiian Islands is a ridge, the Murray fracture zone, which extends to the southern coast of California and may be represented there by the Transverse Ranges.

North of the Hawaiian-Midway Ridge is the

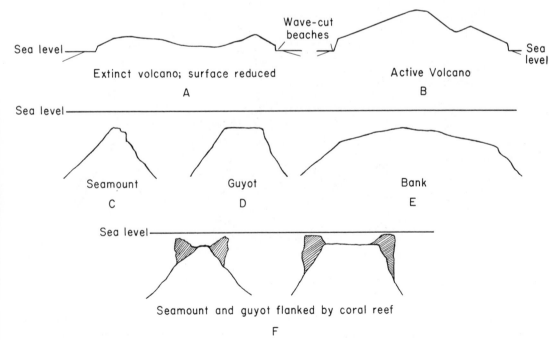

Figure 19.1 *Diagrammatic cross sections illustrating three different kinds of mountains in the Pacific Ocean.*

North Pacific Basin, which extends northward to a broad low ridge separating it from the Aleutian Trench. West of Midway is the Northwest Pacific Basin, which extends westward to a broad ridge separating it from the trenches bordering Japan and the Kurile Islands.

In the eastern half of the Pacific Ocean the topographic and structural grain trends easterly at a high angle to the Pacific Mountain System along the coast of North America. Except for the alignment of the Murray fracture zone with the Transverse Ranges, the trends of the oceanic and continental structures are quite different. Moreover, both gravity and seismic data indicate that the Pacific Mountain System is composed chiefly of light rock, about the density of granite, and that the ocean floor and its ridges and mountains are composed chiefly of dense rock, about the density of basalt. So far as specimens can be

obtained, they confirm this interpretation. If we could see the ocean bottom, we might find its structure and composition similar to that of the Columbia Plateau.

There are five principal Hawaiian Islands and four smaller ones (Fig. 19.3), all basaltic volcanoes. Volcanic activity began in the west and moved eastward, so the youngest islands and the ones with the highest peaks are toward the east. Hawaii, the most easterly and the largest of the islands, has peaks more than 13,000 feet in altitude, and some volcanoes there still are active. This island is not flanked by coral; the older islands, more reduced and lower, are flanked by coral reefs. Farther west, between Kauai and Midway, are shoals and small islands of coral, some with basaltic remnants; these are still older islands.

The islands are hilly and mountainous, especially toward the east. About a fourth of the area is below 650 feet in altitude; a half is

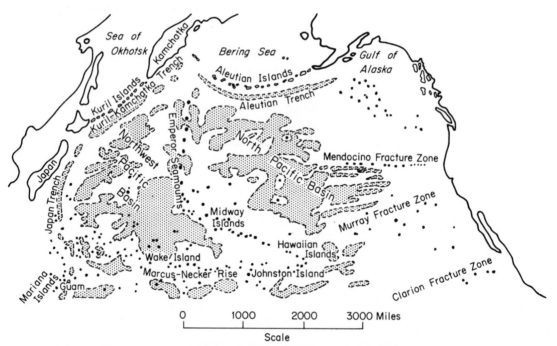

Figure 19.2 *Diagram of the North Pacific Ocean, showing the basins that are deeper than 18,000 feet (stippled area) and the general distribution of seamounts, guyots, and islands (dots) along the ridges separating the basins. (Generalized from Scripps Institute of Oceanography and National Geographic Society.)*

between 650 and 2,000 feet, and a fourth is above 2,000 feet. The coast lines are mostly rocky and rough. Erosion at the exposed, windward (northeast) shores in places has produced seacliffs 3,000 feet high. Only Oahu and Niihau have much coastal plain. There is only one harbor, Pearl Harbor, which is west of Honolulu, and there is a bay at Hilo.

The Hawaiian volcanoes developed during the Tertiary and seem to have been built above sea level late in Tertiary time. Most of the parts that are built above sea level were formed during late Tertiary and Quaternary time. The older islands, such as Oahu (Fig. 19.4), have been reduced by erosion, some coastal plain has been built, and the shores are fringed with coral reefs.

On the big island, Hawaii, the volcanoes at Mauna Loa and Kilauea are still active and erupt every few years; three other volcanoes on the island are dormant. One of these, Mauna Kea, had alpine glaciers in late Pleistocene time.

Climate

The Hawaiian Islands have a pleasant climate. The latitude is tropical, but the surrounding ocean and the highly persistent northeast trade winds maintain uniform climatic conditions throughout the year (Fig. 19.5).

At any given location temperature and precipitation are nearly uniform, but they both vary tremendously with altitude and with exposure. The windward slopes receive as much as 450 inches of rainfall annually, whereas lee slopes are semiarid, with less than 20 inches average annual rainfall. Temperatures de-

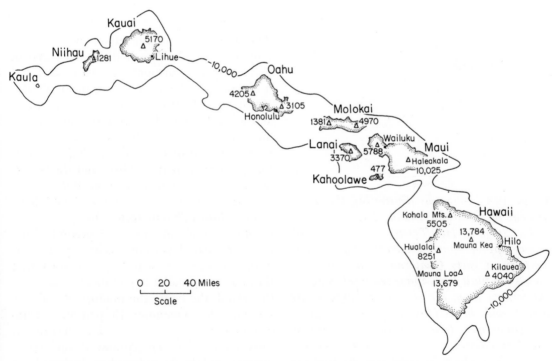

Figure 19.3 *Map of Hawaiian Islands, showing the principle volcanic cones and their altitudes and relation to the −10,000-foot submarine contour. (After U.S.G.S.)*

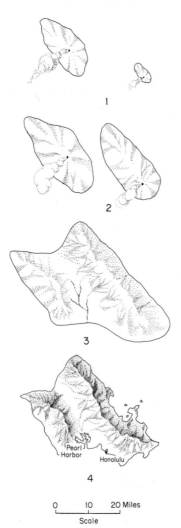

Figure 19.4 *Diagrams illustrating the development of a volcanic island. The example is Oahu. Stage 1: late Tertiary time; two volcanoes appear above sea level. Stage 2: late Tertiary or early Quaternary time; the volcanoes are built high above sea level. Stage 3: Quaternary time; the volcanic mountains are joined, and the activity has ceased. Stage 4: late Quaternary time; the mountains are reduced by erosion; they are fringed by coastal plain and in places by coral reef. Erosion has been particularly vigorous on the northeast side, which is to the windward. The northeast coast is very rocky. (After U.S.G.S.)*

crease about $3\frac{1}{2}°$F for each 1,000 feet of altitude. Below 4,000 feet frost is rare and has never been recorded below 2,500 feet. The lowest *officially recorded* temperature is 25°F, at an altitude of 6,500 feet, but temperatures are lower on the high peaks, where snow may fall during any month of the year and where there is permanent ice in deep cracks.

The islands are free of tornadoes and typhoons. Thunderstorms are infrequent and never severe. Hail is rare. The windward sides are cloudy (Fig. 19.6), but the clouds are high and fogs rarely interfere with shipping or airplane schedules.

Despite the oceanic setting, the climate was different during the Pleistocene, when glaciers formed on Mauna Kea. The lateritic soils (p. 438), which are ancient deposits, possibly formed under climatic conditions different from those of the present.

Vegetation

The native flora of the Hawaiian Islands is unique. Not only does it differ from that of the continents surrounding the Pacific, but it differs from the other islands in the Pacific. When the Hawaiian Islands first appeared above sea level in late Tertiary time, a few millions of years ago, they were barren lavas. Seeds were transported there, perhaps by floating, perhaps in part by birds, and the islands became covered with vegetation. But in isolation from their parent stocks these plants evolved into different forms. Before man arrived on the islands, about 85 percent of the flora consisted of endemic species—species that have so changed from their parent stock that they now are peculiar to the islands. The older the island, the larger the number of endemic species. The remaining 15 percent are indigenous species that retain characteristics of these species elsewhere. Almost all the flowering trees and shrubs and food-producing plants have been introduced by man, and have spread at the expense of the indigenous plants. Stands of native plants on the islands include shrub, forest, bog, and moss-lichen.

Most of the shrub land is along the coastal lowlands, on the lee sides of the mountains, but extends to considerable altitudes where the rainfall is slight. Such areas are Hawaii's deserts.

Forests grow above the shrub land on the lee sides of the mountains, but extend to sea level on the windward side. There are at least five kinds of forest, reflecting differences in moisture availability. One kind occurs on the dry lands on the lee sides of the mountains up to about 2,500 feet. Wetter areas, up to about 6,000 feet, support a forest that includes one of the principal lumber trees, *Ohia*. With it are tree-like ferns. A third kind of forest is found above the *Ohia* forests on Maui and Hawaii up to about 9,500 feet in altitude. A fourth kind of forest is characterized by the koa tree, which is the largest Hawaiian tree, growing 60 feet high and attaining diameters up to 12 feet. These four kinds of forests consist of native plants; the fifth kind of forest is composed predominantly of introduced species.

Shrubs mixed with scattered trees grow on the upper slopes of the high mountains. Bogs with a distinctive plant growth are common in areas of high rainfall, mostly between 4,000 and 6,000 feet in altitude. Mosses and lichens grow above timberline on the summits of the highest mountains, where rainfall is low and frost is frequent. The relationship of the vegetation to the topography and soils is illustrated in Figure 19.7.

The agricultural crops are principally sugar and pineapple, but various other special crops are becoming important: coffee, banana, papaya, citrus fruits, mango, macadamia nut, and avocado. Native woods are used for cabinet making or other special uses.

Surficial Deposits and Soils

Surficial deposits in Hawaii include, at one extreme, the glacial deposits on Mauna Kea; at the other, the saline deposits in some of

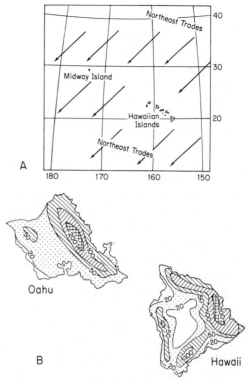

Figure 19.5 *Climatic maps. The four major factors controlling the climate of the Hawaiian Islands are the latitude, surrounding ocean, altitude, and exposure to the northeast trade winds. At sea level the average January temperature is about 70°F; the average July temperature is about 75°F. (A) Exposure to the northeast trade winds. (B) Isohyetal map of Oahu and Hawaii. Precipitation is heavy on the windward sides of the mountains; the leeward sides are semiarid.*

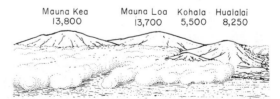

Figure 19.6 *Airplane view south to the peaks on Hawaii, with clouds banked against the windward (north) side by the northeast trade winds. Hualalai has no trade wind clouds, but the west slope has clouds at midday due to landward breezes.*

the desert areas. The soils include, at one extreme, the highly leached soils of the rain forests; at the other, the calcareous (pedocal) soils in the deserts. Deep lateritic soils are widespread on old lavas forming the older islands, whereas young lavas on the younger islands are still bare rock.

Calcareous desert soils are found at low altitudes—below 2,500 feet—where the annual rainfall averages less than 20 inches. The layer of carbonate accumulation is 2 to 20 inches thick and 15 to 24 inches below the surface. The surface layers have little organic matter and are reddish. The sparse vegetation consists mostly of shrubs.

Calcareous grassland soils in Hawaii resemble those on the Great Plains. They occur on the lee sides of the mountains, but the average annual rainfall may be as great as 65 inches, and the soils extend to about 4,000 feet in altitude. These soils have organic-rich surface layers a foot thick. Although the rainfall may be considerable, the year-round growth of grasses suffices to return bases to the surface soil.

In general, the bulk composition of these calcareous soils is like that of the parent rocks —the lavas and volcanic ash. The calcareous soils are developed mostly on volcanic ash, which is more extensive and thicker on the lee sides of the volcanoes than on the windward sides. These deposits and the soils on them are young, for ash has been repeatedly added to them.

The lateritic soils in Hawaii, which contrast strikingly with the calcareous soils, are the result of intensive leaching of the bases and silica. There has been residual enrichment of iron, titanium, and aluminum because of the removal of other elements, but there is no horizon in which elements have accumulated that were leached from another layer. Four varieties of these soils are distinguished.

One kind, found in dry or moderately humid areas, has little organic matter, and is slightly acid. The soil is residually enriched in iron, titanium, and aluminum; the matrix is mostly the clay mineral kaolin. Manganese dioxide has accumulated in the upper part of these soils and forms nodules in the lower part.

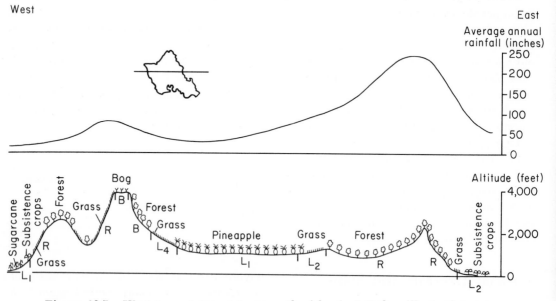

Figure 19.7   *West to east transect across the island of Oahu, illustrating some relationships between topographic position, rainfall, vegetation, soils, and land use. L₁, low-humic laterite; L₂, humic laterite; L₄, ferrugenous laterite; B, bog soil; R, stoney ground. (After U.S.D.A.)*

These soils have developed on all the islands where the average annual precipitation is 10 to 80 inches, but where there is a dry season. The vegetation consists of shrubs and grasses. These are known as low-humic laterites, and at least those in the driest areas probably are relics of an ancient soil that developed when there was more moisture and different vegetation than there is today. It seems doubtful that time has been sufficient for even the volcanic ash to be so weathered in areas that receive as little as 10 inches of rain and in areas where the acidity is so slight.

A second kind of laterite is found at altitudes up to 3,000 feet, where the rainfall averages 40 to 150 inches. These support a considerable growth of shrubs, grasses, or forest, and since there is considerable organic matter in the soil, they are more acid. More silica and aluminum have been lost from these soils than from the low-humic laterites, and they contain little or no manganese dioxide.

A third kind of laterite occurs under the rain forests, and is very acidic. These soils, which occur where the rainfall is considerable and where there is no dry season, are continually wet. They are porous and retain much water, but when dried they become very hard and are difficult to wet again.

The fourth kind of laterite, apparently the oldest, seems to represent the most advanced kind of weathering. This laterite is characterized by upper layers strongly enriched in iron and titanium oxides. In places these layers form crusts. These ferruginous lateritic soils are not found on Hawaii, the youngest of the islands; they are best developed on Kauai, the oldest of the islands. They are found where the present rainfall is as low as 25 inches annually and as high as 150 inches, and at altitudes up to 4,000 feet. In the low-rainfall areas these soils probably are ancient ones that formed when the rainfall was greater than it is now.

Differences between the four kinds of laterite reflect differences in their degree of weathering or stage of development. The least developed, and probably the youngest of these soils, is the low-humic laterite; weathering is most advanced in the ferruginous laterite, which probably is the oldest. The differences are strikingly shown by differences in their chemical composition. Analyses show progressive depletion of silica, alkalis, and alkali earths and residual enrichment in iron and alumina (Fig. 19.8). Even the low humic laterites are more altered than is the residuum, or saprolite, that is parent material for the Red and Yellow Podzols previously described in the other states.

Other soils in Hawaii include some that are so young and unweathered that the parent material still dominates the profile. Others, still younger, have no profile and are simply unweathered surficial deposits, whether alluvium, volcanic ash, volcanic cinders, coral sand, basaltic beach sand, or lavas. In places these are young surficial deposits; in other places they are old deposits that have been freshly exposed by erosion. Soils in poorly drained areas are classed as bog or paddy soils. Some near the coast are saline. Salts also have accumulated locally in some of the desert soils.

Volcanic Eruptions and Tsunami

In most parts of the world, people flee when volcanoes erupt, but in Hawaii people travel to the scenes of the eruptions to watch the display. In a century and a half only one person has been killed by a volcano. Indeed, the volcanoes have been made into a National Park! Hawaiian eruptions are quiet effusions of highly fluid basaltic lava, and not explosive like those in the Aleutian Arc. The active volcanoes are Mauna Loa and Kilauea on the island of Hawaii.

In the last two hundred years Mauna Loa has erupted about 35 times; about half of these eruptions occurred at the summit, the other half occurred along rifts on the flanks

(Figs. 19.9 and 19.10). Kilauea, which has produced 12 flank eruptions, has maintained a lake of active lava at the summit. A volcano observatory is operated by the U. S. Geological Survey in Hawaii National Park.

The start of an eruption may be announced by earthquakes focused about 35 miles below the surface, and located by seismographs distributed over the island. In a matter of weeks (or months) the earthquake focus rises to within a few miles of the surface, and the flanks of the volcano bulge outward (detected by tiltmeters). Attempts to predict the time of eruptions have thus far been only partly successful, but a high degree of success has been achieved in predicting the place of eruption—that is, which volcano and where—on the summit or the flank?

The eruptions usually occur along a few miles of a fissure and begin as fountains of molten lava. At first the molten spray of the fountains forms a "curtain of fire," sometimes

as high as 800 feet. The falling, cooling spray builds ramparts along the fissure. Gradually the activity becomes concentrated at a few places along the fissure, and the fountains at these centers build cones of spatter and cinder. Most of the erupted lava, however, moves downslope like rivers confined between banks of their own construction or forms a lake in the summit caldera. The hottest lavas come to rest with a smooth surface of quenched vesicular glass (*pahoehoe*); cooler lavas have a rough spiny surface of crystallized clinker (*aa*).

Hawaii is exposed to tsunami like those generated along the Aleutian Trench and the coast of Chile (p. 417ff). Figure 19.11 illustrates heights reached by water during the destructive tsunami of April 1, 1946 (p. 418).

The height and intensity of waves caused by a tsunami are not uniform along the coast, and are controlled by several factors. In general, the greatest heights are reached on the side facing the wave's origin. The shape of the

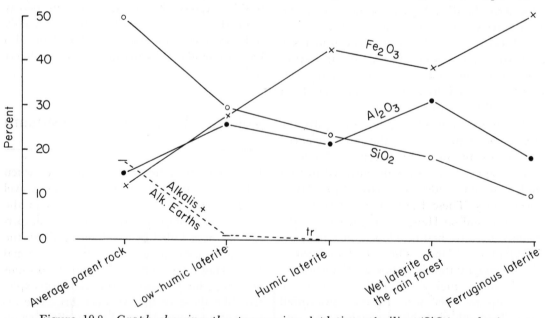

Figure 19.8 *Graph showing the progressive depletion of silica (SiO₂) and of alkalis (K₂O + Na₂O) and alkali earths (CaO + MgO) and the changes (mostly increases) in iron (Fe₂O₃) and alumina (Al₂O₃) in Hawaiian lateritic soils. Percentages refer to total of constituents illustrated in the graph; other constituents in the parent rock total less than 10 percent; in the lateritic soils they may total 30 percent and are mostly water and organic matter.*

island has an effect in refracting the waves, and lee sides of round islands like Kauai experience higher waves than do the lee sides of angular or elongate islands, like Molokai. Waves on the lee sides are likely to be highest where the waves meet after being refracted around the two sides of the island. Exposure is an important factor because storm waves, which are most frequent and generally highest on the windward side, are carried shoreward by the tsunami. The near-shore submarine topography affects the waves because shallow water slows a wave and increases its height.

Fringing reefs, however, reduce the intensity of the waves.

The tsunami warning system (p. 418) can provide a few hours' warning of the arrival of a tsunami.

Water Supply

Despite the very high annual rainfall in much of the Hawaiian Islands, the water supply is not abundant, because the ground, being composed of lavas, is highly porous, and most of

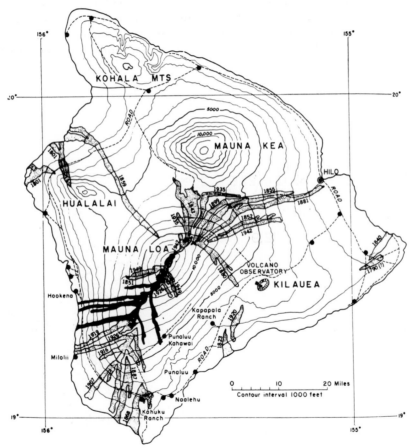

Figure 19.9 *The island of Hawaii, showing the five major volcanic mountains and the historic lava flows to 1953. (After U.S.G.S.) The eruptions of Mauna Loa are centered along the rift that crosses the summit; the eruptions of Kilauea occur at the summit and on the flanks, but the lava flows are mostly from flank eruptions. Note that Kilauea is low on the east flank of Mauna Loa.*

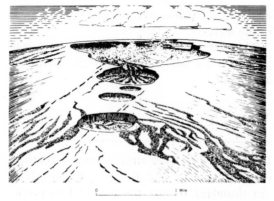

Figure 19.10   *View northeast along the summit of Mauna Loa, showing the large caldera on the summit and the adjoining pit craters. The summit caldera is 9,000 feet wide. (From U.S.G.S.)*

the rainwater runs through it and all the way to the base of the island, where it collects in a lense over salt water (Fig. 19.12). Salt water is about 1/40th heavier than fresh water, and the fresh water can float on the salt water. A lense of fresh water projects above the salt water table 1/40th the thickness of the lense, in the same way that only a small part of an iceberg protrudes above sea level. The fresh-water lense, however, contains a brackish zone in which the two waters mix.

The brackish zone is a very important factor in developing supplies of groundwater from such a lense, because overdrafts by wells cause salt water to rise in cones into the fresh-water lense and contaminate it (Fig. 5.10). The water that can be supplied by such a lense without

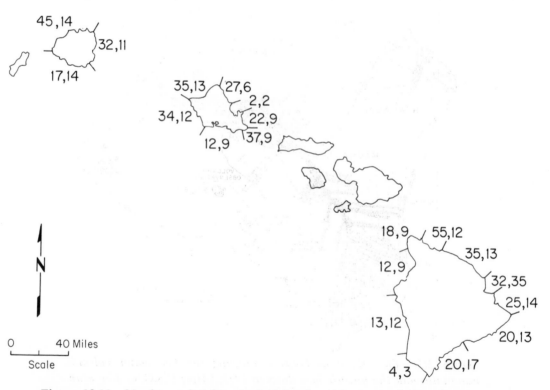

Figure 19.11   *Maximum heights reached by the 1946 tsunami (first figure) and the 1960 tsunami (second figure) along some coastal sections of Hawaii. The 1946 tsunami originated in the Aleutian Trench, to the north; the 1960 tsunami came from the direction of Chile, southwest. (Data from University of Hawaii.)*

disturbing the salt-water–fresh-water boundary is equal to the annual recharge by infiltration. To preserve the supply, water must be skimmed from the top of the lense rather than pumped from lower down. This skimming is done by tunnels with infiltration galleries, and these are replacing wells in the Hawaiian Islands. Most of this water is soft; the average hardness of water in the municipal systems is about 50.

On the high parts of the islands the depth to this basal lense of groundwater makes drilling uneconomic. Some water is obtained from groundwater perched on impervious beds, but these supplies are limited. Most water supplies on the mountains are obtained by collecting rain water in cisterns. It seems strange, in such a high-rainfall area, to see no surface water and to see buildings equipped with cisterns and storage tanks for collecting water!

Differences in the geology introduce considerable differences in the mode of occurrence of the water supplies. For example, Kauai is exceptional in that more than half of its rainfall is discharged in streams. On the other islands, large areas have practically no runoff.

Other Resources

Hawaii's greatest resource is its people. In this state, racial integration is more satisfactorily developed than anywhere else, not only in the United States but in the world. As a result, the several races of people have borrowed traits from each other, and the better traits of each race seem to have prevailed.

The 1960 population of the islands was about 630,000. About half the population lives in Honolulu. The total population on Oahu is 500,000. Kauai and the islands neighboring it have fewer than 30,000 people; Maui, Molokai, and the small islands near them have about 40,000 people. The big island, Hawaii, has about 60,000.

The racial groups (1950) are: Japanese, 37

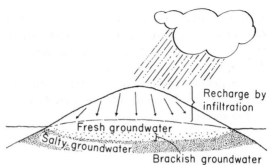

Figure 19.12 *Diagram illustrating occurrence of groundwater on the Hawaiian Islands. Because the islands are composed largely of very permeable lavas, surface water is scanty and a large fraction of the annual rainfall infiltrates the ground and sinks to nearly sea level. It collects at the base of the islands as a lens of fresh water floating on salt water. The groundwater is brackish in a zone where the two waters are mixed.*

percent; Caucasian, 23 percent; part-Hawaiian, 14.8 percent; Filipino, 12 percent; Chinese, 6.5 percent; full-blooded Hawaiian, 2.5 percent; and all others, including Korean, 4.2 percent. Every race is a minority group. When Captain James Cook discovered the islands in 1778, he estimated the population to be about 300,000, though some think this estimate about twice too high. The Hawaiians had been so isolated that they had no resistance to the diseases brought by the whites, and by 1872 only about 50,000 survived. About that time the sugar industry began to expand and other races began moving to the islands in large numbers.

Less than 10 percent of the islands is cultivated, and almost all of the cultivated land is used for raising sugar cane and pineapple. About half the land is in pasture, about 30 percent is forest reserve, and 5 percent is in National Parks. Most of the rest is wasteland. There is considerable livestock, but beef production meets only two-thirds of the local demand. The carrying capacity of the range land averages about one beef animal per 10 acres.

The islands are without important mineral

resources other than volcanic rock, which furnishes road metal and some building stone. Deposits of pumice are considerable but not developed.

A major resource is the climate, and the increasing development of the islands as a tourist mecca.

Also important to the islands' economy is the income from the armed forces stationed there. This income exceeds that obtained from sugar and pineapple production. If the rest of the world were as pacific as Hawaii, the islands might be a depressed area, which is a sad commentary on this phase of our system.

20 Puerto Rico

The Commonwealth of Puerto Rico, like the State of Hawaii, occupies a tropical oceanic position just south of the Tropic of Cancer. The island is one of the easternmost peaks of a partly submerged mountain range composed of Cretaceous and older rocks. This mountain range forms the Greater Antilles and extends eastward to the Virgin Islands (Fig. 20.1). The Lesser Antilles, which form an arc at the east side of the Caribbean, are largely Cenozoic volcanoes, some of them still active, and some with raised platforms of Cenozoic limestone.

Some of the outstanding features of Puerto Rico are its

1. Mountainous topography composed of ridges in an east-trending belt extending the length of the island. The summit is more than 4,000 feet high; the adjoining oceanic abyss is 6 miles deep.
2. Tropical climate relieved by marine environment and by the trade winds, with the result that there is little seasonal change in temperature.
3. Exposure to hurricanes.
4. Tropical rain forest and tropical fruits; meager land fauna, except for birds, bats, and lizards; coral reefs and sports fishing (but not much food fish).
5. Lateritic soils.
6. Scanty mineral resources; considerable hydroelectric power; manufacturing economy ($432,000,000 in 1963), agriculture ($220,-000,000 in 1963), and tourism.

The area is 3,435 square miles, about half that of Hawaii. The population is $2\frac{1}{2}$ million (1965 estimate), more than 700 per square mile. Despite the large population and modest resources, the literacy rate and per capita income compare favorably with those of the southeastern United States.

Structural Framework and Topography

At Puerto Rico the total relief of the mountain range forming the Greater Antilles is almost 35,000 feet. To the north, the base of the island lies 75 miles away in the Puerto Rico Trench (Fig. 20.2) and is 6 miles below sea level. To the south, the base of the island lies in the Caribbean Sea about 3 miles below sea level. The east-west trending ridges and peaks forming the backbone of the island, the Cordillera Central (Fig. 20.3), make up about a third of the island. Local relief is considerable and slopes are steep. The crest is crowded toward the south side of the island. Sierra de Luquillo, an isolated high mountain in the northeast corner of the island, lies slightly north of the eastern extension of the Cordillera Central. About 20 miles southeast of the island, along the eastern extension of the Cordillera Central, is Vieques Island. The rocks forming the mountains are mostly Cretaceous lavas and sedimentary formations derived from volcanic sources (Fig. 20.2). They are cut

by granitic intrusions of Cretaceous and Tertiary age. This terrain is flanked by Tertiary marine limestone that forms low plateaus having karst topography pitted with scattered caverns and sinkholes and surmounted by peculiar, steep-sided, haystack-like hills of limestone. In the limestone country, some rivers disappear underground and reappear near the coast. The Cretaceous formations and granitic intrusions had been uplifted and folded before the limestone was deposited.

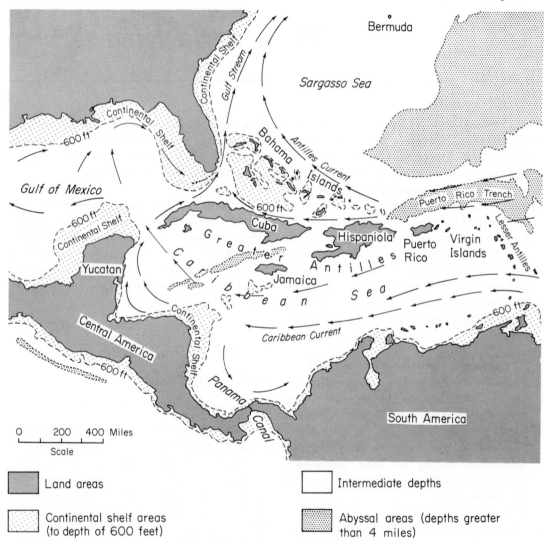

Figure 20.1 *Index map of the West Indies, showing the location of Puerto Rico at the east end of the Greater Antilles. Arrows show ocean currents.*

Further uplift in late Tertiary time raised the limestones to form the plateaus. In latest Tertiary and in Quaternary time there was further uplift and faulting: Puerto Rico was arched, tilted northeastward, and on the west became separated from Hispaniola by downfaulting in the strait between the two islands.

Puerto Rico is located in a seismically active belt that extends southeastward along the volcanic arc of the Lesser Antilles and westward to South America by way of Hispaniola and the trench between Jamaica and Cuba (Fig. 20.1), yet aside from a severe shock that was centered near Puerto Rico's west coast in 1918, earthquakes have been minor. Shore features (p. 451) indicate that there has been little if any structural movement in the last several thousand years.

The subcrustal structure responsible for the island uplift and for the trench might be steep faults that have raised the island and dropped the trench, or might be low-angle faulting directed northward, similar to the structure inferred under the Aleutian Islands (Fig. 18.9).

Climate

Four important factors controlling the climate of Puerto Rico are the latitude, the surrounding ocean, the trade winds, and the topogra-

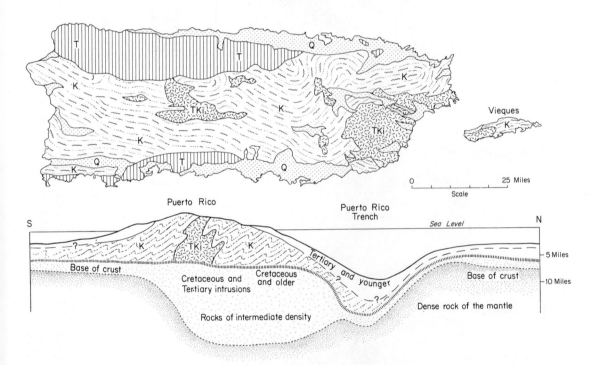

Figure 20.2 *Geologic map and cross section of Puerto Rico. The island is an uplift of Early Tertiary and Cretaceous (K) rocks invaded by Cretaceous and early Tertiary intrusions (TKi) and flanked by middle Tertiary limestone (T). Quaternary deposits include coral reefs, dunes and beach sand in part cemented to eolianite and to beachrock along the shores, and alluvium along valley bottoms. The axis of the uplift parallels the Puerto Rico Trench, which is underlain by a thick mass of light crustal rock. The dense rock of the mantle is very much shallower under the shelf north of the trench and under the Caribbean Sea.*

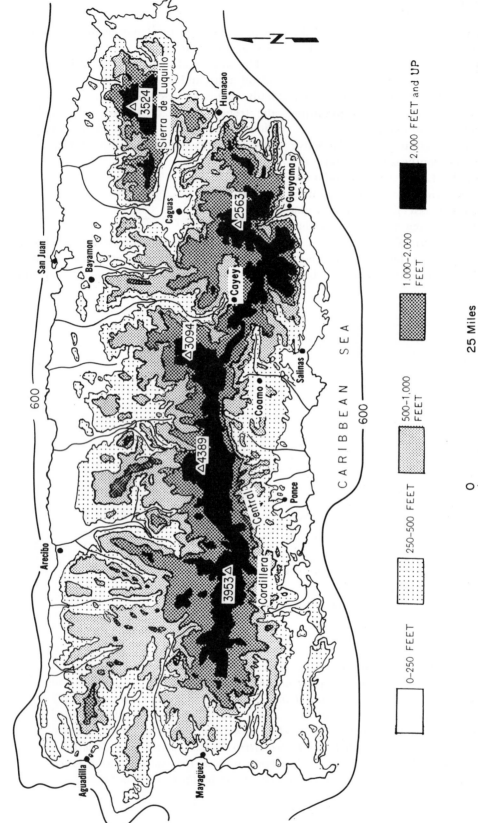

Figure 20.3 *Map of Puerto Rico, showing the east-west-trending mountain range, the Cordillera Central, that forms the backbone of the island. (After U.S.D.A.)*

phy. Although Puerto Rico is located south of the Tropic of Cancer and within the tropical zone, its climate is agreeable due to the temporizing effects of the other three factors.

An effect of the oceanic environment is the low seasonal change in temperature, especially near the coast. At San Juan the January average is 74.8°F, and the July average is 80°F. The maximum is 94°F and the minimum 62°F. The south coast is only a trifle warmer. At Ponce the January average is 75.4°F, and the July average is 81.1°F. The maximum is 96°F and the minimum 55°F. In the interior, the average temperature is lower, because of altitude, and the fluctuations greater than near the coast. At Cayey the January average is 69.2°F, and the July average is 75.6°F. The maximum is 94°F and the minimum 44°F.

The trade winds, blowing from just slightly north of east (Fig. 20.4), first reach the Sierra de Luquillo, and annual rainfall there averages more than 200 inches. Rainfall is considerable in the Cordillera Central, especially in the western part of the island. Leeward of Sierra de Luquillo is rain shadow. Annual rainfall on the north coast, at San Juan, averages 61 inches; on the south coast, which is leeward of the Cordillera, the rainfall is much less, and at Ponce averages 35 inches. The rainfall occurs mostly as showers, but on some windward slopes these may occur daily.

A second major effect of the winds is evaporation. Humidity is high, averaging above 75 percent throughout the day. As a consequence, areas protected from the wind are uncomfortably muggy, but exposed areas are pleasantly cool. Because winds are persistent, evaporation rates are high and the effective moisture is far less than seems indicated by the amount of precipitation. Areas with less than 35 inches of annual rainfall are semiarid.

Puerto Rico is in the belt of hurricanes, which originate in the eastern part of the Caribbean Sea and in the ocean farther east. The hurricane season is mostly July 1 to November 1. July and October hurricanes generally form over the eastern Caribbean, and these rarely attain maximum intensity until they pass Puerto Rico. August and September storms form farther east, over the ocean, and these may develop into major storms by the time they reach the island. Hurricane winds may exceed 100 miles per hour and be accompanied by torrential rain. The storms usually move at 5 to 15 miles per hour.

Water Supplies and Vegetation

Water supplies in Puerto Rico are obtained both from surface water and from groundwater. Because of the abundant limestone, most of the water is hard; in municipal systems the hardness averages about 125, which is much higher than in Hawaii, where the islands are mostly lavas and not carbonates.

Groundwater supplies in Puerto Rico are obtained principally from the Tertiary and Quaternary formations; Cretaceous formations have not been important sources. The intrusive igneous rocks yield the softest water, but the supplies are small. Much of the developed water, both surface water and groundwater, is used for irrigation.

Most of Puerto Rico is under cultivation, and the natural vegetation is undisturbed in only a few places. Areas with high rainfall, like Sierra de Luquillo, are covered by dense forest (Fig. 20.5), including such trees as mahogany, ebony, mamey, tree ferns, sierra palm,

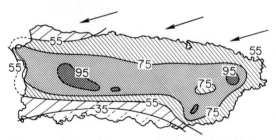

Figure 20.4 *Average annual precipitation (inches) Puerto Rico. Arrows indicate the direction of trade winds. (After U.S.D.A.)*

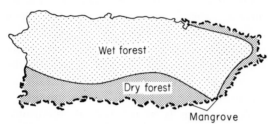

Figure 20.5. *Distribution of three types of forest in Puerto Rico. (After U.S.D.A.) Most of the island is under cultivation, and little forest remains. On the windward (north) slope there is wet forest; on the leeward (south) slope, dry forest. Mangrove forest (greatly exaggerated in figure) grows along the coast in an interrupted belt less than a mile wide.*

mango, Spanish cedar, sandalwood, and rose-wood. Growing with these are orchids, jungle vines, and matojo grass.

The southern slope of the island, which is semiarid, supports dry forest consisting of acacia, royal palm, yucca, cacti, and dry grasses. Mangrove grows along much of the coast. Mangrove swamps include bogs with reeds, sedges, cattails, ferns, and grasses.

Agriculturally the island consists of a coastal belt planted chiefly in sugar cane, supplemented with coconut and sea island cotton.

Of the alluvial areas, about 85 percent is planted in sugar cane and 10 percent in a grass (malojilla) used for forage and hay. The remaining 5 percent is bog. The lower foot-hills are planted in citrus fruits, pineapple, and various subsistence crops; some are used for pasture. The north sides of the higher hills are used for growing tobacco, and the highest for coffee. The wood of the mangrove and other trees is burned for charcoal and used for fuel.

The meager fauna reflects the island's long isolation. Offshore there is considerable coral (Fig. 20.7) and sports fish, but not much food fish.

Surficial Deposits and Soils

Surficial deposits in Puerto Rico include alluvium in valley bottoms, and beach sand, dune sand, and swamp deposits along the coasts. North coast sands at and near the shore are cemented with calcium carbonate to form eolianite and beachrock (see p. 452). Much of the island is covered by thick residual soils, including various laterites, Red and Yellow Podzols, Gray-Brown Podzols, Rend-

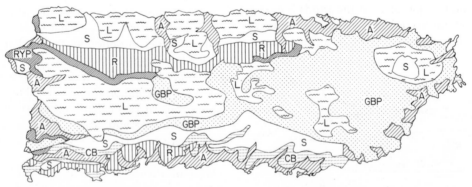

Figure 20.6 *Soil map of Puerto Rico. L, lateritic soils; RYP, Red and Yellow Podzols; GBP, Gray-Brown Podzols; R, Rendzina Soils; CB, mostly pedocals—Chernozem, Reddish Chestnut, and Reddish-Brown Soils with small areas of Reddish Desert and Reddish Prairie Soils; A, alluvial soils; S, mostly shallow soils. (After U.S.D.A.)*

zina Soils, and a series of pedocals that include Chernozem, Reddish-Chestnut, and Brown Soils. The Lateritic and the Red and Yellow Podzolic Soils are as much as 80 feet deep and are developed on the wet, windward side of the island; the pedocals are thinner and are developed on the dry, leeward side (Fig. 20.6). The Rendzina Soils are developed on the plateaus of Tertiary limestone. The thick, well-developed, residual soils, especially the laterites and the Red and Yellow Podzols, are paleosols and are of Pleistocene age or older, for they are overlapped by Pleistocene surficial deposits.

Where developed on Cretaceous volcanic rocks or Tertiary limestone, the lateritic soils are yellow, brown, or red, acid and clayey to a depth of 40 feet, and the clay is aggregated to give a granular and loamy texture. On granitic rocks the surface soil is bright red and clayey; this grades downward to disintegrated rock and is as much as 80 feet deep in places. On serpentine the soil is a deep-red, iron-rich laterite that grades to yellow with depth, is 30 or more feet deep, and, like the parent rock, contains considerable nickel and chromite. Along the coast, these lateritic soils are overlain by Pleistocene terrace deposits about 100 feet above sea level. The relationship is quite like that found along the coast of Florida (Fig. 10.17,B) except that the Puerto Rico terrace is much higher, probably because of uplift since the soil and terrace were formed.

Elsewhere the granitic rocks have weathered to a dense, granular material like sand, but composed of the minerals of the parent rock in varying stages of decomposition. These soils are younger than the laterite, and the mineral alteration is less advanced.

The Gray-Brown Podzols also are developed on the granitic intrusions and on the Cretaceous volcanic rocks. They are shallow soils, 1 to 2 feet thick, granular, and well drained. Surface layers are gray-brown to black clay, slightly acidic and about 6 inches thick. Below these layers there is a brown, slightly acidic, silty clay layer that is 8 to 18 inches thick.

The Rendzina Soils have a black, calcareous surface layer 4 to 10 inches thick that grades downward into parent rock, which is soft white limestone or marl.

The pedocals have surface layers ranging from brown to black. All are calcareous mixtures of sand and clay. The subsoils are clayey and highly calcareous, being the layer of lime accumulation. Other soils included with the pedocals have no layer of lime accumulation and are Prairie Soils; others have clay hardpans like planosols.

The alluvial deposits are by far the most productive ground on the island. The ground is irrigated where rainfall averages less than about 60 inches. The lateritic soils are leached of most of their bases and other plant nutrients and require fertilizer. Moreover, the old lateritic and Red and Yellow Podzolic soils are highly susceptible to erosion, like the Red and Yellow Podzolic soils in the United States (p. 93; Fig. 6.2).

Shore Features

Puerto Rico's shore features exhibit considerable variety. The northeast coast, highly indented and dotted with small islands, has a pattern like that of the New England coast. This might suggest submergence and drowning of the valleys, but the bottom offshore is a shallow, nearly level bank with coral reefs, and is not at all suggestive of submergence.

Along the southeastern coast rocky headlands, built chiefly of granitic rocks (Fig. 20.2), are separated by broad, alluviated valleys fronted by long, arcuate beaches of quartz sand. The configuration of this stretch of shore seems to be controlled by the structural geology of the old rocks, whose surface here slopes eastward below sea level. The relation between topography and structural geology is similar on the west side of the island and western end of the south coast, except that the headlands there are mostly Cretaceous formations.

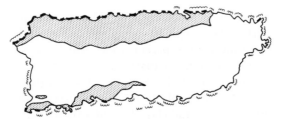

Figure 20.7 *Map of Puerto Rico shows principal areas of limestone (stippled), beachrock (black), and coral reef (wavy pattern). (After U.S.G.S.)*

The central part of the south coast is mostly alluvial plain with beaches composed of sand from the Cretaceous volcanic formations in the mountains. The western part of the north coast is a cliff of Miocene limestone (Fig. 20.7) 150 to 200 feet high; the eastern part of that coast is broad alluvial plain with swamps and lagoons. The reason for this difference is obscure, but may be due to eastward tilting.

Beach sands along the north coast are quite different from those at the south. Instead of quartz sand, they are mostly carbonate—shell fragments, fragments of coral, calcareous algae, and grains of limestone. Along much of this coast the beach sand in the intertidal zone is cemented with calcium carbonate to form *beachrock* (Fig. 20.7). Dune sand is similarly cemented but to depths below low tide and to heights about 100 feet above high-tide level. In the spray zone above high-tide level the cemented dune sand is roughened with solution pits and residual pinnacles and is terraced with erosional platforms in the intertidal zone.

The origins of the calcium carbonate cement in beachrock and related deposits are obscure. In Puerto Rico the cemented deposits are largely limited to limestone areas, yet the calcium carbonate content of the ocean water at such places is very little greater than where there is no limestone. Moreover, in other parts of the world, similar deposits formed where there is no limestone. Such deposits can form rapidly; in many places trash only a few years old is firmly cemented. Some deposits may be due to physicochemical precipitation, others

may be due to biochemical activity of organisms. The problem may have some parallels with the development of some kinds of caliche in deserts (p. 331; Fig. 15.15).

Curiously, the coral around Puerto Rico grows along the shores, away from the limestone and beachrock (Fig. 20.7). This has been attributed partly to the turbidity of the water along the north coast when the rivers flood. The muddy water, which inhibits coral growth, drifts westward; the coral grows toward the east. Moreover, the ocean floor off the north coast is sandy as well as exposed to strong waves, and the foundation may be unsuitable for the growth of young coral.

Recent studies of shoreline details around Puerto Rico indicate that there has been little variation in sea level during the last 2,000 years. Four thousand years ago sea level may have been about 12 feet lower than it is now. This suggests crustal stability in this area during that time.

Puerto Rico has only two harbors, one at San Juan on the north coast and another at Ponce on the south. The west end of the island, however, is sheltered from the prevailing winds, and two shipping ports, Aguadilla and Mayaguez, are located there.

Land—The Major Resource Problem

Puerto Rico's greatest resource problem is shortage of land for its large and growing population. Despite the overcrowding and the limited resources, the commonwealth has successfully reduced illiteracy and has raised per-capita income and the general standard of living. One wonders how long this can be continued if the population continues to increase. Progress has been substantial, although much remains to be done to relieve poverty that persists in city slums as well as in rural areas away from the luxurious tourist centers.

Place Index

Subject Index

(Principal references are indicated in **boldface** type. References in *italic* type are figure numbers.)